GEOMETRY
A TEACHING TEXTBOOK

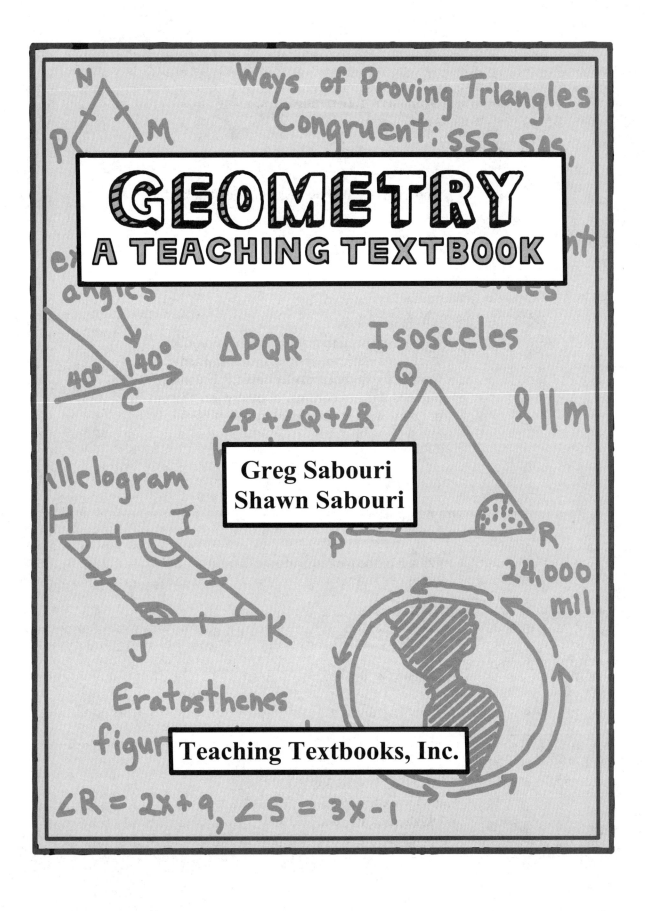

Geometry: A Teaching Textbook™
First Edition

Copyright © 2005 by Teaching Textbooks, Inc.

Printed in the United States of America.

Library of Congress Control Number:

ISBN: 0-9749036-0-4

Teaching Textbooks, Inc.
P. O. Box 60529
Oklahoma City, OK 73146
www.teachingtextbooks.com

Acknowledgements

The authors would like to express their special thanks
to Matt Maloney for his invaluable assistance.

Table of Contents

Letter to Parents ———————————————————————— 1

Suggestions on How to Use This Product ———————— 2

Chapter 1: Geometry Beginnings ——————————— 3

Lesson 1—Inductive Reasoning in Egypt and Babylon   4

Lesson 2—Deductive Reasoning and the Greeks   10

Lesson 3—Self-Evident Truths   17

Lesson 4—Logic Chains   21

Lesson 5—Euclid: The Father of Geometry   26

Chapter 2: Lines and Angles ———————————— 33

Lesson 6—Too Simple to Define   34

Lesson 7—Some Definitions and Postulates   39

Lesson 8—Line Segments   46

Lesson 9—Rays and Angles   53

Lesson 10—Measuring Angles   58

Lesson 11—Kinds of Angles   64

Lesson 12—Midpoints and Bisectors   70

Lesson 13—Properties of Equality   76

Chapter 3: Angle Pairs & Perpendicular Lines ——————— 83

Lesson 14—Formal (and Informal) Proofs   84

Lesson 15—Complementary Angle Pairs   92

Lesson 16—Supplementary Angle Pairs   99

Lesson 17—Adjacent Angles   104

Lesson 18—Vertical Angles   110

Lesson 19—Right Angles and Perpendicular Lines   115

Lesson 20—Drawing Perpendicular Lines through Points   121

Lesson 21—Measuring Distances   127

Chapter 4: Parallel Lines ——————————————— 133

Lesson 22—Lines That Never Meet   134

Lesson 23—Parallel Lines and Angles   140

Lesson 24—More on Parallel Lines   145

Lesson 25—Measuring the Earth   152

Lesson 26—Converse Statements   159

Lesson 27—Proving Lines are Parallel   166

Chapter 5: Triangles — 173

Lesson 28—A Triangle and its Parts   174
Lesson 29—Kinds of Triangles   180
Lesson 30—Adding Up the Angles   186
Lesson 31—Exterior Angles   193
Lesson 32—Congruent Triangles   198
Lesson 33—Side-Angle-Side   205
Lesson 34—Angle-Side-Angle and Angle-Angle-Side   210
Lesson 35—Hypotenuse-Leg   216
Lesson 36—Side-Side-Side   222
Lesson 37—Overlapping Triangles   228

Chapter 6: Using Congruent Triangles — 235

Lesson 38—Proving Corresponding Parts are Congruent   236
Lesson 39—Proving Bisectors   243
Lesson 40—Proving Lines Parallel or Perpendicular   248
Lesson 41—Altitudes and Medians of Triangles   254
Lesson 42—Base Angles of an Isosceles Triangle   261
Lesson 43—Proving That a Triangle is Isosceles   267

Chapter 7: Inequalities — 273

Lesson 44—Inequalities: The Basics   274
Lesson 45—Triangle Side Inequality   281
Lesson 46—Exterior Angle Inequality Theorem   287
Lesson 47—Indirect Proofs   293
Lesson 48—More on Logic   300
Lesson 49—Unequal Sides, Unequal Angles   307

Chapter 8: Quadrilaterals — 313

Lesson 50—A Four-Sided Polygon   314
Lesson 51—Trapezoids   321
Lesson 52—Parallelograms   327
Lesson 53—Congruent Sides and Bisecting Diagonals   333
Lesson 54—Proving that it's a Parallelogram: Part 1   340
Lesson 55—Proving that it's a Parallelogram: Part 2   347
Lesson 56—Rectangles, Rhombuses, and Squares   354
Lesson 57—The Big Picture   359

Chapter 9: Polygons — 367

Lesson 58—Polygons with More Sides — 368
Lesson 59—Adding Up the Angles of any Polygon — 374
Lesson 60—Adding Up the Exterior Angles — 380
Lesson 61—Regular Polygons — 387
Lesson 62—Perimeter of a Polygon — 394

Chapter 10: Similar Triangles — 401

Lesson 63—Ratios — 402
Lesson 64—Proportions — 408
Lesson 65—Similar Figures — 416
Lesson 66—Similar Figures in the Real World — 423
Lesson 67—Splitting a Triangle... Not in the Middle — 429
Lesson 68—Angle-Angle Similarity — 436
Lesson 69—Side-Angle-Side and Side-Side-Side Similarity — 443
Lesson 70—Using Similar Triangles — 451
Lesson 71—Altitudes, Medians, and Perimeters — 459

Chapter 11: Right Triangles & Trigonometry — 467

Lesson 72—Proportions in a Right Triangle — 468
Lesson 73—The Pythagorean Theorem — 474
Lesson 74—Irrational Lengths and Pythagorean Triples — 481
Lesson 75—The Isosceles Right Triangle — 489
Lesson 76—The 30-60 Right Triangle — 496
Lesson 77—Trigonometry: The Basics — 504
Lesson 78—The Tangent Ratio — 511
Lesson 79—The Sine and Cosine Ratios — 519
Lesson 80—Measuring the Solar System — 526

Chapter 12: Circles — 533

Lesson 81—Circles and Lines — 534
Lesson 82—Theorems on Chords — 541
Lesson 83—Theorems on Tangents — 548
Lesson 84—Arcs and Angles — 555
Lesson 85—More on Measuring Arcs — 563
Lesson 86—Arcs and Chords — 569
Lesson 87—Inscribed Angles — 577
Lesson 88—Vertex Inside and Outside — 585
Lesson 89—Segment Products Inside and Out — 593

Chapter 13: Area —————————————————— 601
   Lesson 90—Area of a Rectangle 602
   Lesson 91—Area of a Triangle and Parallelogram 609
   Lesson 92—Area of Other Quadrilaterals 616
   Lesson 93—Area of Polygons with More Sides 623
   Lesson 94—Area of a Circle, Etc. 631

Chapter 14: Solid Geometry —————————— 639
   Lesson 95—Rectangular Solids 640
   Lesson 96—Prisms 647
   Lesson 97—Pyramids 654
   Lesson 98—Cylinders and Cones 661
   Lesson 99—Spheres 668
   Lesson 100—Areas and Volumes of Similar Solids 675

Chapter 15: Coordinate Geometry ———————— 683
   Lesson 101—Merging Geometry with Algebra 684
   Lesson 102—Distance and Midpoint Formulas 691
   Lesson 103—Slope of a Line 699
   Lesson 104—Linear Equations 707
   Lesson 105—Coordinate Proofs 714
   Lesson 106—Circles and Coordinate Proofs 720

Additional Topics —————————————————— 727
   Lesson 107—Constructions 728
   Lesson 108—More Constructions 735
   Lesson 109—Transformations 742
   Lesson 110—Non-Euclidean Geometries 749

Definitions, Theorems, and Postulates ————— 757

A Letter to Parents

Dear Parents,

Finally, there's a Geometry book designed specifically for independent learners. Let us tell you about it.

Textbook and Teacher Combined

Unlike traditional classroom textbooks, which are meant to be used only with the help of a teacher, the Geometry Teaching Textbook™ is both a textbook and a teacher combined into one. The print lessons explain each of the concepts in an easy-to-digest conversational tone. Plus, each lesson includes a 10-15 minute audiovisual lecture.

SAT and ACT Prep Built-In

Also, nearly every problem set includes several problems that were modeled after those found on the SAT and ACT. And since all Teaching Textbooks use the well-known review method, students become better and better at solving these important problem types each day.

Never Get Stumped Again

But what really sets the Geometry Teaching Textbook™ apart is its audiovisual step-by-step solutions for every single one of the 3,500 homework and test problems! This is far more teaching than is offered by any other product on the market. In fact, it's even more teaching than is available in most traditional classes. With this unprecedented CD-ROM package, the frustration of missing a problem and not being able to figure out what you did wrong is over. A student or parent need never get stumped again!

Friendly Text and Fun Illustrations

Parents choose Teaching Textbooks™ primarily as a safety net for tough problems and for the extra preparation they provide for college entrance exams. But if you ask students what makes a Teaching Textbook™ the best, they almost always say the same thing: *It's more fun*. Students say that reading the text is like having a friendly tutor or coach gently guiding you through each concept and problem type. They also enjoy the fascinating (and sometimes entertaining) real-world examples and humorous illustrations. Together these features put students at ease and keep them totally engaged in the learning process. And again, because the problem sets employ the review method, students are more likely to actually retain what they've learned.

Thank you for your purchase of the Geometry Teaching Textbook™ and for the opportunity to serve you and your family's educational needs.

Greg Sabouri and Shawn Sabouri

1

Suggestions on How to Use This Product

Please feel free to use this powerful and versatile product as you see fit. However, when families ask us to suggest a "best" method for using the Geometry Teaching Textbook™, here is the advice we give.

How to "Best" Use the Teaching Textbook

1) Read the printed lesson in your book.

2) Watch the lecture on CD.

3) Work any of the five practice problems that seem difficult.

4) Watch the CD lectures that explain those practice problems. These are on the LECTURE & PRACTICE CDs.

5) Work all of the problems in the problem set.

6) Grade the assignment.

7) Watch the step-by-step solutions on CD for any problems that were missed. These are on the STEP-BY-STEP SOLUTIONS CDs.

8) After finishing each chapter, take and grade the chapter test (found in the Answer Key & Test Bank).

Practice Problems

We should also mention a few things about the practice problems and highlighted text. First of all, practice problems are not required. They are additional examples to help the student with the assigned problem set. Each of the five practice problems is labeled with a letter (**a**, **b**, **c**, **d**, or **e**). These problems are very similar to the problems in the problem set that are labeled with those same letters. So if a student is having trouble with number 16, and it's labeled **b**, he or she can see how a very similar problem was solved by referring back to practice problem b. Usually, the hardest problems have a practice problem to match them. So this system gives students a hint for the toughest problems in each problem set.

Highlighted Text

You've already noticed that we use a text highlighter. The purpose of the highlighting is to emphasize the most important points in a lesson. This improves reading comprehension and makes it easier for students to go back and review material that has already been covered. That can be particularly helpful with this book, since every problem set uses the review method. Also, some students may just want to watch the lectures on CD (instead of reading the lessons in the book) and then only read the highlighted text as reinforcement.

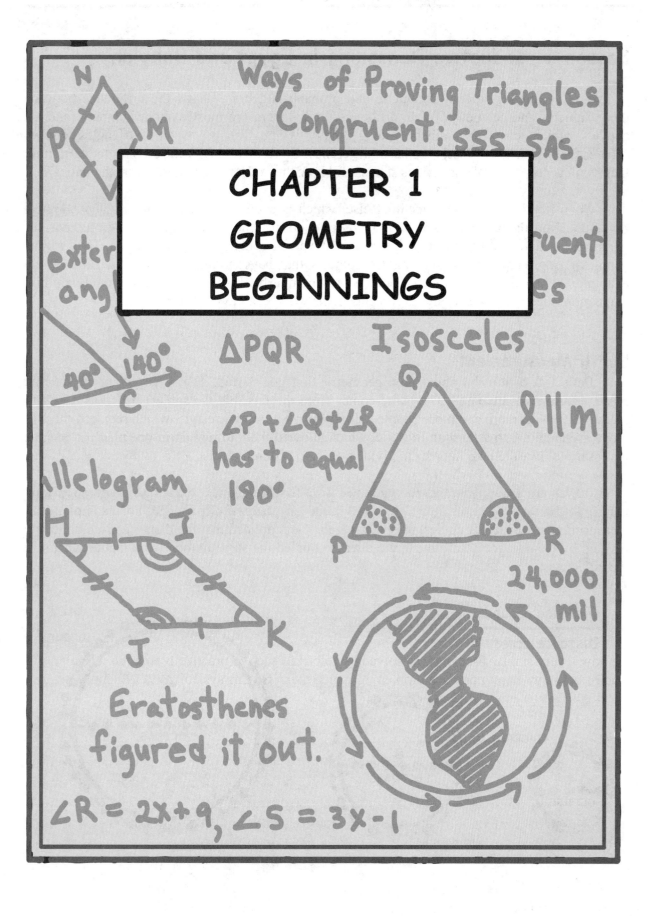

CHAPTER 1
GEOMETRY
BEGINNINGS

Ways of Proving Triangles Congruent: SSS, SAS,

N

P

M

exter
ang

40° 140°
C

ΔPQR

∠P+∠Q+∠R
has to equal
180°

llelogram

H   I

J   K

Isosceles

Q

P   R

ruent
es

ℓ ‖ m

24,000
mil

Eratosthenes
figured it out.

∠R = 2x+9, ∠S = 3x-1

Lesson 1—Inductive Reasoning in Egypt and Babylon

You've already studied arithmetic and probably algebra. What's the difference between those subjects and geometry? Well, arithmetic and algebra are mostly about numbers (and *x*'s and *y*'s, which represent numbers), but geometry is about shapes, such as triangles, circles, squares, and rectangles. That's the basic difference. So in this book, you're going to learn more than you ever dreamed about various shapes and how they relate to one another mathematically.

Geometry is also about something else, which is even more important. It's about logical thinking. Even though it takes plenty of logic to do arithmetic and algebra, the methods for thinking through a problem logically aren't covered formally until geometry. That means geometry can sharpen your thinking for subjects that have nothing to do with math. As an example, Abraham Lincoln studied geometry as an adult because he believed it would help him make more logical and persuasive arguments in his work as a lawyer and politician.

Earth Measurement

Let's talk a little bit about how geometry first got started. The word geometry actually means "earth measurement." The name comes from the fact that the subject began as a way to measure land. As more and more people shifted from a hunting lifestyle, which required them to move around a lot, to a farming lifestyle, which allowed them to remain in one place, it became necessary to measure land in order to divide it up into different farms.

It was the Egyptians and Babylonians who first developed rules that made such land measurement easier. All of their rules were based on practical experience. For example, after measuring many different circles, these early geometers noticed that the distance around a circle divided by the distance across the circle always equaled the same number—no matter what size the circle was.

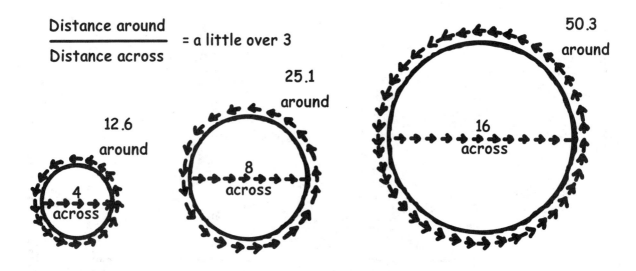

$$\frac{\text{Distance around}}{\text{Distance across}} = \text{a little over 3}$$

12.6 around
4 across

25.1 around
8 across

50.3 around
16 across

So they assumed that for *all* circles the distance around the circle divided by the distance across was always equal to a little over 3. This became one of their rules of Geometry.

Over time, the Egyptians and Babylonians created other such rules covering everything from how to figure out a farm's area, to the amount of crops that the farm might yield in a growing season, to the quantity of bricks needed to build a pyramid. And it was with these practical rules that Geometry first began.

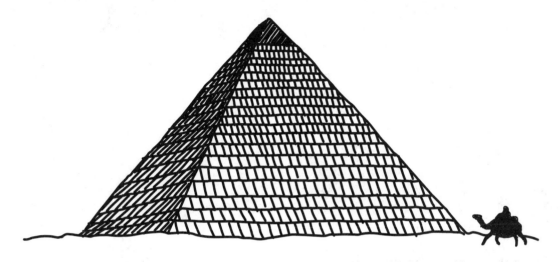

Inductive Reasoning

There's a special name for the kind of thinking that the Egyptians and Babylonians used to develop those first rules for geometry. It's called inductive reasoning. In **inductive reasoning**, or **induction**, we look at several examples of something, as with the circles above, and find a fact that holds true for those examples. Then we conclude that the fact is true for all other possible examples (for all possible circles).

Inductive reasoning can be applied to just about any situation. For instance, Katie, the cat lover, might notice that all eight of her cats have tails. From these examples, Katie could conclude that all the cats in the world have tails. That's inductive reasoning. Or a young science student might heat several pans of water and notice that the water boils each time when it reaches 212 degrees Fahrenheit. From those experiments, the student might conclude that water always boils at 212 degrees Fahrenheit. This too is inductive reasoning.

Practice 1

Use inductive reasoning to finish the conclusion from each set of facts below.

    a.   A coin is tossed 10 times and each time it falls tails.

        Conclusion: _____ fall tails.

b. The foreman asked whether the top four workers on the loading dock had returned from lunch and none had.

Conclusion: _____ on the loading dock had returned from lunch.

c. In rhombus *ABCD*, all sides equal 0.4 inches. In rhombus *EFGH*, all sides equal 1 inch. In rhombus *IJKL*, all sides equal 1.5 inches.

 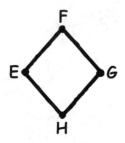 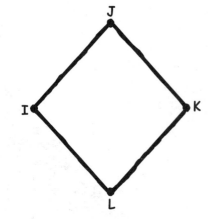

Conclusion: In any rhombus, _____ .

d. In the Murdock family, the father, mother, and youngest son have blue eyes.

Conclusion: _____ has blue eyes.

Assuming inductive reasoning was used, finish the set of facts to fit the conclusion below.

e. When a _____ object has no force applied to it, the object continues to travel at a constant velocity. When a _____ object has no force applied to it, the object continues to travel at a constant velocity. When a _____ object has no force applied to it, the object continues to travel at a constant velocity.

Conclusion: When an object of any mass has no force applied to it, the object continues to travel at a constant velocity.

Problem Set 1

Tell whether each sentence below is True or False.

1. Geometry is about shapes such as triangles, circles, squares, and rectangles.

2. Geometry is also about logical thinking.

3. The word "geometry" actually comes from a Latin word meaning "complex mathematics."

4. The Americans and Russians were the first to develop practical rules for geometry.

Complete each sentence below with the best of the choices given.

5. Geometry first began when people needed to _____ in order to create farms.

    A. milk cows   B. measure land
    C. chop wood   D. keep their children busy
    E. develop new crops

6. The early geometry rules were based on _____.

    A. practical experience   B. writings in encyclopedias
    C. textbooks   D. formulas in ancient scrolls
    E. algebra equations

7. In _____ we look at several examples of something and find a fact that holds true for those examples. Then we conclude that the fact is true for all other possible examples.

    A. deductive reasoning   B. algebraic reasoning
    C. inductive reasoning   D. trigonometric reasoning
    E. geometry reasoning

Use inductive reasoning to finish the conclusion from each set of facts below.

(a) 8. Twelve cans from the factory were examined, and all 12 had been contaminated.

    Conclusion: _____ from the factory were contaminated.

9. The magician pulled the Ace of Spades from the card deck 17 times in a row.

    Conclusion: The magician will pull the Ace of Spades from the card deck _____.

10. The first three donuts from the box were chocolate-covered.

    Conclusion: _____ in the box are chocolate-covered.

(b) 11. The teacher asked the first five students in the class to hand in their homework and none of them had it.

Conclusion: _____ in the class have their homework.

12. The temperature in Anchorage, Alaska has fallen below freezing every year for the past 100 years.

Conclusion: The temperature in Anchorage, Alaska will fall below freezing _____.

(c) 13. In square *ABCD*, all sides equal 0.5 inches. In square *EFGH*, all sides equal 1 inch. In square *IJKL*, all sides equal 2 inches.

Conclusion: In any square, _____.

14. In circle *O*, the distance from the center *O* to point *P* equals 1 centimeter, the distance from the center *O* to point *Q* equals 1 centimeter, and the distance from the center *O* to point *R* equals 1 centimeter.

Conclusion: The distance from the center *O* to any point on the circle is _____.

(d) 15. In the Burgess family, the father, mother, and oldest daughter have blonde hair.

Conclusion: _____ has blonde hair.

16. The first three balls the tennis player took out of the basket were yellow.

Conclusion: _____ are yellow.

17. Every one of Todd's friends lost their money when they bought a lottery ticket.

Conclusion: _____ when they buy a lottery ticket.

Assuming inductive reasoning was used, finish the set of facts to fit each conclusion below.

(e) 18. When a _____ object is dropped to the ground, it accelerates at 32 feet per second each second. When a _____ object is dropped to the ground, it accelerates at 32 feet per second each second. When a _____ object is dropped to the ground, it accelerates at 32 feet per second each second.

Conclusion: When an object of any weight is dropped to the ground, it will accelerate at 32 feet per second each second.

19. The police officer _____ of the first five drivers who stopped at the traffic light.

Conclusion: The police officer will ask to see the driver's license of all the drivers who stop at the traffic light.

20. In the first seven experiments _____ melted at 450 degrees Celsius.

Conclusion: The chemical compound will always melt at 450 degrees Celsius.

Lesson 2—Deductive Reasoning and the Greeks

As we learned in Lesson 1, the Egyptians and Babylonians discovered rules of geometry through practical experience. They used inductive reasoning, remember, which involves looking at a few examples and then concluding that all other possible examples work the same way. Although these early rules were helpful, the subject of geometry didn't really blossom until the Ancient Greeks began to work with it.

Enter the Greeks

The Greeks were great mathematicians and philosophers who had brilliant ideas on many subjects. They weren't satisfied with the practical geometry from Egypt and Babylon, because it seemed too uncertain. Being philosophers, the Greeks were very concerned with discovering facts that were absolutely true. They didn't want facts that were probably true. They wanted to know for sure.

We need certainty!

It didn't take these Greeks long to realize that inductive reasoning, the method used by the Egyptians and Babylonians, only gives probable facts. For example, what if we met four red-headed men and they all had mustaches. Using inductive reasoning, we could conclude that all red-headed men have mustaches. But this is false, because there are plenty of clean-shaven red-headed men in the world. Even in science, inductive reasoning doesn't always work. For instance, we could conduct experiments with copper, brass, iron, and a dozen other substances, and every one would expand when heated. From that, we might conclude that all substances expand when heated. That would be a false conclusion, however, because water actually contracts (shrinks) when heated at temperatures that are near freezing. So inductive reasoning doesn't always give accurate conclusions. It works some of the time, but not all of the time.

Deductive Reasoning

The Greeks couldn't accept this. They wanted all their rules of geometry to be absolutely correct, beyond a shadow of a doubt. That's why they used another type of logical thinking that today is called **deductive reasoning**, or just **deduction**. With this type of thinking, we start with an accurate assumption and then, as long as we've reasoned correctly, our conclusion *has* to be true.

To show you how it works, let's go through a simple example.

> If a person lives in California, then that person lives in the United States. If Marsha lives in California, then Marsha must live in the United States.

As long as it's true that a person living in California also lives in the United States (and we know that's right), there's no way that the conclusion about Marsha can possibly be wrong. That's deductive reasoning. Here's another example, which is very well known.

> If all men are mortal and if Socrates (a famous Greek philosopher) is a man, then Socrates must be mortal.

Again, since we've used deductive reasoning, there's no way the conclusion about Socrates's being mortal can be wrong.

Conditional Statements

Notice the statements in our examples use the words "if" and "then." *If* something is true, *then* something else has to be true. The "if" statement is the assumption. Its technical name is **premise**.[1] The "then" statement is called the **conclusion**. And "if-then" statements in general are called **conditional statements**. Our Marsha example contains two conditional statements. In the first one, the premise is "If a person lives in California," and the conclusion is "then that person lives in the United States." In the second conditional statement, the premise is "If Marsha lives in California," and the conclusion is "then Marsha must live in the United States." If-then or conditional statements are used a lot in deductive reasoning because they show clearly what is being assumed (the "if" statement) and what is being concluded (the "then" statement) using logic.

Using Diagrams

One easy way to tell if a deduction has been done correctly is to draw a diagram of it. The statements can be represented with circles, or any other closed shapes. Here are diagrams of the Marsha and Socrates examples.

---

[1] The premise is also sometimes called the "hypothesis."

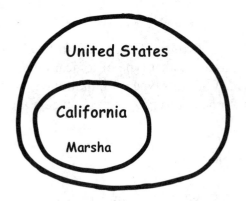

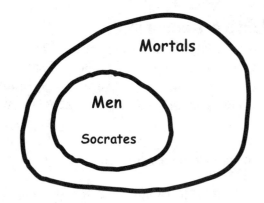

Since California is inside the United States, we put the California circle inside the U.S. circle. And since Marsha lives in California, she goes inside the California circle. That means Marsha has to also be inside the U.S. circle. Therefore, Marsha must live in the U.S. The diagram makes it very clear that there's no way Marsha could live outside the U.S.

The diagram for the Socrates example shows that all men are mortal by putting the circle for men completely inside the circle for mortals. But since Socrates is a man he has to go inside the Men circle, which automatically puts him inside the mortal circle as well. Therefore, Socrates has to be mortal. So diagrams can be really helpful in making sure that deductive reasoning is done correctly. These kinds of reasoning diagrams are called **Venn diagrams** or **Euler diagrams** (pronounced "oiler" after the mathematician Leonhard Euler).

Valid and Invalid Reasoning

It's very important to be able to tell whether a deduction has been done correctly or incorrectly. To see why, take a look at this example.

> If a watch is gold, then it's expensive. If Ray's watch is expensive, then Ray's watch is gold.

This looks like deductive reasoning, so it's tempting to believe that the conclusion—that Ray's watch is gold must be right. The problem is that the deduction wasn't done correctly. A diagram makes this clear.

The premises ("if" statements) tell us that gold watches and Ray's watch are expensive, so we have to put both of those inside the expensive watches circle. But the statements don't say anything about Ray's watch having to go inside the gold watches circle, which means that we cannot conclude that Ray's watch is gold.

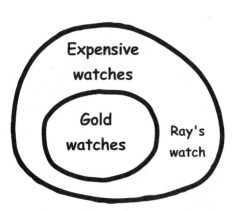

When a deduction is done incorrectly, we say that the reasoning (or the "argument" as it's also called) was **invalid**. So the reasoning in our watch example was invalid. When a deduction is done correctly we say that the reasoning (or argument) is **valid**. The earlier examples with Marsha and Socrates were both valid. And the easiest way to figure out whether a deduction is valid or invalid is to draw a diagram.

So the main point of this lesson—and it's an important one—is that deductive reasoning can give you conclusions that are absolutely true. That's why the Greeks preferred it to inductive reasoning, which only gives conclusions that might be true.

Practice 2

a. Tell whether the argument below is an example of inductive or deductive reasoning.

If all the dogs in the kennel are collies, and if Tim's dog, Rover, is in the kennel, then Rover must be a collie.

b. Draw a Venn diagram to represent the set of conditional statements below.

If a being is a Saturnite, then it is striped. If RJ4 is a Saturnite, then RJ4 is striped.

c. Write conditional statements to represent the Venn diagram on the right.

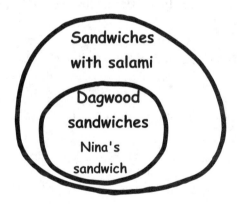

d. Tell whether the argument below is a valid or invalid deduction.

If a person is a good surfer, then she has excellent balance. If Tonya has excellent balance, then she must be a good surfer.

e. Use deductive reasoning to write the conclusion for the statements below.

If a person is a licensed driver, then she must be over 16 years old. If Patti is a licensed driver, _____.

Problem Set 2

Tell whether each sentence below is True or False.

1. Inductive reasoning, the method used by the Egyptians and Babylonians, only gives probable facts.
2. In deductive reasoning, you start with an accurate assumption, then, as long as you've reasoned correctly, the conclusion *has* to be true.

3. When a deduction is done incorrectly, we say that the reasoning is "valid," and when it's done correctly, we say the reasoning is "invalid."

Complete each sentence below with the best of the choices given.

4. The "if" statement is the assumption and it's called the _____.

   A. intercept   B. conditional statement
   C. induction   D. conclusion
   E. premise

5. The "then" statement is called the _____.

   A. intercept   B. conditional statement
   C. induction   D. conclusion
   E. premise

6. "If-then" statements in general are called _____.

   A. intercepts   B. conditional statements
   C. inductions   D. conclusions
   E. premises

Use inductive reasoning to finish the conclusion from each set of facts below.

7. The doctor said that in all 50 cases reported, the treatment cured the disease.

   Conclusion: _____ cure the disease.

8. All 140 customers in the survey said they were satisfied with the company's new Silly Billy doll.

   Conclusion: _____ are satisfied with the company's new Silly Billy doll.

Identify the premise and the conclusion of each conditional statement below.

9. If you run the 100 yard dash in 10 seconds, then you are a good sprinter.

10. If Bruce Teller wins the election, then he will become mayor of Cove Creek.

Tell whether each argument below is an example of inductive or deductive reasoning.

11. The product of 2 and 1 is 2, which is an even number. The product of 2 and 2 is 4, which is an even number. The product of 2 and 3 is 6, which is an even number.

Conclusion: The product of 2 and any positive integer is an even number.

(a) 12. If all the people at Myra's party are 16 years old, and if Sarah is at Myra's party, then Sarah must be 16 years old.

13. If the first 3 contestants on the game show won prizes, then all of the contestants will win prizes.

Draw a Venn diagram to represent each set of conditional statements below.

(b) 14. If a being is a Martian, then it is red. If XMQ is a Martian, then XMQ is red.

15. If a dentist is dressed up like Robin Hood, he must be on his way to a costume party. If Linda's dentist is dressed up like Robin Hood, he must be on his way to a costume party.

Write conditional statements to represent each Venn diagram below.

(c) 16.   **17.**

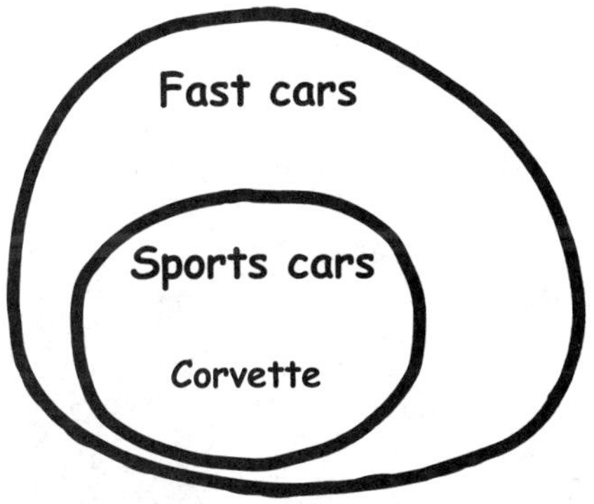

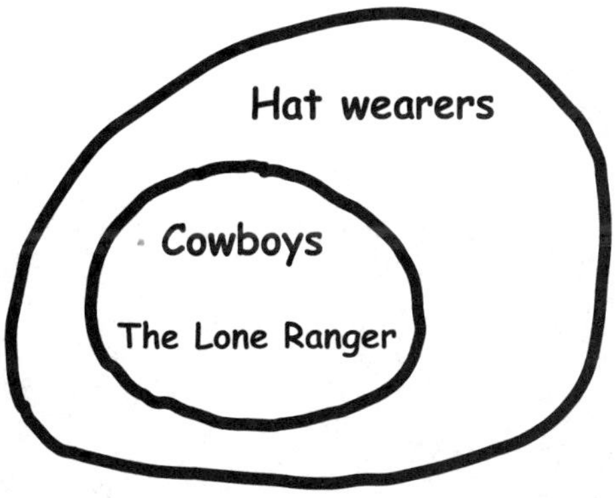

Tell whether the arguments below are valid or invalid deductions.

(d) 18. If a guy wears cowboy boots, then he must like country music. If Jake likes country music, then he must wear cowboy boots.

19. If a planet is in our solar system, then it orbits the sun. If Neptune is a planet in our solar system, then Neptune must orbit the sun.

Use deductive reasoning to write the conclusion for each set of statements below.

20. If a person is a teenager, then he or she must love jeans. If Terry is a teenager, _____.

(e) 21. If someone is a registered voter, then he must be over 18 years old. If Sam is a registered voter, _____.

Lesson 3—Self-Evident Truths

We've been learning about deductive reasoning, which the Greeks discovered gives absolutely correct results. Deductive reasoning does have a weakness, though. It turns out that the conclusion is only absolutely certain if the premises are true. Remember, the premises are the assumptions or "if" statements that the deduction starts out with.

Valid Deduction/Wrong Answer

To show you what a problem this can be, here's an example of a deduction with a false premise.

If a student is a sixth grader, then he is in high school. If Marty is a sixth grader, then he must be in high school.

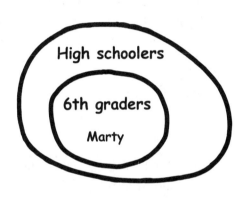

The reasoning for this deduction is valid. The diagram for it is on the right. Since the first premise says that a sixth grader is in high school, we're justified in putting the sixth grader circle inside the high schoolers circle. And since the second premise says that Marty is a sixth grader, we can put him inside the sixth grader circle. That means Marty has to be inside the high schoolers circle too, which makes him in high school. But obviously, the conclusion is false. Marty can't be in high school, because he is only in sixth grade. The problem is that the first premise is wrong. A sixth grade student is actually not in high school. This shows that even if the reasoning in a deduction is valid, the conclusion can still be wrong if a premise is false.

Postulates

After seeing this example, you may be thinking that the Greeks weren't so smart after all. They chose to use deductive reasoning in their Geometry because it supposedly always gives correct results. But now we see that deductive reasoning only works when the premises are true. The Greeks were plenty smart, though, and they had a way around this difficulty. What they decided to do was only use incredibly simple premises. They wanted ones that were so simple and obvious that you'd have to be crazy to disagree with them. They called these premises "self-evident truths" or **postulates**. (The word "postulate" actually comes from a Latin word which means literally "self-evident truth.") Here's an example of a postulate from Greek Geometry:

Two points determine a unique straight line.

No one would argue with the truth of this statement. The Greeks felt that if they only started out with these obviously true postulates, and if they always used deductive reasoning, then all their conclusions would have to be true as well. That was their plan for making sure that all of their rules of Geometry were absolutely correct. The Greeks were also careful to limit the number of postulates. They didn't want to make any more assumptions than necessary. In this way, the Greeks built up a set of Geometry rules that were much more reliable than any of the Egyptian or Babylonian rules.

An interesting story about postulates is that they were used in the U.S. Declaration of Independence. Thomas Jefferson, the author of the declaration, was an intellectual who knew a lot about geometry. That's why he based his argument for the American colonies' independence on important postulates. Jefferson even used the phrase "self-evident truths." Here is the sentence as it appears in the declaration.

Thomas Jefferson
(author: Declaration of Independence)

We hold these *truths* to be *self-evident*, that all men are created equal and endowed by their Creator with certain unalienable Rights, that among these are Life, Liberty and the pursuit of Happiness.

Practice 3

a. Rewrite the sentence below in conditional ("if-then") form.

All the ice cream stores on Wylie Drive sell chocolate malts.

b. Write conditional statements to represent the Venn diagram on the right.

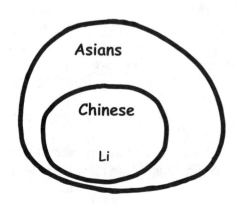

18

c. Tell whether the argument below is a valid or invalid deduction.

Since all tortoises are slow and Wally is slow, Wally must be a tortoise.

d. Use deductive reasoning to write the conclusion for the set of statements below.

All of the modern poet's works were classics and *I Say Tomato, You Say Radish* was written by him. Therefore, _____.

e. Indicate whether the statement below seems "self-evident" or "not self-evident."

If equal numbers are added to two quantities that are equal, the results are equal.

Problem Set 3

Tell whether each sentence below is True or False.

1. Even if the reasoning in a deduction is valid, the conclusion can still be wrong if the premises are false.

2. Postulates or "self-evident truths" are statements that seem obviously true.

3. The Greeks felt that all their conclusions in geometry would have to be correct if they just used inductive reasoning.

Identify the premise and the conclusion of each conditional statement below.

4. If all of Salvador Dominguez's napkin drawings are great works of art, then Salvador Dominguez was a great napkin drawer.

5. If all the players on the team are injured, then the team will have to forfeit tonight's game.

Rewrite each sentence below in conditional ("if-then") form.

(a) 6. All the pizza joints in Melville serve pepperoni.

7. An attorney who wears a robe to work is a judge.

Draw a Venn diagram to represent each set of conditional statements below.

8. If a person is a bull rider, then he has broken a bone. If Jeff is a bull rider, then Jeff has broken a bone.

9. If a person is a linguist, then he loves words. If Gustav is a linguist, then Gustav loves words.

10. If a player is in the league, then he is taller than 6 feet. If Bo Price is a player in the league, then Bo Price is taller than 6 feet.

Write conditional statements to represent each Venn diagram below.

(b) 11.

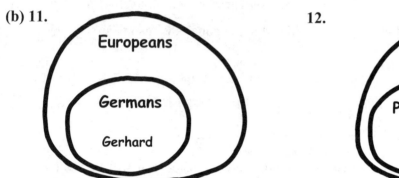

12.

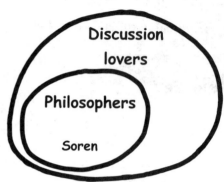

Tell whether the arguments below are valid or invalid deductions.

(c) 13. Since all deep-sea divers wear flippers and Brita wears flippers, she must be a deep-sea diver.

14. Puppies always have to be walked in the morning, and Pedro is a puppy, so Pedro has to be walked in the morning.

Use deductive reasoning to write the conclusion for each set of statements below.

15. If an event is a pig roast, then lots of barbecue sauce will be served. If we are going to a pig roast on Friday night, _____.

(d) 16. All of Heinrich's novels were based on his travels in Africa. The novel *As Free as the Grass Grows* was written by Heinrich. Therefore, _____.

17. Digital cameras don't need film. I have a digital camera, so _____.

Indicate whether each statement below seems "self-evident" or "not self-evident."

(e) 18. Things equal to the same thing are equal to each other.

19. All right angles are equal.

20. The sum of the three angles of any triangle always equals 180 degrees.

Lesson 4—Logic Chains

We learned in the last lesson that the Greeks figured out a way to make their Geometry rules as certain as possible. They started with the simplest premises, called self-evident truths or "postulates." These are statements that are incredibly obvious. The Greeks felt that if their premises were definitely true and if they used deductive reasoning to come up with their conclusions, then those conclusions would have to be true. Remember, one of their postulates—which no one would disagree with—was "Two points determine a unique straight line."

If-then-If-then-If-then...

It might seem hard to come up with very many geometry rules by starting out with such simple postulates. But what makes deductive reasoning so powerful is that it can be used over and over again to create long chains of logic. Here's a somewhat silly (and non-geometric) example.

Madame Pompadour

If the butler was home at noon,
then he couldn't have committed the murder.

If the butler didn't commit the murder,
then Lila Langone must be lying.

If Lila Langone is lying,
then Mr. Bragg must have stolen the murder weapon.

If Mr. Bragg stole the murder weapon,
then he must have visited the clubhouse at noon.

If Mr. Bragg visited the clubhouse at noon,
then Madame Pompadour must not have been in the clubhouse alone.

If Madame Pompadour was not in the clubhouse alone,
then Madame Pompadour and Mr. Bragg must be accomplices.

Notice that this logic chain is made up of several "if-then" (conditional) statements. Notice also that each "if" statement is the same as the "then" statement just before it. That's how the chain is connected. A logic chain, because it can go on indefinitely, can lead to a surprising conclusion. What's more, if the premises are true, and if the logic chain uses only deductive reasoning, then the conclusion will have to be true as well. In our example, from the starting point of the butler being home at noon, we were able to conclude that Madame Pompadour and Mr. Bragg were accomplices. So with logic chains, starting with true postulates and applying deductive reasoning really can uncover valuable new facts. This is the method used in geometry.

Terms and Symbols

Logic chains are actually called **direct proofs**. The word "proof" means that we have "proven" something is true by using deduction, which is the most reliable form of reasoning. Since proofs are used so much in geometry, mathematicians have come up with short ways of writing about them. For instance, each of the lines in the proof above can be represented by a letter. The line "If the butler was home at noon," can be shown with the letter a and the line "then he couldn't have committed the murder" can be shown with the letter b. Those two lines together make up an "if-then" (conditional) statement that can then be written as $a \rightarrow b$. This just means that if a is true, then b is true. Or, another way of saying it is, "a implies b." By representing the other lines with letters of the alphabet, we could show the whole direct proof in symbol form.

$$a \rightarrow b, \ b \rightarrow c, \ c \rightarrow d, \ d \rightarrow e, \ e \rightarrow f, \ f \rightarrow g$$

The symbols $f \rightarrow g$ stand for the last two lines: "If Madame Pompadour was not in the clubhouse alone, then Madame Pompadour and Mr. Bragg must be accomplices." The entire argument proves the following statement:

> If the butler was home at noon, then Madame Pompadour and Mr. Bragg must be accomplices.

This final conclusion is called a **theorem**, which is just the end result of an argument that has been proven with deductive reasoning. The theorem above can also be written in symbols as $a \rightarrow g$.

Practice 4

a. Rewrite the sentence below in conditional ("if-then") form.

A pastry from Mel's Bakery is delicious.

b. Tell whether the argument below is a valid or invalid deduction.

If all conductors are flamboyant and if Carlos is flamboyant, then Carlos is a conductor.

c. Tell whether the argument below is a valid or invalid deduction.

The Millers have meatloaf every Thursday and today is Thursday, so the Millers must be having meatloaf.

d. Tell the theorem that is proved by the statements below.

If Dana goes shopping tomorrow, then she'll buy a sweater.
If Dana buys a sweater, then she won't be able to afford the theater tickets.
If Dana can't afford the theater tickets, then she'll have to stay home on Friday.
If Dana stays home on Friday, then she'll have to eat leftovers.

e. Complete a direct proof for the theorem by rearranging the statements in logical order.

Theorem: If Melanie wins her match, she'll lose in the semi-finals.

If Melanie is in the semi-finals, then she'll have to play on Saturday.
If Melanie is too tired, then she'll lose in the semi-finals.
If Melanie wins her match, then she'll be in the semi-finals.
If Melanie plays on Saturday, then she'll be too tired.

Problem Set 4

Tell whether each sentence below is True or False.

1. What makes deductive reasoning so powerful is that it can be used over and over again to create long chains of logic.

2. A logic chain is made up of several conditional statements, where each "if" statement is the same as the "then" statement before it.

3. A conditional statement ("if-then") can be written as $a \rightarrow b$, where a represents the premise ("if" statement) and b represents the conclusion ("then" statement).

Complete each sentence below with the best of the choices given.

4. Logic chains are actually called _____.

    A. intercepts   B. inductive statements
    C. direct proofs   D. premises
    E. geometrical complexities

5. The final conclusion of an argument that has been proven with deductive reasoning is called a(n) _____.

    A. syllogism   B. inductive statement
    C. direct proof   D. theorem
    E. geometrical complexity

Use inductive reasoning to finish the conclusion from each premise below.

6. The bowler bowled a strike 8 times in a row.

Conclusion: _____ bowl a strike.

7. Sales at the restaurant chain have risen every year for the last 10 years.

Conclusion: _____.

Rewrite each sentence below in conditional ("if-then") form.

8. A well-balanced diet will give your body the vitamins it needs.

(a) 9. Radioactive material is very dangerous.

Draw a Venn diagram to represent each set of conditional statements below.

10. If a soldier is always brave, and if Ryan is a soldier, then Ryan is brave.

11. If all mules are stubborn, and if Bertha is a mule, then Bertha is stubborn.

Write conditional statements to represent each Venn diagram below.

12.   **13.**

 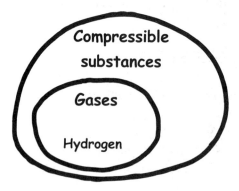

Tell whether the arguments below are valid or invalid deductions.

(b) 14. If all scientists are intelligent and if Peter is intelligent, then Peter is a scientist.

(c) 15. It rains every Tuesday and today is Tuesday, so it must be raining today.

Use deductive reasoning to write the conclusion for each set of statements below.

16. If the medical intern is sleep-deprived, and if sleep-deprived people are grouchy, then _____.

17. All of Beethoven's string quartets are masterpieces, and the Quartet in F major, op. 135 is one of Beethoven's string quartets. Therefore, _____.

Tell the theorem that is proved by each set of statements below.

(d) 18. If Joey's locker is empty, then he lost his glove,
If Joey lost his glove, then he won't be able to practice this afternoon.
If Joey doesn't practice this afternoon, then he'll have to stay home.
If Joey has to stay home, then he'll have to clean the garage.

19. If the sky is turbulent, then the flight will be delayed by 2 hours.
If the flight is delayed by 2 hours, then Mr. Russell will be late for his meeting.
If Mr. Russell is late for his meeting, then he won't be able to close the sale.
If Mr. Russell doesn't close the sale, then he'll get fired.

Complete a direct proof for each theorem by rearranging the statements in logical order.

(e) 20. Theorem: If the team wins the game, they will lose in the playoffs.

If the team is in the playoffs, they'll have to play in Dallas.
If the team wins the game, they'll be in the playoffs.
If the fans are against the team, they will lose in the playoffs.
If the team plays in Dallas, the fans will be against them.

21. Theorem: If the flowers aren't watered, the bride will be upset.

If the flowers aren't shown at the wedding, the bride will be upset.
If the flowers wither, they'll have to be thrown away.
If the flowers aren't watered, they will wither.
If the flowers are thrown away, they can't be shown at the wedding.

Lesson 5—Euclid: The Father of Geometry

The Greek mathematician Euclid is considered to be the father of geometry. That seems strange when you consider the fact that Euclid didn't discover a lot of new geometry rules himself. And he came along hundreds of years after the Egyptians and Babylonians discovered their practical rules for geometry. Euclid even lived years after the first Greek geometers, who decided that deductive reasoning was superior to inductive reasoning.

Nothing but Deduction

If Euclid didn't discover anything new, why is he considered the father of geometry? As it turns out, Euclid was the first person to organize all of the geometry rules into a completely deductive system. In other words, he was the first one to start with just a few "self-evident" postulates and then use deductive reasoning to prove all of the rules of geometry that others had figured out through practical experience.

Euclid
(father of geometry)

Euclid began with only 10 postulates. All of these were statements that seemed obviously true to everybody. Euclid's postulates are listed in the box below. Although the wording is a little different, these 10 postulates are basically the same ones Euclid used.

Euclid's Postulates

1.	Two points determine a unique straight line.
2.	A straight line extends indefinitely far in either direction.
3.	A circle may be drawn with any given center and any given radius.
4.	All right angles are equal.
5.	Given a line ℓ and a point P not on that line, there exists in the plane of P and ℓ and through P one and only one line m, which does not meet the given line ℓ.

Euclid's Postulates (continued)

6.	Things equal to the same thing are equal to each other.
7.	If equals be added to equals, the sums are equal.
8.	If equals be subtracted from equals, the remainders are equal.
9.	Figures which can be made to coincide are equal.
10.	The whole is greater than any part.

Euclid realized that precise definitions were important, so he also defined 23 geometrical words, like line, triangle, and angle. Then, using those postulates and definitions, Euclid proceeded to prove theorems (geometry rules) one by one. And the neat thing is that after a theorem was proved deductively, Euclid was able to use it as an assumption in proving something else. In that way, he built up a very large number of geometry rules, every one based on those original postulates and definitions. What's more, since all the rules were proved with deductive reasoning, Euclid was satisfied that they were absolutely correct. So Euclid was the first person to make the subject of geometry completely logical.

The Elements

Euclid's geometry system can be found in his book *The Elements*. It's the most famous textbook in history, which is why more copies of *The Elements* have been printed in the Western world than any other book besides the Bible. And even though it was written 2,300 years ago, *The Elements* can still be found in bookstores and libraries today.

The Elements is made up of 13 small "books" (which are actually like chapters), each one covering a different topic of geometry. All high school Geometry courses, including this one, are based on information found in *The Elements*. Euclid's book is very long, though—it has about 465 major theorems—and many of the proofs are really tough. So in high school we don't cover everything in *The Elements*, just the most important topics.

Main Themes

Euclid's book is not just a bunch of rules thrown together haphazardly. If you read *The Elements* carefully, you'll find that it has several main themes. One theme is the concept of congruent figures. **Congruent figures** are figures that are the same shape and the same size. For example, here are two congruent triangles.

In *The Elements*, Euclid discusses lots of methods for determining whether two figures are congruent. To you, congruent figures might seem like a ridiculously simple concept. After all, it only takes a quick glance to tell if figures are the same shape and size. And if we were really worried about it, we could just measure the triangles. But remember Euclid and all other mathematicians want as much

Congruent Triangles

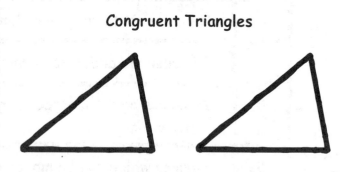

certainty as possible. A glance can be deceiving; everybody's had experiences with optical illusions. And even a careful measurement can never be precise, because a ruler only has so many marks on it (and your eyes are only so good). So the only way Euclid was willing to accept that two figures are congruent is if that fact could be proven using deductive reasoning. That's why *The Elements* has methods for *proving* two figures (whether they're triangles or other shapes) are congruent. And this is one of the main themes of the book.

The concept of congruent figures is not just a pie-in-the-sky math idea. It has many uses in the real world. For example, when an automobile company is manufacturing car parts, it has to make sure that all the parts of a particular kind are congruent: they have to be exactly the same shape and size. Otherwise, when your car broke down, and you wanted to buy a new part to fix it, that new part wouldn't fit well in your car.

Another main theme in *The Elements* is the concept of similar figures. **Similar figures are figures that have the same shape but are different sizes.** Take the two similar rectangles to the right as an example. Even though the rectangles have the same shape, the one on the left is smaller than the one on the right. Euclid's *Elements* contains a lot of theorems that allow us to figure out deductively that two figures are similar.

Similar Rectangles

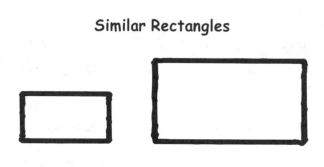

The concept of similar figures is also practical. For example, the blueprint for a house uses similar figures. The blueprint has drawings of the different rooms and closets in the house, and those rooms are the exact same shape as the actual house, but much smaller. Another example is a model of a new building that is about to be constructed. That model will be the same shape as the actual building, but smaller.

A third major theme of *The Elements* is the concept of equivalent figures. **Equivalent figures are just figures that have the same area.** As you know, the area of a figure is just the space inside of it. Even figures that have totally different shapes can have the same area. Here is a rectangle and a triangle, each with an area of 12 square inches.

Euclid's book has a lot of theorems for calculating the area of figures of different shapes, and all these procedures have been proven deductively. Everybody knows that area calculations are extremely practical in everyday life and lots of situations.

So congruent figures, similar figures, and equivalent figures are three of the major themes of Euclid's famous book. These same concepts will be major themes for us as we go through our Geometry course.

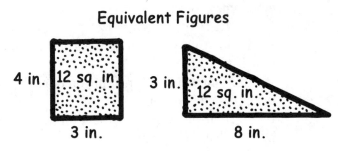

Equivalent Figures

Both figures have area = 12 square inches.

Practice 5

a. Draw a Venn diagram to represent the conditional statement below.

All drummers are loud, and Robbie is a drummer. So Robbie is loud.

b. Write conditional statements to represent the Venn diagram on the right.

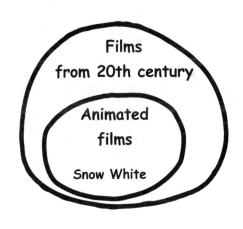

c. Tell whether the argument below is a valid or invalid deduction.

People who watch TV a lot usually don't have a wide vocabulary. George does not have a wide vocabulary, so he must watch TV a lot.

d. Tell the theorem that is proved by the statements below.

If the cat gets outside, he'll climb onto the roof.
If the cat climbs onto the roof, the noise will wake up the baby.
If the noise wakes up the baby, the baby will cry.
If the baby cries, Mom will have to sing the baby to sleep.

e. Complete a direct proof for the theorem by rearranging the statements in logical order.

Theorem: If Mrs. Johnson has the driveway redone, Mr. Johnson will have to go to the emergency room.

If Mr. Johnson gets wet cement on his shoes, he will also get some on Mrs. Johnson's new carpet.
If Mrs. Johnson hits Mr. Johnson over the head with a frying pan, he will have to go to the emergency room.
If Mr. Johnson gets wet cement on Mrs. Johnson's new carpet, she will hit him over the head with a frying pan.
If Mrs. Johnson has the driveway redone, Mr. Johnson will get wet cement on his shoes.

Problem Set 5

Tell whether each sentence below is True or False.

1. The Greek mathematician Euclid is considered the father of geometry.

2. Euclid wrote a famous book entitled *The Elements*, which starts with 10 postulates.

3. Euclid decided not to use deductive reasoning in his book.

Complete each sentence below with the best of the choices given.

4. Congruent figures are figures that _____.

    A. are the same shape and the same size   B. are the same shape and different size
    C. have the same area   D. have the same line thickness
    E. none of the above

5. Similar figures are figures that _____.

    A. are the same shape and the same size   B. are the same shape and different size
    C. have the same area   D. have the same line thickness
    E. none of the above

6. Equivalent figures are figures that _____.

    A. are the same shape and the same size   B. are the same shape and different size
    C. have the same area   D. have the same line thickness
    E. none of the above

Identify the premise and the conclusion of each conditional statement below.

   7. If Odysseus returns home within one year, then Penelope will be pleased.

   8. If justice is served, then Lady Macbeth will be punished.

Rewrite each sentence below in conditional ("if-then") form.

   9. A Rolls Royce is a very expensive car.

   10. It's too dangerous to cross the tracks when a train is within sight.

Draw a Venn diagram to represent each set of conditional statements below.

   11. All good students are conscientious, and Annette is a good student. So Annette is conscientious.

(a) 12. Interpreters are bilingual and Niels is an interpreter. So Niels is bilingual.

Write conditional statements to represent each Venn diagram below.

   13.   (b) 14.

Tell whether the arguments below are valid or invalid deductions.

   15. All competent lifeguards are fast swimmers. Mitch is a fast swimmer, therefore he is a competent lifeguard.

(c) 16. A starving population always leads to a revolution. There was a revolution in France in the late 18th century, so the population of France must have been starving.

31

Use deductive reasoning to write the conclusion for each set of statements below.

17. If all puppeteers have strong forearms, and Randy is a puppeteer, then _____.

18. If all stationary satellites must orbit 24,000 miles above the earth's surface, and X-Y45 is a stationary satellite, then _____.

Tell the theorem that is proved by each set of statements below.

(d) 19. If Olga falls asleep on the private plane, she will get a crick in her neck.
If Olga gets a crick in her neck, she will not be able to turn her head to the left.
If Olga can't turn her head to the left, she will not be able to perform in the ballet.
If Olga does not perform in the ballet, thousands of ticket buyers will feel cheated.

20. If the office water cooler is removed, then Todd and Steve will no longer have a place to talk about the game.
If Todd and Steve no longer have a place to talk about the game, then their friendship will suffer.
If Todd and Steve's friendship suffers, then their wives will stop having tea together.
If their wives stop having tea together, then Steve's wife will no longer have a reason to make little cucumber sandwiches.

Complete a direct proof for each theorem by rearranging the statements in logical order.

(e) 21. Theorem: If Twila Glisten points to the grand prize, contestant #3 will be the runner-up.

If contestant #3 misses the question, then he will be the runner-up.
If Twila Glisten points to the grand prize, then the audience will say "ooh" and "ahh".
If contestant #3 gets nervous, then he will miss the question.
If the audience says "ooh" and "ahh," then contestant #3 will get nervous.

22. Theorem: If the florist delivers the roses to the wrong office, Jane will end up wrapping presents on Christmas Eve.

If Jane postpones her Christmas shopping again, she will end up wrapping presents on Christmas Eve.
If Jane thinks she has a secret admirer, she will make a hair appointment for tomorrow.
If Jane makes a hair appointment for tomorrow, she will have to postpone her Christmas shopping again.
If the florist delivers the roses to the wrong office, Jane will think she has a secret admirer.

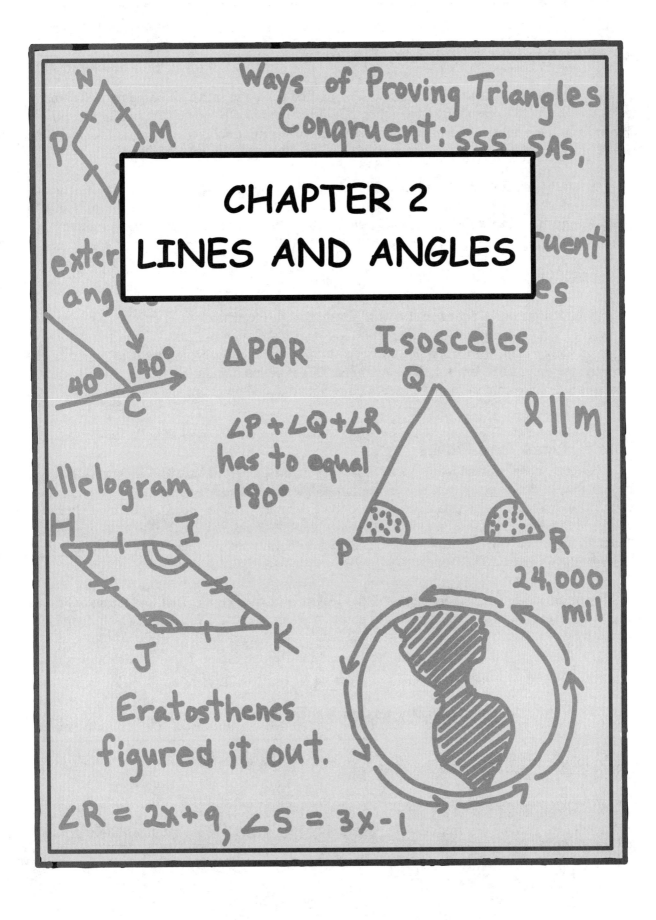

N

P

M

Ways of Proving Triangles
Congruent: SSS, SAS,

exter
ang

ruent
es

40° 140°
C

ΔPQR

Isosceles
Q

ℓ || m

∠P+∠Q+∠R
has to equal
180°

llelogram

H   I

P   R

24,000
mil

J   K

Eratosthenes
figured it out.

∠R = 2x + 9, ∠S = 3x - 1

CHAPTER 2
LINES AND ANGLES

Lesson 6—Too Simple to Define

In Chapter 1, we learned that Euclid was the first person to prove all of the major geometry rules with deductive reasoning. Remember, he started with just 10 postulates and 23 definitions. By limiting the number of postulates and defining every term, Euclid was trying to take all of the uncertainty out of geometry.

Even though Euclid was an incredibly logical person, after 2,300 years, mathematicians have found a few errors in Euclid's thinking. One thing they realized was that it's impossible to define every geometry term that's used. Think about it. To define a term like "triangle," we might want to use the words "points" and "sides." But then what do "points" and "sides" mean? We'd have to define those words too. In giving definitions for points and sides, though, we would need other words that would also require definitions.

Dictionaries don't define every word, even though they claim to. You may have had an experience with a dictionary like this. You look up a word such as "insane" and the definition given is "crazy." But then when you look up "crazy," the dictionary defines it as "insane." So actually, the dictionary hasn't defined anything. This is called circular reasoning. And if you try to define every possible word that's used, you're bound to end up going in a circle.

Points, Lines, and Planes

Modern mathematicians are more logical than dictionary writers and they realized that geometry would ultimately need some words that are not defined. Appropriately enough, they called these **undefined terms**. They left only extremely simple words undefined, because everybody understands those intuitively. Three important undefined terms used in geometry are "point," "line," and "plane." Mathematicians give no definitions for these words, although they describe them vaguely.

A **point** indicates position, and it has no length, width, or depth. That just means it has no size at all. Nevertheless, when showing a point on paper, we use a little dot (which does have some size).

• A

A point actually has no length, width, or depth.

Notice that there's a letter *A* next to the dot. That's the way we name points when talking about them in geometry. We always use a capital letter.

A second undefined term is line. Of course, everybody knows what a line is. But the mathematician's vague description is that a **line** is a set of points that extend indefinitely in either direction. A line has length, but no width or depth. (The lines we draw on paper have width, so they're not entirely accurate.) Importantly, in geometry, the word line refers only to a line that goes on forever in both directions. That's shown by putting arrows on either end, like this.

A line has length but no width or depth, and goes on forever in both directions.

Notice there are two points on the line: *A* and *B*. Those two points can be used to name the line. We can just call it "line *AB*" and write it as $\overrightarrow{AB}$. The little line on top with arrows on both ends shows that the line goes forever. It doesn't matter where the points *A* and *B* fall on the line. As long as we have two points, then we can use them to give the line its name. If we don't have two points on the line, we can still name the line by using a single lower case letter. For instance, without the points *A* and *B*, we could just call the line *l*. Then we would put the letter *l* next to the line like this.

A line can also be named with a single lower case letter.

Of course, any other lower case letter would work just as well.

One more undefined term is plane. A **plane** can be (vaguely) described as a set of points that forms a flat surface which extends forever in all directions. So a plane has length and width, but no depth. It's not possible to show a picture of a plane that goes on forever (we can't do it for a line either). So when drawing a plane, we put a border around it, as you can see. And notice the letter *P* in the upper left corner of the plane. As with points, we name planes with a single capital letter.

A plane has length and width but no depth, and goes forever in all directions.

So three undefined terms in geometry are point, line, and plane. Using these terms, it's possible to write definitions for other important words. Those definitions, along with some postulates, can then be used with deductive reasoning to prove a lot of geometry rules, which is what we'll do in this book. Unlike Euclid, though, we won't limit ourselves to just 10 postulates and 23 definitions. We'll throw in some extra postulates and definitions to make the concepts a little clearer. We won't prove every single rule (the way Euclid did) either. As we mentioned, some of Euclid's proofs are really tough. So we'll just tell you those and move on.

Practice 6

a. Tell whether the symbol "*n*" could represent a plane, point, or line.

b. Tell whether the symbol "*Q*" could represent a plane, point, or line.

c. Name the line below. Write your answer in proper form.

d. Rewrite the sentence below in conditional ("if-then") form.

A tree surgeon operates on trees.

e. Tell whether the arguments below are valid or invalid deductions.

All real cowboys own a pair of cowboy boots. Justin owns a pair of cowboy boots. So Justin must be a real cowboy.

Problem Set 6

Tell whether each sentence below is True or False.

1. In geometry every single term must be defined.

2. A point indicates position, and it has no length, width, or depth.

Complete each description below by filling in the blank.

3. A _____ is a set of points that extend indefinitely in either direction, and it has length, but no width or depth.

4. A _____ is a set of points that forms a flat surface which extends forever in all directions and has length and width, but no depth.

Tell whether each symbol below could represent a plane, point, or line. You can have more than one answer to a problem.

(a) 5. *m*   **6.** $\overleftrightarrow{AB}$ **(b) 7.** *P*

Name each line below. Write your answer in proper form.

(c) 8.

9.

Use inductive reasoning to finish the conclusion from each premise below.

10. The door-to-door vacuum cleaner salesman was rejected on his first 27 attempts.

Conclusion: _____ of his attempts.

11. The first 14 samples from the expedition were bauxite.

Conclusion: _____ were bauxite.

Rewrite each sentence below in conditional ("if-then") form.

12. A violin is an instrument played in an orchestra.

(d) 13. An investigative reporter looks for corruption.

Draw a Venn diagram to represent each set of conditional statements below.

14. If someone is a brain surgeon, then he must have gone to college. If Brad is a brain surgeon, then Brad has gone to college.

15. Kentucky Derby winners are fast and Summer Breeze is a Kentucky Derby winner. So Summer Breeze is fast.

Write conditional statements to represent each Venn diagram below.

16.   **17.**

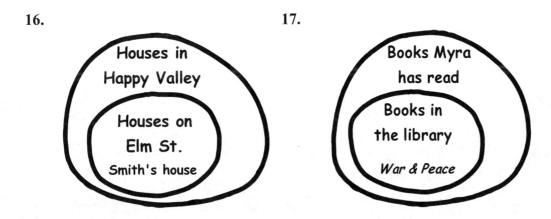

Tell whether the arguments below are valid or invalid deductions.

18. All soldiers are wearing camouflage clothing. Bobby is a soldier, therefore he is wearing camouflage clothing.

19. All good putters have steady nerves. Craig has steady nerves. So Craig must be a good putter.

(e) 20. All movie stars wear sunglasses. Edna wears sunglasses. So Edna is a movie star.

Use deductive reasoning to write the conclusion for each set of statements below.

21. If all industrial economies have recessions and if China's economy is industrial, then _____.

22. If all clowns are funny, and if Bobo is a clown, then _____.

Tell the theorem that is proved by the statements below.

23. If the groundhog sees its shadow, then we'll have six more weeks of winter.
If we have six more weeks of winter, then the flowers will not bloom.
If the flowers do not bloom, then the birds will not sing.
If the birds do not sing, then love will not fill the air.

Complete a direct proof for the theorem below by rearranging the statements in logical order.

24. Theorem: If the rebels enter the demilitarized zone tomorrow, then all hope for democracy is lost.

If negotiations break down, then the government will attack.
If the rebels are crushed, then all hope for democracy is lost.
If the government attacks, then the rebels will be crushed.
If the rebels enter the demilitarized zone tomorrow, then negotiations will break down.

Lesson 7—Some Definitions and Postulates

In the last lesson, we covered several basic, undefined terms of geometry: point, line, and plane. Now we're going to use those terms to write some definitions and postulates. We'll always number our definitions and postulates, as well as our theorems. That will make them easier to keep track of. (We'll also list all the definitions, postulates, and theorems used in each chapter at the end of the book. That way, you can quickly look up whatever information you need when working on a problem set.)

Collinear and Noncollinear Points

Here's our first definition, which is called Definition 1 (surprise, surprise).[1]

Definition 1	*Collinear points* are points that lie on the same line.

Collinear points are pretty easy to understand. But just to make sure you're getting the concept, an example of 3 points that are collinear is on the right. Points *P*, *R*, and *S* all lie on the same line.

Points P, R, and S are collinear.

Another, closely related definition is of **noncollinear points**.

Definition 2	*Noncollinear points* are points that do not lie on the same line.

An example is on the right. Notice that points *C*, *D*, and *E* do not all lie on the same line, which is what makes them noncollinear.

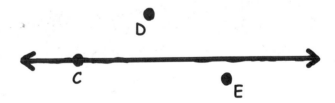

Points C, D, and E are noncollinear.

The Reversibility Test

Now that we're working with definitions, we should talk a little about how to make sure that a definition is good. In everyday life people tend to be sloppy about their definitions. For example, a person might define a friend like this: "Joe is a really tall guy." That's not a good

---

[1] Notice that we use the undefined term "points" in this definition.

definition of Joe, because it doesn't provide enough information for us to distinguish him from all of the other really tall guys in the world. Another example of a poor definition is "Lincoln was a good president." That's too vague again. There are other presidents who were good, so we need more information to distinguish Lincoln from them. A better definition of Lincoln would be "Lincoln was the 16th president of the United States." The main point is that for a definition to be good, it must be specific.

There's a simple way to tell if a definition contains enough specific information. It's called **the reversibility test**. All we have to do is turn the definition around. If the new statement makes sense, then the definition is good. Let's try it on our definition of collinear points. Here's the original definition again.

"Collinear points are points that lie on the same line."

Turning it around gives us this.

"Points that lie on the same line are collinear points."

That does make sense, because the first part of the sentence is a description of "collinear points" and nothing else. So the definition is good.

But now let's apply the reversibility test to the first definition of Lincoln. Here it is again.

"Lincoln was a good president."

Turning the definition around, we get this.

"A good president was Lincoln."

This doesn't work, because a good president could be lots of other people besides Lincoln.

So the reversibility test makes sure that there's enough information given to zero in on the word being defined. It's important to use this test when writing math definitions, since, as you know, mathematicians are very precise people.

Determining a Line

We've looked at two definitions. Now let's look at two postulates. The first one—which is number 1 on Euclid's list as well—is about how to "determine" a line.

Postulate 1	Two points determine a unique straight line.

Postulate 1 just means that it only takes 2 points on a line to pin down the entire line. In other words, we can only run one line through any 2 points. Otherwise the second line would have to bend or curve.

The only way two lines could go through the same two points is if one line was bent or curved.

So Postulate 1 tells us how much information we need in order to pinpoint a particular line. Remember, since this is a postulate, we're assuming that it's true without doing a deductive proof. The postulate seems pretty obvious, but postulates are supposed to be obvious. When coming up with postulates, the key is to identify every assumption clearly. That way we'll have a strong logical foundation for all of the geometry rules that we're going to prove with deductive reasoning.

Determining a Plane

Here's a postulate about planes.

Postulate 2	Three noncollinear points determine a unique plane.

Instead of telling us how much information is needed to determine a line, Postulate 2 tells us what is required to determine a plane. It takes 3 points instead of 2 (as with a line) and those points have to be noncollinear. To get a better understanding of this postulate, let's look at two pictures. The first one is a plane going through 3 noncollinear points, which is shown on the right.

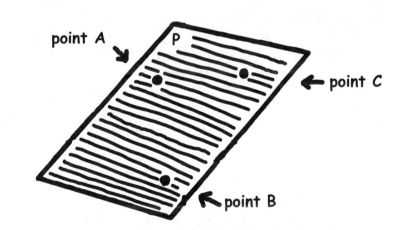

It takes 3 noncollinear points to pin down a plane.

Notice that points *A*, *B*, and *C* do not lie on a single line. And there's only one plane that we can run through them—that's plane P.

Now let's look at another picture. In this one, the 3 points do lie on a single line.

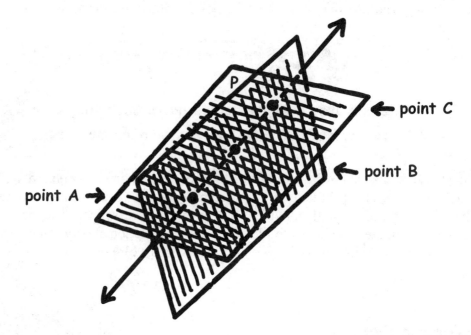

Since the 3 points lie on the same line, a unique plane is not determined.

Notice that we can now run 2 planes through these points. In fact, we could run even more than 2 planes through them. That's because the points are collinear. So it's 3 *noncollinear* points that will determine a unique plane.

Practice 7

a. In the diagram on the right, are points *C*, *B*, and *D* collinear?

b. In the diagram on the right, do points *A*, *B*, and *D* determine plane *P*?

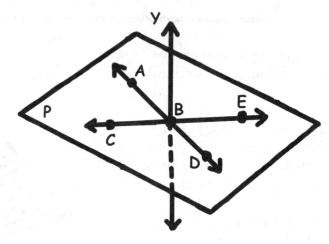

c. From the diagram on the right, name a fourth point that is in the same plane as the points *P*, *Q*, and *R*.

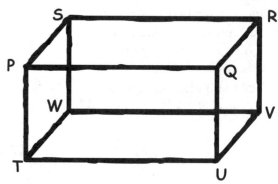

d. Tell whether the argument below is a valid or invalid deduction.

All of the members of the wrestling team were defeated. Brock is a member of the wrestling team. Therefore, Brock must have been defeated.

e. Reverse the definition below and tell whether it passes the reversibility test.

Germany is a country in Europe.

Problem Set 7

Tell whether each sentence below is True or False.

1. Collinear points are points that lie on the same line.

2. Noncollinear points are points that do not lie on the same line.

3. The "reversibility test" is a simple way to tell if a definition contains enough specific information.

Complete each postulate below by filling in the blank.

4. Two points determine a unique _____.

5. Three noncollinear points determine a unique _____.

Answer each of the questions below using the diagram.

(a) 6. Are points *T*, *O*, and *R* collinear?

7. Are points *R*, *O*, and *S* noncollinear?

8. Do points *T*, *O*, and *W* lie in plane *Q*?

(b) 9. Do points *T*, *O*, and *W* determine plane *Q*?

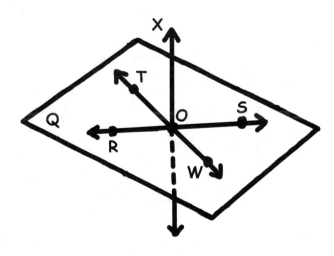

From the diagram, name a fourth point that is in the same plane as each set of points listed.

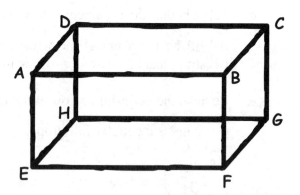

(c) 10. *A, B, C*

11. *D, H, G*

12. *B, G, C*

Rewrite each sentence below in conditional ("if-then") form.

13. All Faberge eggs are from Russia.

14. All of the pencils at the car rental agency say "Swifty Rentals."

Draw a Venn diagram to represent each set of conditional statements below.

15. If a man is an Olympic sprinter, he can run the 100 yard dash in under 10 seconds. If Maurice is an Olympic sprinter, then he can run the 100 yard dash in under 10 seconds.

16. If everybody on the desert island was a castaway, and if Gilligan is on the desert island, then Gilligan is a castaway.

Write conditional statements to represent each Venn diagram below.

17.

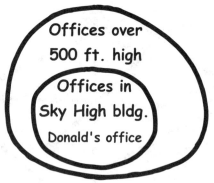

18.

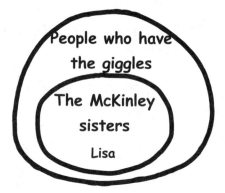

Tell whether the arguments below are valid or invalid deductions.

    19. Every person at the convention is a republican. Nancy Bender is a republican. Therefore, she must be at the convention.

(d) 20. All planets in the solar system orbit the sun. Jupiter is a planet in the solar system. Therefore, Jupiter must orbit the sun.

Use deductive reasoning to write the conclusion for each set of statements below.

    21. If all good guys wear white hats, and Wyatt is a good guy, then _____.

    22. If all of the actors in the play memorized their lines, and Thurgood is an actor in the play, then _____.

Reverse each definition below and tell whether it passes the reversibility test.

 (e) 23. Texas is a state in America.

    24. A bumblebee is a large, hairy, social bee that nests underground.

Lesson 8—Line Segments

A couple of lessons back we covered several undefined terms. One of them was a line, and you remember that lines go on forever in both directions. Well, as it turns out, there's also such a thing as a **line segment**, which is just part of a line. Here's the formal definition.[2]

Definition 3	A *line segment* is a part of a line consisting of two points, called *end points*, and the set of all points between them.

On the right is an actual example of a line segment. See, this is just a part of a line. Instead of going on forever, segment *DE* stops at both ends. The stopping points are called **end points**. So the end points of this line segment are points *D* and *E*. We actually use the end points to name a line

A line segment with end points D and E.

segment. So this is "line segment *DE*" and it's written like this: $\overline{DE}$. Notice there are no arrows on the ends of the little line above. We only put arrows in when naming a line that goes on forever (not a line segment, which ends).

Measuring Line Segments

It's not possible to measure lines, because lines go on forever. But since line segments are finite, they can be measured. There's nothing complicated about the process. All we have to do is use a ruler.

The mathematicians do have special ways of writing the length of a line segment, however. Let's say that a particular line segment $\overline{AB}$ has a length of 2 inches. That's written as $m\overline{AB} = 2$. The little *m* stands for "measure," so $m\overline{AB} = 2$ means "the measure (or length) of line segment *AB* is 2 inches." Another way of writing it is $AB = 2$. This actually means "the distance between points *A* and *B* is 2." The two methods mean exactly the same thing. Be careful about one thing, though. It is incorrect to write the length of a line segment as $\overline{AB} = 2$. The *AB* has a line over it, but there's no *m* in front. This is wrong. Just remember that the line above and the letter *m* go together. If you leave one out, then you need to leave both out.

---

[2] If you check, you'll find that this definition passes the reversibility test.

Congruent Line Segments

In Chapter 1 we talked about three main themes of geometry: congruent figures, similar figures, and equivalent figures. Just to refresh your memory, congruent figures are figures that have the same size and shape.

It turns out that line segments can be congruent. Since line segments have only length (but no width or depth), for two line segments to be **congruent**, they only need to have the same length.

Definition 4	Congruent line segments are line segments that have equal lengths.

An example is on the right. Since line segments $\overline{DE}$ and $\overline{JK}$ have the same length, they're congruent. Here's the way we write it: $\overline{DE} \cong \overline{JK}$. The symbol $\cong$ means "congruent."

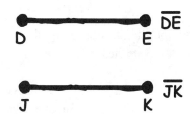

The Ruler Postulate

There's also a postulate, called the Ruler Postulate, that covers the measurement of line segments. **The Ruler Postulate** basically says that for any point on a line, there's a number for that point, and for any number there's a point on the line for it. The reason this postulate is necessary is that until the real number system was created (Remember, real numbers include integers, rational numbers, such as fractions, and irrational numbers, like the square root of 2), there were some lengths that didn't have a number to represent them. But that problem is eliminated with The Ruler Postulate.

The Ruler Postulate also talks about how to calculate the distance between two points on a line or line segment. Technically, the way to do it is to subtract the coordinates of the points and then take the absolute value between them.

As a quick example, let's say we want to calculate the length of line segment $\overline{DE}$. We'll assume that the numbered units on the ruler are inches. Notice that point D is over the coordinate 3 on the ruler, and point E is over the coordinate 6. So to find the distance between the points and the length of the line segment, we

Subtract the coordinates of the points and take the absolute value of the result.

subtract 6 and 3 and take the absolute value of the result.

$$|6-3| = 3$$

The absolute value of a quantity is shown by putting little bars around it, as you can see. **Absolute value** just means to take the positive of whatever quantity is inside those bars. Absolute value focuses on the magnitude of a quantity and doesn't pay attention to whether the quantity is positive or negative. It's the "absolute" difference between the numbers. So the absolute value of $6-3$ equals 3, which tells us that the line segment is 3 inches in length.

The reason absolute value is used to calculate distances is that it doesn't matter which of the points we list first. For instance, if we had listed the coordinate for point D (which is 3) first and the coordinate for point E (which is 6) second, we would have ended up with this.

$$|3-6| = 3$$

Even though 3 minus 6 equals -3, since the absolute value of -3 is 3, we still end up with an answer of 3 inches.

So The Ruler Postulate covers the measurement of line segments. Specifically, it says that there's a real number for every point on a line, and it also gives a technical way for calculating the distance between two points on a line. Here's The Ruler Postulate, which for us is Postulate 3, written out formally.

The Ruler Postulate (Postulate 3)

1.	To every point on a line, there corresponds exactly one real number called its coordinate.
2.	To every real number, there corresponds exactly one point of the line.
3.	To every pair of points there corresponds exactly one real number called the distance between the points.
4.	And the distance between two points is the absolute value of the difference between their coordinates.

Betweenness of Points

There's one last definition related to lines and line segments that we should talk about before finishing this lesson. In his book *The Elements*, Euclid was not as precise as modern mathematicians would have liked. One thing Euclid did was to assume that certain things were true without writing those things down. One incredibly simple assumption Euclid made—which bothered modern mathematicians, believe-it-or-not —has to do with the position of points along a line. Take the line below as an example.

Notice that point *G* is between points *F* and *H*. It wasn't enough for the mathematicians to be able to just look at the line and see that *G* was between *F* and *H*. They wanted to be able to determine that without even having to look at the diagram! So what they did was make a postulate covering the concept of "betweenness." Instead of using a postulate, we'll just use the following definition, which is called "Betweenness of Points."

Betweenness of Points

Definition 5	If F, G, and H are collinear and FG + GH = FH, then G is between F and H.

According to **Betweenness of Points**, when 3 points—we'll call them *F*, *G*, and *H*—are on the same line (are collinear), the only way that *G* can be between *F* and *H* is if the equation $FG + GH = FH$ is true. Here's the line again (to the right), showing *FG* and *GH* added together to get *FH*.

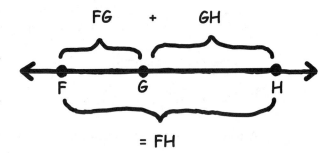

It's not too hard to see why this definition works. If *G* were to the right of *H*, then *FG* alone would be greater than *FH*, as the bottom diagram shows. We would run into a similar problem if *G* were to the left of *F*, because then *FH* would be less than *GH*. So Betweenness of Points gives us a method for determining when a point is between two other points, without having to rely on a diagram.[3]

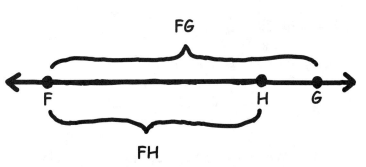

FG is now greater than FH.

---

[3] The reason mathematicians don't want to rely on diagrams is that diagrams can never be drawn precisely. Also, they want everything to be based on postulates and deductive reasoning, not on our sense perceptions, which are limited.

There's also a short way to write the fact that a point is between two other points. To show that G is between F and H, we write F-G-H.

Practice 8

a. Write the measure of the line segment on the right. Make sure your answer is in proper form.

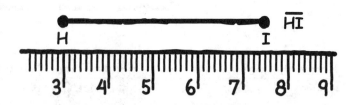

b. Use Betweenness of Points to answer the question below.

Is point O between points L and P? Given: $m\overline{LO} = 3$, $m\overline{OP} = 2$, and $m\overline{LP} = 5$.

c. Use Betweenness of Points to answer the question below.

Is point S between points R and T? Given: $m\overline{RS} = 6$, $m\overline{RT} = 4$, and $m\overline{ST} = 10$.

d. Identify the premise and the conclusion of the conditional statement below.

Zookeepers love animals.

e. Reverse the definition below and tell whether it passes the reversibility test.

A mile is an English unit of measure that is 5,280 feet long.

Problem Set 8

Tell whether each sentence below is True or False.

1. According to the Ruler Postulate, for any point on a line there's a number for that point, and for any number there's a point on the line for it.

2. According to Betweenness of Points, if points A, B, and C are collinear and $AB + BC = AC$, then B is between A and C.

Complete each definition below by filling in the blanks.

3. _____ line segments are line segments that have equal lengths.

4. A _____ is a part of a line consisting of two points, called _____, and the set of all points between them.

Complete each description below by filling in the blank.

5. A _____ is a set of points that extend indefinitely in either direction, and it has length, but no width or depth.

6. A _____ is a set of points that forms a flat surface which extends forever in all directions and has length and width, but no depth.

Write the measure of each line segment below. Make sure each answer is in proper form.

(a) 7.

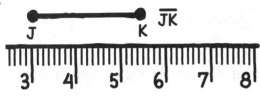

8.

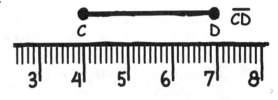

Use Betweenness of Points to answer each question below.

(b) 9. Is point B between points A and C? Given: $m\overline{AB} = 4$, $m\overline{BC} = 5$, and $m\overline{AC} = 9$.

(c) 10. Is point E between points D and G? Given: $m\overline{DE} = 5$, $m\overline{DG} = 7$, and $m\overline{EG} = 12$.

Identify the premise and the conclusion of each conditional statement below.

11. If the truck arrives by 5:30, then the shipment will be on time.

(d) 12. Firefighters are brave.

Draw a Venn diagram to represent each set of conditional statements below.

13. If an executive at XYZ Technologies gets promoted, the executive's salary goes up. If Thomas gets promoted to vice president at XYZ, then his salary will go up.

14. To pass your driver's test, you have to stop at all red lights. Delphina passed her driver's test, so she must have stopped at all red lights.

Write conditional statements to represent each Venn diagram below.

15.

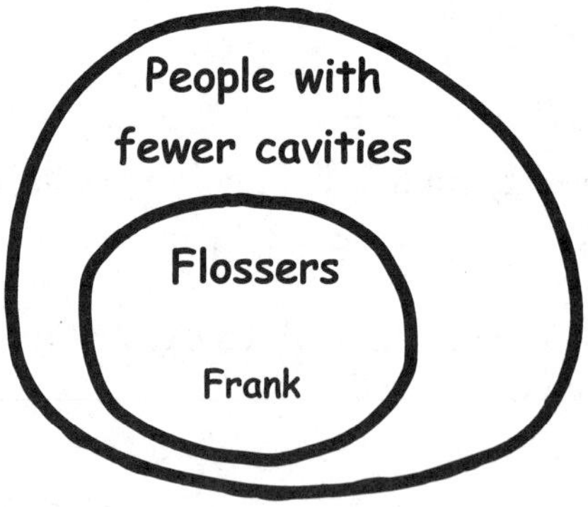

People with
fewer cavities

Flossers

Frank

16.

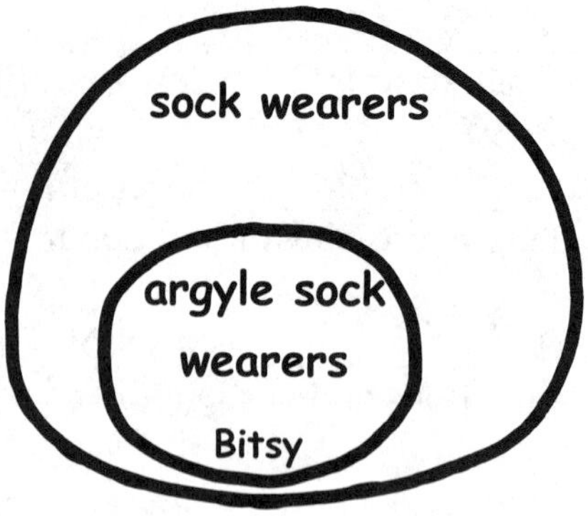

sock wearers

argyle sock
wearers

Bitsy

Tell whether the arguments below are valid or invalid deductions.

17. All beginning bowlers seem to aim for the gutter. Scott seems to aim for the gutter. Therefore, Scott is a beginning bowler.

18. Johnson is a scientist. And since all scientists prefer the metric system, Johnson must prefer the metric system.

Use deductive reasoning to write the conclusion for each set of statements below.

19. If all cities in Nebraska are in the United States, and if Lincoln is in Nebraska, then _____.

20. All of the hotel rooms on the 4th floor have been cleaned. If room 412 is on the 4th floor, then _____.

Complete a direct proof for the theorem below by rearranging the statements in logical order.

21. Theorem: If the auctioneer raises the bid for the painting, then the library will be able to build a new wing.

If Rutherford wins the auction, the proceeds will go to the library.
If the auctioneer raises the bid for the painting, then Mrs. Higgins will drop out.
If Mrs. Higgins drops out, then Rutherford will win the auction.
If the proceeds go to the library, then the library will be able to build a new wing.

Reverse each definition below and tell whether it passes the reversibility test.

22. Julius Caesar was a Roman military leader.

(e) 23. A foot is an English unit of measure that is 12 inches long.

Lesson 9—Rays and Angles

So far we've covered lines and line segments. Remember, a line goes on forever in both directions and a line segment has end points on both sides. Well, there's also something called a ray.

Rays

A **ray** has an end point on one side but goes on forever on the other side. A real-world example of a ray is a sun ray, where light starts at the sun (the end point) but then goes on forever through the universe.

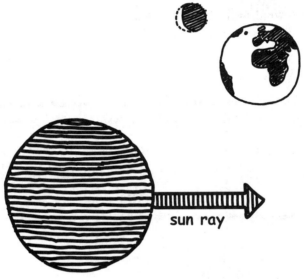

The ray starts at the sun and goes forever in one direction.

Here is the formal definition of a ray.

Definition 6	A *ray* is a part of a line consisting of a given point, called the end point, and the set of all points on one side of the end point.

We draw a picture of a ray by putting an end point at one end and an arrow at the other end. Since the ray on the right has two points on it (points *A* and *B*), we were able to use those for a name. This is "ray *AB*" and it's written as $\overrightarrow{AB}$. Notice that instead of a plain line on top, the line has just one arrow on it. And the arrow always points toward the right, no matter which direction the ray itself points. Also, the end point of the ray has to be listed first (in other words, *A* is

before *B*). We know that a line segment can be measured with a ruler. But since a ray goes on forever, there's no way to measure it. It's like a line in that way.

Angles

If we take two rays and put them together so that they have the same end point, we get an angle. Rays $\overrightarrow{AB}$ and $\overrightarrow{AC}$ form an angle shown on the right. The end point is called the **vertex** of the angle. And the rays form the **sides** of the angle. So the vertex of the angle above is point *A* and the sides are rays $\overrightarrow{AB}$ and $\overrightarrow{AC}$. Here's the formal definition of an angle, which says pretty much the same thing.

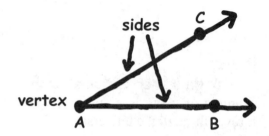

Two rays with the same end point form an angle.

Definition 7	An *angle* is the union of two rays having the same end point. The end point is called the *vertex* of the angle; the rays are called the sides of the angle.

Ways of Naming Angles

There are actually several ways to name an angle. If we have three points on the angle, we can use the letters for these points in the angle's name. The center letter should represent the vertex. So the angle in our example can be named $\angle BAC$. The symbol $\angle$ is just a little angle. That's the symbol we use to represent an angle. And $\angle BAC$ is pronounced "angle *BAC*." We could also write $\angle CAB$. The order of the letters doesn't matter as long as the vertex, *A*, is in the middle.

The second way to name an angle is with a number at the vertex, inside the angle. The number method is good when we don't have any points on the angle. The little curved arc (on the right) is just a way to highlight the angle. This is now "angle 1" and as a symbol it's written like this: $\angle 1$. Of course, any other number besides 1 would work just as well.

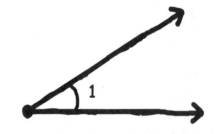

An angle can also be named with a number.

A third way to name an angle is to just use the vertex letter. The vertex of the original angle was *A*. But instead of calling this angle *BAC* (∠*BAC*), we could just call it angle *A*, and write it like this: ∠*A*. This shorter method is nice, but it can only be used if it doesn't cause any confusion.

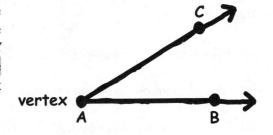

On the bottom right is an example where the shorter method doesn't work. We can't just write ∠*M* for the angle shown by the little arc. With that name, it's unclear whether we're talking about ∠*LMO*, ∠*OMN*, or ∠*LMN*. On this one, we have to use the name ∠*LMO*. That eliminates all the confusion.

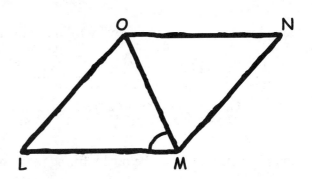

Practice 9

a. Name the angle below. Write your answer in proper form.

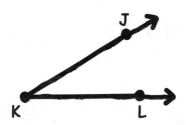

b. Name the angle indicated by the arc below. Write your answer in proper form.

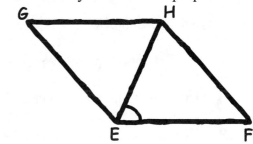

c. Use Betweenness of Points to answer the question below.

Is point *Y* between points *T* and *Z*? Given: $m\overline{YZ} = 2.7$, $m\overline{TZ} = 1.9$, and $m\overline{TY} = 4.6$.

d. Tell whether the arguments below are valid or invalid deductions.

All the people in the library are book lovers. Rick is a book lover. Therefore, Rick is in the library.

e. Reverse the definition below and tell whether it passes the reversibility test.

Bitsy is a sales clerk at Smith's Department Store.

Problem Set 9

Tell whether each sentence below is True or False.

1. A ray has an end point on one side but goes on forever on the other side.

2. Two rays put together so that they have the same end point make an angle.

Complete each postulate below by filling in the blank.

3. Two points determine a _____.

4. Three noncollinear points determine a _____.

Complete each sentence below by filling in the blank.

5. An angle's end point is called the _____ of the angle.

6. The rays of an angle are called the angle's _____.

Answer each question below.

7. How many end points does a ray have?

8. How many end points does a line have?

9. How many end points does a line segment have?

Name each angle below. Write your answers in proper form.

(a) 10.   **11.**   **(b) 12.**

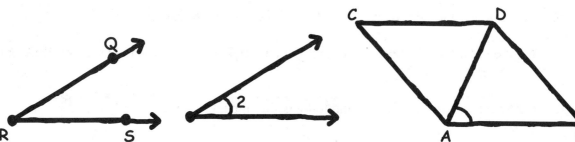

Write the measure of each line segment below. Make sure each answer is in proper form.

13.

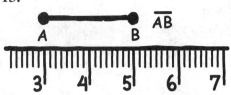

14.

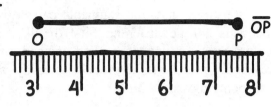

Draw a Venn diagram to represent each set of conditional statements below.

15. All of the incumbents were elected. Congressman Perkins is an incumbent, so he was elected.

16. All felons are under suspicion. Carter is a felon, therefore he's under suspicion.

Use Betweenness of Points to answer each question below.

17. Is point M between points L and N? Given: $m\overline{LM} = 5.2$, $m\overline{MN} = 2.9$, and $m\overline{LN} = 8.1$.

(c) 18. Is point X between points S and Z? Given: $m\overline{XZ} = 3.4$, $m\overline{SZ} = 1.6$, and $m\overline{SX} = 5$.

Tell whether the arguments below are valid or invalid deductions.

(d) 19. All the people at the town meeting are good citizens. Mr. Dirkson is a good citizen. Therefore, he is at the town meeting.

20. Every manager at Rainbow Sprinkled Donuts is super strict. Steve is night manager at Rainbow Sprinkled Donuts. So Steve must be super strict.

Use deductive reasoning to write the conclusion for each set of statements below.

21. If all the stocks in the Dow Jones Industrials Average rose on Tuesday, and Combined Consolidated Corp. is in the Dow Jones Industrials Average, then _____.

22. If all pets named Rover are dogs, and if our next door neighbor's pet is named Rover, then _____.

Reverse each definition below and tell whether it passes the reversibility test.

23. Washington, D.C. is the capital of the United States.

(e) 24. Randolph Simpson is a sophomore at State University.

Lesson 10—Measuring Angles

We know that line segments can be measured. As it turns out, angles can too, but the process is a little different. First of all, the unit of measure for an angle is not inches, or centimeters; it's **degrees**.[4] And instead of using a ruler, we use an instrument called a **protractor**, which you're probably already familiar with. Here's a picture of a protractor with an angle being measured on it.

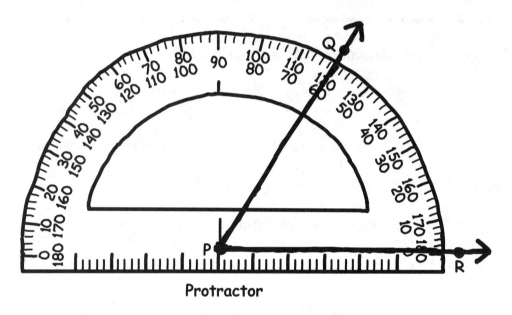

Protractor

Notice that the protractor has two sets of numbers around it. The bottom row starts with 0 degrees on the right and goes to 180 degrees on the left. The top row starts with 0 degrees on the left and goes to 180 degrees on the right. The bottom row is used to measure angles that open to the right (like the angle in the picture). The top row is used to measure angles that open to the left.

To actually measure an angle, we can put the vertex at the center of the protractor near the bottom. There's usually a circle in the exact spot where the vertex goes. Then we put one ray horizontally along the bottom of the protractor, lined up with one of the zero marks. Once the angle is in the right place, we just read the angle's measure by looking at the number that the top ray crosses. The angle in the picture, $\angle QPR$, crosses 60, so we say the "measure of angle QPR is 60." (We used the bottom row of numbers, because the angle opened to the right.) The symbol for "degrees" is a little circle. So 60 degrees can be written as $60°$. The "measure of angle QPR is 60" is written like this: $m\angle QPR = 60$. The m stands for "measure." And notice that the degree symbol is left off. By the way, it's wrong to leave off the m and write $\angle QPR = 60$.

---

[4] There's actually another unit for measuring angles, which is covered in Trigonometry.

Congruent Angles

As with line segments, angles can also be congruent. Here's the formal definition.

Definition 8	Congruent angles are angles that have equal measures.

Now look at $\angle QPR$ and $\angle TSU$. Both have measures of $60°$, the two angles are congruent. And we write that as $\angle QPR \cong \angle TSU$. Notice that in the drawing the rays of the two angles have different lengths. That doesn't matter one bit. Since the angles both have a measure of $60°$, they still have to be congruent. It seems a little strange at first, but it makes

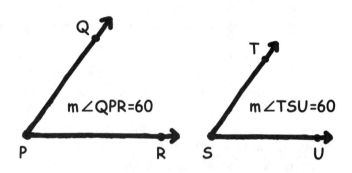

sense if you think about it. Rays go on forever in one direction, so they don't even have a finite length. We just draw them as if they do. Just remember that it's not the length of the rays in a drawing that determines whether two angles are congruent, but the measure of their angles.

The Protractor Postulate

You may remember that we have a postulate for measuring line segments called The Ruler Postulate. Basically, The Ruler Postulate says that there's a real number for every point on a line and a point for every real number. The Ruler Postulate ensures that there's a number for a line segment of any possible length. Well, it turns out that there's a similar postulate for measuring angles. It's called **The Protractor Postulate**. It says that there's a degree measure for every angle from 0 to 180 degrees, and an angle for every degree measure. Here are the first two parts of the postulate.

The Protractor Postulate (Postulate 4)

1.	The rays in a half rotation (180 degrees) can be numbered so that to every ray there corresponds exactly one real number called its coordinate.
2.	And to every real number from 0 to 180, there corresponds exactly one ray.

The Protractor Postulate also explains a method for measuring angles that's a little more complicated than the one we just showed you. The method involves absolute value, so it's similar to the Ruler Postulate in this way too. Here's that part of the postulate.

The Protractor Postulate (cont.)

3.	To every pair of rays there corresponds exactly one real number called the measure of the angle that they determine.
4.	And the measure of the angle is the absolute value of the difference between the coordinates of its rays.

In this second way of measuring an angle, instead of putting one ray horizontally along the bottom of the protractor, as we showed earlier, you put it anywhere you want (as long as the vertex is in its usual place). Next, you read off the numbers that both rays cross on the protractor. Then you subtract those numbers and take the absolute value of the result.

Betweenness of Rays

There's another definition involving angles that you need to know about. It's called the **Betweenness of Rays**. This definition allows us to tell whether a ray is between two other rays, without looking at a diagram. If that sounds familiar, it's because Betweenness of Rays is a lot like Betweenness of Points, which allows us to tell whether a point is between two other points. To show you how this new definition works, take a look at the picture to the right. Notice there's a point S between $\angle QPR$, and we've drawn in a ray from P through S ($\overrightarrow{PS}$). With Betweenness of Rays, we can know that $\overrightarrow{PS}$ is between $\overrightarrow{PR}$ and $\overrightarrow{PQ}$, without looking at the diagram.[5] The way we can tell is by adding up angles. Specifically, if the measure of angle SPR plus the measure of angle SPQ equals the measure of angle QPR, then $\overrightarrow{PS}$ has to be between $\overrightarrow{PR}$ and $\overrightarrow{PQ}$. Here's the Betweenness of Rays definition written out formally.

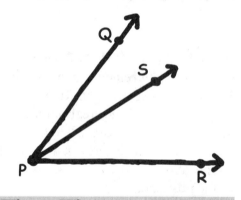

Betweenness of Rays

Definition 9	$\overrightarrow{PS}$ is between $\overrightarrow{PQ}$ and $\overrightarrow{PR}$, if point S lies in the interior of $\angle QPR$ and $m\angle SPR + m\angle QPS = m\angle QPR$.

---

[5] Remember, the mathematicians are concerned about this kind of thing.

Practice 10

a. Tell whether the symbol $\overleftrightarrow{XY}$ could represent a point, line, plane, line segment, ray, or angle.

b. Name the angle indicated on the right. Write your answer in proper form.

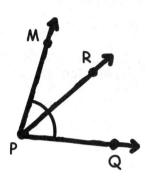

c. Use a protractor to measure the angle below. Write your answer in proper form.

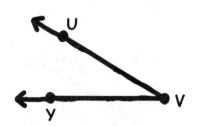

d. Use a protractor to measure the angle below. Write your answer in proper form.

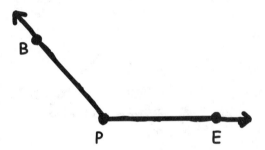

e. Tell whether the argument below is a valid or invalid deduction.

All junk food is unhealthy. Potato chips are unhealthy. Therefore, potato chips are junk food.

Problem Set 10

Tell whether each sentence below is True or False.

1. The unit of measure for angles is kilometers.

2. Angles are measured with an instrument called a protractor.

3. The Protractor Postulate says that there's a degree measure for every angle from 0 to 180 degrees, and an angle for every degree measure.

Complete each definition below by filling in the blank.

4. _____ angles are angles that have equal measures.

5. If point O lies in the interior of $\angle ABC$ and $m\angle OBC + m\angle ABO = m\angle ABC$, then _____.

6. A _____ is a part of a line consisting of a given point, called the end point, and the set of all points on one side of the end point.

Tell whether each symbol below could represent a point, line, plane, line segment, ray, or angle.

(a) 7. $\overrightarrow{FT}$ 8. $\overline{DS}$ 9. $\angle B$

Name each angle below. Write your answers in proper form.

10.
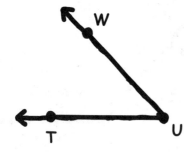

(b) 11.
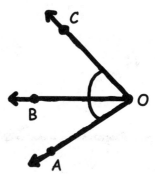

Use a protractor to measure each angle below.

(c) 12.   13.   (d) 14.

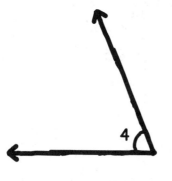
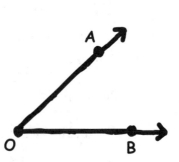
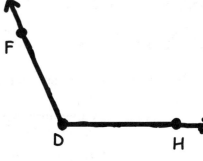

Draw a Venn diagram to represent each set of conditional statements below.

15. If all of the towns in Florida are in the United States and Orlando is in Florida, then Orlando is in the United States.

16. The hostess welcomed all of her guests. Marie was her guest, so the hostess welcomed Marie.

Tell whether the arguments below are valid or invalid deductions.

17. All pianists are musicians. Mrs. Buswell is a pianist. So Mrs. Buswell is a musician.

(e) 18. All rich desserts are fattening. Chocolate éclairs are fattening. Therefore, chocolate éclairs are rich desserts.

Use deductive reasoning to write the conclusion for each set of statements below.

19. A man who can't control his temper shouldn't be in a leadership position. If Mr. Jones can't control his temper, then _____.

20. If the recruits can scale the wall, then they'll make it through boot camp. Tommy can scale the wall, therefore _____.

Complete a direct proof for the theorem below by rearranging the statements in logical order.

21. Theorem: If the batter hits a double, then the street cleaners will have to work overtime.

If the batter drives in one run, then the Tigers will win the playoffs.
If the city celebrates, then the street cleaners will have to work overtime.
If the Tigers win the playoffs, then the city will celebrate.
If the batter hits a double, then he'll drive in one run.

Reverse each definition below and tell whether it passes the reversibility test.

22. A mule is a hybrid offspring of a male donkey and a female horse.

23. Ralph Waldo Emerson is a well-known author.

Lesson 11—Kinds of Angles

We've been learning about angles. As it turns out, angles can be divided up into several different types, based on their measure.

Right Angles

The simplest type of angle, which you're probably already familiar with, is a **right angle**. It has a measure of 90°. Here's the formal definition.

Definition 10	A *right* angle is an angle with a measure of 90°.

A right angle is very easy to spot, because the angle is shaped like an L. Here's a picture.

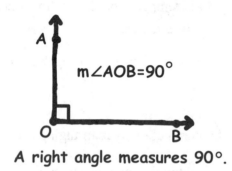

A right angle measures 90°.

Notice the box down by the vertex. That is the symbol for a right angle. Instead of showing the angle with a curved arc, as we do sometimes with other angles, we use a box for a right angle.

Here's another right angle. This one opens to the left instead of the right, so it has the shape of a backwards L.

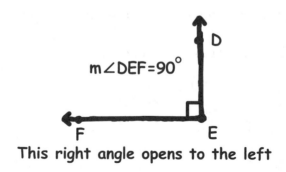

This right angle opens to the left

It's also possible for a right angle to open downward (toward the right or left) or to slant in any direction.

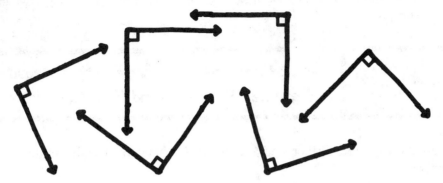

Every one is a right angle (90°).

All of these are right angles, because the two rays of each form an L shape. That's how you can tell that you're dealing with a right angle. Of course, another way to tell is to put a protractor over the angle and measure it.

Acute Angles

A second kind of angle is an **acute angle**, which is just an angle that's less than 90°. Here's the formal definition.

Definition 11	An *acute* angle is an angle with a measure of less than 90°.

So all the angles ranging from less than 1° to just under 90° qualify as acute angles. You can usually tell an acute angle at a glance, because the rays are closer together than the L shape of a right angle. Here are pictures of several acute angles. Notice that instead of a box, each angle is shown with a curved arc.

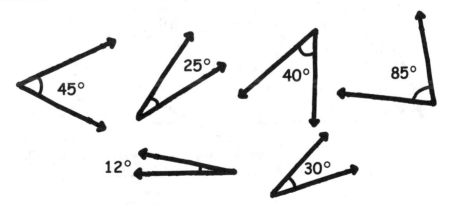

Every one is an acute angle (less than 90°).

Obtuse Angles

The last kind of angle is an **obtuse angle**, which is just an angle that's greater than 90°.[6] The formal definition is below.

| Definition 12 | An *obtuse* angle is an angle with a measure of greater than 90° (and less than 180°). |

In these angles, the rays are farther apart than the L shape of a right angle. Here are a few pictures of obtuse angles.

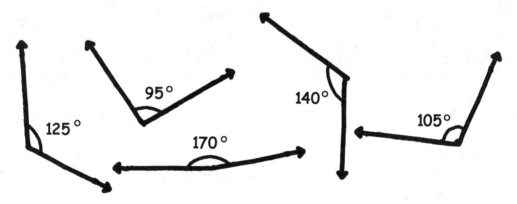

125°   95°   140°   105°

170°

Every one is an obtuse angle (greater than 90°).

Practice 11

a. Use the protractor to measure ∠*BOC* below.

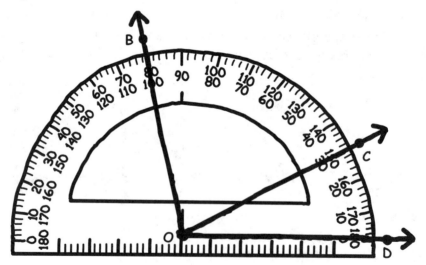

---

[6] An obtuse angle also has to be less than 180° . We haven't talked about angles that are greater than 180° , but they exist. Angles of that kind are covered in Trigonometry.

b. From the diagram below, tell what kind of angle is ∠AOB.

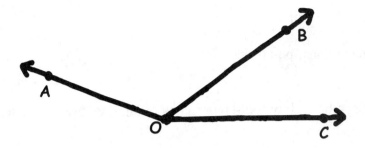

c. Use Betweenness of Points to answer the question below.

If points *F*, *G*, and *H* are collinear and *FG* = 5, *FH* = 8, and *GH* = 13, which point is between the other two?

d. Use Betweenness of Rays to answer the question below.

If point *L* lies in the interior of ∠AOB and $m\angle AOL = 25°$, $m\angle LOB = 55°$, and $m\angle AOB = 80°$, then which of the following rays is between the other two: $\overrightarrow{OB}$, $\overrightarrow{OL}$, $\overrightarrow{OA}$.

e. Reverse the definition below and tell whether it passes the reversibility test.

A Formula 1 race car is a machine used for transportation.

Problem Set 11

Tell whether each sentence below is True or False.

1. All right angles are congruent.

2. All acute angles are congruent.

Complete each definition below by filling in the blank.

3. A(n) _____ is an angle with a measure of less than 90°.

4. A right angle is an angle with a measure of _____ .

5. A(n) _____ is an angle with a measure of greater than 90° (but less than 180°).

Complete each postulate below by filling in the blank.

6. Two points determine a _____ .

7. Three noncollinear points determine a _____ .

Tell whether each symbol below could represent a point, line, plane, line segment, ray, or angle.

8. ∠4

9. $\overrightarrow{GH}$

Use the protractor to measure each angle below.

10. ∠*LOM*   **11.** ∠*POM*   **(a) 12.** ∠*LOP*

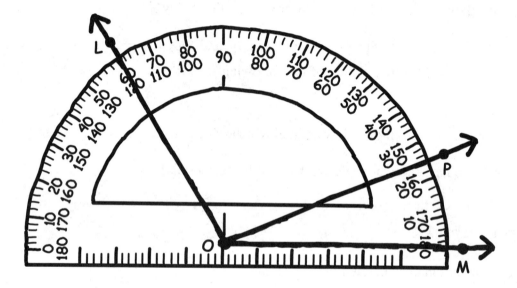

Tell the kind of each angle below.

13. ∠*KOH*   **14.** ∠*JOH*   **(b) 15.** ∠*JOK*

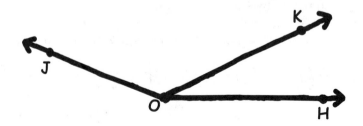

Use Betweenness of Points to answer each question below.

16. Is point W between points T and B? Given: $m\overline{TW} = \dfrac{3}{4}$, $m\overline{WB} = \dfrac{1}{3}$, and $m\overline{TB} = \dfrac{13}{12}$.

(c) 17. If points U, V, and Q are collinear and $UV = 7$, $UQ = 9$, and $VQ = 16$, which point is between the other two?

Use Betweenness of Rays to answer each question below.

18. If point P lies in the interior of $\angle CDE$ and $m\angle CDP = 30°$, $m\angle PDE = 40°$, and $m\angle CDE = 70°$, then which of the following rays is between the other two: $\overrightarrow{DC}$, $\overrightarrow{DE}$, $\overrightarrow{DP}$.

(d) 19. If point Q lies in the interior of $\angle RST$ and $m\angle RSQ = 35°$, $m\angle QST = 50°$, and $m\angle RST = 85°$, then which of the following rays is between the other two: $\overrightarrow{ST}$, $\overrightarrow{SQ}$, $\overrightarrow{SR}$.

Tell whether the arguments below are valid or invalid deductions.

20. All bodybuilders lift weights. Arnold lifts weights. Therefore, Arnold is a bodybuilder.

21. Bernadette loves to twirl her baton. And since all drum majors love to twirl their batons, Bernadette must be a drum major.

Complete a direct proof for the theorem below by rearranging the statements in logical order.

22. Theorem: If the cat burglar leaves his flashlight, then the maid will faint.

If the maid finds the safe open, then she will faint.
If the cat burglar leaves his flashlight, then the maid will think something is wrong.
If the maid thinks something is wrong, then she will check the safe.
If the maid checks the safe, then she will find it open.

Reverse each definition below and tell whether it passes the reversibility test.

23. A snowman is a figure of a person made from packed snow.

(e) 24. A necktie is an article of clothing worn by men.

Lesson 12—Midpoints and Bisectors

So far in this chapter, we've been learning mostly about line segments and angles. Sometimes it's necessary to cut a line segment or an angle into two equal parts. We'll cover that in this lesson.

Midpoint of a Line Segment

Let's start with the line segment below.

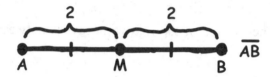

Point M is the midpoint of $\overline{AB}$.

Point M is exactly in the middle of $\overline{AB}$. We know that's true, because $m\overline{AM} = 2$ and $m\overline{MB} = 2$. That's why M is called the **midpoint** of $\overline{AB}$. Basically, a point is a midpoint when it's between the end points of a line segment, and when the two little line segments on either side are equal to each other. Notice that we show that the halves are equal by putting little marks through each one. Here's the formal definition of a midpoint.

Definition 13	The midpoint of a line segment is the point that divides the line segment into two congruent line segments.

Not only does $m\overline{AM} = m\overline{MB}$,[7] but there are several other things that must also be true because M is the midpoint of $\overline{AB}$. It follows that both of the little segments, $\overline{AM}$ and $\overline{MB}$, have to equal half of the complete segment, $\overline{AB}$. Here are those relationships written as equations.

$$AM = \frac{1}{2}AB \qquad\qquad MB = \frac{1}{2}AB$$

Segment Bisectors

A segment bisector is something that divides a line segment into two equal parts. "Bisector" comes from the word "bisect," which just means to divide something in half. In our

---

[7] Or we could also say that these two little segments are congruent.

example, point (*M*) is a bisector of $\overline{AB}$. But it's also possible for a line, a ray, or another line segment to be a bisector of $\overline{AB}$. Here are examples of those cases.

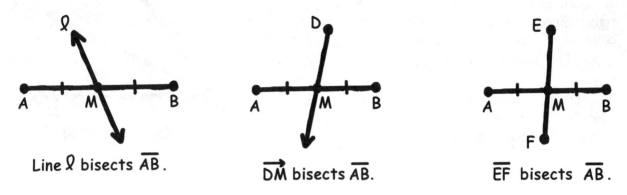

Line ℓ bisects $\overline{AB}$. $\overrightarrow{DM}$ bisects $\overline{AB}$. $\overline{EF}$ bisects $\overline{AB}$.

Notice that the bisectors don't have to run straight up and down. They can slant at any angle. They're still bisectors as long as they intersect (cross) $\overline{AB}$ at the midpoint *M*. So a line segment actually has an infinite number of bisectors, because we can slice through the midpoint at all sorts of different angles.

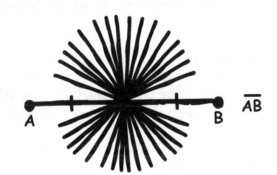

$\overline{AB}$ actually has an infinite number of bisectors.

Here's the formal definition of a segment bisector.

Segment Bisector

Definition 14	A *bisector* of $\overline{AB}$ is any line, ray, or line segment which passes through the midpoint of $\overline{AB}$.

Angle Bisectors

It's not just line segments that can be bisected. An angle can be bisected too (see the diagram on the right). Since the measures of angles *POR* and *RON* are equal, ray *OR* is exactly between rays *OP* and *ON*. That makes $\overrightarrow{OR}$ an angle bisector of the big angle, ∠*PON*.

On the diagram, we show that the little angles are equal by drawing an arc through each one. Here's the formal definition of an angle bisector.

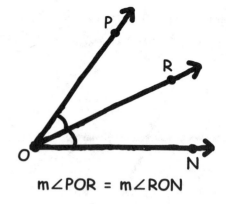

m∠POR = m∠RON

Angle Bisector

Definition 15	$\overrightarrow{OR}$ is the bisector of ∠PON if R lies in the interior of ∠PON and m∠POR = m∠RON .

You know that when a line segment is bisected there are simple relationships that are created between the little segments and the original, big segment. Well, the same thing happens when an angle is bisected. It turns out that both of the little angles, ∠*POR* and ∠*RON* , have to equal half of the big angle, ∠*PON* . Here are those relationships written as equations.

$$m\angle POR = \frac{1}{2}m\angle PON \qquad\qquad m\angle RON = \frac{1}{2}m\angle PON$$

We should make one last quick point about angle bisectors. Even though line segments have an infinite number of bisectors (as we showed on the previous page), angles have just one bisector. There's only one ray that will divide ∠*PON* into two equal halves, and that's $\overrightarrow{OR}$.

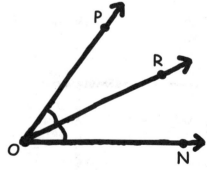

$\overrightarrow{OR}$ is the *only* ray that bisects ∠PON.

Practice 12

a. Use Betweenness of Points or Rays to answer the question below.

If point K lies in the interior of $\angle LMN$ and if $m\angle KMN = 30°$, $m\angle LMN = 75°$, and $m\angle LMK = 45°$, then which of the following rays is between the other two: $\overrightarrow{MK}$, $\overrightarrow{MN}$, $\overrightarrow{ML}$.

b. Use the definition of a segment bisector to answer the question below.

If point P is the midpoint of $\overline{LQ}$ and if $m\overline{LP} = 2\frac{1}{7}$, then find $m\overline{PQ}$.

c. Use the definition of a segment bisector to answer the question below.

If $\overleftrightarrow{AB}$ bisects $\overline{QT}$ at point R, and if $QT = 10$, then find the length of QR.

d. Use the definition of an angle bisector to answer the question below.

If $\overrightarrow{PQ}$ bisects $\angle CPD$, and if $m\angle CPQ = 36°$, then find $m\angle QPD$.

e. Use the definition of an angle bisector to answer the question below.

If $\overrightarrow{CV}$ bisects $m\angle BCE$, and if $m\angle BCE = 56°$, then find $m\angle BCV$ and $m\angle VCE$.

Problem Set 12

Tell whether each sentence below is True or False.

1. A point is a midpoint when it's between the end points of a line segment, and when the two little line segments on either side are equal to each other.

2. Any line segment has just one bisector.

3. Any angle has just one bisector.

Complete each definition below by filling in the blank.

4. The _____ of a line segment is the point that divides the line segment into two congruent line segments.

5. A _____ of $\overline{AB}$ is any line, ray, or line segment which passes through the midpoint of $\overline{AB}$.

6. $\overrightarrow{BD}$ is the _____ of $\angle ABC$ if D lies in the interior of $\angle ABC$ and $m\angle ABD = m\angle DBC$.

7. A _____ is a part of a line consisting of two points, called end points, and the set of all points between them.

Complete each sentence below by filling in the blank.

8. _____ angles are angles that have the same measure.

9. An angle's end point is called the _____ of the angle.

10. The _____ of an angle are called the angle's sides.

Use Betweenness of Points or Rays to answer each question below.

11. If points E, J, and L are collinear and $EJ = 4$, $JL = 7$, and $EL = 11$, which point is between the other two?

(a) 12. If point X lies in the interior of $\angle TUV$ and if $m\angle TUV = 50°$, $m\angle XUV = 35°$, and $m\angle TUX = 15°$, then which of the following rays is between the other two: $\overrightarrow{UT}$, $\overrightarrow{UV}$, $\overrightarrow{UX}$.

Use the definition of a segment bisector to answer each question below.

(b) 13. If point S is the midpoint of $\overline{RT}$ and if $m\overline{RS} = 5\frac{1}{4}$, then find $m\overline{ST}$.

14. If $\overleftrightarrow{CE}$ bisects $\overline{DG}$ at point F, and if $DF = 8$, then find the length of FG.

(c) 15. If $\overleftrightarrow{OR}$ bisects $\overline{JL}$ at point K, and if $JL = 6$, then find the length of JK.

Use the definition of an angle bisector to answer each question below.

(d) 16. If $\overrightarrow{YR}$ bisects $\angle XYZ$, and if $m\angle XYR = 48°$, then find $m\angle RYZ$.

17. If $\overrightarrow{BD}$ bisects $m\angle ABC$, and if $m\angle ABC = 32°$, then find $m\angle ABD$.

(e) 18. If $\overrightarrow{OL}$ bisects $m\angle MOP$, and if $m\angle MOP = 74°$, then find $m\angle MOL$ and $m\angle LOP$.

Tell the kind of each angle below.

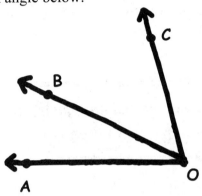

19. $\angle AOB$ **20.** $\angle BOC$ **21.** $\angle AOC$

Use deductive reasoning to write the conclusion for each set of statements below.

22. E-mail attachments from unknown senders should not be opened. The sender of the last e-mail attachment was unknown. Therefore, _____.

23. All of the World War II veterans at the banquet were honored. If Mr. McKenna is a World War II veteran and he was at the banquet, then _____.

Reverse each definition below and tell whether it passes the reversibility test.

24. An icicle is a hanging mass of ice formed by the freezing of dripping water.

25. Calculus is a hard subject.

Lesson 13—Properties of Equality

For the last few lessons, we've learned a lot of new definitions. But there are several more postulates or "properties," as they're called, that we should cover before starting to do geometry proofs.[8] These are familiar to you, because they're used in algebra. In this book, though, we'll be using them a lot on line segments and angles.

Addition and Subtraction Properties

In simple language, the **Addition Property of Equality** says that if two things are equal and then if we add the same quantity to each one, the results will still be equal. Here it is written formally.

Addition Property	If equals are added to equals, the results are equal: If a = b, then a + c = b + c

This property is used all the time when solving equations. For example to solve $x - 6 = 10$, we would add 6 to both sides. Because of the Addition Property of Equality, we know that the left and right sides are still equal. That gives us $x - 6 + 6 = 10 + 6$ or just $x = 16$.

The Addition Property can also be applied to geometry problems. Let's say that line segments AB and CD have the same length.

$$AB = CD$$

Now, if we add the length of line segment FG to each one, we get this.

$$AB + FG = CD + FG$$

Since equals are being added to equals, we know that the left and right sides of the equation are still equal. The same process works on angles. For instance, if $m\angle X = m\angle Y$, then $m\angle X + m\angle Z = m\angle Y + m\angle Z$.

---

[8] These are called "properties" instead of a "postulates" because, technically, some of them can be proved deductively using others. But we will work with these properties in the same way that we do postulates.

There's also a **Subtraction Property of Equality**. It's almost identical to the Addition Property, only instead of adding we subtract a quantity from two equal things. Here's this property written formally.

Subtraction Property	If equals are subtracted from equals, the results are equal: If a = b, then a - c = b - c

The Subtraction Property is also used a lot in solving algebra equations. For example, to solve $x + 3 = 14$ we would subtract 3 from both sides to get $x + 3 - 3 = 14 - 3$ or $x = 11$. The Subtraction Property will work in geometry as well. For example, if the lengths of two line segments are the same, then we can subtract the same length from each and the resulting lengths will be equal.

$$\text{If } JK = LM \text{, then } JK - OR = LM - OR$$

Likewise, if the measures of two angles are the same, we can subtract the same measure from each and the results will be equal.

$$\text{If } m\angle AOP = m\angle SRT \text{, then } m\angle AOP - m\angle DEF = m\angle SRT - m\angle DEF$$

Multiplication and Division Properties

The next property involves multiplication. And you can probably guess that it's the **Multiplication Property of Equality**, which just says that if two quantities are equal, we can multiply each one by the same number and the results have to be equal. Here's this one written out in formal language.

Multiplication Property	If equals are multiplied by equals, their products are equal: If a = b, then ac = bc.

This property is used in algebra on equations like $\frac{x}{2} = 27$. To solve, we multiply both sides by 2 to get $\frac{x}{2} \cdot 2 = 27 \cdot 2$ or $x = 54$.

There's also a **Division Property of Equality**. And it just says that if two quantities are equal, we can divide each one by the same number and the results have to be equal. There is one exception to the Division Property, though. We can't divide the quantities by 0, because division by 0 is not allowed. Here's this property written formally.

Division Property	If equals are divided by nonzero equals, their quotients are equal: If a = b, then $\frac{a}{c} = \frac{b}{c}$ as long as c ≠ 0.

The Multiplication and Division Properties can also be used in geometry.

Substitution and Transitive Properties

The next property is a little bit different from the first four. This one is called the **Substitution Property** and it says that if two quantities are equal, then one of them can be substituted for the other one. Here it is written out.

Substitution Property	If a = b, then either a or b may be substituted for the other in any equation.

You may remember that this property is used in algebra when solving a system of equations such as $\begin{cases} 2y - 3x = 1 \\ y = 4x \end{cases}$. Since y and $4x$ are equal, we can substitute $4x$ for y in the top equation. The same kind of thing can be done in geometry. As an example, let's say that the measures of angles 1 and 2 add to equal 180°, and that angle 2 is equal in measure to an angle 3.

$$m\angle 1 + m\angle 2 = 180$$

$$m\angle 2 = m\angle 3$$

Since the measure of angle 2 and angle 3 are the same, using the Substitution Property we can "substitute" $m\angle 3$ for $m\angle 2$ in the top equation to get

$$m\angle 1 + m\angle 3 = 180$$

So the process works basically the same way it does in algebra.

Another property that's very closely related to Substitution is the **Transitive Property**. This says that if two quantities are equal to the same quantity, then they are equal to each other. Here it is written formally.

Transitive Property	If two quantities are equal to the same quantity, then they are equal to each other: If a = b and b = c, then a = c.

As a simple geometry example of this property, assume that line segments AB and DE have the same measure and also that line segments DE and FG have the same measure.

$$AB = DE \qquad\qquad DE = FG$$

Since both AB and FG are equal to DE, they must be equal to each other.

$$AB = FG$$

Reflexive and Symmetric Properties

There are two more properties which seem incredibly obvious. But remember that postulates (and properties) are supposed to state the obvious. The first of these is the **Reflexive Property of Equality**. It says, believe-it-or-not, that a quantity is equal to itself. Here's the formal way of writing it.

Reflexive Property	Any quantity is equal to itself: a = a.

The second property is the **Symmetric Property of Equality** which says that the positions of expressions on either side of an equals sign or congruent symbol may be reversed. In other words, $x = 4$ is the same as $4 = x$. Or in geometry, $UV = ST$ is the same as $ST = UV$. Here's the Symmetric Property written formally.

Symmetric Property	The positions of the expressions on either side of an equals sign may be reversed: If a = b, then b = a.

Practice 13

a. If a right angle is bisected, are the resulting little angles right, acute, or obtuse?

b. Use Betweenness of Points or Rays to answer the question below.

If U-I-Y (point I is between points U and Y), and if $IY = 3\frac{1}{4}$ and $UY = 9\frac{1}{2}$, then find UI.

c. Use the definition of a segment bisector to answer the question below.

If $\overrightarrow{RS}$ bisects $\overline{CX}$ at point N, and if $CX = 11.7$, then find the length of CN.

d. Use the definition of an angle bisector to answer the question below.

If $\overrightarrow{QT}$ bisects $m\angle PQR$, and if $m\angle TQR = 14°$, then find $m\angle PQR$.

e. Tell whether the argument below is a valid or invalid deduction.

Tom loves Notre Dame football. All Notre Dame graduates love Notre Dame football. Tom must be a Notre Dame graduate.

Problem Set 13

Tell whether each sentence below is True or False.

1. There are several "properties of equality" from algebra that are also used in geometry.

2. The Division Property doesn't work when dividing by 0.

Complete each sentence below by filling in the blanks. Also name the property it states.

3. If equals are added to equals, the results are _____ : If $a = b$, then _____ .

4. If equals are _____ by equals, the results are _____ : If $a = b$, then $ac = bc$.

5. If $a = b$, then either a or b may be _____ for the other in any equation.

6. The positions of the _____ on either side of an equal sign may be _____ : If $a = b$, then $b = a$.

Complete each definition below by filling in the blank.

7. A(n) _____ is an angle with a measure of less than $90°$.

8. A _____ of $\overline{AB}$ is any line, ray, or line segment which passes through the midpoint of $\overline{AB}$.

9. _____ line segments are line segments that have equal lengths.

Answer each question below.

10. How many end points does a line segment have? a ray? a line?

(a) 11. If an obtuse angle is bisected, are the resulting little angles right, acute, or obtuse?

Use Betweenness of Points or Rays to answer each question below.

12. If point Z lies in the interior of $\angle WQS$ and if $m\angle ZQS = 8°$, $m\angle WQS = 61°$, and $m\angle WQZ = 53°$, then which of the following rays is between the other two: $\overrightarrow{QZ}$, $\overrightarrow{QW}$, $\overrightarrow{QS}$.

(b) 13. If F-J-W (point J is between points F and W), and if $JW = 4\frac{1}{2}$ and $FW = 8\frac{3}{4}$, then find FJ.

Use the definition of a segment bisector to answer each question below.

14. If point M is the midpoint of $\overline{DE}$ and if $m\overline{DM} = 3.75$, then find $m\overline{DE}$.

(c) 15. If $\overrightarrow{RP}$ bisects $\overline{AB}$ at point P, and if $AB = 14.9$, then find the length of AP.

Use the definition of an angle bisector to answer each question below.

16. If $\overrightarrow{OA}$ bisects $\angle XOY$, and if $m\angle XOA = 23°$, then find $m\angle AOY$.

(d) 17. If $\overrightarrow{FH}$ bisects $m\angle EFG$, and if $m\angle HFG = 18°$, then find $m\angle EFG$.

Tell the kind of each angle below.

18. $\angle STQ$ **19.** $\angle RTQ$

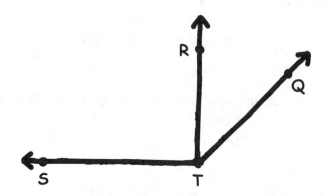

Tell whether the arguments below are valid or invalid deductions.

(e) 20. Rick wears a suit. All bankers wear suits, so Rick must be a banker.

21. All mammals have lungs, and all whales are mammals. Therefore, all whales have lungs.

Reverse each definition below and tell whether it passes the reversibility test.

22. Leonardo da Vinci was a famous painter.

23. A torpedo is a self-propelled submarine missile.

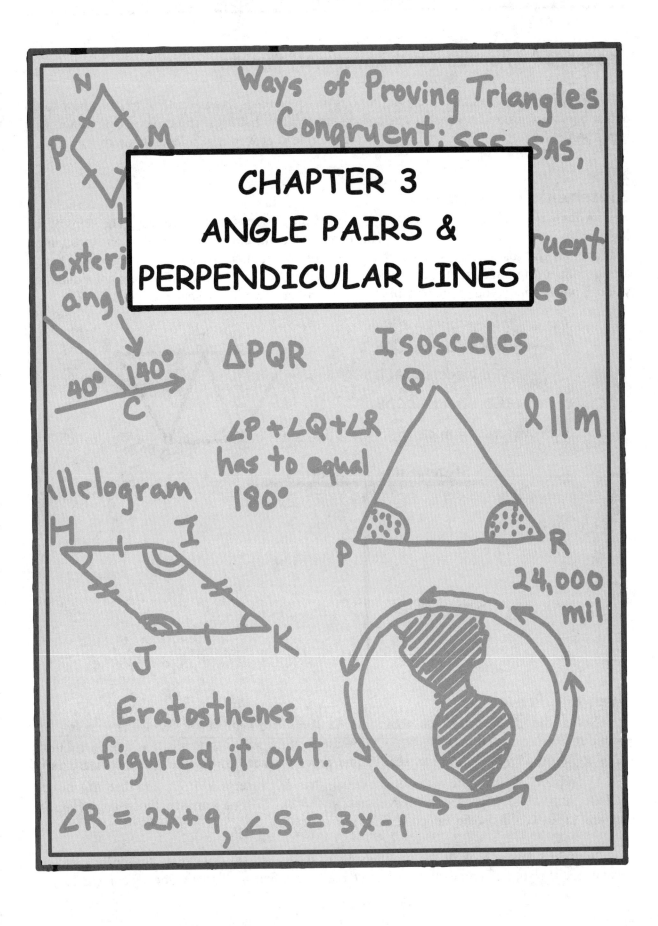

Ways of Proving Triangles
Congruent: SSS, SAS,

CHAPTER 3
ANGLE PAIRS &
PERPENDICULAR LINES

exteri
angl

40° 140°
C

ΔPQR

∠P + ∠Q + ∠R
has to equal
180°

Isosceles
Q

ℓ ‖ m

P   R

24,000
mil

llelogram
H   I

J   K

Eratosthenes
figured it out.

∠R = 2x + 9, ∠S = 3x - 1

Lesson 14—Formal (and Informal) Proofs

We've shown you quite a few definitions and postulates. Now it's time to learn how to do actual geometry proofs. A proof is basically a logic chain that uses deductive reasoning to show that a particular rule of geometry is true. Once the rule is proved it's called a theorem.

Statements and Reasons

A **formal proof** is just a proof that is written out in a very organized way. The steps of the logic chain go in a column on the left. Those are called **statements**. The definitions, postulates, or properties that justify each step go in a column on the right. Those are called **reasons**. There's also usually a diagram of some geometric figure that relates to the proof. If there's not a diagram, you can always draw your own. But all of this is written down in a T shape like this.

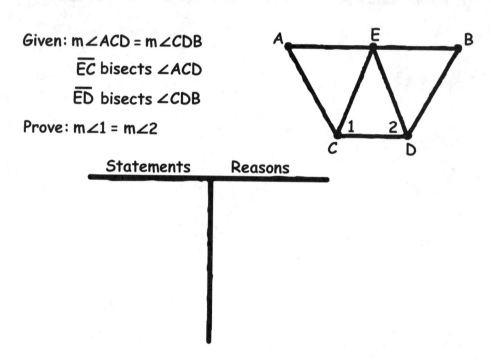

Given: $m\angle ACD = m\angle CDB$

      $\overline{EC}$ bisects $\angle ACD$

      $\overline{ED}$ bisects $\angle CDB$

Prove: $m\angle 1 = m\angle 2$

Statements   Reasons

Given and Prove

Notice the **given** statements above the T. These are statements that we're supposed to assume to be true for the proof. Then, below those is the **prove** statement, which is the thing we're trying to prove. As you can see, in this proof we need to assume that the measures of $\angle ACD$ and $\angle CDB$ from the diagram are equal, that $\overline{EC}$ bisects $\angle ACD$, and that $\overline{ED}$ bisects $\angle CDB$. And we're supposed to prove that $m\angle 1 = m\angle 2$. You can see those angles in the diagram. (They could also be named $\angle ECD$ and $\angle EDC$.)

Now let's take a look at the proof itself. It shows all the statements on the left and the reasons on the right that prove, with deductive reasoning, that $m\angle 1$ really does equal $m\angle 2$.

Given: $m\angle ACD = m\angle CDB$

$\overline{EC}$ bisects $\angle ACD$

$\overline{ED}$ bisects $\angle CDB$

Prove: $m\angle 1 = m\angle 2$

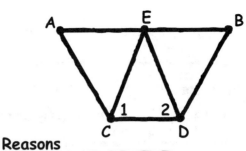

	Statements		Reasons
1.	$\overline{EC}$ bisects $\angle ACD$	1.	Given
2.	$\overline{ED}$ bisects $\angle CDB$	2.	Given
3.	$m\angle 1 = \frac{1}{2}m\angle ACD$	3.	Definition of angle bisector
4.	$m\angle 2 = \frac{1}{2}m\angle CDB$	4.	Definition of angle bisector
5.	$m\angle ACD = m\angle CDB$	5.	Given
6.	$\frac{1}{2}m\angle ACD = \frac{1}{2}m\angle CDB$	6.	Multiplication Property
7.	$m\angle 1 = m\angle 2$	7.	Substitution Property

Now let's go through the logic. The first steps are to state the givens that $\overline{EC}$ bisects $\angle ACD$ and that $\overline{ED}$ bisects $\angle CDB$. The next steps are to state that the measure of angle 1 is half of the measure of angle ACD and that the measure of angle 2 is half of the measure of angle CDB. We know this is true from the definition of an angle bisector, and so those are the reasons given for steps 3 and 4. The important thing about steps 3 and 4 is that they relate angles 1 and 2, which are in the "prove" statement, to angles ACD and CDB, which are in the given statements.

At this point, we bring in the remaining given statement, that $m\angle ACD = m\angle CDB$. Of course, the reason for this step is "given." Next, we want to change $m\angle ACD$ on the left to $\frac{1}{2}m\angle ACD$ and $m\angle CDB$ on the right to $\frac{1}{2}m\angle CDB$. This can be done by multiplying both sides of the equation $m\angle ACD = m\angle CDB$ by $\frac{1}{2}$ to get $\frac{1}{2}m\angle ACD = \frac{1}{2}m\angle CDB$. The reason for this step is the Multiplication Property of Equality (that we can multiply equals by equals and the results will still be equal). We already proved in steps 3 and 4 that $m\angle 1 = \frac{1}{2}m\angle ACD$ and $m\angle 2 = \frac{1}{2}m\angle CDB$. So the final step is to substitute $m\angle 1$ for $\frac{1}{2}m\angle ACD$ and $m\angle 2$ for

$\frac{1}{2}m\angle CDB$ in the equation $\frac{1}{2}m\angle ACD = \frac{1}{2}m\angle CDB$. That gives us $m\angle 1 = m\angle 2$, which is what we were trying to prove. And that ends the proof. The final theorem can be written as follows:

Practice Theorem	If $m\angle ACD = m\angle CDB$, $\overline{EC}$ bisects $\angle ACD$, and $\overline{ED}$ bisects $\angle CDB$, then $m\angle 1 = m\angle 2$.

Since this was just a practice proof, we won't number the theorem. But we will number all of the important theorems that we prove in this book.

There are a few things that you should notice about this proof. First, all of the statements and reasons are numbered. Number 1 on the left goes with number 1 on the right, number 2 on the left goes with number 2 on the right, and so on. That helps us keep track of which statement goes with which reason. Another thing is that the given statements are part of the actual proof. And when we write down a given statement, the reason is always just "given." The given statements are frequently at the beginning of the proof, but they don't have to be. For instance, we didn't list $m\angle ACD = m\angle CDB$ as a statement until step 5. The key is to bring the given statements into the proof when it makes sense logically.

Something else to notice is that some of our reasons are definitions and others are postulates or properties. (The given statements are really like postulates, because we're supposed to assume those are true.) We can also use previously proved theorems as reasons for statements. So as we prove more and more theorems, we'll have more reasons that can be used in new proofs. That's how we'll be able to prove more and more geometry rules as we go through the book.

Getting the Hang of Proofs

If this proof seemed kind of hard, don't worry. It takes a while to get the hang of doing proofs. The process is easier if you'll plan ahead. Before writing down any statements or reasons, go through quickly how you can show that the prove statement has to be true. You can get all the details down later. It also helps to make marks on the diagrams to show certain things that you know have to be true. We'll do that a lot ourselves when going through proofs. Whatever you do, don't get frustrated. It's normal to have some trouble in the beginning. The only way to learn to do proofs is to practice a lot.

Informal Proofs

Our example was a "formal" proof, because we wrote out all the statements and reasons in a T shape, with the givens and prove statement written neatly on top. Formal proofs are also called **two-column proofs**, since the statements and reasons go in two columns. There's also such a thing as an informal proof, though. In this kind of proof, we just go through the essential steps quickly in paragraph form, without worrying about all the details. Here's an informal proof for our example.

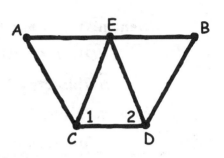

In the figure on the right, since $\overline{EC}$ bisects $\angle ACD$ and $\overline{ED}$ bisects $\angle CDB$, we know that $m\angle 1 = \frac{1}{2}m\angle ACD$ and $m\angle 2 = \frac{1}{2}m\angle CDB$ (Definition of angle bisector). Also, $m\angle ACD = m\angle CDB$ (given). Then, multiplying both sides by $\frac{1}{2}$ gives $\frac{1}{2}m\angle ACD = \frac{1}{2}m\angle CDB$ (Multiplication Property). Finally, we substitute $m\angle 1$ for $\frac{1}{2}m\angle ACD$ and $m\angle 2$ for $\frac{1}{2}m\angle CDB$ to get $m\angle 1 = m\angle 2$.

It's the same logic as the formal proof, but it's a lot shorter and faster. In this book, some of our proofs will be formal and others will be informal. For your problem sets, you should always do formal proofs unless the instructions explicitly say to do an informal proof.

Practice 14

a. From the given statement below, tell the definition, property, or postulate that justifies the prove statement.

   Given: $\angle C + \angle V = \angle X$ and $\angle Y = \angle C + \angle V$; Prove: $\angle Y = \angle X$

b. From the given statement below, tell the definition, property, or postulate that justifies the prove statement.

   Given: $\overline{JL}$ (shown below), J, K, and L are collinear, and $JK + KL = JL$; Prove: K is between J and L.

c. Use Betweenness of Points or Rays to answer the question below.

   If D-H-J (point H is between points D and J), and if $DH = 4.6$ and $DJ = 7.1$, then find HJ.

d. If $\overrightarrow{IJ}$ bisects $\overline{MO}$ at point N, and if $MN = 14.1$, then find the length MO.

e. Complete the proof below by filling in the blanks.

Given: m∠UOR = m∠TOS
    $\overline{VO}$ bisects ∠UOR
    $\overline{WO}$ bisects ∠TOS

Prove: m∠1 = m∠2

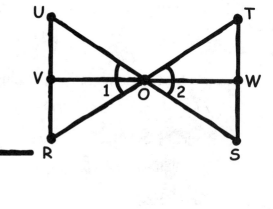

	Statements		Reasons
1.	$\overline{VO}$ bisects ∠UOR	1.	Given
2.		2.	Given
3.		3.	Definition of angle bisector
4.	$m\angle 2 = \frac{1}{2} m\angle TOS$	4.	
5.	m∠UOR = m∠TOS	5.	
6.		6.	Multiplication Property
7.	m∠1 = m∠2	7.	

Problem Set 14

Tell whether each sentence below is True or False.

1. A formal (two-column) proof is just a proof that is written out in a very organized way.

2. In a proof, the "given" statements are assumed to be true.

Complete each sentence below by filling in the blank.

3. An angle's end point is called the _____ of the angle.

4. A _____ is a set of points that extend indefinitely in either direction, and it has length, but no width or depth.

Comp lete each sentence below by filling in the blanks. Also name the property it states.

5. If two quantities are equal to the same quantity, then they are _____ to each other: If $a = b$ and $b = c$, then _____ .

6. If equals are _____ by nonzero equals, their quotients are equal: If $a = b$, then _____ .

7. If equals are _____ from equals, the results are _____ : If $a = b$, then $a - c = b - c$.

8. Any quantity is equal to _____ : $a = a$.

From each given statement below, tell the definition, property, or postulate that justifies the prove statement.

9. Given: $\frac{1}{2} m\angle WDR = 23°$; Prove: $m\angle WDR = 46°$

(a) 10. Given: $\angle O + \angle R = \angle T$ and $\angle S = \angle O + \angle R$; Prove: $\angle S = \angle T$.

(b) 11. Given: $\overline{DG}$ (shown below), D, F, and G are collinear, and $DF + FG = DG$; Prove: F is between D and G.

12. Given: $\overline{AC}$ (shown below) and $m\overline{AB} = m\overline{BC}$; Prove: B is the midpoint of $\overline{AC}$.

Use Betweenness of Points or Rays to answer each question below.

13. If $\overrightarrow{NW}$ - $\overrightarrow{NX}$ - $\overrightarrow{NY}$ ($\overrightarrow{NX}$ is between $\overrightarrow{NW}$ and $\overrightarrow{NY}$) and if $m\angle WNX = 32$ and $m\angle XNY = 27$, then find $m\angle WNY$.

(c) 14. If A-B-C (point B is between points A and C), and if $AB = 6.3$ and $AC = 15.2$, then find BC.

Use the definition of a segment bisector to answer each question below.

15. If $\overrightarrow{IO}$ bisects $\overline{AB}$ at point Q, and $AQ = 2.7$, then find the length of QB.

(d) 16. If $\overleftrightarrow{XY}$ bisects $\overline{UW}$ at point V, and $UV = 12.3$, then find the length of UW.

Use the definition of an angle bisector to answer each question below.

17 If $\overrightarrow{BW}$ bisects $\angle ABC$, and if $m\angle WBC = 38°$, then find $m\angle ABW$.

18. If $\overrightarrow{MO}$ bisects $m\angle LMN$, and $m\angle LMO = 29°$, then find $m\angle LMN$.

Use deductive reasoning to write the conclusion for each set of statements below.

19. All of the trees in Bryan Park are over 10 feet tall. The old oak tree is in the center of Bryan Park. Therefore, _____.

20. Every one in the Percy family is wearing a red sweater in the Christmas card photograph. Clara is in the Percy family, so Clara _____.

Tell whether the arguments below are valid or invalid deductions.

21. All the matter in the universe is made up of chemical elements. That chair is a piece of matter. Therefore, that chair is made up of chemical elements.

22. Super Duper Saver Mart's customers pay less. John is a Super Duper Saver Mart customer. Therefore, John pays less.

Reverse each definition below and tell whether it passes the reversibility test.

23. Photosynthesis is a process that occurs inside of plants.

24. The kidney is an important organ of the body.

Complete the proof below by filling in the blanks.

(e) 25.

Given: $m\angle DAC = m\angle DBC$

$\overline{AB}$ bisects $\angle DAC$

$\overline{AB}$ bisects $\angle DBC$

Prove: $m\angle 1 = m\angle 2$

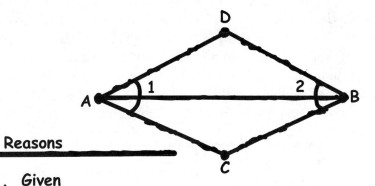

	Statements		Reasons
1.	$\overline{AB}$ bisects $\angle DAC$	1.	Given
2.		2.	Given
3.	$m\angle 1 = \frac{1}{2}m\angle DAC$	3.	
4.		4.	Definition of angle bisector
5.	$m\angle DAC = m\angle DBC$	5.	
6.	$\frac{1}{2}m\angle DAC = \frac{1}{2}m\angle DBC$	6.	
7.		7.	Substitution Property

Lesson 15—Complementary Angle Pairs

For the next several lessons, we're going to focus on several different kinds of angle pairs (taking angles two at a time, in other words) that have things in common. The first angle pair we'll discuss is **complementary angles**. These are just angles that add to equal 90° (a right angle). A quick example is $\angle A$, which we'll say has a measure of 35°, and $\angle B$, which we'll assume has a measure of 55°. Since $35° + 55° = 90°$, $\angle A$ and $\angle B$ are complementary. Another way of saying it is that $\angle A$ is the "complement" of $\angle B$ and $\angle B$ is the complement of $\angle A$. Here's the formal definition of complementary angles.

Definition 16	Complementary angles are angles with measures that add to 90°.

The Law of Reflection

Just so you can get a better of idea of the concept, let's quickly go through an example of complementary angles from science. In ordinary air light travels along straight lines. But when light runs into a mirror, it bounces off or "reflects" in another direction. Let's say that there's a light bulb at point A and that a light ray from the bulb travels down and strikes a mirror at point P. The light will reflect off the mirror in the direction of point B, as shown below.

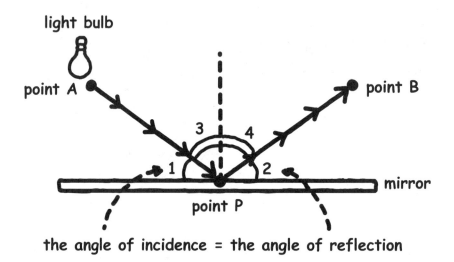

the angle of incidence = the angle of reflection

Angle 1, which is on the bottom left, is called the "angle of incidence." Angle 2, on the bottom right, is called "the angle of reflection." According to the Law of Reflection, no matter what the angle at which the light shines down on the mirror, the angle of incidence must equal the angle of reflection.

That means if the light bulb is really low and far to the left so that ∠1 has a measure of just 15°, then the light will reflect off of the mirror in such way that the angle of reflection (∠2) will just be 15°. Or if the light bulb is really high and to the right, so that ∠1 has a measure of 65°, then the angle of reflection (∠2) will also equal 65°.

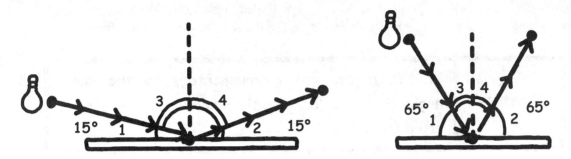

Now instead of focusing on ∠1 and ∠2, take a look at ∠3 and ∠4. Those angles are formed by the vertical dotted line, which rises up from point *P* (where the light ray strikes the mirror). Those angles have different measures than angles 1 and 2. We show that in the diagram by drawing two arcs through each of those angles, instead of just one arc (the way we've done with ∠1 and ∠2). It turns out that those angles are equal to each other, no matter where the light bulb is located.

But what's important for this lesson is that no matter what angle the light bulb shines down at, the measure of ∠1 added to the measure of ∠3 always equals 90°, and the measure of ∠2 added to the measure of ∠4 must always equal 90°.

$$m\angle 1 + m\angle 3 = 90 \qquad\qquad m\angle 2 + m\angle 4 = 90$$

That means ∠1 and ∠3 are complementary angles, as are ∠2 and ∠4.

Finding Angles 3 and 4

Using this fact, we can easily figure out the measures of ∠3 and ∠4 in each of our examples. When the light bulb is low and to the left so that ∠1, the angle of incidence, is just 15°, since ∠3, which is complementary to ∠1, has to equal 75° (since 15° + 75° = 90°). And since ∠2, the angle of reflection, must also equal 15°, and since ∠2 and ∠4 are complementary angles, ∠4 has to equal 75° as well.

Using the same thinking, we can quickly find the measures of ∠3 and ∠4 in the other example, when the light bulb is high and to the right. In this case, the angles of incidence and reflection are 65°. Then, since ∠3 is complementary to ∠1 and ∠4 is complementary to ∠2, ∠3 and ∠4 must each have a measure of 25° (because 65° + 25° = 90°).

A Proof Involving Complementary Angles

One of the interesting things about our example was that $\angle 1$ and $\angle 2$ each had a complementary angle: $\angle 3$ and $\angle 4$. But then it turned out that those complements were equal to each other. In other words, $\angle 3$ was equal to $\angle 4$. That was no coincidence. There's actually an important rule (theorem) of geometry, which says that complements of the same angle or of equal angles have to always be equal to each other. Here's the theorem written formally.

Theorem 1	If two angles are complementary to the same angle or equal (congruent) angles, then they are equal (congruent).

Here's the formal proof of this theorem.[1] Notice that this proof doesn't have a diagram. Even though a diagram is usually needed in a proof, in this case it doesn't help much, so we left the diagram out.

Given: $\angle A$ and $\angle B$ are complements of $\angle C$

Prove: $m\angle A = m\angle B$

Statements	Reasons
1. $\angle A$ and $\angle B$ are complements of $\angle C$	1. Given
2. $m\angle A + m\angle C = 90$	2. If two angles are complementary, the sum of their measures is 90°.
3. $m\angle B + m\angle C = 90$	3. If two angles are complementary, the sum of their measures is 90°.
4. $m\angle A = 90 - m\angle C$	4. Subtraction Property
5. $m\angle B = 90 - m\angle C$	5. Subtraction Property
6. $m\angle A = m\angle B$	6. Substitution Property

One important thing to understand about this proof is that it covers all possible complementary angles. That's why the proof doesn't say anything about the measures of angles A, B, or C. The proof is true for all sorts of different angle measurements. That's what makes math so powerful. With a single deductive proof, we can cover lots and lots of possibilities.

---

[1] This is the proof for the case where two angles are complements of the *same* angle. With just one more step, we can prove the case where two angles are complements of *equal* angles.

Practice 15

a. From the given statement below, tell the definition, property, or postulate that justifies the prove statement.

Given: $\dfrac{1}{3}m\angle TYW = m\angle 1$ and $m\angle 1 = \dfrac{1}{3}m\angle ZSA$; Prove: $m\angle TYW = m\angle ZSA$

b. In the figure on the right, there are three angles with vertex D. Name all three. Be sure to write your answers in proper form.

c. Use Betweenness of Points or Rays to answer the question below.

If E-M-L, and if $EM = 3x - 1$, $ML = x + 2$, and $EL = 9$ then find x.

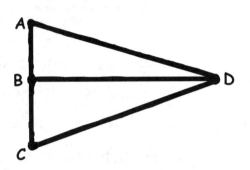

d. Use the protractor below to name the measure of an angle that is complementary to $\angle FOG$.

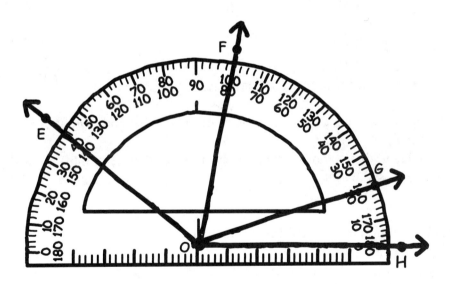

e. Complete the proof below by filling in the blanks.

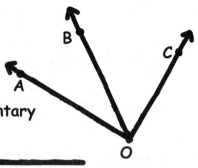

Given: $\overrightarrow{OC}$ - $\overrightarrow{OB}$ - $\overrightarrow{OA}$

∠COA is a right angle

Prove: ∠COB and ∠BOA are complementary

Statements	Reasons
1. $\overrightarrow{OC}$ - $\overrightarrow{OB}$ - $\overrightarrow{OA}$	1.
2. ∠COB + ∠BOA = ∠COA	2.
3. ∠COA is a right angle	3.
4. m∠COA = 90	4.
5. m∠COB + m∠BOA = 90	5.
6. ∠COB and ∠BOA are complementary	6.

Problem Set 15

Tell whether each sentence below is True or False.

1. Complementary angles are angles with measures that add to equal 180°.

2. According to the Law of Reflection, the angle of incidence must equal the angle of reflection.

Complete each definition below by filling in the blank.

3. A(n) _____ is an angle with a measure of greater than 90° (but less than 180°).

4. A right angle is an angle with a measure of _____.

5. _____ points are points that do not lie on the same line.

6. The rays of an angle are called the angle's _____.

From each given statement below, tell the definition, property, or postulate that justifies the prove statement.

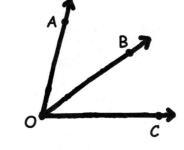

7. Given: $\angle AOC$ (shown on the right), B which lies in the interior of $\angle AOC$, and $m\angle AOB = m\angle BOC$.
   Prove: $\overrightarrow{OB}$ bisects $\angle AOC$

8. Given: $3PQ = 3ST$; Prove: $PQ = ST$

9. Given: $JK + KR = JR$; Prove: $JK = JR - KR$

(a) 10. Given: $\dfrac{1}{2}m\angle EFG = m\angle 2$ and $m\angle 2 = \dfrac{1}{2}m\angle JKL$; Prove: $m\angle EFG = m\angle JKL$

Answer each question below using the figure on the right.

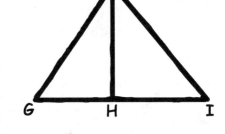

11. There are six line segments in the figure. Name all six.

12. There are two angles in the figure that can be named with just one letter. Name both angles.

(b) 13. There are three angles with vertex K. Name all three. Be sure to write your answers in proper form.

Use Betweenness of Points or Rays to answer each question below.

14. If $\overrightarrow{PA}$-$\overrightarrow{PB}$-$\overrightarrow{PC}$ and if $m\angle APB = 51$ and $m\angle APC = 89$, then find $m\angle BPC$.

(c) 15. If D-M-G, and if $DM = 2x$, $MG = x - 5$, and $DG = 7$ then find x.

Use the protractor to name the measure of an angle that is complementary to each angle below.

16. $\angle COD$

(d) 17. $\angle BOC$

18. $\angle AOB$

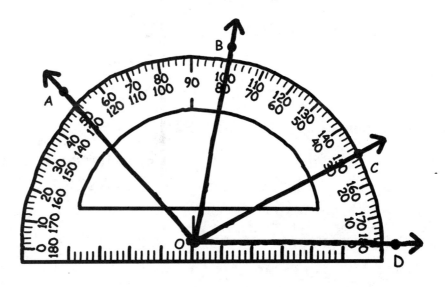

Draw a Venn diagram to represent each set of conditional statements below.

19. All rational numbers are real numbers, and $\frac{5}{7}$ is a rational number. Therefore, $\frac{5}{7}$ is a real number.

20. Fyodor is a novelist, and all novelists are writers. So Fyodor is a writer.

Tell whether the arguments below are valid or invalid deductions.

21. All wise men own a pair of galoshes. Mr. Thompson owns a pair of galoshes, so he must be wise.

22. Dr. Breeley is knowledgeable about the past. All historians are knowledgeable about the past. So Dr. Breeley must be a historian.

Complete the proof below by filling in the blanks.

(e) 23.

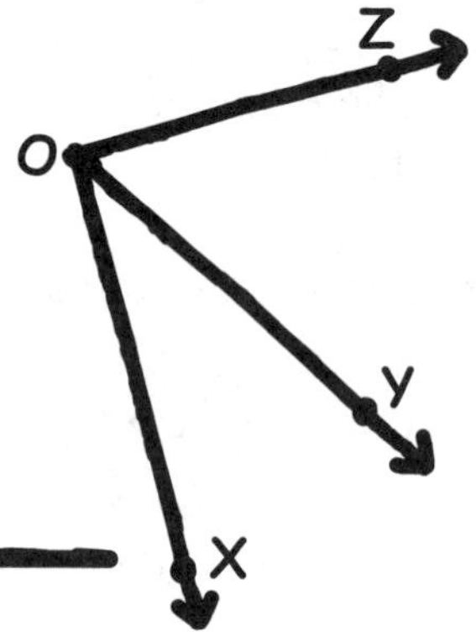

Given: $\overrightarrow{OZ} - \overrightarrow{OY} - \overrightarrow{OX}$

∠ZOX is a right angle

Prove: ∠ZOY and ∠YOX are complementary

	Statements	Reasons
1.	$\overrightarrow{OZ} - \overrightarrow{OY} - \overrightarrow{OX}$	1.
2.	∠ZOY + ∠YOX = ∠ZOX	2.
3.		3. Given
4.	m∠ZOX = 90	4.
5.	m∠ZOY + m∠YOX = 90	5.
6.		6. Definition of complementary angles

98

Lesson 16—Supplementary Angle Pairs

We've learned about complementary angles, which are angles that add to equal 90°. Now we're going to cover another kind of angle pair called **supplementary angles**. These are angles that add to equal 180°. Here's the formal definition.

Definition 17	Supplementary angles are angles with measures that add to 180°.

As a quick example, if $m\angle Q = 105°$ and $m\angle R = 75°$, then, since $105° + 75° = 180°$, $\angle Q$ and $\angle R$ are supplementary angles. We could also say that $\angle Q$ is a supplement of $\angle R$ or that $\angle R$ is a supplement of $\angle Q$.

Bouncing Billiard Balls

In the last lesson, we used the concept of complementary angles to study light rays. In this lesson, we're going to use supplementary angles for something a little less practical: to play billiards. A billiard table, as you know, has cushioned sides so that the billiard balls can bounce off of. Interestingly, when a billiard ball bounces off those sides, it follows the same basic rules as a light ray hitting a mirror. Specifically, it follows the Law of Reflection, which says that the angle of incidence equals the angle of reflection. So let's do a billiard ball example that uses this law. This one is a little more complicated than the example in the last lesson.

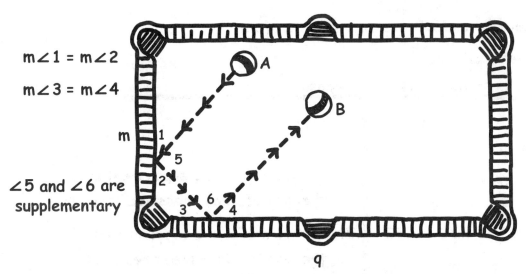

The billiards player must be pretty advanced, because he wants to hit ball A in such a direction that it will bounce off side m, then head toward side q and bounce off that side to finally go in the direction of ball B. As it turns out, because of the Law of Reflection, the slant of ball A's path will be the same going in as it is going out (after bouncing off walls m and q). The diagram shows that clearly. You don't yet have enough knowledge of geometry to understand a proof of this rule, but it's true. Basically, the reason is that angles 1 and 2 are angles of incidence and reflection for the first bounce (off wall *m*), so they have to be equal. And angles 3 and 4 (from the second bounce, off wall *q*) are also equal for the same reason. That's what makes the slant of the ball's path the same on the way in as it is on the way out.

What, you may be wondering, does this have to do with supplementary angles? Well, since the paths in and out have the same slant, $\angle 5$ and $\angle 6$ always have to add to equal 180°. So $\angle 5$ and $\angle 6$ area supplementary angles. Interestingly, those two angles will be supplementary no matter **what** the particular slant of the ball's path in and out. That's an example, then, of supplementary angles in action (so to speak).

A Supplementary Proof

You may remember that if two angles are complementary to the same angle, then the angles have to be congruent to each other. We proved that theorem in the last lesson. As it turns out, there's a similar theorem about supplementary angles: If two angles are supplementary to the same angle, then the two angles are congruent to each other. First, we'll show you the official statement of the theorem and then the proof.

Theorem 2	If two angles are supplementary to the same angle or equal (congruent) angles, then they are equal (congruent).

Given: $\angle A$ and $\angle B$ are supplements of $\angle C$

Prove: $m\angle A = m\angle B$

Statements	Reasons
1. $\angle A$ and $\angle B$ are supplements of $\angle C$	1. Given
2. $m\angle A + m\angle C = 180$	2. If two angles are supplementary, the sum of their measures is 180°.
3. $m\angle B + m\angle C = 180$	3. If two angles are supplementary, the sum of their measures is 180°.
4. $m\angle A = 180 - m\angle C$	4. Subtraction Property

5. $m\angle B = 180 - m\angle C$	5. **Subtraction Property**
6. $m\angle A = m\angle B$	6. **Substitution Property**

Practice 16

a. Find the measures of the complement and supplement to $\angle R$ if $m\angle R = y$.

b. From the given statement below, tell the definition, property, postulate, or theorem that justifies the prove statement.

Given: $\angle A$ and $\angle B$ are complements of $\angle C$; Prove: $\angle A \cong \angle B$

c. In the figure on the right, $\angle FOG$ and $\angle GOH$ are complementary. If $m\angle FOG = 2x + 10$ and $m\angle GOH = 2x$, find x.

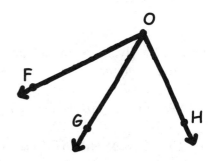

d. Use the definition of a segment or angle bisector to answer the question below.

If $\overrightarrow{PQ}$ bisects $\angle SPF$, and if $m\angle SPQ = 3x - 2$ and $m\angle QPF = 2x + 9$ then find $m\angle SPF$. Is $\angle SPF$ acute, right, or obtuse?

e. Do the proof below.

Given: $\overline{GD}$ bisects $\angle EDF$
$\qquad$ $\angle 1$ and $\angle 3$ are supplementary
$\qquad$ $\angle 2$ and $\angle 4$ are supplementary
Prove: $m\angle 1 = m\angle 2$

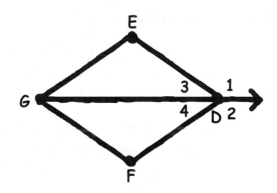

Problem Set 16

Tell whether each sentence below is True or False.

1. Supplementary angles are angles with measures that add to equal $180°$.

2. The supplement of an acute angle is acute.

Complete each sentence below by filling in the blanks.

3. The _____ of a line segment is the point that divides the line segment into two congruent line segments.

4. A _____ is a set of points that forms a flat surface which extends forever in all directions and has length and width, but no depth.

5. Two points determine a unique _____.

Find the measures of the complement and supplement of each angle below.

6. $m\angle A = 25$ **7.** $m\angle B = 88$ **(a) 8.** $m\angle C = x$

From each given statement below, tell the definition, property, postulate, or theorem that justifies the prove statement.

9. Given: $AB + DE = GH$; Prove: $GH = AB + DE$.

10. Given: $m\angle PST + m\angle LQR = 90°$ and $m\angle DEF = m\angle LQR$; Prove: $m\angle PST + m\angle DEF = 90°$.

11. Given: $OM + MP = OP$; Prove: O-M-P.

(b) 12. Given: $\angle 1$ and $\angle 2$ are supplements of $\angle 3$; Prove: $\angle 1 \cong \angle 2$.

Answer each question below.

(c) 13. In the figure on the right, $\angle SOT$ and $\angle TOU$ are complementary. If $m\angle SOT = 2x + 4$ and $m\angle TOU = x - 16$, find x.

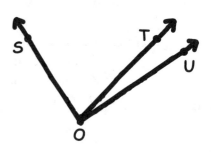

14. $\angle ABC$ and $\angle DEF$ are supplementary. If $m\angle ABC = 2y$ and $m\angle DEF = 3y - 5$, find y.

Use Betweenness of Points or Rays to answer each question below.

15. If points Q, R, and S are collinear and if $RS = 15.7$, $RQ = 9.1$, and $QS = 6.6$, which point is between the other two?

16. If point K lies in the interior of $\angle JML$ and if $m\angle KML = 24$, $m\angle JML = 71$, and $m\angle JMK = 47$, then which of the following rays is between the other two: $\overrightarrow{MK}$, $\overrightarrow{MJ}$, $\overrightarrow{ML}$.

Use the definition of a segment or angle bisector to answer each question below.

17. If $\overrightarrow{PQ}$ bisects $\overline{CX}$ at point J, and if $JX = 4y$ and $CJ = y + 9$, then find y.

(d) 18. If $\overrightarrow{OL}$ bisects $\angle HOP$, and if $m\angle HOL = 2x - 5$ and $m\angle LOP = x + 11$ then find $m\angle HOP$. Is $\angle HOP$ acute, right, or obtuse?

Write conditional statements to represent each Venn diagram below.

19.

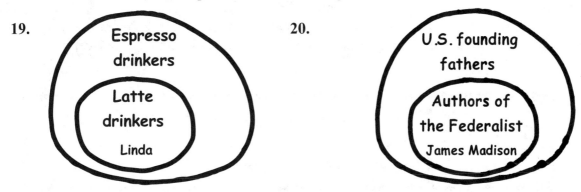

Espresso drinkers

Latte drinkers

Linda

20.

U.S. founding fathers

Authors of the Federalist

James Madison

Reverse each definition below and tell whether it passes the reversibility test.

21. A unicycle is a vehicle with a single wheel that is propelled by pedals.

22. A department store is a place to purchase clothing.

Do the proof below.

(e) 23. Given: $\overrightarrow{MO}$ bisects $\angle NPQ$;
               $\angle NPO$ and $\angle NPM$ are supplementary;
               $\angle OPQ$ and $\angle QPM$ are supplementary
      Prove: $m\angle QPM = m\angle NPM$

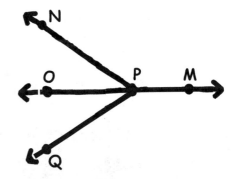

Lesson 17—Adjacent Angles

We've learned about complementary angles and supplementary angles. Our next angle pair is adjacent angles. The word adjacent basically means "right next to each other." So **adjacent angles** are angles that are next to each other because they have one side in common. Actually, several of our past lessons have had pictures of adjacent angles. We just didn't call them by name. Two adjacent angles, $\angle AOB$ and $\angle BOC$, are shown on the right. Notice that $\overrightarrow{OB}$ is a side of both angles. That's what it means to say that

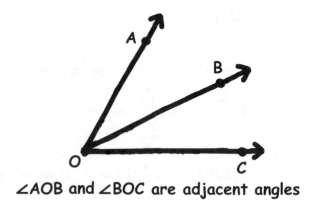

$\angle AOB$ and $\angle BOC$ are adjacent angles

$\angle AOB$ and $\angle BOC$ have a side in common. The rays on the outside, $\overrightarrow{OA}$ and $\overrightarrow{OC}$, are called **exterior sides** of the angles. The two angles also have the same vertex, point O. That, too, is a requirement for two angles to be adjacent. Below is the formal definition of adjacent angles.

Definition 18	*Adjacent* angles are angles that have the same vertex, share a common side, and have no interior points in common.

The last part of the definition says that adjacent angles can't have any interior points in common. That just means that the angles can't overlap. For example, $\angle AOC$ and $\angle BOC$ don't qualify as adjacent angles, because they overlap in the shaded area shown below.

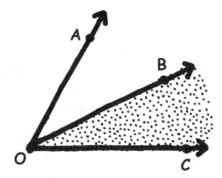

$\angle AOC$ and $\angle BOC$ are not adjacent because they overlap.

104

Linear Pairs

One special pair of adjacent angles is a pair whose exterior sides form a straight line. Here's an example.

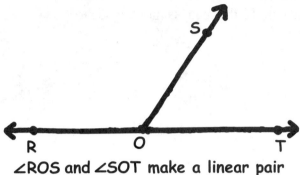

∠ROS and ∠SOT make a linear pair

See, the adjacent angles are ∠*ROS* and ∠*SOT*. And the exterior sides $\overrightarrow{OR}$ and $\overrightarrow{OT}$ make up a straight line. This line can also be considered an angle with point *O* for its vertex and rays *OR* and *OT* for its sides. Angles of this type are sometimes called "straight angles," obviously because they're shaped like straight lines. A straight angle always has a measure of 180 degrees. So *m*∠*ROT* = 180. Adjacent angles such as ∠*ROS* and ∠*SOT* are called **linear pairs**. Here's the formal definition.

Definition 19	A *linear pair* is two adjacent angles whose exterior sides form a straight line.

A Proof on Linear Pairs

It turns out that the angles of a linear pair are always supplementary. The actual theorem is shown below.

Theorem 3	If two angles are a linear pair, then they are supplementary.

The proof is pretty easy, so we'll show it informally.

Linear pair ∠*ROS* and ∠*SOT* have exterior sides, $\overrightarrow{OR}$ and $\overrightarrow{OT}$, that form a straight line. So *m*∠*ROT* = 180. $\overrightarrow{OS}$ is between $\overrightarrow{OR}$ and $\overrightarrow{OT}$ and ∠*ROS* + ∠*SOT* = ∠*ROT* (Betweenness of Rays). By substitution, we get ∠*ROS* + ∠*SOT* = 180°. So ∠*ROS* and ∠*SOT* are supplementary (Definition of supplementary angles).

Practice 17

a. Tell whether the pair of angles $\angle BAC$ and $\angle COD$ is adjacent. If the pair is not adjacent, briefly tell why not.

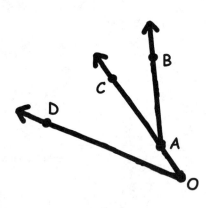

b. From the given statement below, tell the definition, property, postulate, or theorem that justifies the prove statement.

Given: $\angle JKM$ and $\angle MKL$ (shown on the right) are a linear pair;
Prove: $\angle JKM$ and $\angle MKL$ are supplementary.

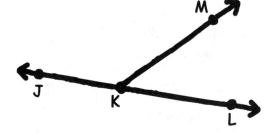

c. Use Betweenness of Points or Rays to answer the question below.

If $\overrightarrow{XA}$ - $\overrightarrow{XB}$ - $\overrightarrow{XC}$ and if $m\angle AXB = 2x$, $m\angle BXC = x$, and $m\angle AXC = 60$, then find $m\angle AXB$.

d. Use the definition of a segment or angle bisector to answer the question below.

If line q bisects $\overline{EG}$ at point T, and if $ET = \dfrac{1}{3}x$ and $TG = x - 2$, then find EG.

e. Do the proof below.

Given: $\angle 5$ and $\angle 6$ are a linear pair;
$\angle 4$ and $\angle 6$ are supplementary
Prove: $m\angle 4 = m\angle 5$

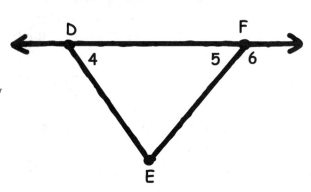

Problem Set 17

Tell whether each sentence below is True or False.

1. A linear pair is two adjacent angles whose exterior sides form a straight line.

2. If two angles are a linear pair, then they are complementary.

Complete each sentence below by filling in the blanks. If the sentence is a property, name the property.

3. _____ are angles that have the same vertex, share a common side, and have no interior points in common.

4. If equals are _____ by equals, the results are _____ : If $a = b$, then $ac = bc$.

5. If two angles are supplementary to the same angle or equal (congruent) angles, then they are _____.

Tell whether each pair of angles below is adjacent. If a pair is not adjacent, briefly tell why not.

(a) 6. $\angle TPU$ and $\angle UOV$

7. $\angle UOV$ and $\angle VOW$

8. $\angle UOW$ and $\angle UOV$

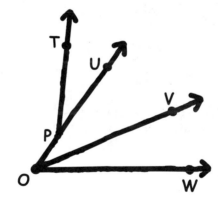

From each given statement below, tell the definition, property, postulate, or theorem that justifies the prove statement.

9. Given: H-M-S and $m\overline{HM} = m\overline{MS}$; Prove: M is the midpoint of $\overline{HS}$.

10. Given: $\dfrac{1}{2}m\angle EDG = m\angle FDG$;
    Prove: $m\angle EDG = 2m\angle FDG$

(b) 11. Given: $\angle AOB$ and $\angle BOC$ (shown on the right) are a linear pair;

Prove: $\angle AOB$ and $\angle BOC$ are supplementary.

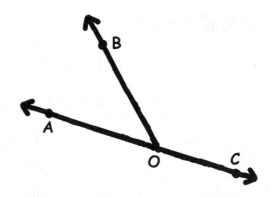

Answer each question below.

12. $\angle URH$ and $\angle KLJ$ are complementary. If $m\angle URH = 3z - 1$ and $m\angle KLJ = z + 7$, then find z.

13. $\angle P$ and $\angle Q$ are supplementary. If $m\angle P = 2x$ and $m\angle Q = x - 3$, find x.

Use Betweenness of Points or Rays to answer each question below.

14. If points B, P, and R are collinear and if $BP = 7.3$, $PR = 9.2$, and $BR = 1.9$, which point is between the other two?

(c) 15. If $\overrightarrow{OD} - \overrightarrow{OE} - \overrightarrow{OF}$ and if $m\angle DOE = 2x$, $m\angle EOF = x + 5$, and $m\angle DOF = 50$, then find $m\angle DOE$.

Use the definition of a segment or angle bisector to answer each question below.

16. If $\overrightarrow{RJ}$ bisects $\angle IRK$, and if $m\angle IRJ = 2x + 1$ and $m\angle JRK = x + 28$ then find $m\angle IRK$. Is $\angle IRK$ acute, right, or obtuse?

(d) 17. If line m bisects $\overline{AB}$ at point P, and if $AP = \frac{1}{2}y$ and $PB = y - 2$, then find AB.

Find the measure of each angle below.

18. x

19. y

20. z

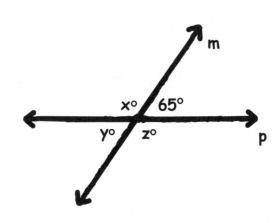

Tell whether the arguments below are valid or invalid deductions.

21. All of the angles in the triangle are acute. $\angle HJK$ is acute. So it must be one of the angles in the triangle.

22. Every parachuter opened his chute within 10 seconds. Pete was the first parachuter. Therefore, Pete opened his chute within 10 seconds.

Do the proof below.

(e) 23. Given: $\angle 2$ and $\angle 3$ are a linear pair
   $\angle 1$ and $\angle 3$ are supplementary
   Prove: $m\angle 1 = m\angle 2$

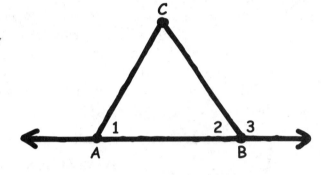

Lesson 18—Vertical Angles

The next kind of angle pair we're going to study is vertical angles. **Vertical angles are made when two lines intersect** (cross). As shown in the diagram on the right, angles 1 and 2 are adjacent angles, as are angles 3 and 4. (They're both linear pairs.) But $\angle 2$ and $\angle 3$ are not adjacent. They share a vertex, but don't share a common side. They happen to be vertical angles. The other pair of vertical angles in this diagram are $\angle 1$ and $\angle 4$. Basically, vertical angles are the "nonadjacent angles" that are formed when two lines (or line segments) intersect. They have the same vertex (as do adjacent angles). Their vertex is where the two lines cross. But vertical angles are on opposite sides of that intersection point. Here's the formal definition.

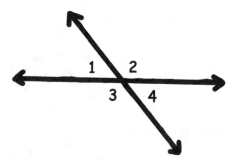

$\angle 2$ and $\angle 3$ are vertical angles.
$\angle 1$ and $\angle 4$ are vertical angles.

Definition 20	Vertical angles are a pair of nonadjacent angles formed by two intersecting lines.

In general, any time two lines cross, four linear pairs of angles will be created and two pairs of vertical angles will be created. In the figure above, the linear pairs are $\angle 1$ and $\angle 2$, $\angle 3$ and $\angle 4$, $\angle 1$ and $\angle 3$, and $\angle 2$ and $\angle 4$. The vertical angles are $\angle 2$ and $\angle 3$, as well as $\angle 1$ and $\angle 4$.

Vertical Angles in the Movies

Since intersecting lines are so common, there are lots of examples of vertical angles in the real world. One simple example is a movie reel that feeds the film of the movie into the projector. The "spokes" of a movie reel represent intersecting lines that form pairs of vertical angles.

Vertical Angles are Congruent

There is a very simple but important theorem about vertical angles. Even though two lines can intersect at lots of different slants, each pair of vertical angles

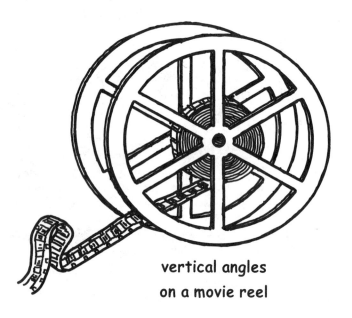

vertical angles
on a movie reel

that is formed will always be congruent (have equal measures). You can see this principle in each of the figures below.

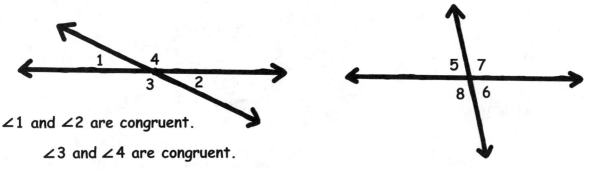

∠1 and ∠2 are congruent.

∠3 and ∠4 are congruent.

∠5 and ∠6 are congruent.

∠7 and ∠8 are congruent.

Here is the theorem stated formally, followed by its proof.

Theorem 4	Pairs of vertical angles are congruent (equal).

Given: Lines m and n intersect at point. P.

Prove: m∠1 = m∠3

	Statements	Reasons
1.	Lines m and n intersect at point P.	1. Given
2.	∠1 and ∠2 are supplementary.	2. If two angles are a linear pair, then they are supplementary.
3.	∠2 and ∠3 are supplementary.	3. If two angles are a linear pair, then they are supplementary.
4.	m∠1 = m∠3	4. If two angles are supplementary to the same angle, then they are equal.

Practice 18

a. From the given statement below, tell the definition, property, postulate, or theorem that justifies the prove statement.

Given: $DS = ER$ and $ER = TW$; Prove: $DS = TW$.

b. Find the measure of $\angle KOJ$.

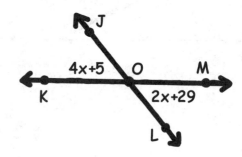

c. Write an equation to represent the question below; then solve the equation to get your answer.

A supplement of an angle is 4 times as large as the angle's complement. Find the measure of the angle.

d. Draw a Venn diagram to represent the set of conditional statements below.

All Texans are Americans and Isabella is not an American. Therefore, Isabella is not a Texan.

e. Do the proof below.

Given: $\angle ABO$ is complementary to
$\angle AOB$;
$\angle CDO$ is complementary to
$\angle DOC$
Prove: $m\angle ABO = m\angle CDO$

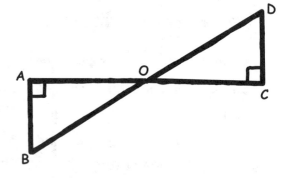

Problem Set 18

Tell whether each sentence below is True or False.

1. Vertical angles are a pair of nonadjacent angles formed by two intersecting lines.

2. Pairs of vertical angles are congruent.

Complete each sentence below by filling in the blanks.

3. _____ angles are angles with measures that add to equal $90°$.

4. A _____ of $\overline{AB}$ is any line, ray, or line segment which passes through the midpoint of $\overline{AB}$.

5. _____ are angles that have the same vertex, share a common side, and have no interior points in common.

6. A _____ is a part of a line consisting of two points, called end points, and the set of all points between them.

Find the measures of a complement and supplement of each angle below.

7. $m\angle ABC = 47$

8. $m\angle DEF = 3y$

From each given statement below, tell the definition, property, postulate, or theorem that justifies the prove statement.

9. Given: $\angle JKL$ and $\angle MNP$ are complements of $\angle T$
   Prove: $\angle JKL \cong \angle MNP$

(a) 10. Given: $CV = HY$ and $HY = GW$
    Prove: $CV = GW$

11. Given: Intersecting lines l and m (shown on the right)
    Prove: $m\angle 1 = m\angle 2$

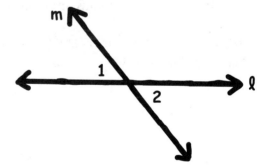

Find the measure of each angle below.

(b) 12. $\angle AOD$

13. $\angle AOB$

14. $\angle DOC$

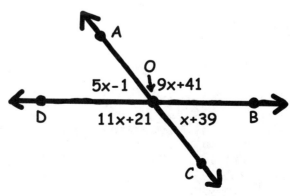

Write an equation to represent each question below; then solve the equation to get your answer.

15. An angle's measure is equal to 24 less than its complement. Find the measure of the angle.

(c) 16. A supplement of an angle is 6 times as large as the angle's complement. Find the measure of the angle.

Use Betweenness of Points or Rays to answer each question below.

17. If $\overrightarrow{OA}$-$\overrightarrow{OB}$-$\overrightarrow{OC}$ and if $m\angle AOB = 10$, $m\angle BOC = 9x + 2$, and $m\angle AOC = 11x - 2$, then find $m\angle BOC$.

18. If R-S-T, and if $RS = 3x$, $RT = 6x - 2$, and $ST = 19$ then find RT.

Use the definition of a segment or angle bisector to answer each question below.

19. If $\overrightarrow{OF}$ bisects $\angle EOG$, and if $m\angle EOF = 3x - 4$ and $m\angle FOG = 2x + 7$ then find $m\angle EOG$.

20. If line q bisects $\overline{KM}$ at point V, and if $KV = 2.5z$ and $VM = 5z - 10$, then find KM.

Draw a Venn diagram to represent each set of conditional statements below.

21. Since all anthems are songs, the national anthem must be a song.

(d) 22. All Californians are Americans and Otto is not an American. Therefore, Otto is not a Californian.

Do the proof below.

(e) 23. Given: $\angle 1$ is complementary to $\angle 3$,
$\angle 2$ is complementary to $\angle 4$.
Prove: $m\angle 3 = m\angle 4$

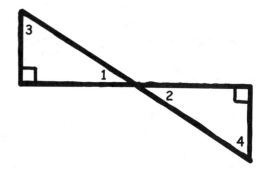

Lesson 19—Right Angles and Perpendicular Lines

We've been learning about different angle pairs. Now we're going to switch gears and talk about the connection between right angles and perpendicular lines. When two lines (or line segments) intersect to form a right angle, the lines are said to be **perpendicular**. Here's a picture.

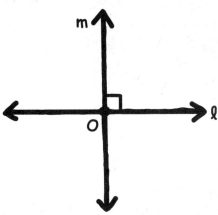

Lines m and ℓ are perpendicular, because they
intersect to form a right angle.

See, lines m and ℓ are perpendicular because they make a right angle at their intersection point. To show on paper that m and ℓ are perpendicular, we write $m \perp \ell$. We use an upside down T as our symbol, because it looks like a right angle. If, instead of m and ℓ, the lines had been named $\overleftrightarrow{AB}$ and $\overleftrightarrow{CD}$, we would have written $\overleftrightarrow{AB} \perp \overleftrightarrow{CD}$ to show that they're perpendicular.

Crossing Streets and the Leaning Tower of Pisa

There are all sorts of examples of perpendicular lines in the real world. A very simple one is two streets that intersect. Although intersecting streets don't have to be perpendicular, most of them are.

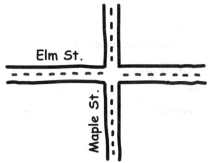

Most intersecting streets
are perpendicular.

115

Another example that's used a lot to explain the perpendicular concept is the Leaning Tower of Pisa in Italy. As you probably know, this building leans to one side pretty seriously. If we think of the tower as a line and the ground as another line, then the tower does *not* make a right angle with the ground, the way most buildings do. So, really, the Leaning Tower of Pisa is an example of two lines that are not perpendicular. But, by looking at it, we realize that most (properly constructed) buildings *are* perpendicular to the ground.

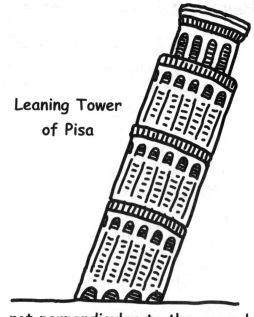

Leaning Tower of Pisa

not perpendicular to the ground

Now that you're grasping the concept, here is the formal definition of perpendicular lines. It's basically the same definition we gave above.

Definition 21	*Perpendicular lines* are lines which intersect to form right angles.

Not One but Four

You may have noticed in our diagrams that perpendicular lines don't just make one right angle. Actually, they make four right angles: on top and bottom of both sides. And even though it seems pretty obvious, this fact has been proven deductively by the mathematicians.

Here's the official theorem, followed by the proof.

Theorem 5	Perpendicular lines intersect to form 4 right angles.

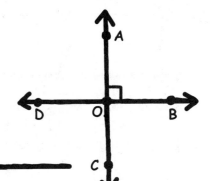

Given: Lines $\overleftrightarrow{AC}$ and $\overleftrightarrow{BD}$ are perpendicular.

Prove: ∠AOB, ∠AOD, ∠DOC, and ∠BOC are right angles.

	Statements		Reasons
1.	Lines $\overleftrightarrow{AC}$ and $\overleftrightarrow{BD}$ are perpendicular.	1.	Given
2.	∠AOB is a right angle.	2.	Definition of perpendicular lines.
3.	m∠AOB = 90	3.	Definition of right angle.
4.	∠AOB and ∠AOD are a linear pair.	4.	Definition of linear pair.
5.	∠AOB and ∠AOD are supplementary.	5.	If two angles are a linear pair, then they are supplementary.
6.	m∠AOB + m∠AOD = 180	6.	Definition of supplementary angles.
7.	90 + m∠AOD = 180	7.	Substitution Property
8.	m∠AOD = 90	8.	Subtraction Property
9.	∠AOD and ∠DOC are a linear pair.	9.	Definition of linear pair
10.	∠AOD and ∠DOC are supplementary.	10.	If two angles are a linear pair, then they are supplementary.
11.	m∠AOD + m∠DOC = 180	11.	Definition of supplementary angles.
12.	90 + m∠DOC = 180	12.	Substitution Property
13.	m∠DOC = 90	13.	Subtraction Property
14.	∠AOD and ∠DOC are right angles.	14.	Definition of right angle.

∠BOC can be proven to be a right angle by following the exact same steps.

A Very Easy Theorem

That last theorem was very tough. So tough that we couldn't fit the entire proof on the page. To finish up the lesson, we'll show you a very easy theorem. Here it is.

Theorem 6	All right angles are congruent (equal).

This seems very obvious. Of course, all right angles are congruent, you may be thinking. But this is a theorem that can be proved using the definition of a right angle (that they all equal 90°). We're going to need this simple theorem to do some proofs on future lessons.

Practice 19

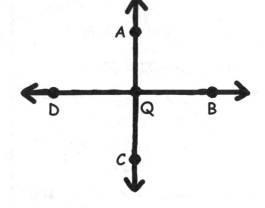

a. From the given statement below, tell the definition, property, postulate, or theorem that justifies the prove statement.

Given: $\overleftrightarrow{AC} \perp \overleftrightarrow{DB}$ (shown on the right).
Prove: $\angle AQB$, $\angle AQD$, $\angle BQC$, and $\angle DQC$ are right angles.

b. Find the measure of $\angle KOJ$ below.

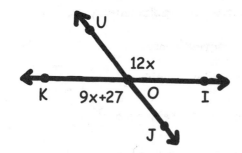

c. Write an equation to represent the question below; then solve the equation to get your answer.

The difference between three times an angle's measure and its complement is 46. Find the measure of the angle.

d. If $\overrightarrow{PN}$ bisects $\angle MPL$, and if $m\angle MPN = 8x - 2$ and $m\angle MPL = 12x + 24$ then find $m\angle NPL$.

e. Tell whether the argument below is a valid or invalid deduction.

All Brazilians are South Americans. If Luis is not South American, then he is not Brazilian.

Problem Set 19

Tell whether each sentence below is True or False.

1. When two lines intersect to form right angles, the lines are said to be perpendicular.
2. Intersecting perpendicular lines actually make two right angles.

Complete each sentence below by filling in the blanks.

3. $\overrightarrow{BD}$ is the _____ of $\angle ABC$ if D lies in the interior of $\angle ABC$ and $m\angle ABD = m\angle DBC$.

4. An angle's end point is called the _____ of the angle.

5. _____ are a pair of nonadjacent angles formed by two intersecting lines.

Complete each property below by filling in the blanks. Also name the property it states.

6. The positions of the _____ on either side of an equal sign may be _____ : If $a = b$, then $b = a$.

7. If equals are _____ by nonzero equals, their quotients are equal: If $a = b$, then _____.

From each given statement below, tell the definition, property, postulate, or theorem that justifies each prove statement.

8. Given: $m\angle ABC + m\angle DEF = 90$
   Prove: $\angle ABC$ and $\angle DEF$ are complementary.

9. Given: Lines $\overleftrightarrow{AB}$ and $\overleftrightarrow{RQ}$ intersect (shown on the right)
   Prove: $\angle ROB$ and $\angle AOQ$ are congruent.

10. Given: $AD = DB$ and $CD = DE$
    Prove: $AD + CD = DB + DE$

(a) 11. Given: $\overleftrightarrow{FG} \perp \overleftrightarrow{JK}$ (shown on the right)
    Prove: $\angle FPK$, $\angle FPJ$, $\angle JPG$, and $\angle KPG$ are right angles.

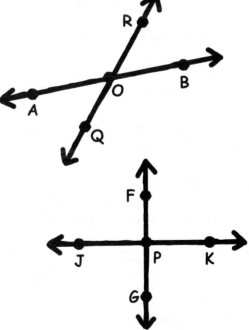

Find the measure of each angle below.

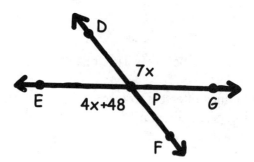

(b) 12. ∠EPF

13. ∠DPE

Write an equation to represent each question below; then solve the equation to get your answer.

14. An angle's measure is 12 less than twice its complement. Find the measure of the angle.

(c) 15. The difference between twice an angle's measure and its supplement is 27. Find the measure of the angle.

Answer each question below.

16. If A-P-B, and if $AP = 2x - 9$, $AB = 32$, and $PB = 1.5x + 6$ then find PB.

(d) 17. If $\overrightarrow{QS}$ bisects $\angle RQT$, and if $m\angle RQS = 7x + 7$ and $m\angle RQT = 9x + 54$ then find $m\angle SQT$.

Rewrite each sentence below in conditional ("if-then") form.

18. No NBA players are short.

19. None of the Barkers are musicians.

Tell whether the arguments below are valid or invalid deductions.

20. All museum curators are snooty. Mr. Clawson is a museum curator. Therefore, Mr. Clawson is snooty.

(e) 21. All French people are Europeans. If Pierre is not European, then he is not French.

Do the proof below.

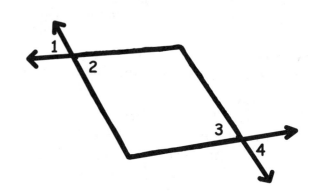

22. Given: $m\angle 1 = m\angle 4$
Prove: $m\angle 2 = m\angle 3$

Lesson 20—Drawing Perpendicular Lines through Points

We've been learning about perpendicular lines. It turns out that a perpendicular line can be used to bisect a line segment. Remember, "bisect" just means to cut the line segment into two equal parts. So instead of using any old line to do the bisecting, we can use a line that is perpendicular to the segment, as in the diagram on the right. See, line CM is perpendicular to segment AB, and since $m\overline{AM} = m\overline{MB}$, $\overleftrightarrow{CM}$ also cuts $\overline{AB}$ into two equal halves. That means $\overleftrightarrow{CM}$ is a "perpendicular bisector" of $\overline{AB}$. That's the technical name. And here's the formal definition.

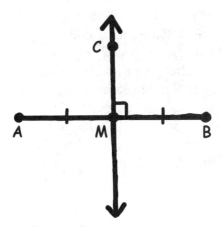

$\overleftrightarrow{CM}$ is perpendicular to $\overline{AB}$ and it also bisects $\overline{AB}$.

Definition 22	A *perpendicular bisector* is a line that is perpendicular to a line segment and intersects the line segment at its midpoint.

The interesting thing about a perpendicular bisector is that every line segment has just one. In other words, there's only one line, $\overleftrightarrow{CM}$, that is both perpendicular to $\overline{AB}$ and that cuts $\overline{AB}$ in half. That's not true for non-perpendicular bisectors. You may remember from several lessons ago that if we don't care about the slant of the bisector, then lots of different lines will cut a segment in half.

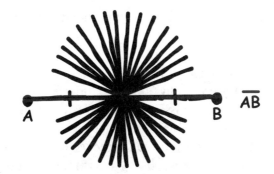

There are lots of non-perpendicular bisectors of $\overline{AB}$.

Perpendiculars through Other Points on a Line

This idea of a single perpendicular line going through a midpoint can actually be extended. It turns out that, no matter where a point is along a line, there's just one perpendicular line that can be drawn through it. As an example, let's randomly choose a point R along line ST in the figure on the right. There's just one line that will run through R and that's also perpendicular to $\overleftrightarrow{ST}$. And the same thing is true for any other point along $\overleftrightarrow{ST}$ that we might choose. There is a theorem which covers this principle. Here's the theorem stated formally.

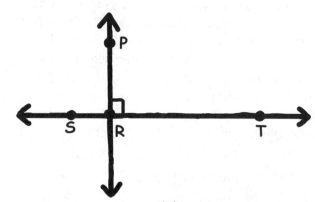

There's just one line ($\overleftrightarrow{PR}$) that goes through point R and that's also perpendicular to $\overleftrightarrow{ST}$.

Theorem 7	Through a given point on a line, there exists exactly one perpendicular to the given line.

The proof of the theorem is pretty simple, so we'll go through it informally.

According to the Protractor Postulate, there's only one ray above $\overleftrightarrow{ST}$ that will give $\angle PRT$ a measure of $90°$. And that's $\overrightarrow{RP}$. That means $m\angle PRT = 90$ and is a right angle (by the definition of a right angle). And since $\angle PRT$ is a right angle, $\overrightarrow{PR}$ must be perpendicular to $\overleftrightarrow{ST}$ (Definition of perpendicular lines).

Theorem 6 is very helpful when doing proofs that require us to draw an extra line in the proof's diagram (which is pretty common on harder proofs). When we have to draw a line, it's important to make sure that only one possible line meets the requirements in the proof's "given" statement. Only then do the mathematicians say that the line is "determined." If more than one line can be drawn, with both meeting the requirements in the given statement, then the line is "underdetermined." So Theorem 6 allows us to determine a unique perpendicular line through any point on a line.

Perpendiculars through Points *Not* on a Line

Sometimes it's necessary to draw a line through a point that's not even on a line. Let's take the line $\overleftrightarrow{JK}$ and point P (on the right) as an example.

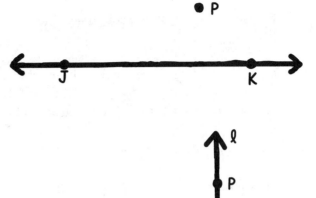

It turns out that there's just one line that we can draw through point P that is also perpendicular to $\overrightarrow{JK}$ The perpendicular line ℓ is shown in the diagram on the right. The same principle would apply if we chose some other point besides P that was not on $\overrightarrow{JK}$. We would be able to draw just one line through that point as well (and have the line also be perpendicular to $\overrightarrow{JK}$).

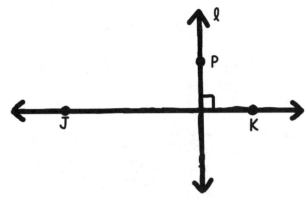

There's just one line (ℓ) that goes through point P and that's also perpendicular to $\overleftrightarrow{JK}$.

Instead of proving this rule deductively, we'll accept it as a postulate. Here's the postulate stated formally.

Postulate 5	Through a given point *not* on a line, there exists exactly one perpendicular to the given line.

Practice 20

a. From the given statement below, tell the definition, property, postulate, or theorem that justifies the prove statement.

Given: $m\angle 1 + m\angle 2 = 90$;
$\quad\quad m\angle 1 = m\angle 2$
Prove: $m\angle 1 = 45$

b. Find the measure of $\angle HKL$ below.

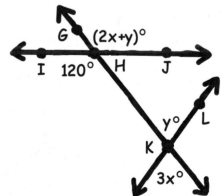

123

c. Write an equation to represent the question below; then solve the equation to get your answer.

The measure of an angle is 3 greater than 2 times its supplement. Find the measure of the angle.

d. Draw a Venn diagram to represent the set of conditional statements below.

All vegetarians eat tofu. If Lucy doesn't eat tofu, then she isn't a vegetarian.

e. Tell whether the arguments below are valid or invalid deductions.

All of the swimmers are wearing goggles. If Eric is not a swimmer, then he must not be wearing goggles.

Problem Set 20

Tell whether each sentence below is True or False.

1. Through a given point on a line, there exist an infinite number of perpendiculars to the given line.

2. Through a given point *not* on a line, there exist exactly two perpendiculars to the given line.

Answer each question below.

3. $\overline{CE}$ has two bisectors. The first, $\overrightarrow{OR}$, is a perpendicular bisector. What can you conclude about the second bisector, $\overleftrightarrow{ST}$.

4. Point P is not on $\overleftrightarrow{AB}$. $\overrightarrow{BV}$ and $\overrightarrow{FG}$ both run through P and $\overleftrightarrow{AB}$. What can you conclude about $\overrightarrow{BV}$ and $\overrightarrow{FG}$?

Complete each sentence below by filling in the blanks.

5. A _____ is a line that is perpendicular to a line segment and intersects the line segment at its midpoint.

6. _____ are angles that have the same vertex, share a common side, and have no interior points in common.

7. _____ angles are angles with measures that add to equal 180°.

8. The _____ of a line segment is the point that divides the line segment into two congruent line segments.

From each given statement below, tell the definition, property, postulate, or theorem that justifies each prove statement.

9. Given: $\angle 1$ and $\angle 2$ are a linear pair. Prove: $\angle 1$ and $\angle 2$ are supplementary.

10. Given: $FG = KL$ and $QP = ST$; Prove: $FG - QP = KL - ST$.

(a) 11. Given: $m\angle A + m\angle B = 180$ and $m\angle A = m\angle B$; Prove: $m\angle A = 90$.

Find the measures of a complement and supplement of each angle below.

12. $m\angle UHJ = 21$

13. $m\angle LPW = 90 - 2x$

Find the measure of each angle below.

14. $\angle ABC$

(b) 15. $\angle BEF$

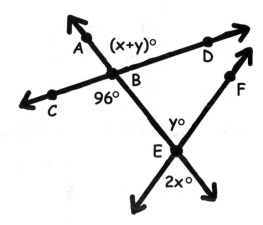

Write an equation to represent each question below; then solve the equation to get your answer.

16. The measure of an angle is 5 times as great as the measure of its complement. Find the measure of the angle.

(c) 17. The measure of an angle is 8 greater than 3 times its supplement. Find the measure of the angle.

Draw a Venn diagram to represent each set of conditional statements below.

18. If all of the walruses will clap for food, and Whiskers is a walrus, then Whiskers will clap for food.

(d) 19. All professors wear tweed jackets. If Dr. Johnson doesn't wear a tweed jacket, then he isn't a professor.

Tell whether the arguments below are valid or invalid deductions.

20. Every Koala bear has a funny-shaped nose. If Mr. Cuddly has a funny-shaped rose, then he must be a Koala Bear.

(e) 21. All of the voters are angry with Senator Olson. If James is not a voter, then he must not be angry with Senator Olson.

Complete the proof below by filling in the blanks. This will become our Theorem 8.

22.

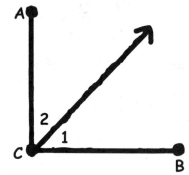

Given: $\overline{AC} \perp \overline{BC}$
        $\angle 1$ and $\angle 2$ are adjacent.
Prove: $m\angle 1 + m\angle 2 = 90$

Statements	Reasons
1.	1. Given
2.	2. Given
3. $\quad m\angle ACB = 90$	3.
4. $m\angle ACB = m\angle 1 + m\angle 2$	4.
5.	5.

Theorem 8	If the exterior sides of a pair of adjacent angles are perpendicular, the angles are complementary.

Lesson 21—Measuring Distances

We're going to continue our discussion of perpendicular lines. In this lesson, we'll see how perpendicular lines can be used to measure distances.

Point to Point

The simplest distance to measure is the distance between two points. On the top right are two points *A* and *B*. In geometry, the distance between two objects is the *shortest* path from one to the other. That means it would be wrong to measure the distance between *A* and *B* as shown on the middle right. The curve between the points is not the distance between them, because it's not the shortest path from *A* to *B*. According to the shortest path rule, we should measure the distance with a straight line segment (bottom right). Therefore, the measure of $\overline{AB}$ is the distance between the points. And, generally, the distance between any two points is defined as the length of the line segment connecting them. Here's the formal definition.

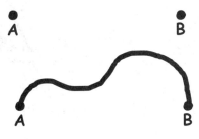

This is not the shortest
path from A to B.

Line segment AB is the shortest path,
so it is the distance between the points.

Definition 23	The distance *between two points* is the length of the line segment joining the points.

Point to Line

That's how to measure the distance between two points. But how do we measure the distance between a point and a line? Let's look at an example.

A fisherman is traveling to a river to fish. If the fisherman's position is represented by the point shown on the right, what is the distance between the fisherman and the river?

● Fisherman

How far is it from the fisherman to the river?

127

Actually, there are lots of ways to measure the distance from the point to the river. That's because we could draw line segments to many different points along the riverbank.

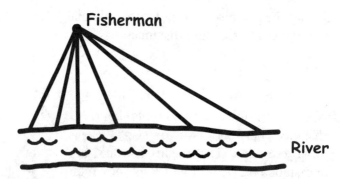

Which line segment do we use for the distance?

All of these line segments have different lengths. The question is which segment represents the distance between the fisherman and the river.

What we do is use the shortest path rule again. We want the shortest line segment between the two. As it turns out, the shortest distance is the line segment that is perpendicular to the riverbank. So here is the line segment we need.

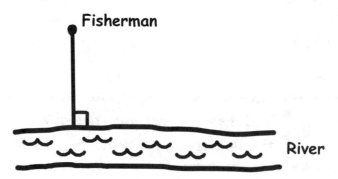

**The shortest path is the line segment that is
perpendicular to the river.**

Since it's the shortest path, the length of this line segment is the distance between the fisherman and the river.

Obviously, this same principle can be applied to lots of other situations. The fisherman is just a point and the river is a line. So the distance between any point A and any line ℓ is the line segment between the two that is also perpendicular to ℓ. Here's the formal definition, along with a diagram.

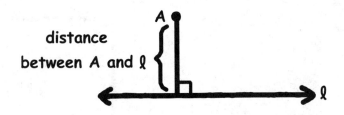

distance
between A and ℓ

Definition 24	The distance *between a line and a point not on the line* is the length of the perpendicular segment drawn from the point to the line.

Practice 21

a. From the given statement below, tell the definition, property, postulate, or theorem that justifies the prove statement.

Given: $\overleftrightarrow{RW} \perp \overleftrightarrow{TW}$ (shown on the right);
$\angle RWS$ and $\angle SWT$ are adjacent angles.
Prove: $\angle RWS$ and $\angle SWT$ are complementary.

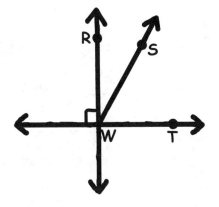

b. Find the measure of $\angle MOL$ below.

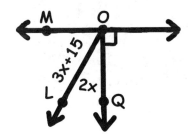

c. The difference between 2 times an angle's supplement and 120 is 30. Find the measure of the angle.

d. Complete the sentence below with *always*, *sometimes*, or *never*.

The angles of a linear pair are _____ supplementary.

e. Do the proof below.

Given: $\overline{LM} \perp \overline{MN}$, $\overline{PN} \perp \overline{MN}$, and $\angle 5 \cong \angle 8$.
Prove: $\angle 6 \cong \angle 7$

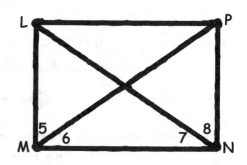

Problem Set 21

Tell whether each sentence below is True or False.

1. In geometry, the distance between two objects is the *shortest* path from one to the other.

2. The distance between any two points is the length of the line segment joining the two points.

Complete each sentence below by filling in the blanks.

3. _____ angles are angles with measures that add to equal 180°.

4. Pairs of _____ angles are congruent.

5. Through a given point on a line, there exists exactly one _____ to the given line.

6. If the exterior sides of adjacent angles are perpendicular, the angles are _____.

Measure each distance below with a ruler.

7. the distance between points *A* and *B*   **8.** the distance between point *C* and line *m*

C •

A

•
B

m

9. the distance between point D and line n

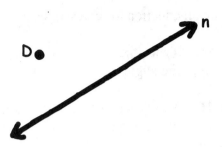

From each given statement below, tell the definition, property, postulate, or theorem that justifies each prove statement.

10. Given: $\angle A$ and $\angle B$ are supplements, and $\angle B$ and $\angle C$ are supplements.
Prove: $\angle A \cong \angle C$.

11. Given: $m\overline{RT} + m\overline{TW} = m\overline{RW}$. Prove: R-T-W.

(a) 12. Given: $\overleftrightarrow{AO} \perp \overleftrightarrow{OC}$ (shown on the right);
$\angle AOB$ and $\angle BOC$ are adjacent angles.
Prove: $\angle AOB$ and $\angle BOC$ are complementary.

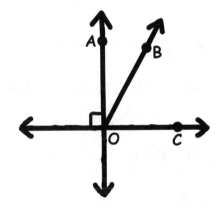

Find the measure of each angle below.

(b) 13. $\angle FOG$

14. $\angle JOI$

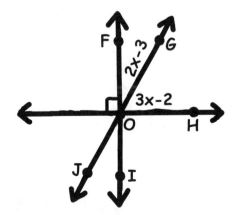

Write an equation to represent each question below; then solve the equation to get your answer.

15. Twice the measure of an angle's complement less 6 is equal to 124. Find the measure of the angle.

(c) 16. The difference between 3 times an angle's supplement and 100 is 17. Find the measure of the angle.

Complete each sentence below with *always*, *sometimes*, or *never*.

(d) 17. Adjacent angles are _____ supplementary.

18. The midpoint of a line segment is _____ equidistant (equally far) from each end point.

19. Vertical angles are _____ adjacent.

Answer each question below.

20. If $\overrightarrow{QX}\text{-}\overrightarrow{QY}\text{-}\overrightarrow{QZ}$ and if $m\angle XQY = 4a + 8$, $m\angle XQZ = 8a$, and $m\angle YQZ = 28$, then find $m\angle XQZ$.

21. If line ℓ bisects $\overline{AB}$ at point M, and if $AM = 4x$ and $MB = 5x - 4$, then find AB.

Tell whether the arguments below are valid or invalid deductions.

22. All the players on the volleyball team have sand in their toes. Allison is not a player on the volleyball team, so she must not have sand in her toes.

23. All of the ballerinas are wearing tutus. Hank is not wearing a tutu, so he must not be a ballerina.

Do the proof below.

(e) 24. Given: $\overline{FJ} \perp \overline{FG}$, $\overline{GH} \perp \overline{FG}$, and $\angle 2 \cong \angle 4$.
Prove: $\angle 1 \cong \angle 3$

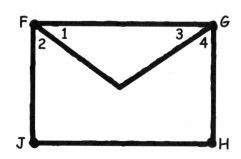

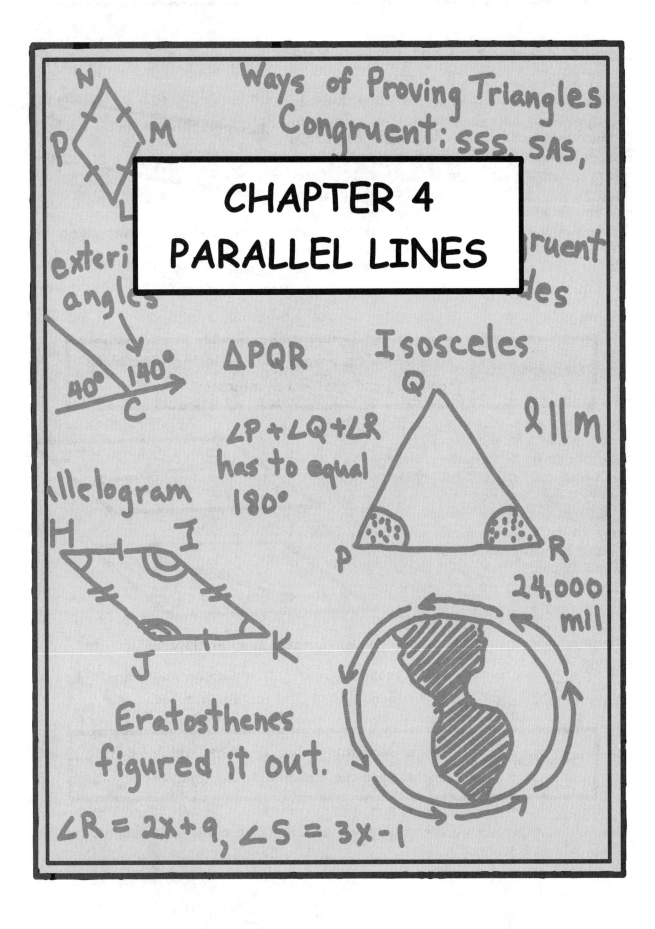

Ways of Proving Triangles
Congruent: SSS, SAS,

N

P   M

L

CHAPTER 4
PARALLEL LINES

exteri   ruent
angles   des

40° 140°

C

ΔPQR

∠P + ∠Q + ∠R
has to equal
180°

Isosceles

Q

ℓ ‖ m

P   R

llelogram

H   I

J   K

24,000
mil

Eratosthenes
figured it out.

∠R = 2x + 9, ∠S = 3x - 1

Lesson 22—Lines That Never Meet

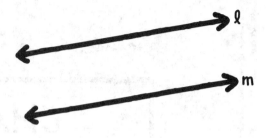

In Chapter 3, we spent several lessons focusing on perpendicular lines. In Chapter 4, we're going to concentrate on parallel lines. You're probably already familiar with parallel lines from earlier math courses. A simple, everyday definition of parallel lines is "lines that never meet." (shown on the right) Since these are lines and not line segments, they go on forever in both directions. But the main thing is that because the lines slant in the same way, they never meet (or intersect).

Parallel lines never meet.

That's why we say that lines ℓ and m are parallel. To show that on paper, we write: $\ell \parallel m$. The two little vertical lines are the symbol for "parallel." Here is the formal definition for parallel lines.

Definition 25	*Parallel lines* are lines that lie in the same plane (coplanar) and that never intersect.

Notice that the definition says that the lines have to lie in the same plane. That's because non-parallel lines don't have to intersect when they are in different planes. An example is shown in the diagram on the right. Notice that, even though these lines are not parallel, they still don't intersect. The reason is that they lie in different planes. But the only way that lines in the same plane cannot intersect is if they are parallel. That's why our definition has to include the

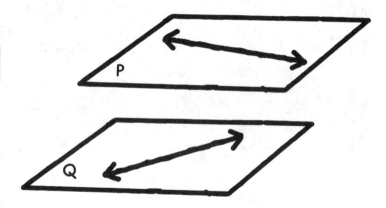

Non-parallel lines in different planes

part about the lines being in the same plane. By the way, "coplanar" means "lie in the same plane," just as "collinear" means "lie on the same line." Here's that definition.

Definition 26	Lines, segments, rays, or points which lie in the same plane are said to be *coplanar.*

From now on, whenever we talk about groups of lines, assume that those lines are coplanar unless you're told otherwise.

A Few Terms

Now let's go over a few important terms that we're going to use a lot in our study of parallel lines. Many times two lines, whether they're parallel or not, will have a third line crossing them, as shown on the right. See, lines ℓ and m are not parallel, but they have another line (line n) running through them. Line n is called a **transversal**. Here's the formal definition of the term.

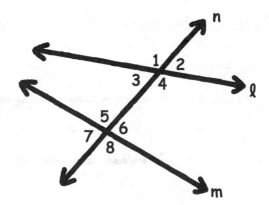

Line n is a transversal.

Definition 27	A *transversal* is a line that intersects two or more lines in different points.

A transversal makes 4 angles at each point of intersection, for a total of 8 angles. Certain pairs of these angles are given special names.

Alternate interior angles are angles that are in the "interior" part of the diagram, meaning that they are inside the space between lines ℓ and m. And they also lie on "alternate" or opposite sides of the transversal (line n). In the below left diagram, angles 3 and 6 are alternate interior angles and so are angles 4 and 5. Other angles given a special name are **corresponding angles**. These are angles that are on the same side of the transversal. Also, one angle of a corresponding angle pair is an interior angle and the other is an exterior angle. In the below right diagram, angles 1 and 5 and angles 2 and 6 are corresponding angles.

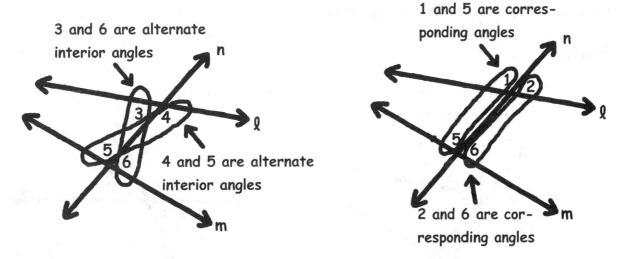

In the diagram at the top of this page, angles 3 and 7 and angles 4 and 8 are corresponding angles as well.

135

Parallel Line Segments and Rays

If two lines are parallel, then parts of those lines are also parallel. Take the lines below as an example.

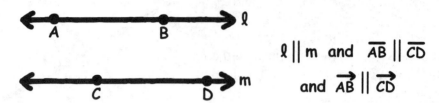

$\ell \parallel m$ and $\overline{AB} \parallel \overline{CD}$

and $\overrightarrow{AB} \parallel \overrightarrow{CD}$

Since lines ℓ and m are parallel, then line *segments* AB and CD, which are parts of those lines, must also be parallel. The same thing is true for rays AB and CD. This rule is important to remember when doing proofs.

Another thing that's helpful when doing proofs (or any other kind of geometry problem) is to label any parallel lines or parts of lines on a diagram. Parallel lines are labeled with arrowheads. For example, in the diagram below, line segments AB and DC and line segments AD and BC are parallel.

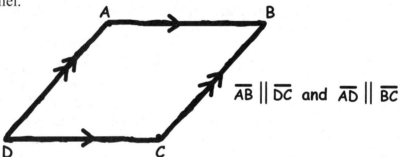

$\overline{AB} \parallel \overline{DC}$ and $\overline{AD} \parallel \overline{BC}$

To label the parallel lines, we put arrowheads on each pair. And to distinguish between the pairs, we use one arrowhead on $\overline{AB}$ and $\overline{DC}$ but two arrowheads on $\overline{AD}$ and $\overline{BC}$.

Practice 22

a. Name all pairs of alternate interior angles in the diagram below.

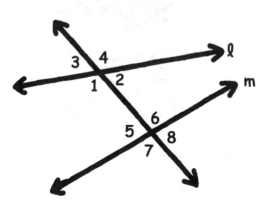

b. Find the measure of $\angle QKE$ below.

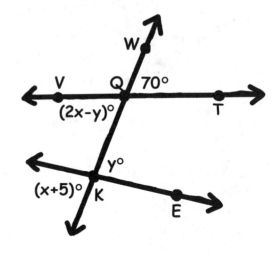

c. $\angle C$ and $\angle F$ are a linear pair. If $m\angle C = 3x$ and $m\angle F = 3x + 18$, find $m\angle F$.

d. If $\overrightarrow{KM}$ bisects $\angle LKN$, and if $m\angle LKM = 3x + 6$ and $m\angle LKN = 7x + 1$ then find $m\angle LKN$.

e. Write a conditional statement to represent the Venn diagram on the right.

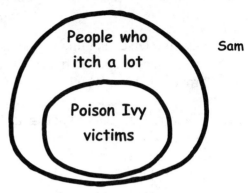

Problem Set 22

Tell whether each sentence below is True or False.

1. Parallel lines are lines that lie in the same plane and that never intersect.

2. Lines, segments, rays, or points that lie in the same plane are said to be collinear.

Complete each sentence below by filling in the blanks.

3. A(n) _____ is a line that intersects two or more lines in different points.

4. $\overleftrightarrow{EF} \parallel \overleftrightarrow{GH}$ means that _____.

5. Through a given point *not* on a line, there exists exactly one _____ to the given line.

6. A(n) _____ is an angle with a measure of less than $90°$.

Answer each question below based on the accompanying diagram.

(a) 7. Name all pairs of alternate interior angles.

8. Name all pairs of corresponding angles.

9. Do the lines ℓ and m appear parallel? Do the alternate interior angles appear to be congruent? Do the corresponding angles appear to be congruent?

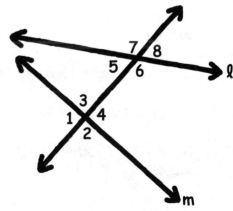

From each given statement below, tell the definition, property, postulate, or theorem that justifies each prove statement.

10. Given: $AD = BC$; Prove: $\frac{1}{2}AD = \frac{1}{2}BC$.

11. Given: Intersecting line segments TV and SU (shown on the right)
    Prove: $\angle TXS \cong \angle UXV$.

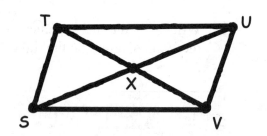

12. Given: $\angle F \cong \angle G$ and $\angle G \cong \angle H$
    Prove: $\angle F \cong \angle H$

13. Given: $\angle TQC$ and $\angle KJL$ are right angles; Prove: $\angle TQC \cong \angle KJL$.

Complete each sentence below with *always*, *sometimes*, or *never*.

14. Complementary angles are _____ congruent.

15. An angle bisector _____ divides the angle into two congruent angles.

Find the measure of each angle below.

(b) 16. $\angle LNO$

17. $\angle KLN$

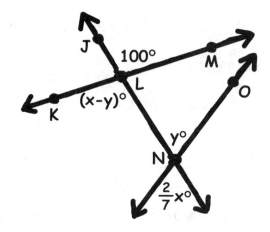

Answer each question below.

18. $\angle ADS$ and $\angle BCT$ are comple-
    mentary. If $m\angle ADS = 3z - 1$ and
    $m\angle BCT = z + 7$, then find
    $m\angle ADS$.

(c) 19. $\angle R$ and $\angle J$ are a linear pair. If $m\angle R = 3x - 5$ and $m\angle J = 5x + 1$, find $m\angle J$.

20. If G-H-I, and if $GH = 2x - 9$, $HI = 14$, and $GI = 3x - 8$, then find GI.

(d) 21. If $\overrightarrow{PB}$ bisects $\angle APC$, and if $m\angle APB = 2x + 9$ and $m\angle APC = 3x + 35$ then find
    $m\angle APC$.

Write conditional statements to represent each Venn diagram below.

22.

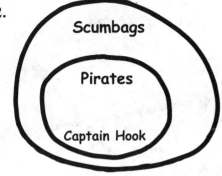

(e) 23.

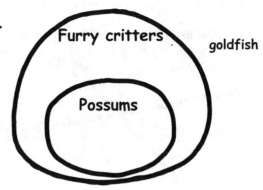

Complete the proof below by filling in the blanks.

24.   Given: $\overline{CD} \perp \overline{AD}$, $\overline{BC} \perp \overline{AB}$
          $\overline{AC}$ bisects $\angle DCB$
          $\angle 1 \cong \angle 3$, $\angle 2 \cong \angle 4$

     Prove: $\angle 5 \cong \angle 6$

	Statements	Reasons
1.	$\overline{CD} \perp \overline{AD}$, $\overline{BC} \perp \overline{AB}$	1.
2.	$\overline{AC}$ bisects $\angle DCB$	2.
3.		3. Given
4.		4. Definition of angle bisector
5.	$\angle 1 \cong \angle 4$	5. Transitive (or Substitution)
6.	$\angle 3 \cong \angle 4$	6.
7. $\angle 5$ is complementary to $\angle 3$		7.
8.		8. If the exterior sides of a pair of adjacent angles are perpendicular, then the angles are complementary.
9.		9.

Lesson 23—Parallel Lines and Angles

Let's compare the alternate interior angles in two diagrams. Look below.

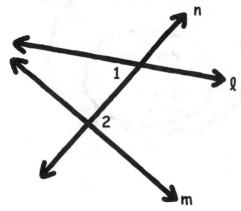

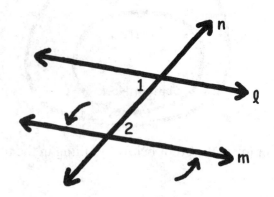

Lines ℓ and m are not parallel,
and m∠1 is less than m∠2.

Now ℓ and m are parallel,
and m∠1 is equal to m∠2.

Notice that on the left, $m\angle 1$ appears to be less than $m\angle 2$. And the reason is that lines ℓ and m are not parallel. Line m has more of a slant downward than line ℓ. But in the diagram on the right, $m\angle 1$ appears to equal $m\angle 2$. And that's because line m has been rotated so that ℓ and m are parallel.

Parallel Lines = Congruent Alternate Interior Angles

If you play around with parallel lines and angles in this way, you'll find that whenever the lines are parallel, the alternate interior angles are congruent (equal). And whenever the lines are not parallel, the alternate interior angles are not congruent (equal). It always works that way. This rule can be proven deductively. But the proof is hard, so we'll accept it as a postulate.

Postulate 6	If two parallel lines are cut by a transversal, then their *alternate interior angles* are congruent (equal).

Parallel Lines = Congruent Corresponding Angles

Now that we have the alternate interior angles postulate, we can use it to prove that when two lines are parallel and cut by a transversal, all the corresponding angles are also congruent (equal). Here's the theorem followed by the proof.

Theorem 9	If two parallel lines are cut (crossed) by a transversal, then their *corresponding angles* are congruent (equal).

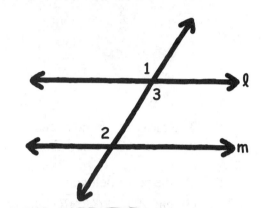

Given: $\ell \parallel m$

Prove: $\angle 1 \cong \angle 2$

Statements	Reasons
1. $\ell \parallel m$	1. Given
2. $\angle 1 \cong \angle 3$	2. Pairs of vertical angles are congruent.
3. $\angle 2 \cong \angle 3$	3. If two parallel lines are cut by a transversal, then their alternate interior angles are congruent.
4. $\angle 1 \cong \angle 2$	4. Transitive (or Substitution)

Practice 23

a. Identify the pair of angles $\angle 5$ and $\angle 7$, $\angle 2$ and $\angle 6$, as adjacent angles, vertical angles, alternate interior angles, corresponding angles, or supplementary angles.

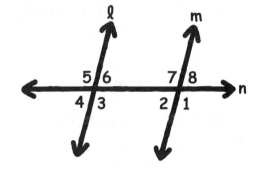

b. From the given statement below, tell the definition, property, postulate, or theorem that justifies the prove statement.

Given: $m\angle 3 + m\angle GHK = 90$ and $m\angle WSA + m\angle 3 = 90$; Prove: $m\angle GHK = m\angle WSA$.

c. Given $\ell \parallel m$, find the measure of $\angle EFP$ on the right.

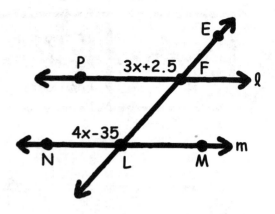

d. The measure of one of two complementary angles is 14 less than three times the measure of the other. Find *both* angles.

e. Do the proof below
Given: $\overline{AD} \parallel \overline{BC}$, $\overline{AB} \parallel \overline{DC}$
Prove: $m\angle ABC = m\angle ADC$

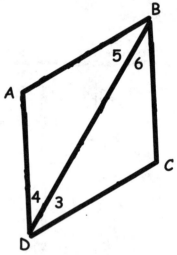

Problem Set 23

Tell whether each sentence below is True or False.

1. If two parallel lines are cut (crossed) by a transversal, then their alternate interior angles are congruent.

2. If two parallel lines are cut (crossed) by a transversal, then their corresponding angles are congruent.

Complete each sentence below by filling in the blanks. If the sentence is a property, name the property.

3. A (n) _____ is a line that is perpendicular to a line segment and intersects the line segment at its midpoint.

4. _____ are angles with measures that add to equal $90°$.

5.   Any quantity is equal to _____ : $a = a$

6.   A(n) _____ is an angle with a measure of greater than $90°$ (but less than $180°$).

Identify each pair of angles below as adjacent angles, vertical angles, alternate interior angles, corresponding angles, or supplementary angles.

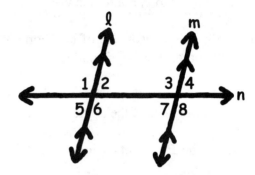

7. $\angle 1$ and $\angle 4$,
     $\angle 3$ and $\angle 6$

8. $\angle 4$ and $\angle 8$,
     $\angle 2$ and $\angle 5$

(a) 9. $\angle 6$ and $\angle 8$,
     $\angle 4$ and $\angle 7$

From each given statement below, tell the definition, property, postulate, or theorem that justifies each prove statement.

10.   Given: $QT = ZP$ and $VB = NM$; Prove: $QT + VB = ZP + NM$.

11.   Given: $A\text{-}M\text{-}B$ and $m\overline{AM} = \dfrac{1}{2}m\overline{AB}$; Prove: M is the midpoint of $\overline{AB}$.

(b) 12.   Given: $m\angle RST + m\angle 2 = 90$ and $m\angle 2 + m\angle DEF = 90$; Prove: $m\angle RST = m\angle DEF$.

Given $\ell \parallel m$, find the measure of each angle below.

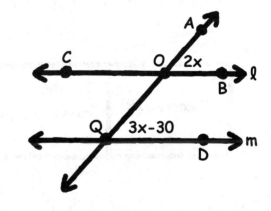

(c) 13. $\angle AOB$

14. $\angle COQ$

Answer each question below.

15.   If $\overrightarrow{OG}\text{-}\overrightarrow{OH}\text{-}\overrightarrow{OI}$ and if $m\angle GOH = 6x - 2$, $m\angle GOI = 8x + 1$, and $m\angle HOI = 17$, then find $m\angle GOI$.

16.   If line p bisects $\overline{CT}$ at point D, and if $CD = 7x - 10$ and $DT = 5x + 6$, then find CT.

17. Find the measure of ∠AOB (shown on the right).

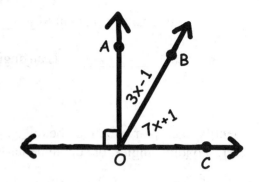

Write an equation to represent each question below; then solve the equation to get your answer.

(d) 18. The measure of one of two complementary angles is 6 less than twice the measure of the other. Find *both* angles.

19. Three times the measure of a supplement of an angle is 8 times the measure of a complement of the angle. Find the measure of the angle.

Tell whether the arguments below are valid or invalid deductions.

20. All of the brave houseflies landed on Mrs. Patterson's wig. Housefly #4 did not land on Mrs. Patterson's wig. Therefore, Housefly #4 must not be a brave housefly.

21. All chemists have heard of the periodic table. Dr. Einstein is not a chemist. Therefore, Dr. Einstein must not have heard of the periodic table.

Do each proof below.
Number 22 will become our Theorem 10.

22. Given: ∠AOB and ∠BOC are a linear pair;
  $m\angle AOB = m\angle BOC$
  Prove: ∠AOB and ∠BOC are right angles.

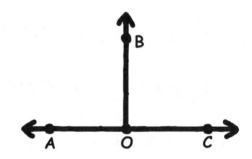

Theorem 10	If the two angles in a linear pair have equal measures (are congruent), then each is a right angle.

(e) 23. Given: $\overline{DE} \parallel \overline{GF}$, $\overline{EF} \parallel \overline{DG}$
  Prove: $m\angle EDG = m\angle EFG$

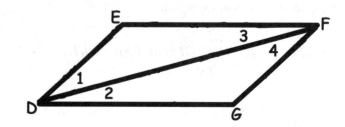

144

Lesson 24—More on Parallel Lines

In the last lesson, we learned that when two parallel lines are cut by a transversal, their alternate interior angles are congruent and so are their corresponding angles. As it turns out, there's also another pair of angles that are congruent when parallel lines are involved.

Alternate Exterior Angles

Take a look at the diagrams below.

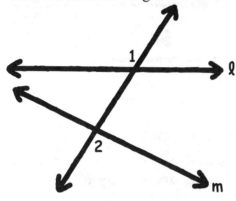

∠1 and ∠2 are alternate exterior angles.

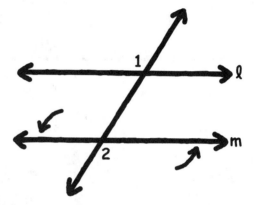

When lines ℓ and m are parallel, ∠1 and ∠2 are congruent.

Angles 1 and 2 are called **alternate exterior angles**. They're "alternate" angles because they are on opposite (or alternate) sides of the transversal. They're "exterior" angles because, instead of being on the inside (interior) of lines ℓ and m, they're on the outside (exterior) of those lines. Now notice that on the left, where lines ℓ and m are not parallel, ∠1 and ∠2 are not congruent. However, on the right, where lines ℓ and m *are* parallel, ∠1 and ∠2 *are* congruent.

Actually, there are always two sets of alternate exterior angles in a diagram like this. Another pair of alternate exterior angles is shown on the right. Angles 3 and 4 are also alternate exterior angles, because they too lie on opposite sides of the transversal and are outside the parallel lines. So the main point is that when parallel lines are cut by a transversal, not only are the alternate interior and corresponding angles congruent, but the alternate *exterior* angles are congruent as well. The proof that

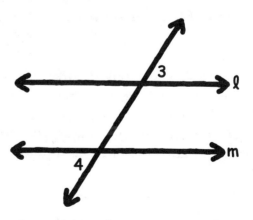

∠3 and ∠4 are also alternate exterior angles.

alternate exterior angles are congruent is shown below, along with the formal theorem.

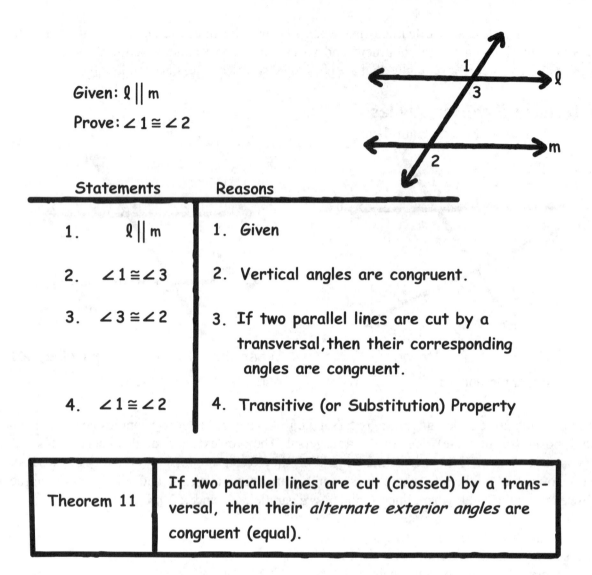

Given: $\ell \parallel m$

Prove: $\angle 1 \cong \angle 2$

Statements	Reasons
1. $\ell \parallel m$	1. Given
2. $\angle 1 \cong \angle 3$	2. Vertical angles are congruent.
3. $\angle 3 \cong \angle 2$	3. If two parallel lines are cut by a transversal, then their corresponding angles are congruent.
4. $\angle 1 \cong \angle 2$	4. Transitive (or Substitution) Property

Theorem 11	If two parallel lines are cut (crossed) by a transversal, then their *alternate exterior angles* are congruent (equal).

Interior Angles on the Same Side of the Transversal

By now you realize that parallel lines cut by a transversal have a lot of congruent angle pairs. Actually, though, they also have some supplementary angle pairs. For instance, any two angles that are inside (interior) the parallel lines and on the same side of the transversal are supplementary. Take a look on the next page.

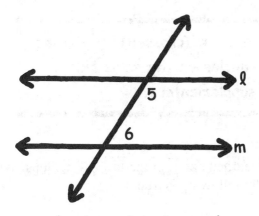

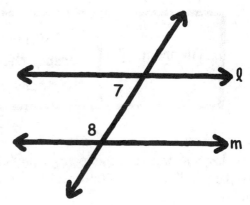

∠5 and ∠6 are interior angles on the same side of the transversal. They are supplementary

∠7 and ∠8 are interior angles on the same side of the transversal. They are supplementary

See, pair ∠5 and ∠6 and pair ∠7 and ∠8 are called **interior angles on the same side of the transversal**. And both pairs are supplementary. Here's the proof and the formal theorem.

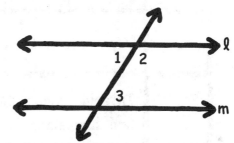

Given: ℓ ‖ m

Prove: ∠2 and ∠3 are supplementary.

Statements	Reasons
1. ℓ ‖ m	1. Given
2. ∠1 ≅ ∠3	2. If two parallel lines are cut by a transversal, then their alternate interior angles are congruent.
3. ∠1 and ∠2 are linear angles	3. A linear pair is two adjacent angles whose exterior sides form a straight line.
4. m∠1 + m∠2 = 180	4. If two angles are a linear pair, then they are supplementary.
5. m∠3 + m∠2 = 180	5. Substitution Property
6. ∠2 and ∠3 are supplementary	6. Definition of supplementary angles.

Theorem 12	If two parallel lines are cut (crossed) by a transversal, then interior angles on the same side of the transversal are supplementary.

Let's summarize all the angle pairs that we've learned about in the last two lessons. When two parallel lines are cut (crossed) by a transversal, the following is true:

Angle Relationships When Lines are Parallel

1.	Alternate interior angles are congruent.
2.	Corresponding angles are congruent.
3.	Alternate exterior angles are congruent.
4.	Interior angles on the same side of the transversal are supplementary.

Practice 24

a. Given that $\overline{UR} \parallel \overline{PQ}$ (on the right), identify the angle pair $\angle SRU$ and $\angle RQP$ below. Tell whether the pair is congruent or supplementary.

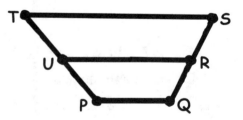

b. From the given statement below, tell the definition, property, postulate, or theorem that justifies the prove statement.

Given: $\ell \parallel m$
Prove: $\angle 2 \cong \angle 8$.

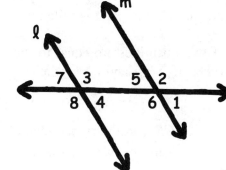

Given $\overline{RS} \parallel \overline{UT}$, $m\angle 5 = 118$, $m\angle 3 = 5x$, and $m\angle 4 = 4x - 1$, find the measure of each angle below.

c. $\angle 3$

d. $\angle S$

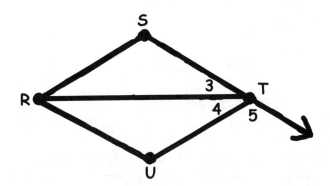

e. Given: $\overline{DE} \parallel \overline{FG}$, $\angle D \cong \angle E$.
Prove: $\angle DFG \cong \angle EGF$

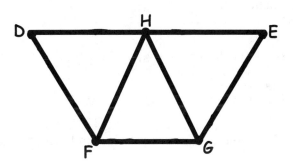

Problem Set 24

Tell whether each sentence below is True or False.

1. If two parallel lines are cut by a transversal, then their alternate exterior angles are supplementary.

2. If two parallel lines are cut by a transversal, then interior angles on the same side of the transversal are congruent.

Complete each sentence below by filling in the blanks. If the sentence is a property, name the property.

3. _____ angles are angles with measures that add to equal 180°.

4. A(n) _____ is a line that intersects two or more lines in different points.

5. An angle's end point is called the _____ of the angle.

6. If two quantities are equal to the same quantity, then they are _____ to each other: If $a = b$ and $b = c$, then _____ .

Given that $\overline{BA} \parallel \overline{CE}$ (on the right), identify the type of each angle pair. Tell whether each pair is congruent or supplementary.

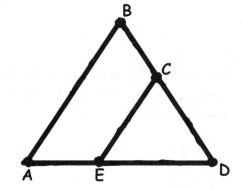

(a) 7. $\angle BAE$ and $\angle CED$

8. $\angle ABC$ and $\angle BCE$

9. $\angle BCE$ and $\angle ECD$

From each given statement below, tell the definition, property, postulate, or theorem that justifies each prove statement.

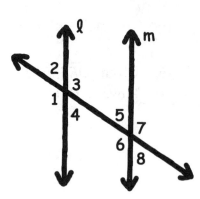

(b) 10. Given: $\ell \parallel m$; Prove: $\angle 1 \cong \angle 7$.

11. Given: $\ell \parallel m$; Prove: $\angle 4 \cong \angle 5$.

12. Given: $\ell \parallel m$; Prove: $\angle 3$ and $\angle 5$ are supplementary.

Complete each sentence below with *always*, *sometimes*, or *never*.

13. Alternate exterior angles are _____ congruent.

14. Vertical angles are _____ congruent.

Given $\overline{AB} \parallel \overline{DC}$, $m\angle 1 = 112$, $m\angle 2 = 4x$, and $m\angle 3 = 3x + 12$, find the measure of each angle below.

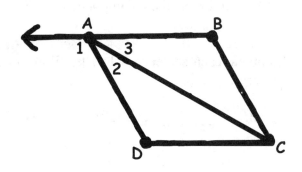

(c) 15. $\angle 2$

16. ∠3

(d) 17. ∠D

Answer each question below.

18. If L-M-N, and if $LM = 2x$, $MN = 3x - 1$, and $LN = 24$, then find MN.

19. If $\overrightarrow{OJ}$ bisects ∠IOK, and if $m\angle IOJ = 5x + 2$ and $m\angle JOK = 6x - 9$ then find $m\angle IOJ$.

Write an equation to represent each question below; then solve the equation to get your answer.

20. A supplement of an angle is twice as large as the angle. Find the measure of the angle.

21. The difference between the measures of two supplementary angles is 42. Find *both* angles.

Do each proof below.

22. Given: $\overline{PT} \parallel \overline{WV}$, $\overline{RQ} \parallel \overline{SU}$
Prove: ∠1 ≅ ∠2

(e) 23. Given: $\overline{CP} \parallel \overline{QL}$, ∠Q ≅ ∠L
Prove: ∠C ≅ ∠P

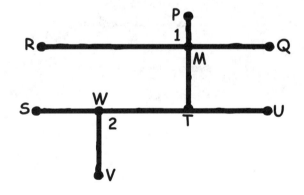

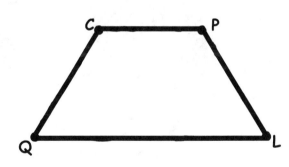

Lesson 25—Measuring the Earth

We've been learning about parallel lines and angles. In this lesson, we're going to see how these basic rules were used to do one of the most famous and important calculations in history: calculating the distance around the earth.

A Great Greek Discovery

In ancient times—long before spaceships, satellites, or even airplanes—people had no way to see the actual shape of the earth. Since land looks basically flat, most people just assumed that the entire earth was flat. Only a few scientists realized that the earth might actually be round (spherical). One of those was Eratosthenes, the brilliant Greek mathematician and astronomer. Eratosthenes was way ahead of his time, because he not only knew the earth's true shape, but actually succeeded in measuring its size. Specifically, using simple geometry, Eratosthenes calculated the distance all the way around the earth, with incredible accuracy—a feat that even most people today might think is impossible.

Here's how Eratosthenes did it. First, he noticed that at noon on the summer solstice (which is in late June), the sun's rays were shining down from a different place in the sky in the city Alexandria than they were in another city, Syene, which was about 500 miles away.[1]

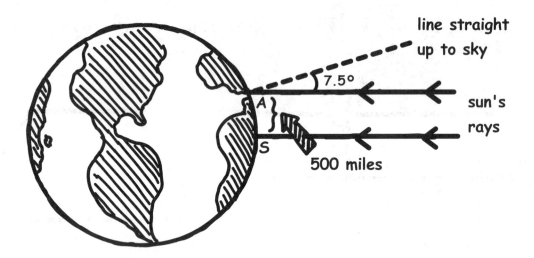

Point *A* is Alexandria and point *S* is Syene. The sun's rays are represented by the two parallel lines streaming onto the earth's surface from the right. And you can see that the top line is hitting Alexandria and the bottom line is hitting Syene. The important thing, though, is that the sun's rays are shining down from straight up in the sky in Syene, while in Alexandria the rays are coming down at an angle. Notice the dotted line is straight up in the sky over Alexandria, and the

---

[1] The rays come down at a different angle in the two cities because the earth is round. If the earth were flat, the sun would shine down at the same angle everywhere.

actual sun rays are at a different angle from that line. Eratosthenes was able to measure the angle formed by the dotted line (straight up into the sky) and the sun ray line in Alexandria. It came out to be 7.5 degrees. (The angle in the drawing is actually bigger than 7.5°).

Here's what Eratosthenes did next. He imagined a line segment extending from Alexandria all the way to the center of the earth. Then he imagined another line segment extending from Syene to the earth's center. Those lines make another angle, which we'll call angle x.

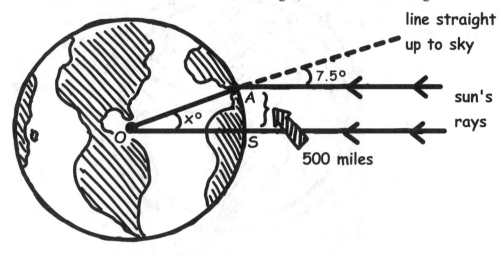

Now take a good look at our diagram. The sun's rays are parallel, and the line that's part dotted is a transversal. That means the 7.5° angle and angle x (or $\angle AOS$) are corresponding angles, which have to be equal. Eratosthenes understood this and concluded that angle x has a measure of 7.5° also.

All the Way Around = 360 Degrees

Eratosthenes's final step in solving the problem was to set up an equation. But to understand his equation, we need to make a quick point about angles. An angle that's shaped like a straight line is 180 degrees. So an angle that goes half way around the earth is 180°. Well, if that's true then an angle that goes all the way around the earth has to be 360°.

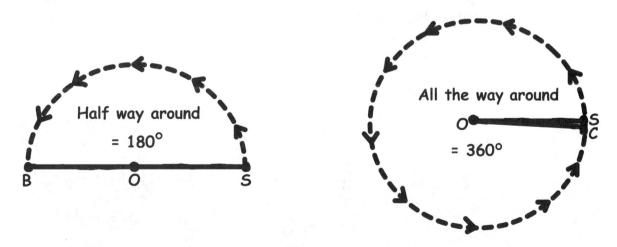

Eratosthenes set up his equation like this. He reasoned that the ratio of the 500 mile distance from Alexandria to Syene and the distance all the way around the earth must be the same as the ratio of angle x to an angle that goes all the way around the earth.

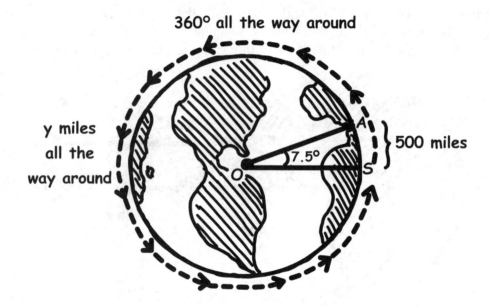

In other words, if we divide 500 by the distance around the earth, that fraction should equal 7.5° divided by 360°.

$$\frac{500}{y} = \frac{7.5}{360}$$

The distance around the earth is what Eratosthenes was trying to find, so we'll represent that unknown by y. This is a pretty simple equation. To solve, the fractions can be cleared first by multiplying both sides by the lowest common denominator, which is $360y$.

$$360y \cdot \frac{500}{y} = 360y \cdot \frac{7.5}{360}$$

The y's cancel on the left and the 360s on the right to get

$$360 \cdot 500 = 7.5y$$

Finally, we simplify and solve for y.

$$180{,}000 = 7.5y$$

$$\frac{180{,}000}{7.5} = \frac{7.5y}{7.5} \qquad \text{divided both sides by 7.5}$$

$$24{,}000 = y$$

Eratosthenes measured the distance around the earth as being 24,000 miles. That's just about right! And the incredible thing is that Eratosthenes did this important calculation using only a little knowledge of parallel lines and angle relationships.

Practice 25

a. Given that $\overline{QR} \parallel \overline{PT}$ (on the right), identify the angle pair $\angle Q$ and $\angle T$. Tell whether the pair is congruent or supplementary.

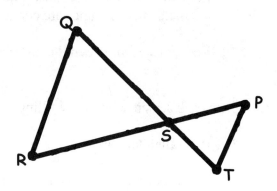

b. Given $\overrightarrow{JK} \parallel \overrightarrow{HI}$ (on the right), find x.

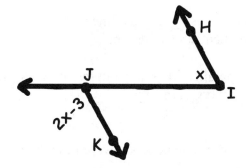

c. Write an equation to represent each question below; then solve the equation to get your answer.

One angle of a linear pair is 4 less than a third of the other angle. Find *both* angles.

d. Tell whether the arguments below are valid or invalid deductions.

All air guitarists dream of being real guitarists. Eugene is not an air guitarist. Therefore, Eugene does not dream of being a real guitarist.

e. Do the proof below.

Given: $\overline{GH} \parallel \overline{KL}$;

$\overrightarrow{IH}$ bisects $\angle GHK$;
$\overrightarrow{JK}$ bisects $\angle HKL$
Prove: $m\angle GHI = m\angle JKL$

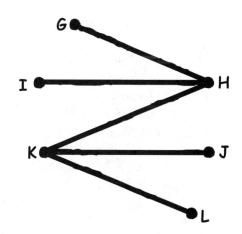

Problem Set 25

Tell whether each sentence below is True or False.

1. Eratosthenes used the postulate that if parallel lines are cut by transversal, their alternate interior angles are congruent.

2. Eratosthenes measured the distance around the earth.

Complete each sentence below by filling in the blanks.

3. If parallel lines are cut by a transversal, alternate exterior angles are _____.

4. If the exterior sides of adjacent angles are perpendicular, the angles are _____.

5. A _____ is a line that is perpendicular to a line segment and intersects the line segment at its midpoint.

6. If parallel lines are cut by a transversal, interior angles on the same side of the transversal are _____.

From each given statement below, tell the definition, property, postulate, or theorem that justifies each prove statement.

7. Given: $\angle R \cong \angle W$ and $\angle W \cong \angle S$; Prove: $\angle R \cong \angle S$.

8. Given: $\overrightarrow{OL}$ bisects $\overline{AB}$ at point O and A-O-B; Prove: $m\overline{AO} = m\overline{OB}$.

9. Given: $\angle 1 + \angle 4 = 180$ and $\angle 2 + \angle 3 = 180$; Prove: $\angle 1 + \angle 4 = \angle 2 + \angle 3$.

Given that $\overline{ED} \parallel \overline{AB}$ (below), identify the type of each angle pair. Tell whether each pair is congruent or supplementary.

10. $\angle ECD$ and $\angle ACB$

(a) 11. $\angle D$ and $\angle A$

12. $\angle E$ and $\angle B$

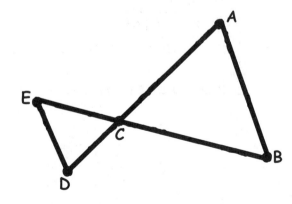

156

Answer each question below, given $\overrightarrow{FT} \parallel \overrightarrow{RG}$ on the left and $\ell \parallel m$ on the right.

(b) 13. Find x

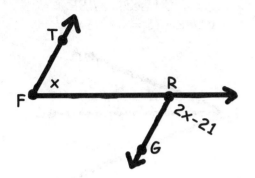

14. Find $m\angle QPR$

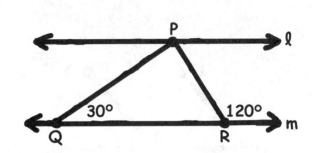

Answer each question below.

15. If $\overrightarrow{SD} \text{-} \overrightarrow{SE} \text{-} \overrightarrow{SG}$ and if $m\angle DSE = 5x - 4$, $m\angle ESG = 3x + 4$, and $m\angle DSG = 72$, then find $m\angle DSE$.

16. If line ℓ bisects $\overline{KP}$ at point L, and if $KL = 7x + 1$ and $LP = 8x - 3$, then find KP.

17. Find $m\angle AOB$ if $m\angle AOB = 4y - 3$ and $m\angle BOC = 6y - 17$.

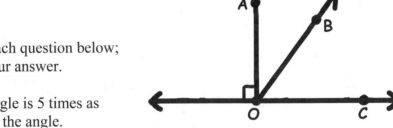

Write an equation to represent each question below; then solve the equation to get your answer.

18. A complement of an angle is 5 times as large as the angle. Find the angle.

(c) 19. One angle of a linear pair is 12 less than half the other angle. Find *both* angles.

Tell whether the arguments below are valid or invalid deductions.

(d) 20. All of the true hockey players have had their teeth knocked out. Ed has never had his teeth knocked out. Therefore, Ed is not one of the true hockey players.

21. Every beach bum owns a pair of flip-flops. Randy is not a beach bum. Therefore, Randy does not own a pair of flip-flops.

Do each proof below.

22. Given: $\overline{MN} \parallel \overline{PQ} \parallel \overline{SR}$, $\overline{MR} \parallel \overline{ST}$

Prove: $\angle 1 \cong \angle 2$

(e) 23. Given:, $\overline{AB} \parallel \overline{FE}$, $\overline{BC}$ bisects $\angle ABE$,

$\overline{DE}$ bisects $\angle BEF$

Prove: $m\angle ABC = m\angle DEF$

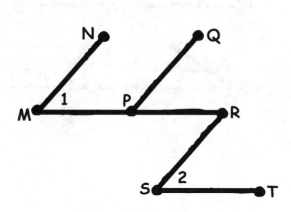

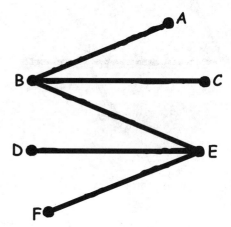

Lesson 26—Converse Statements

So far in this chapter, when doing proofs involving parallel lines, we've started with a given statement about how two lines are parallel, and then we've proven that certain angle pairs (like alternate interior angles) are congruent.

The Perils of Flipping

But what if we have the opposite situation? What if we know that two alternate interior angles are congruent, but then want to prove that the lines forming them are parallel? Take the proof shown on the right as an example. See, the given statement tells us that $\angle 1$ and $\angle 2$ are congruent. And even though the lines look like they have the same slant, we're supposed to prove deductively that they are actually parallel. It's tempting to use Postulate 6. Here's the postulate again, just to refresh your memory.

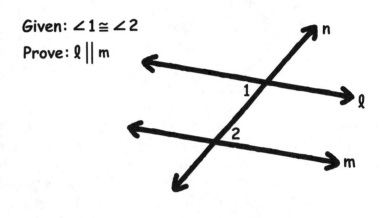

Given: $\angle 1 \cong \angle 2$
Prove: $\ell \parallel m$

Postulate 6	If two parallel lines are cut by a transversal, then their *alternate interior angles* are congruent (equal).

Notice the way this is written. The "if" statement says that the lines are parallel, which means we're assuming that to be true. The "then" statement concludes that alternate interior angles are congruent. But in our proof, we're starting with the assumption that the angles are congruent. So we actually need the postulate to be flipped around to "If alternate interior angles are congruent, then the lines are parallel." Are we allowed to just flip statements around like this and use them? The answer is no, we can't do that, and here's why.

According to the rules of logic, if we start with a true statement and then flip it around, the new statement doesn't have to be true. Take the simple statement below as an example.

If a vehicle is an automobile, then it has four wheels.

This is obviously a true statement. But now let's flip it around.

If a vehicle has four wheels, then it is an automobile.

Just because a vehicle has four wheels, doesn't necessarily make it an automobile. The vehicle could be a truck, a jeep, or several other things. So the second statement is not true. The diagram on the left shows this clearly.

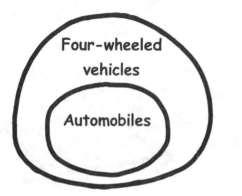 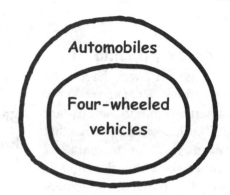

When a vehicle is inside the automobiles circle, it has to be inside the four-wheeled vehicle circle. That's why the first statement is correct. But just because a vehicle is inside the four wheel circle doesn't necessarily mean that it also has to be inside the automobile circle. So the second statement isn't true. A diagram for the second statement would actually look like the one on the right above. This can't be right, because, again, there are lots of four-wheeled vehicles that are not automobiles.

The main point is that you have to be very careful about flipping a statement around. It changes the meaning, and if the original statement is true, the new statement may very well be false. That's why we can't just flip around postulate 6 and use it in our proof.

Converses

When we do flip a statement around by switching the "if" clause with the "then" clause, we create something which is called the **converse** of the original statement. So the converse of "If a vehicle is an automobile, then it has four wheels" is "If a vehicle has four wheels, then it is an automobile."

You may remember from Chapter 1 that conditional statements can be shown in symbols. When the "if" statement is represented by the letter a and the "then" statement by the letter b, the entire statement becomes $a \rightarrow b$. So in symbols, if we start with a statement $a \rightarrow b$, then the converse of that statement is $b \rightarrow a$.

A very common logical error is to assume that if a statement is true, then its converse must also be true. People do this all the time when making arguments. For instance, someone might say "All good citizens believe in democracy and Mr. Jones believes in democracy. Therefore, Mr. Jones must be a good citizen." However, if we write these sentences in "if-then" form, the mistake is obvious.

If a person is a good citizen, then he believes in democracy.

If Mr. Jones (a person) believes in democracy, then he is a good citizen.

The argument is claiming that since the first statement is true, the converse has to be true as well. But we know that's not necessarily the case. Another way to tell that the reasoning is invalid is to draw a Venn diagram, of course. You've been doing that a lot in the problem sets. But now you know *why* the reasoning in this example is invalid.

Converses and Definitions

There is one case when the converse of a statement should also be true. That's when the original statement is a definition. Remember, the test of a good definition is whether it's reversible. Here's an example.

Definition: A transversal is a line that intersects two or more lines in different points.

Reversed: A line that intersects two or more lines in different points is a transversal.

This definition is good because after reversing it, the new statement is still right. Now let's look at both statements in "if-then" form.

Definition: If a line is a transversal, then it intersects two or more lines in different points.

Reversed: If a line intersects two or more lines in different points, then it is a transversal.

Now it's clear that the "reversed" statement is really just the converse of the original. So a good definition is one where both the original statement and the converse are true. And any definition $a \rightarrow b$ can be flipped around to $b \rightarrow a$.

A lot of times, definitions will include both the original statement and the converse.

If a line is a transversal, then it intersects two or more lines in different points,
and
if a line intersects two or more lines in different points, then it is a transversal.

The only problem with showing a definition like this is that it's kind of long. A shorter way of writing the same thing is to phrase the definition this way.

A line is a transversal if and only if it intersects two or more lines in different points.

The phrase "a if and only if b" means both $a \rightarrow b$ and $b \rightarrow a$. It's also written like this: $a \leftrightarrow b$. Sometimes "if and only if" is abbreviated as "iff." So "a if and only if b" can be written as "a iff b." When "iff" is put in the actual definition, it looks like this.

A line is a transversal iff it intersects two or more lines in different points.

Writing a definition this way shows that the definition is reversible without taking up a lot of space.

A New Postulate

Now let's go back to the proof at the beginning of the lesson. Remember, the given statement was that alternate interior angles $\angle 1$ and $\angle 2$ are congruent. And we were supposed to prove that lines ℓ and m are parallel. (See the diagram at the beginning of the lesson.)

To complete this proof, we need to use the reason "If two lines form congruent alternate interior angles with a transversal, then the lines are parallel." This is the converse of our Postulate 6 (If two lines are cut by a transversal, then their alternate interior angles are congruent.). But now you know that we can't automatically assume the converse of a true statement is also true. That's a logical error.

As it turns out, the converse of Postulate 6 can be proven deductively. But since the proof requires knowledge that won't be covered until later in the book, we won't show it to you. And instead of listing it as a theorem (which is a logically proven statement), we'll accept it as a postulate (an assumption).

Postulate 7	If two lines form congruent alternate interior angles with a transversal, then the lines are parallel.

This is how we justify that lines ℓ and m are parallel.

The important thing to understand is that a statement and its converse are two different things. If one is true, the other may be false. That's why we can't use the two interchangeably. In order to use the converse of a theorem or postulate as justification for a step in a proof, we need a proof showing that the converse is true or we have to accept the converse as another postulate. The only time we can assume that the converse of a statement is true is when the statement is a definition.

162

Practice 26

a. From the given statement below, tell the definition, property, postulate, or theorem that justifies the prove statement.

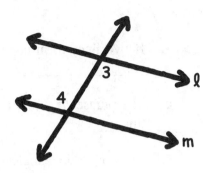

Given: $\angle 3 \cong \angle 4$; Prove: $\ell \parallel m$.

b. Given $\overline{QS} \parallel \overline{PT}$ and $\overline{SP} \parallel \overline{TR}$, find x.

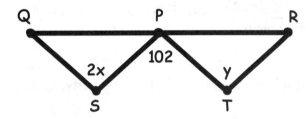

c. Tell whether the argument below is a valid or invalid deduction. (Use your knowledge of converse statements.)

If a person is under 62, then she is not eligible for Social Security. If Mrs. Marlow is not eligible for Social Security, then she must be under 62.

d. Tell whether the definition below passes the reversibility test by writing its converse and determining whether the converse is true.

If an animal is a peacock, then it has feathers.

e. Do the proof below.

Given: $\angle O \cong \angle U$, $\overline{SO} \parallel \overline{WU}$
Prove: $\overline{AO} \parallel \overline{SU}$

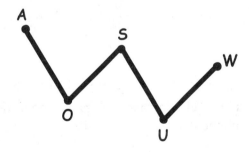

Problem Set 26

Tell whether each sentence below is True or False.

1. When the "if" clause and "then" clause of a statement are flipped around, the "converse" of the original statement is created.

2. A good definition is one where both the original statement and the converse are true.

Complete each sentence below by filling in the blanks. If the sentence is a property, name the property.

3. If two lines form congruent alternate interior angles with a transversal, then the lines are _____.

4. The phrase "*a* if and only if *b*" means both $a \rightarrow b$ and $b \rightarrow a$ and can be written like this: _____.

5. Pairs of vertical angles are _____.

6. The _____ of a line segment is the point that divides the line segment into two congruent line segments.

From each given statement below, tell the definition, property, postulate, or theorem that justifies each prove statement.

7. Given: $\overline{UV} \parallel \overline{XY}$ (shown on the right)
   Prove: $\angle 1$ and $\angle 2$ are supplementary.

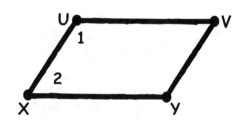

8. Given: $\angle ABC$ and $\angle GHJ$ are complementary;

   $\angle GHJ$ and $\angle RTU$ are complementary.
   Prove: $\angle ABC \cong \angle RTU$.

(a) 9. Given: $\angle 1 \cong \angle 2$ (shown on the right)
   Prove: $\ell \parallel m$

Given that $\overrightarrow{BA} \parallel \overrightarrow{DC}$ (below), identify the type of each angle pair. Tell whether each pair is congruent or supplementary.

10. $\angle 1$ and $\angle 4$

11. $\angle 3$ and $\angle 6$

12. $\angle 4$ and $\angle 5$

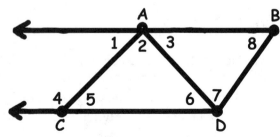

Answer each question below, given $\overline{KL} \parallel \overline{MN}$ and $\overline{LM} \parallel \overline{NO}$.

(b) 13. Find x.

14. Find y.

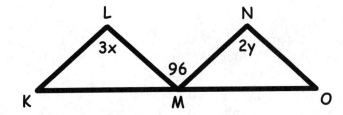

Answer each question below.

15. If J-K-P, and if $JP = 4x - 10$, $KP = 2x + 5$, and $JK = 31$, then find JP.

16. If $\overrightarrow{CE}$ bisects $\angle DCF$, and if $m\angle DCE = x - 11$ and $m\angle ECF = 166 - 2x$ then find $m\angle ECF$.

17. $\angle A$ and $\angle B$ are supplementary. If $m\angle A = 6x + 17$ and $m\angle B = 3x + 10$, find $m\angle A$.

Tell whether the arguments below are valid or invalid deductions. (Use your knowledge of converse statements.)

18. Every member of the chess team lost to the machine. Tyler is on the chess team. Therefore, Tyler lost to the machine.

(c) 19. If a person is under 18, then he is not eligible to vote. If Chauncey is not eligible to vote, then he must be under 18.

Tell whether each definition below passes the reversibility test by writing its converse and determining whether the converse is true.

20. If a person is an architect, then he plans buildings and oversees their construction.

(d) 21. If an animal is a raccoon, then it has a bushy tail.

Do the proof below.

(e) 22. Given: $\angle E \cong \angle G$, $\overline{DE} \parallel \overline{FG}$
Prove: $\overline{EF} \parallel \overline{GH}$

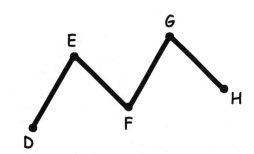

Lesson 27—Proving Lines are Parallel

In the last lesson, we learned that when alternate interior angles are congruent, the two lines forming them are parallel. We accepted that as a postulate. But what about a case where two *corresponding* angles are congruent? Do the lines have to be parallel then too?

Our Theorem 9 deals with corresponding angles. Remember, Theorem 9 says that "If two parallel lines are cut by a transversal, then their corresponding angles are congruent." This won't help us prove that lines are parallel, though, because it assumes that the lines are already parallel. What we need is the converse of Theorem 9. Here it is.

> Converse of Theorem 9: If two lines form congruent corresponding angles with a transversal, then the lines are parallel.

Remember from the last lesson, a statement and its converse are not the same logically. So just because we proved Theorem 9, doesn't mean its converse is also proven. But there's nothing to stop us from doing a separate proof of the converse. That will give us another theorem, saying that when corresponding angles are congruent the lines have to be parallel. Here's the proof. (Notice that it uses Postulate 7 from the last lesson.)

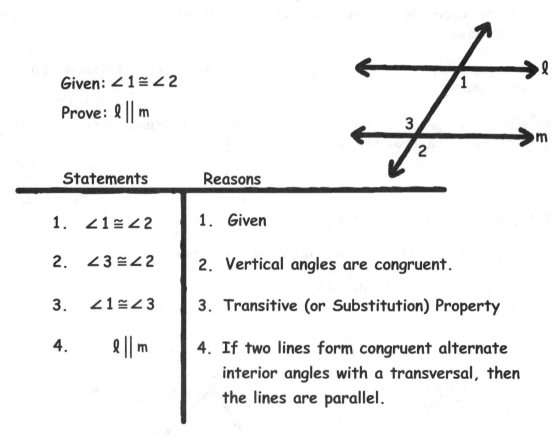

Given: $\angle 1 \cong \angle 2$

Prove: $\ell \parallel m$

Statements	Reasons
1. $\angle 1 \cong \angle 2$	1. Given
2. $\angle 3 \cong \angle 2$	2. Vertical angles are congruent.
3. $\angle 1 \cong \angle 3$	3. Transitive (or Substitution) Property
4. $\ell \parallel m$	4. If two lines form congruent alternate interior angles with a transversal, then the lines are parallel.

And this is the resulting theorem. We'll call it Theorem 13.

Theorem 13	If two lines form congruent corresponding angles with a transversal, then the lines are parallel.

Now we have two ways to prove that lines are parallel: when their alternate interior angles are congruent or when their corresponding angles are congruent.

Two Other Ways to Prove Lines Parallel

As it turns out, there are two other ways to prove that lines are parallel. You can probably guess what they are. One way is to know that their alternate exterior angles are congruent. Here's that proof and the formal theorem for that one.

Given: ∠1 ≅ ∠2

Prove: ℓ ∥ m

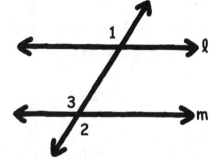

Statements	Reasons
1. ∠1 ≅ ∠2	1. Given
2. ∠2 ≅ ∠3	2. Pairs of vertical angles are congruent.
3. ∠1 ≅ ∠3	3. Transitive (or Substitution) Property
4. ℓ ∥ m	4. If two lines form congruent corresponding angles with a transversal, then the lines are parallel.

Theorem 14	If two lines form congruent alternate exterior angles with a transversal, then the lines are parallel.

The next way to prove parallel lines is by knowing that the interior angles on the same side of the transversal are supplementary. Here is the proof, followed by the formal theorem.

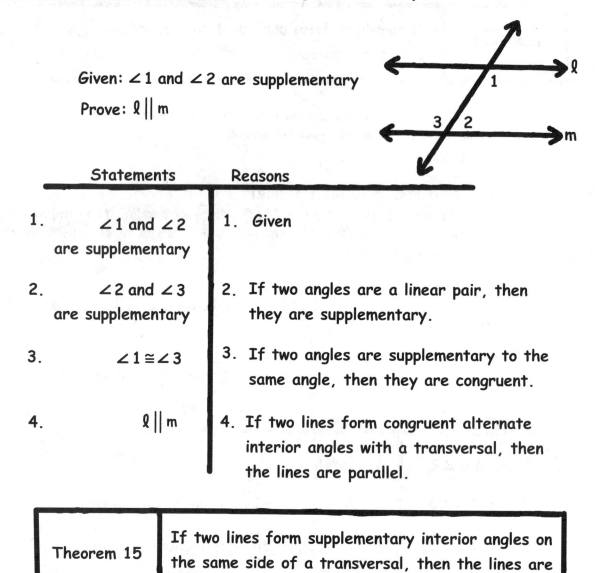

Given: ∠1 and ∠2 are supplementary

Prove: ℓ ∥ m

Statements	Reasons
1. ∠1 and ∠2 are supplementary	1. Given
2. ∠2 and ∠3 are supplementary	2. If two angles are a linear pair, then they are supplementary.
3. ∠1 ≅ ∠3	3. If two angles are supplementary to the same angle, then they are congruent.
4. ℓ ∥ m	4. If two lines form congruent alternate interior angles with a transversal, then the lines are parallel.

Theorem 15	If two lines form supplementary interior angles on the same side of a transversal, then the lines are parallel.

Counting what we learned in the last lesson, we now have a total of four ways to prove that lines are parallel. And interestingly, every one of these is a converse of a theorem or postulate that we learned earlier. For instance, Theorem 9 is one of our earlier theorems. It says that if two lines are parallel, then corresponding angles are congruent. But Theorem 13, from this lesson, says that if we know that corresponding angles are congruent, we can prove that the lines are parallel. That's the converse of Theorem 9. So when it comes to parallel lines and corresponding angles, it's a two way street. The same goes for Postulates 6 and 7, Theorems 11 and 14, and Theorems 12 and 15. These pairs are all converses. It may seem like a waste of time to do separate proofs that say almost the same thing, but it's actually not. Remember, a statement and its converse are not the same logically. If one is true, the other doesn't necessarily have to be true. That's why we had to prove all of those converses separately.

Just to make sure that you've got a handle on all this new information, let's summarize the four ways of proving that lines are parallel.

Ways to Prove Lines are Parallel

1.	If alternate interior angles are congruent.
2.	If corresponding angles are congruent.
3.	If alternate exterior angles are congruent.
4.	If interior angles on the same side of the transversal are supplementary.

Practice 27

a. Write the converse of the statement below. Tell whether the converse is True or False.

If Akio lives in Tokyo, then he lives in Japan.

b. From the given statement below, tell the definition, property, postulate, or theorem that justifies the prove statement.

Given: $\angle T \cong \angle U$; Prove: $\overline{ST} \parallel \overline{VU}$

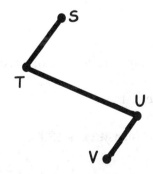

c. Find y, given $d \parallel f$ below.

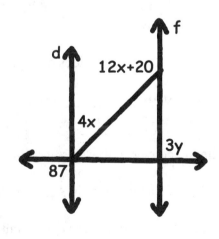

d. From the diagram on the right, name a pair of lines that must be parallel if $\angle 6 \cong \angle 7$ is true. If there are no lines that have to be parallel, write "none" for your answer.

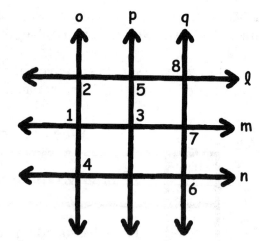

e. Add 16° to the measure of an angle, and the result is a third of the angle's supplement. What is the measure of the angle?

Problem Set 27

Tell whether each sentence below is True or False.

1. Two lines form congruent alternate exterior angles with a transversal iff the lines are parallel.

2. If two lines form supplementary interior angles on the same side of a transversal, then the lines are parallel.

Complete each sentence below by filling in the blanks.

3. If two lines form _____ corresponding angles with a transversal, then the lines are _____.

4. If parallel lines are cut by a transversal, _____ angles on the same side of the transversal are _____.

5. If the exterior sides of adjacent angles are perpendicular, the angles are _____.

6. A(n) _____ is an angle with a measure of less than 90°.

Write the converse of each statement below. Tell whether the converse is True or False.

(a) 7. If Shelley lives in Arizona, then she lives in the United States.

8. If two angles are supplementary, then the sum of their measures is 180°.

9. If two angles are vertical, then they are congruent.

170

From each given statement below, tell the definition, property, postulate, or theorem that justifies each prove statement.

(b) 10. Given: $\angle L \cong \angle M$ (below)
Prove: $\overline{PL} \parallel \overline{MN}$

11. Given: $\overrightarrow{DJ}$ and $\overrightarrow{GF}$ intersect at E (below)
Prove: $\angle DEF$ and $\angle GEJ$ are congruent.

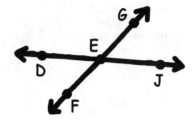

12. Given: $\dfrac{1}{2}m\angle ABC = m\dfrac{1}{2}\angle NMV$; Prove: $m\angle ABC = m\angle NMV$

Complete each sentence below with *always*, *sometimes*, or *never*.

13. Alternate interior angles are _____ congruent.

14. Adjacent angles _____ share the same vertex.

Answer each question below, given $p \parallel n$ on the right.

15. Find x.

(c) 16. Find y.

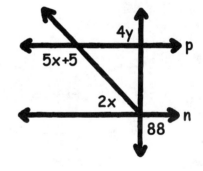

From the diagram on the right, name a pair of lines that must be parallel if each statement below is true. If there are no lines that have to be parallel, write "none" for your answer.

(d) 17. $\angle 2 \cong \angle 5$

18. $\angle 3$ and $\angle 5$ are supplementary

19. $\angle 3 \cong \angle 4$

20. $\angle 6 \cong \angle 8$

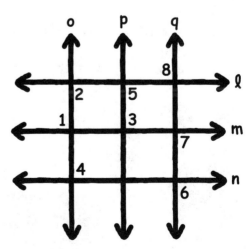

Write an equation to represent each question below; then solve the equation to get your answer.

21. The supplement of an angle is 4 times as large as the angle. Find the angle.

(e) 22. Add 27° to the measure of an angle, and the result is half of the angle's supplement. What is the measure of the angle?

Complete the proof below by filling in the blanks.

23.

Given: $\overline{DE} \perp \overline{EF}$,

∠DFE is complementary to ∠DEG.

Prove: $\overleftrightarrow{DF} \parallel \overleftrightarrow{GH}$.

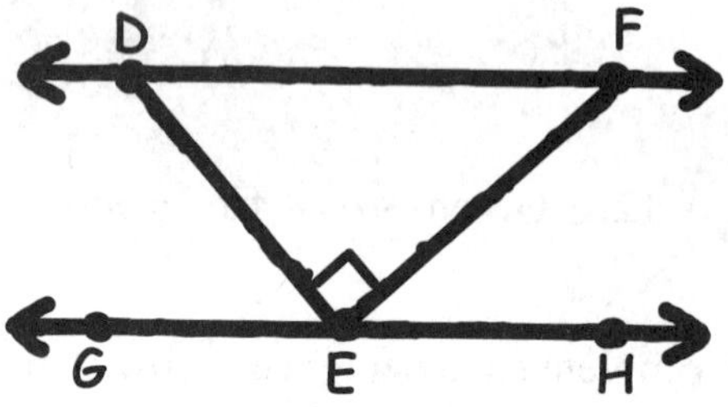

Statements	Reasons
1. $\overline{DE} \perp \overline{EF}$	1.
2.	2. Given
3.	3. Definition of a right angle.
4. m∠DEG + m∠DEF + m∠FEH = 180	4. A straight angle measures 180°.
5. m∠DEG + 90 + m∠FEH = 180	5.
6. m∠DEG + m∠FEH = 90	6.
7. ∠DEG is complementary to ∠FEH	7.
8. ∠FEH ≅ ∠DFE	8.
9.	9.

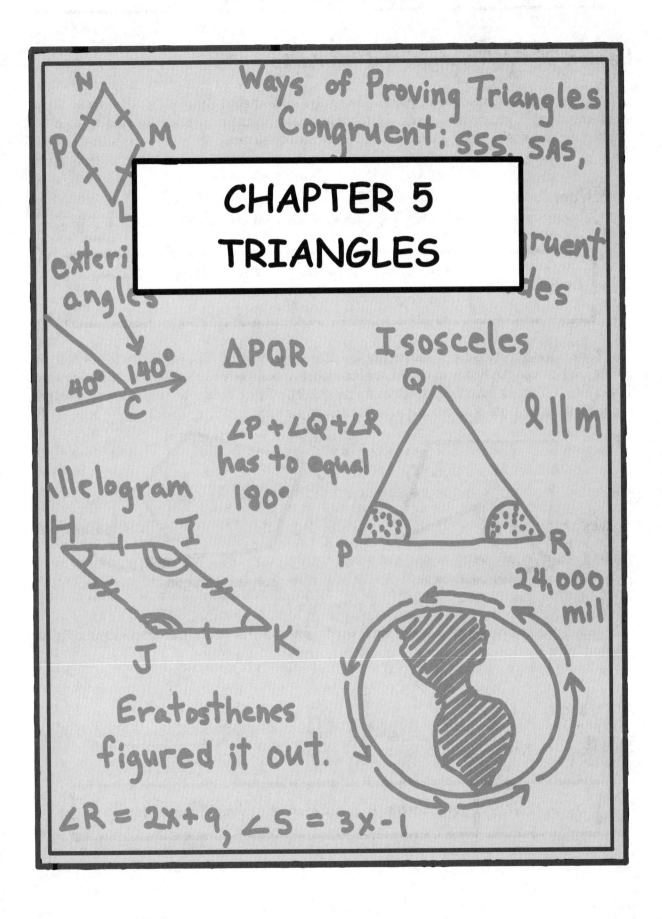

Ways of Proving Triangles
Congruent: SSS, SAS,

CHAPTER 5
TRIANGLES

exterior
angles

40° 140°
C

ΔPQR

∠P + ∠Q + ∠R
has to equal
180°

Isosceles

ℓ ‖ m

llelogram

H   I

J   K

24,000
mill

Eratosthenes
figured it out.

∠R = 2x + 9, ∠S = 3x - 1

Lesson 28—A Triangle and its Parts

So far, we've learned about points, lines, rays, and angles. By putting all of those things together, we make geometric figures like triangles, squares, and rectangles. So starting with this chapter, we're going to study geometric figures of various shapes.

A Polygon

A geometric figure that has straight sides is called a **polygon**. Here's the formal definition.

Definition 28	A *polygon* is a geometric figure whose sides are line segments.

There are two basic kinds of polygons: convex and concave. The simple way to tell the difference between the two is to remember that concave polygons have sides that "cave" inward, and convex polygons have sides that push outward. The figure on the left is a concave polygon and the one on the right is a convex polygon.

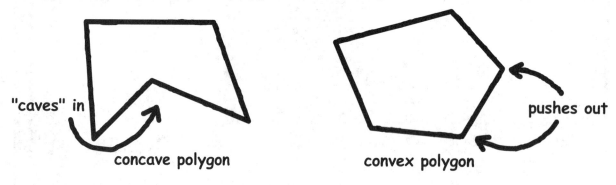

"caves" in   concave polygon   convex polygon   pushes out

In beginning geometry, we only study convex polygons. So you won't hear much about concave polygons after this lesson.

A Triangle

Probably the most common polygon is the triangle. A **triangle** is just a polygon with three sides. Here's the formal definition, followed by a picture.

Definition 29	A triangle is a polygon that has three sides.

The triangle's three sides are line segments. (That's because all polygons have line segments for sides.) There are three points at the end of these segments: points *A*, *B*, and *C*. Each of these is a **vertex** of the triangle. So triangles have vertices (that's plural for vertex) just as angles do. The triangle is named after its three vertices. This is "triangle *ABC*," which is written as $\triangle ABC$.[1] Notice that

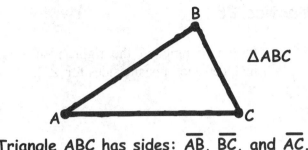

Triangle ABC has sides: $\overline{AB}$, $\overline{BC}$, and $\overline{AC}$.

$\triangle ABC$ also has three angles: $\angle A$, $\angle B$, and $\angle C$. These are at each vertex. So every triangle has six parts: three sides and three angles.

Included and Opposite

The words "included" and "opposite" are used a lot when discussing triangles. In $\triangle ABC$, side $\overline{AB}$ is included by $\angle A$ and $\angle B$, because it sits right between those angles. Side $\overline{AB}$ is opposite side $\angle C$, because it's on the opposite side of the triangle from $\angle C$. Also, $\angle B$ is included by sides $\overline{BA}$ and $\overline{BC}$, since those segments run into $\angle B$. And $\angle B$ is opposite to side $\overline{AC}$, because it is on the opposite side of the triangle from that segment.

Basically, a side of a triangle is "included" by the two angles that are at each of the side's end points, and is opposite to the angle on the opposite side of the triangle from it. Similarly, an angle is "included" by the two sides that connect to it, and is opposite to the third side.

You can tell by looking at the symbols when a side is included between two angles, because the angles' vertices will be named in the line segments. For example, $\overline{AB}$ is included within $\angle A$ and $\angle B$ because $\overline{AB}$ contains

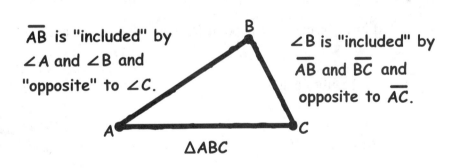

$\overline{AB}$ is "included" by $\angle A$ and $\angle B$ and "opposite" to $\angle C$.

$\angle B$ is "included" by $\overline{AB}$ and $\overline{BC}$ and opposite to $\overline{AC}$.

$\triangle ABC$

both the letters *A* and *B*. The same thing is true for an included angle. The angle's vertex will appear in both line segments. For instance, both $\overline{BC}$ and $\overline{AC}$ have the letter *C*, which is why $\angle C$ is included by $\overline{BC}$ and $\overline{AC}$.

---

[1] We use a little triangle to represent triangles just as we use a little angle symbol ($\angle$) to represent angles.

Practice 28

a. In the triangle on the right, identify the included and opposite sides for $\angle A$.

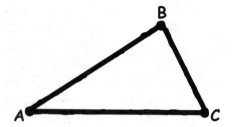

b. Find the measure of $\angle IMN$ below.

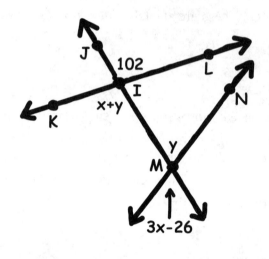

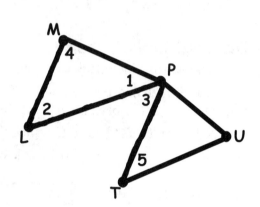

c. Given that $\overline{ML} \parallel \overline{PT}$ (above right), identify the angle pair $\angle 4$ and $\angle MPT$. Tell whether the pair is congruent or supplementary.

d. If line p bisects $\overline{AD}$ at point O, and if $AO = z + 4$ and $AD = 3z - 11$, then find OD.

e. Do the proof below.

Given: $\angle F \cong \angle S$, $m\angle H + m\angle S = 180$
Prove: $\overline{FR} \parallel \overline{HS}$

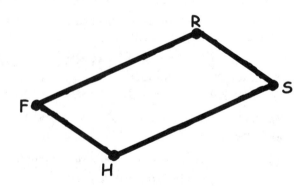

Problem Set 28

Tell whether each sentence below is True or False.

1. A circle is a polygon.

2. A triangle is a polygon that has three sides.

Complete each sentence below by filling in the blanks.

3. A(n) _____ is a line that intersects two or more lines in different points.

4. Every triangle has six parts: three _____ and three _____.

5. If two lines form _____ alternate exterior angles with a transversal, then the lines are parallel.

6. If two lines form _____ interior angles on the same side of a transversal, then the lines are parallel.

Tell whether each of the figures below is a convex or concave polygon.

7.

8.

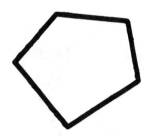

In the triangle on the right, identify the included and opposite sides or angles for each of the following.

(a) 9.   ∠B

10. $\overline{AB}$

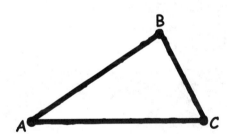

From each given statement below, tell the definition, property, postulate, or theorem that justifies each prove statement.

11. Given: $\overleftrightarrow{DO} \perp \overrightarrow{OF}$ and ∠DOE and ∠EOF are adjacent angles (shown on the right). Prove: ∠DOE and ∠EOF are complementary.

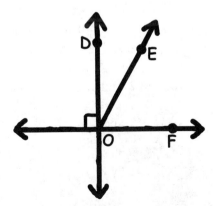

12. Given: line *n* intersects line *p* (shown on the right);
    Prove: $\angle 1 \cong \angle 3$

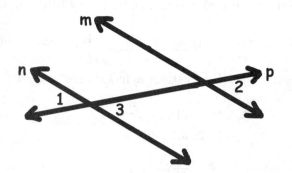

13. Given: $\angle 1 \cong \angle 2$ (shown on the right);
    Prove: $n \parallel m$

Complete each sentence below with *always*, *sometimes*, or *never*.

14. A polygon is _____ convex.

15. Interior angles on the same side of a transversal cutting parallel lines are _____ congruent.

Find the measure of each angle below.

16. $\angle ACB$

(b) 17. $\angle CEF$

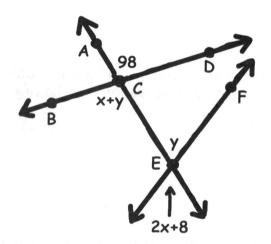

Given that $\overline{SD} \parallel \overline{TF}$ (on the right), identify the type of each angle pair. Tell whether each pair is congruent or supplementary.

18. $\angle 2$ and $\angle 3$

(c) 19. $\angle 5$ and $\angle DFT$

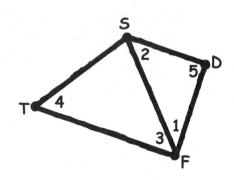

Answer each question below.

20. If $\overrightarrow{DW}$ - $\overrightarrow{DX}$ - $\overrightarrow{DY}$ and if $m\angle WDX = 2x - 5$, $m\angle XDY = 52$, and $m\angle WDY = 5x - 16$, then find $m\angle WDY$.

(d) 21. If line n bisects $\overline{QR}$ at point T, and if $QT = y + 8$ and $QR = 3y - 25$, then find TR.

To tell whether each definition below passes the reversibility test, write its converse and determine whether the converse is true.

22. If a person is from China, then he knows how to use chopsticks.

23. If a polygon is a triangle, then it has three sides.

Do the proof below.

(e) 24. Given: $\angle D \cong \angle L$, $m\angle G + m\angle L = 180$
    Prove: $\overline{DP} \parallel \overline{GL}$

Lesson 29—Kinds of Triangles

We're learning about triangles, and in this lesson we're going to cover all the different kinds. As it turns out, triangles can be categorized in two different ways: by the length of their sides and by the measure of their angles. Let's look at the categories according to sides first.

By Side Length

A **scalene** triangle has no sides equal (congruent). Triangle *ABC* below has sides of all different lengths (4, 5, 6), so it is scalene. An **isosceles** triangle has two sides equal (congruent). Triangle *DEF* is isosceles, since two of its sides equal 7. The sides of an isosceles triangle have special names. The two equal sides are called its **legs**. So in ΔDEF, the legs are $\overline{DE}$ and $\overline{EF}$. The third side of the triangle is called the **base**, which means that the base in ΔDEF is $\overline{DF}$.[2] Something else important for an isosceles triangle is the **vertex angle**. That's the angle between the triangle's legs. The vertex angle of ΔDEF is $\angle E$. Finally, an **equilateral** triangle has all three sides equal (congruent). Triangle *GHJ* is equilateral, because all of its sides equal 5.

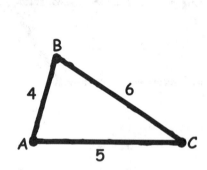

Scalene triangle: no sides equal

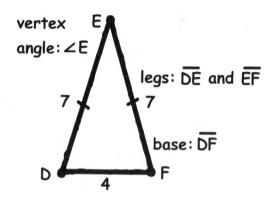

Isosceles triangle: two sides equal

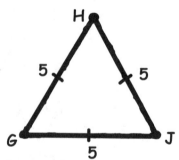

Equilateral triangle: all three sides equal

---

[2] By the way, the word "base" comes from the fact that isosceles triangles are frequently drawn so that the base is on the bottom. That makes the triangle seem like it's sitting on its base.

Notice the little marks on the sides of ΔGHJ. Those are another way to show that the sides are all equal. When the sides are not equal, we can put a different number of marks on each. (For instance, we could put one mark on a side and two marks on the other side.)

By Angle Measure

Now let's classify triangles according to their angles. This will be pretty familiar to you, because we've already studied different kinds of angles. An **acute triangle** is a triangle where all three angles measure less than 90°. Triangle WVU is acute. A **right triangle** has one angle that measures 90°. Our example is ΔMNP. Notice that the sides of a right triangle have special names. The short sides are called **legs**. In ΔMNP, the legs are $\overline{MN}$ and $\overline{MP}$. The long side, which is always opposite the right angle, is called the **hypotenuse**. The hypotenuse in ΔMNP is $\overline{NP}$. Moving on, an **obtuse triangle** has one angle that is greater than 90°. Triangle KLI is obtuse because $m\angle L = 135$. Finally, an equiangular triangle is a triangle where the measures of all three angles are equal. You can see our example, ΔRST, below.

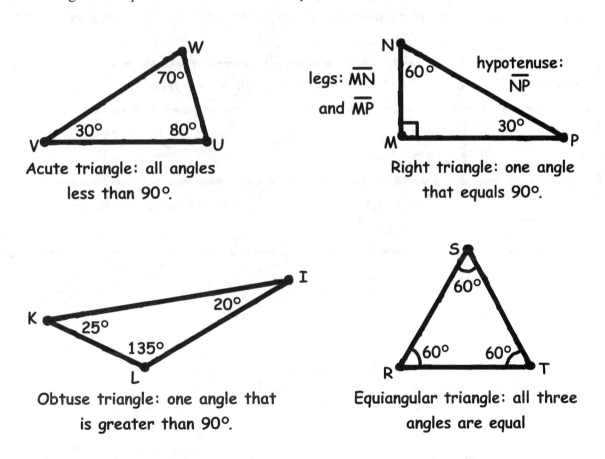

Acute triangle: all angles less than 90°.

Right triangle: one angle that equals 90°.

Obtuse triangle: one angle that is greater than 90°.

Equiangular triangle: all three angles are equal

Notice that we use little arcs to show that all three of the angles in the equiangular triangle have equal measures. If the angles had been different, we could have shown that by putting different numbers of arcs on each angle.

We've covered a lot of definitions in this lesson. Let's summarize everything in two big boxes.

Kinds of Triangles: By Side Length

Definition 30	A *scalene* triangle has no congruent (equal) sides.
Definition 31	An *isosceles* triangle has two congruent (equal) sides.
Definition 32	An *equilateral* triangle has all three congruent (equal) sides.

Kinds of Triangles: By Angle Measure

Definition 33	An *acute* triangle has all three angles with measures of less than 90°.
Definition 34	A *right* triangle has one angle with a measure of 90°.
Definition 35	An *obtuse* triangle has one angle with a measure of greater than 90°.
Definition 36	An equiangular triangle has all three angles with equal measures.

Practice 29

a. What kind of triangle is ΔBLC (shown on the right) with respect to its sides? What kind of triangle is it with respect to its angles?

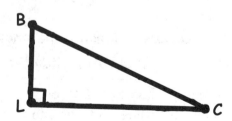

b. Name the legs and hypotenuse of ΔBLC (shown on the right)?

c. Given $\overline{AB} \parallel \overline{JK}$, find y.

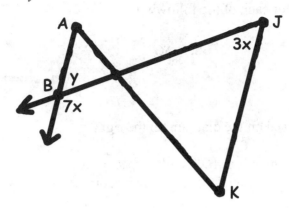

d. The supplement of an angle is 3.5 times as large as the angle. Find the angle.

e. Do the proof below.

Given: $d \parallel f$, $f \parallel g$
Prove: $d \parallel g$

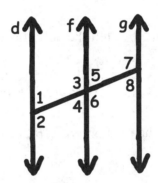

Problem Set 29

Tell whether each sentence below is True or False.

1. Triangles can be categorized in two different ways: by the length of their sides and by the measure of their angles.

2. An isosceles triangle has three congruent sides.

Complete each sentence below by filling in the blanks.

3. A scalene triangle has _____ congruent (equal) sides.

4. A right triangle has one angle with a measure of _____.

5. A(n) _____ triangle has three congruent (equal) sides.

6. A(n) _____ triangle has one angle with a measure of greater than $90°$.

In the triangle on the right, identify the included and opposite sides or angles for each of the following.

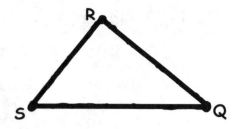

7. $\angle S$ **8.** $\overline{SQ}$

Answer each question based on the diagram on the right.

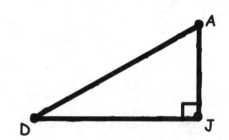

(a) 9. What kind of triangle is $\triangle ADJ$ with respect to its sides? What kind of triangle is it with respect to its angles?

(b) 10. Name the legs and hypotenuse of $\triangle ADJ$.

From each given statement below, tell the definition, property, postulate, or theorem that justifies each prove statement.

11. Given: $m\angle 1 = m\angle 3$ and $m\angle 2 = m\angle 4$; Prove: $m\angle 1 + m\angle 2 = m\angle 3 + m\angle 4$.

12. Given: point M is the midpoint of $\overline{AB}$; Prove: $AM = MB$.

From the diagram below, name a pair of lines that must be parallel if each statement below is true. If there are no lines that have to be parallel, write "none" for your answer.

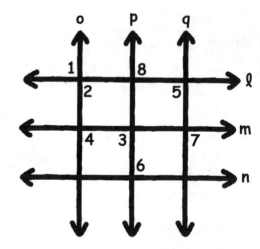

13. $\angle 1 \cong \angle 4$

14. $\angle 5 \cong \angle 7$

Answer each question below, given $\overline{AB} \parallel \overline{JK}$.

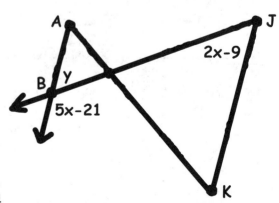

15. Find x.

(c) 16. Find y.

Write an equation to represent each question below; then solve the equation to get your answer.

(d) 17. The complement of an angle is 1.5 times as large as the angle. Find the angle.

18. Three times the measure of an angle is equal to twice the measure of the angle's supplement. What is the measure of the angle?

Draw a Venn diagram to represent each set of conditional statements below.

19. Every one of the angry fans thought the umpire was blind. Mike is an angry fan. Therefore, Mike must think the umpire is blind.

20. All Basset Hounds have sad eyes. Homer does not have sad eyes. Therefore, Homer is not a Basset Hound.

Write the converse of each statement below. Tell whether the converse is True or False.

21. If a triangle is scalene, then all its sides have different lengths.

22. If a triangle is isosceles, then it has two equal sides.

Do each proof below.

(e) 23. Given: $m \parallel n$, $n \parallel q$
      Prove: $m \parallel q$

     This will become our Theorem 16.

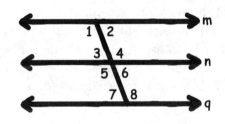

Theorem 16	If two lines are parallel to a third line, then the lines are parallel to each other.

24. Given: $m\angle 1 + m\angle 3 = 180$
     Prove: $t \parallel r$

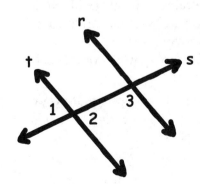

Lesson 30—Adding Up the Angles

We showed a lot of different triangles in the last lesson. If you were observant, you might have noticed something about them. The angles of every one of those triangles added to equal 180° (whenever their measures were shown). That was no coincidence. One of the most important theorems of geometry says that the sum of the angles of *any* triangle—no matter what its shape—is 180°.

Auxiliary Lines

We're going to prove the sum of the angles of a triangle theorem in this lesson. But first, we need to talk about drawing lines. It's not unusual to have to draw an extra line in a diagram in order to complete a proof. The extra line is called an **auxiliary line**. The important thing about drawing the line is to make sure that only one line can be drawn in that particular position. For example, let's say we needed to draw a line between the two points below.

If two different lines could be drawn through *A* and *B*, then we would have a problem, because no one would know which of the two lines we were talking about in our proof. Showing which line on the diagram wouldn't help, because mathematicians don't want us to rely on a diagram any more than necessary. They want every proof to be based on pure logic.

In reality, only one line can be drawn between any two points. The way we justify that mathematically is to rely on the postulate "two points determine a unique straight line." That was our Postulate 1, in case you've forgotten. The word "determine" means that there's just one line that will satisfy the requirements (to go through both *A* and *B*). The main point, though, is that any time we draw a line in a diagram for a proof, we need to make sure that line is "determined."

Proving the Angles Add to 180

Now that we've covered auxiliary lines, we're ready to do our proof. It should be no surprise that the proof requires an auxiliary line. We'll put the diagram up and then show where the line needs to be drawn. Notice that we didn't draw an equilateral or isosceles triangle. We just draw a plain scalene triangle (with all different side lengths). That's because we want our proof to hold for *any* triangle. Making our drawing scalene prevents us from coming up with a proof that only works on a special kind of triangle.

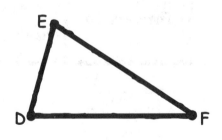

The first step is to draw an auxiliary line through point *E* and parallel to $\overline{DF}$. Remember, we need to make sure that this line is "determined." In other words, we need some way of knowing that only one line can be drawn through a point and also parallel to another line. There's a postulate that covers this. It's called **the parallel postulate**.[3]

Postulate 8	Through a given point not on a line, exactly one line may be drawn parallel to the line.

Postulate 8 will be our reason for drawing line p through E and parallel to $\overline{DF}$. Here is that step, along with the rest of the proof.

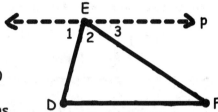

Given: $\triangle DEF$

Prove: $m\angle D + m\angle 2 + m\angle F = 180$

Statements	Reasons
1. $\triangle DEF$	1. Given
2. Through point E, draw line p such that p ∥ $\overline{DF}$.	2. Through a point not on a line, exactly one line may be drawn parallel to that line.
3. $m\angle 1 = m\angle D$ and $m\angle 3 = m\angle F$	3. If two parallel lines are cut by a transversal, then their alternate interior angles are equal.
4. $m\angle 1 + m\angle 2 + m\angle 3 = 180$	4. A straight angle measures 180°.
5. $m\angle D + m\angle 2 + m\angle F = 180$	5. Substitution Property

Here is the important theorem that we've just proven stated formally.

Theorem 17	The sum of the measures of the angles of a triangle is 180.

---

[3] This is actually a very famous postulate—the most famous in all of geometry. You'll learn why at the end of this course.

Corollaries

There are several other things we can now prove using Theorem 17. These are all very closely related to Theorem 17 too. And actually, any theorem that is easy to prove using an existing theorem is called a **corollary**. So what we're about to show you are all corollaries of Theorem 17.

The first one says that the acute angles of a right triangle are complementary. It makes sense if you think about it. A right triangle has one right angle, which measures 90°. And since all three angles of the triangle have to add to 180°, the other two angles must add to equal 90°, which makes them complementary. We'll show you the theorem and then an informal proof.

Corollary 17.1	The acute angles of a right triangle are complementary.

We've numbered this corollary "17.1" to show that it's closely related to Theorem 17. Here's the informal proof.

> If a right triangle has a right angle measuring 90 and two other angles measuring x and y, then $x + y + 90 = 180$ (sum of angles of any triangle equals 180). Subtracting 90 from both sides gives $x + y = 90$. Therefore, x and y are complementary. (Definition of complementary angles)

Our next corollary says that the measure of each angle of an equiangular triangle is 60. Remember, an equiangular triangle has all three angles equal. Here's the corollary and an informal proof.

Corollary 17.2	The measure of each angle of an equiangular triangle is 60.

> If in an equiangular triangle the measure of all three angles equals x, then $3x = 180$ (sum of angles of any triangle equals 180). Dividing both sides by 3 gives $x = 60$. Therefore, all three angles have a measure of 60.

Our last corollary says that if two angles of a triangle are congruent to two angles of another triangle, then the third angles must be congruent. This also follows directly from Theorem 17, because the angles of both triangles have to add to equal 180°. Here's the corollary and an informal proof.

Corollary 17.3	If two angles of a triangle are congruent to two angles of another triangle, then the remaining pair of angles are congruent.

Given $\triangle ABC$ and $\triangle DEF$. Since the measures of each triangle's angles must add to equal 180, we know the following: $m\angle A + m\angle B + m\angle C = 180$ and $m\angle D + m\angle E + m\angle F = 180$. Then, by substitution, $m\angle A + m\angle B + m\angle C = m\angle D + m\angle E + m\angle F$. Two pairs of angles are congruent, so $m\angle A = m\angle D$ and $m\angle B = m\angle E$. By substitution again, we get this: $m\angle A + m\angle B + m\angle C = m\angle A + m\angle B + m\angle F$. Finally, subtracting $m\angle A + m\angle B$ from both sides gives us $m\angle C = m\angle F$.

Practice 30

a. Find the measures of the angles of the triangle described below.

A triangle whose angles have measures x, $x+5$, and $x+10$. What kind of triangle is it with respect to its angles?

b. From the given statement below, tell the definition, property, postulate, or theorem that justifies the prove statement.

Given: $m\angle 6 = 45$ and $m\angle 8 = 35$;
Prove: $m\angle G = 100$.

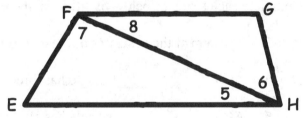

c. Find the value of x and y in the diagram on the right.

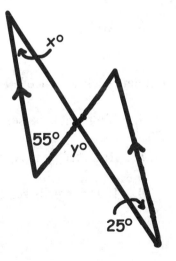

d. Tell whether the argument below is a valid or invalid deduction. (Use your knowledge of converse statements.)

All of the pizza delivery boys have a sign on the roof of their car. Dwayne is a pizza delivery boy, so he must have a sign on the roof of his car.

e. Do the proof below.

Given: $\overline{AB} \perp \overline{AE}$,
Prove: $m\angle B + m\angle E = 90$

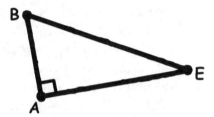

Problem Set 30

Tell whether each sentence below is True or False.

1. According to Postulate 8, through a given point not on a line, exactly one line may be drawn parallel to the line.

2. A corollary is a theorem that is easy to prove using an existing theorem.

Complete each sentence below by filling in the blanks.

3. The sum of the measures of the angles of a triangle is _____.

4. A(n) _____ triangle has three angles with equal measures.

5. A(n) _____ triangle has all three angles with measure less than $90°$.

6. A(n) _____ triangle has two congruent (equal) sides.

Complete each sentence below with *always*, *sometimes*, or *never*.

7. If a triangle is isosceles, then it is _____ equilateral.

8. If a triangle is equilateral, then it is _____ isosceles.

9. If a triangle is scalene, then it is _____ isosceles.

Find the measures of the angles of each triangle described below.

10. A right triangle with one angle whose measure is 30.

11. A right triangle with congruent acute angles.

(a) 12. A triangle whose angles have measures x, $x+10$, and $x+20$. What kind of triangle is it with respect to its angles?

From each given statement below, tell the definition, property, postulate, or theorem that justifies each prove statement.

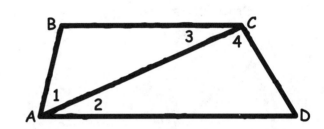

13. Given: $\angle 2 \cong \angle 3$; Prove: $\overline{BC} \parallel \overline{AD}$.

14. Given: $\overline{BC} \parallel \overline{AD}$; Prove; $\angle DAB$ and $\angle B$ are supplementary.

(b) 15. Given: $\triangle ACD$, $m\angle 2 = 25$, and $m\angle 4 = 95$; Prove: $m\angle D = 60$.

Find the value of x and y in each diagram below.

(c) 16.

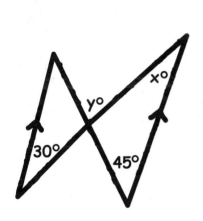

17.

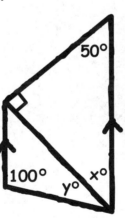

18.

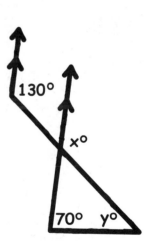

Answer each question below.

19. If A-C-S, and if $AC = 4x-1$, $AS = 6x-4$, and $CS = 7$, then find AC.

20. $\angle 3$ and $\angle 9$ are complementary. If $m\angle 3 = 3x-7$ and $m\angle 9 = 4x-1$, find $m\angle 3$.

Tell whether the arguments below are valid or invalid deductions. (Use your knowledge of converse statements.)

(d) 21. All of the babies had stains on their bibs. Russell is a baby, so he must have stains on his bib.

22. All the trailblazers own a coonskin cap. William owns a coonskin cap. Therefore, William is a trailblazer.

Do each proof below.

23. Given: $\angle C \cong \angle L$,
Prove: $\angle V \cong \angle G$

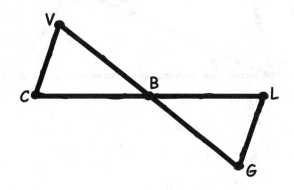

(e) 24. Given: $\overline{RT} \perp \overline{ST}$,
Prove: $m\angle R + m\angle S = 90$

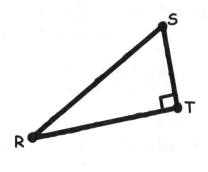

Lesson 31— Exterior Angles

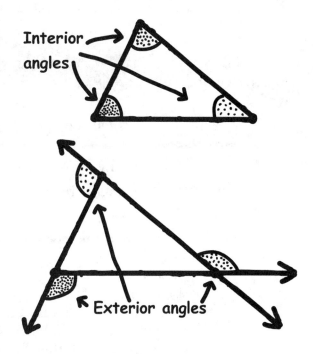

In the last lesson we learned that the three angles of any triangle add to equal 180°. The angles that we were talking about, though, are inside the triangle. They're called **interior angles**, as shown in the top right. These angles have a special name, because a triangle also has "exterior angles," which are outside the triangle. The way to find an exterior angle is to extend the sides of the triangle, like on the bottom right. Basically, an **exterior angle** in a triangle or any polygon is an angle that makes a linear pair with one of the interior angles. Here's the formal definition.

Definition 37	An exterior angle of a polygon is an angle that forms a linear pair with one of the interior angles of the polygon.

That means, by the way, that the exterior and interior angles at any one vertex are supplementary (add to equal 180°).

Exterior Angle of a Triangle Theorem

There's an interesting theorem about the exterior angles of a triangle. It will be easier to explain if we look at a diagram on the right. The interior angles of this triangle are $\angle 1$, $\angle 2$, and $\angle 3$. Angle 4 is an exterior angle. We know that $m\angle 1 + m\angle 2 + m\angle 3 = 180$. And we just learned that $m\angle 3 + m\angle 4 = 180$. Think about what that means. It means that the exterior angle, $\angle 4$, must equal the other two interior angles, $\angle 1$ and $\angle 2$, added together.

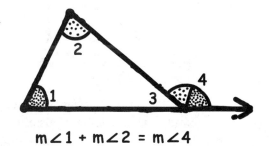

$$m\angle 1 + m\angle 2 = m\angle 4$$

$$m\angle 1 + m\angle 2 = m\angle 4$$

193

Since $\angle 1$ and $\angle 2$ are not adjacent to $\angle 4$, they're actually called **remote interior angles**. The word "remote" just means that they are far away from the exterior angle, instead of right next to it (like $\angle 3$).

So the two remote interior angles always add up to equal the exterior angle. This is called the **Exterior Angle of a Triangle Theorem**. Here's the official version, followed by an informal proof.

Exterior Angle of a Triangle Theorem

Theorem 18	The measure of an exterior angle of a triangle is equal to the sum of the measures of the two remote interior angles.

In the diagram above, $m\angle 1 + m\angle 2 + m\angle 3 = 180$ (The sum of the measures of the angles of a triangle equals 180°). $\angle 3$ and $\angle 4$ are a linear pair, which means that they are supplementary. (If two angles are a linear pair, then they are supplementary). Therefore, $m\angle 3 + m\angle 4 = 180$ (Definition of supplementary angles). Substituting $m\angle 3 + m\angle 4$ for 180 in the first equation gives us $m\angle 1 + m\angle 2 + m\angle 3 = m\angle 3 + m\angle 4$. Finally, subtracting $m\angle 3$ from both sides, we get $m\angle 1 + m\angle 2 = m\angle 4$.

Practice 31

a. Find the value of *y* in the triangle below.

b. Find the value of *y* in the triangle below.

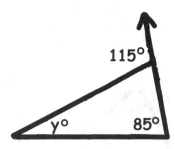

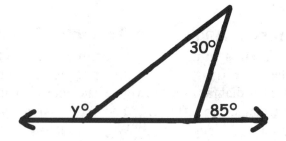

c. Draw a triangle that satisfies the conditions stated. If no triangle can satisfy the conditions, write "not possible."

An obtuse right triangle

d. Write an equation to represent the question below; then solve the equation to get your answer.

The complement of an angle is one fourth of its size. Find the angle.

e. Do the proof below.

Given: $\overline{BV} \perp \overline{VG}$, $\overline{GP} \perp \overline{PZ}$, $\angle 3$ and $\angle 4$ are vertical angles.

Prove: $\angle B \cong \angle Z$.

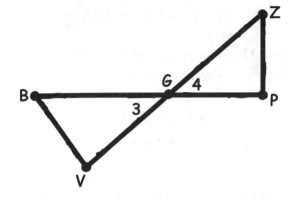

Problem Set 31

Tell whether each sentence below is True or False.

1. The angles inside a triangle are called exterior angles.

2. An exterior angle of a triangle (or any polygon) forms a linear pair with an interior angle.

Complete each sentence below by filling in the blanks.

3. The two equal sides of an isosceles triangle are called _____.

4. If two angles of a triangle are congruent to two angles of another triangle, then the remaining pair of angles are _____.

5. If two lines form _____ interior angles on the same side of a transversal, then the lines are parallel.

6. The measure of an exterior angle of a triangle is _____ the sum of the measures of the _____ remote interior angles.

Find the measures of the angles of each triangle described below.

7. A triangle whose angles have measures of x, $2x$, and $3x$. What kind of triangle is it?

8. An equiangular triangle.

9. A right triangle with one angle whose measure is $10°$.

From each given statement below, tell the definition, property, postulate, or theorem that justifies each prove statement.

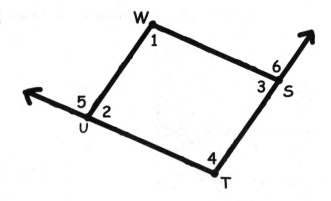

10. Given: $\angle 2$ and $\angle 5$ are a linear pair;
    Prove: $\angle 2$ and $\angle 5$ are
    supplementary.

11. Given: $\overline{UT} \parallel \overline{WS}$
    Prove: $\angle 1 \cong \angle 5$

12. Given: $\overline{UW} \parallel \overline{ST}$
    Prove: $\angle 4 \cong \angle 5$

Find the value of x in each triangle below.

13.

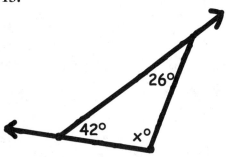

14.

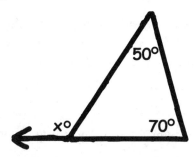

(a) 15.

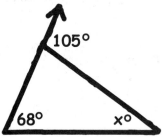

(b) 16.

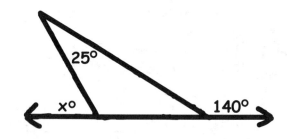

Draw a triangle that satisfies the conditions stated. If no triangle can satisfy the conditions, write "not possible."

17. A right triangle with two angles measuring $45°$.

(c) 18. An obtuse equiangular triangle

Write an equation to represent each question below; then solve the equation to get your answer.

19. The supplement of an angle is 42° more than the angle. Find the angle.

(d) 20. The complement of an angle is half of its size. Find the angle.

To tell whether each definition below passes the reversibility test, write its converse and determine whether the converse is true

21. If a triangle is obtuse, then it has three sides.

22. If a triangle is a right triangle, then it has one angle with a measure of 90°.

Do the proof below.

(e) 23. Given: $\overline{AD} \perp \overline{AF}$, $\overline{FC} \perp \overline{CH}$,
 $\angle 1$ and $\angle 2$ are vertical angles.
 Prove: $\angle D \cong \angle H$

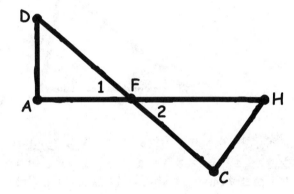

Lesson 32—Congruent Triangles

We've been studying triangles. For the next several lessons, though, we're going to concentrate on congruent triangles. Remember, congruent figures (whether they're triangles or anything else) are figures that have the same size and the same shape. We learned that at the beginning of the course. So congruent triangles have the same size and shape.

But an important question is how do we tell mathematically whether two triangles are actually congruent. For everyday purposes, it may be enough just to glance at them. However in math, everything has to be determined by logic, as you know. A glance, then, is not enough. It turns out that two triangles are congruent when their angles have the same measure and their sides have the same length.

Let's start with an easy example.

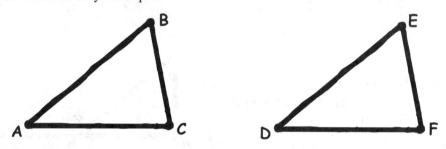

These two triangles are congruent, because all six of their parts are congruent. Specifically, $\angle A \cong \angle D$, $\angle B \cong \angle E$, and $\angle C \cong \angle F$. And for the sides, $\overline{AB} \cong \overline{DE}$, $\overline{BC} \cong \overline{EF}$, and $\overline{AC} \cong \overline{DF}$. It's pretty obvious which angles and which sides go together, because we can imagine picking up $\triangle ABC$ and placing it on top of $\triangle DEF$. That would match up all the congruent angles and the congruent sides perfectly.

But now take a look at these two congruent triangles.

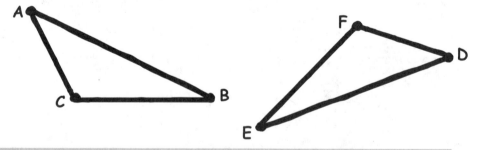

It's not as easy to tell which angles and which sides go together in this example. The reason is that the triangles aren't positioned in the same way. (Actually, we could make $\triangle ABC$ and $\triangle DEF$ look the same by spinning either one of them around a bit.) It turns out that $\angle A \cong \angle D$, $\angle B \cong \angle E$, and $\angle C \cong \angle F$. And for the sides, $\overline{AB} \cong \overline{DE}$, $\overline{BC} \cong \overline{EF}$, and $\overline{AC} \cong \overline{DF}$. So everything matches up in the same way as the first example.

Correspondence

But do you see the problem in working with congruent triangles? Unless the triangles are positioned in exactly the same way, it's hard to tell which angles and which sides match up. To deal with this, the mathematicians created a concept called correspondence. Two figures are put in **correspondence** by matching each vertex of one figure with a specific vertex of the other figure. In our examples, we matched vertex A with vertex D, vertex B with vertex E, and vertex C with vertex F. The correspondence of the vertices can be written like this.

$$A \leftrightarrow D \qquad\qquad B \leftrightarrow E \qquad\qquad C \leftrightarrow F.$$

Or we could group the vertices of each triangle together in this way.

$$ABC \leftrightarrow DEF$$

And to show that the triangles are congruent, we write $\triangle ABC \cong \triangle DEF$. From the diagram on the right, notice that the letters are in the same order as the correspondence. A and D are first; B and E are second; and C and F are third. The vertices need to be in the right order, because that makes it easy to figure out which angles and which sides are congruent. To find the congruent angles from these triangles, all we have to do is match up each pair of corresponding vertices.

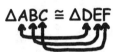

The vertices are in order of their correspondence.

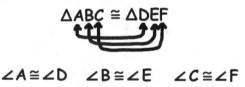

$$\angle A \cong \angle D \quad \angle B \cong \angle E \quad \angle C \cong \angle F$$

To find which angles are congruent, just pair the vertices according to their correspondence.

To find the congruent sides, we just take pairs of vertices in the same order from each triangle.

△ABC ≅ △DEF	△ABC ≅ △DEF	△ABC ≅ △DEF
$\overline{AB} \cong \overline{DE}$	$\overline{BC} \cong \overline{EF}$	$\overline{AC} \cong \overline{DF}$

The matching angles are called "corresponding angles," and the matching sides are called "corresponding sides." So $\angle A$ and $\angle D$ are examples of corresponding angles and $\overline{AB}$ and $\overline{DE}$ are examples of corresponding sides.

Another important point is that we didn't have to write the vertices of the triangles in the order *ABC* and *DEF*. We could have written them as *CBA* and *FED* (to get $\triangle CBA \cong \triangle FED$) or some other combination. As long as the corresponding vertices are in the same position for both triangles, then you will be able to figure out which angles and which sides go together.[4]

Definition of Congruent Triangles

Now that we've explained how correspondence works, we're ready for the formal definition of congruent triangles. Here it is.

Definition of Congruent Triangles

Definition 38	If the vertices of two triangles can be paired in a correspondence so that all pairs of corresponding angles are congruent and all pairs of corresponding sides are congruent, then the triangles are congruent.

According to this definition, we can prove that two triangles are congruent by putting their vertices in some correspondence (matching them up), and then showing that the corresponding sides and angles—based on the order of the vertices in the correspondence—are all congruent.

So going back to our second example, let's say we were told that $\angle A \cong \angle D$, $\angle B \cong \angle E$, and $\angle C \cong \angle F$, and also that $\overline{AB} \cong \overline{DE}$, $\overline{BC} \cong \overline{EF}$, and $\overline{AC} \cong \overline{DF}$. From that information, we could conclude that $\triangle ABC \cong \triangle DEF$. (And notice that the order of the letters matches the correspondence of the angles and sides.)

Henry Ford's Assembly Line

One of the most common uses of congruent figures in the real world is in manufacturing, where assembly lines crank out product after product, all exactly alike. The assembly line was first popularized by Henry Ford, the founder of Ford Motor Company. Before Henry Ford, cars were a luxury that only a few rich people could afford. There were very few roads for cars to drive on. But Ford realized that with assembly line production, the cost of a car could be lowered to a point where the average American family could afford one. So he perfected his "Model T", which was stronger and cheaper than all the other cars then available. Henry Ford played a big role in creating our modern world, with millions of cars zipping down highways all across the country.

---

[4] In other words, since *A* and *D* are corresponding vertices, they both have to be in the same position. The same goes for *B* and *E* and also *C* and *F*.

For assembly line production to work, every part coming off the line must be exactly alike. Otherwise, the parts won't fit into all the cars properly. And imagine the frustration if every time your car broke down, you couldn't get a replacement part that fit right. Mathematically, car parts that are exactly alike are congruent: they're the same shape and the same size.[5] So the challenge that Henry Ford and other early assembly line manufacturers faced was how to produce lots of congruent objects cheaply and efficiently. The principles of geometry played an important role in their efforts.

Practice 32

a. If $\triangle AHE \cong \triangle IUQ$, list all of the congruent sides from the two triangles.

b. Given congruent triangles in the diagram below, fill in the blank: $\overline{QX} \cong$ _____

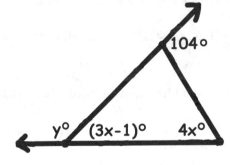

Find the value of x and y in each diagram below.

c.

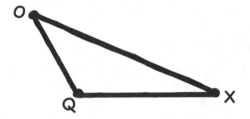

d.

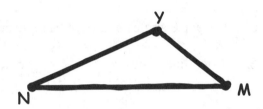

e. Do the proof below.

Given: $\angle 4$ is an exterior angle of $\triangle IKL$.
Prove: $m\angle L = m\angle 4 - m\angle 6$

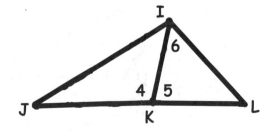

---

[5] Technically congruent car parts are a little different from the congruent triangles we're studying because they are three dimensional. We'll get to 3-D geometry later in the course.

Problem Set 32

Tell whether each sentence below is True or False.

1. Congruent figures are figures that have the same size and shape.

2. Two figures are put in correspondence by matching each vertex of one figure with a specific vertex of the other figure.

Complete each sentence below by filling in the blanks.

3. Two triangles are congruent if their vertices can be paired in a correspondence so that all pairs of _____ are congruent and all pairs of _____ are congruent.

4. Two triangles are congruent when all _____ of their parts are congruent.

5. The acute angles of a right triangle are _____.

6. If two lines form _____ corresponding angles with a transversal, then the lines are _____.

Answer each question below.

7. If $\triangle JKL \cong \triangle DFG$, list all of the congruent angles from the two triangles.

(a) 8. If $\triangle JKL \cong \triangle DFG$, list all of the congruent sides from the two triangles.

Given congruent triangles in the diagram below, fill in each of the blanks.

9. $WVU \leftrightarrow$ _____   10. $\angle V \cong$ _____   (b) 11. $\overline{VU} \cong$ _____

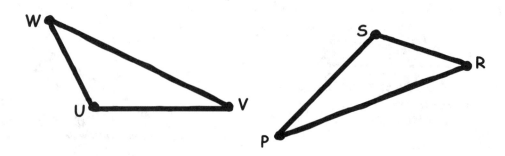

Complete each sentence below with *always*, *sometimes*, or *never*.

12. An acute triangle _____ has an angle that is greater than $90°$.

13. Corresponding angles cutting parallel lines are _____ congruent.

From each given statement below (and the diagram), tell the definition, property, postulate, or theorem that justifies each prove statement.

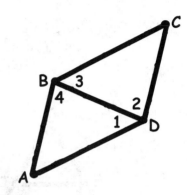

14. Given: $\triangle ABD$; Prove: $m\angle A + m\angle 4 + m\angle 1 = 180$

15. Given: $\angle 1 \cong \angle 3$; Prove: $\overline{AD} \parallel \overline{BC}$

16. Given: $\angle A$ and $\angle ADC$ are supplementary;
Prove: $\overline{AB} \parallel \overline{DC}$

Find the value of *x* and *y* in each diagram below.

17.

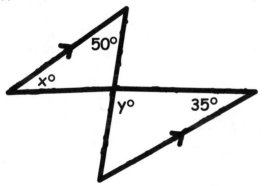

(c) 18.

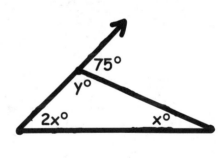

(d) 19.

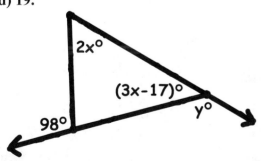

Answer each question below.

20. If $\overrightarrow{OA}\text{-}\overrightarrow{OB}\text{-}\overrightarrow{OC}$ and if $m\angle AOB = 9x + 20$, $m\angle BOC = 7x - 6$, and $m\angle AOC = 142$, then find $m\angle BOC$.

21. If line r bisects $\overline{DG}$ at point E, and if $DE = 2z + 2$ and $DG = 5z - 7$, then find DG.

Do each proof below.

22. Given: ΔDFH and ΔEGI are equiangular.
Prove: $\angle D \cong \angle EGI$

(e) 23. Given: $\angle 1$ is an exterior angle of ΔURS
Prove: $m\angle R = m\angle 1 - m\angle 3$

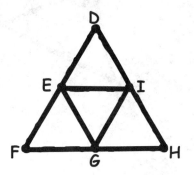

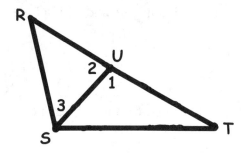

Lesson 33—Side-Angle-Side

In the previous lesson, we learned about congruent triangles. Remember, those are triangles where all six parts are congruent: three sides and three angles. One thing you'll be glad to know, though, is that there are several short cuts for proving two triangles are congruent. In other words, it's not necessary to prove that all six of the triangles' parts are congruent (which could take a long time).

Two Sides and the Angle Between Them

These shortcuts only require us to prove that three of the six parts of each triangle are congruent. To see how the first shortcut works, look at the two partial triangles below.

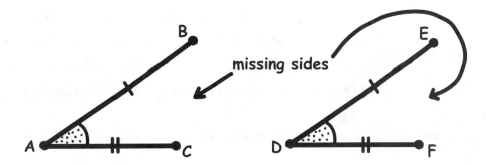

Can the third side make the triangles *not* congruent?

These are "partial" triangles, because each has a missing side. And notice that the existing two sides of each triangle are congruent, as is the angle between them (the included angle). So these partial triangles are exactly alike. But here's an interesting question. Is it possible to draw in the third side on both triangles in such a way that it makes the two triangles *not* congruent? A quick look will tell you that this is not possible. Since the existing two sides of both triangles are exactly the same and since the angle between them (the included angle) is the same, the third side is determined. It has to have a certain length and a certain slant. Otherwise, it won't fit into each triangle. Let's draw in the third sides.

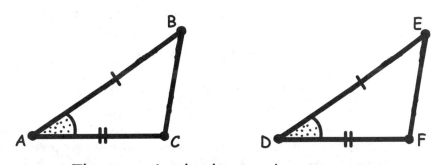

The two triangles have to be congruent.

The triangles are now complete and notice what happened. The third side is the same in both triangles. And so are the other angles that the third side makes with the existing sides. With all sides and angles the same, these triangles are congruent.

This little experiment tells us something important. It tells us that when two sides and the included angle of a pair of triangles are congruent, the entire triangles must be congruent as well. We don't have to know anything about the third side or about the other two angles. Those have to be the same for both triangles as well. There's no way to draw that third side in that would make the triangles not congruent. This rule is called **Side-Angle-Side or S.A.S. for short.** Since we didn't prove SAS, we'll have to accept it as a postulate. Here's the postulate written formally.

Side-Angle-Side Postulate

Postulate 9	If the vertices of two triangles can be paired so that two sides and the included angle of one triangle are congruent to the corresponding parts of the second triangle, then the two triangles are congruent.

A Little Proof

To make sure you're getting the concept, let's use Side-Angle-Side in a little proof. Let's say we want to prove that $\triangle PLM$ and $\triangle RQM$ (on the right) are congruent. We're given that $\overline{PM} \cong \overline{RM}$ and $\overline{LM} \cong \overline{QM}$. Since $\angle 1$ and $\angle 2$ are vertical angles, they also have to be congruent. What's more, $\angle 1$ is included between $\overline{PM}$ and $\overline{LM}$, and $\angle 2$ is included between $\overline{RM}$ and $\overline{QM}$. That means we have two corresponding sides and the angles between them that are congruent. By the Side-Angle-Side Postulate, we can conclude that all the other sides and angles are also congruent, which makes the entire triangles congruent:

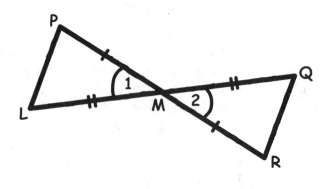

By Side-Angle-Side,
$$\triangle PLM \cong \triangle RQM$$

That's how the S.A.S. shortcut can be used to prove two triangles are congruent. Notice that we only needed to know that three of the six parts of each triangle were congruent to the corresponding parts of the other triangle. That's a time saver.

Practice 33

a. From the given statement below, tell the definition, property, postulate, or theorem that justifies the prove statement.

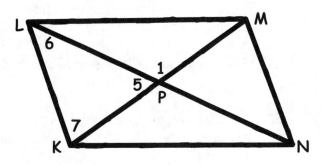

Given: $\overline{LP} \cong \overline{NP}$, $\angle 5 \cong \angle MPN$,
$\overline{PK} \cong \overline{PM}$;
Prove: $\triangle LPK \cong \triangle NPM$

b. Find $m\angle K$ and $m\angle JDK$.

c. Find x and y.

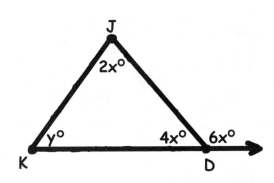

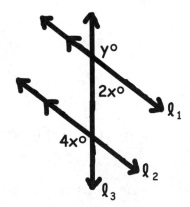

d. Write an equation to represent the question below; then solve the equation to get your answer.

Four times an angle is equal to its supplement. Find the angle.

e. Do the proof below.

Given: $\angle HFG \cong \angle IHF$; J is the midpoint of $\overline{FH}$; $\overline{FG} \cong \overline{HI}$
Prove: $\triangle FGJ \cong \triangle HIJ$

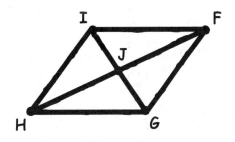

Problem Set 33

Tell whether each sentence below is True or False.

1. There are several shortcuts for proving that two triangles are congruent.

2. According to the Side-Angle-Side postulate, when two sides and the included angle of a pair of triangles are congruent, the entire triangles must be congruent as well.

Complete each sentence below by filling in the blanks.

3. Through a given point not on a line, exactly _____ may be drawn parallel to the line.

4. If two angles of a triangle are congruent to two angles of another triangle, then the remaining pair of angles are _____.

5. The measure of an exterior angle of a triangle is _____ the sum of the measures of the _____ remote interior angles.

6. A(n) _____ triangle has one angle with a measure of greater than $90°$.

Answer each question below.

7. If $\triangle HSU \cong \triangle KLP$, list all of the congruent angles from the two triangles.

8. If $\triangle HSU \cong \triangle KLP$, list all of the congruent sides from the two triangles.

Draw a triangle that satisfies the conditions stated. If no triangle can satisfy the conditions, write "not possible."

9. A scalene isosceles triangle.   10. An acute scalene triangle

From each given statement below, tell the definition, property, postulate, or theorem that justifies each prove statement.

11. Given: $\angle 1$ is an exterior angle of $\triangle CED$. Prove: $m\angle 1 = m\angle 3 + m\angle 4$.

(a) 12. Given: $\overline{BE} \cong \overline{DE}$, $\angle 2 \cong \angle BEA$, $\overline{EA} \cong \overline{EC}$; Prove: $\triangle BEA \cong \triangle DEC$.

13. Given: $\overline{BE} \cong \overline{DE}$, $\angle 1 \cong \angle AED$, $\overline{EC} \cong \overline{EA}$; Prove: $\triangle BEC \cong \triangle DEA$.

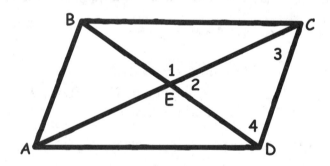

Find the measures of the angles of each triangle described below.

14. A right triangle with one angle measuring $38°$.

15. A triangle with one angle measuring $130°$ and the other two measuring x.

Answer each question below.

16. Find x and y.

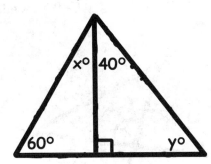

(b) 17. Find $m\angle S$ and $m\angle TRS$.

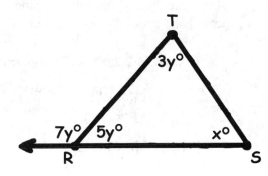

(c) 18. Find x and y.

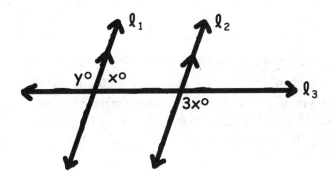

Write an equation to represent each question below; then solve the equation to get your answer.

19. The complement of an angle is $16°$ less than the angle. Find the angle.

(d) 20. Three times an angle is equal to its supplement. Find the angle.

Write the converse of each statement below. Tell whether the converse is True or False.

21. If two triangles are congruent, then all three of their angles are congruent.

22. If a triangle is acute, then it has one angle that measures less than $90°$.

Do the proof below.

(e) 23. Given: $\angle BAD \cong \angle ADC$; E is the midpoint of $\overline{AD}$; $\overline{AB} \cong \overline{CD}$
Prove: $\triangle ABE \cong \triangle DCE$

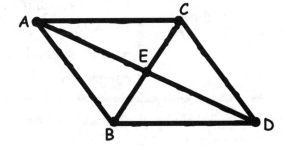

Lesson 34—Angle-Side-Angle and Angle-Angle-Side

There are other shortcuts, besides Side-Angle-Side, for proving that two triangles are congruent. Take a look at this example.

Given: ∠1 and ∠2 are vertical angles;

R is the midpoint of $\overline{PS}$;

∠P ≅ ∠S.

Prove: ∆RPQ ≅ ∆RSO

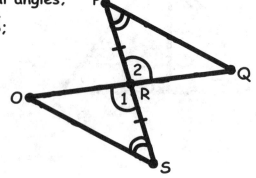

We've already marked the key facts on the diagram. Since ∠1 and ∠2 are vertical angles, those angles have to be congruent. And since R is the midpoint of $\overline{PS}$, $\overline{RP}$ and $\overline{RS}$ must be congruent. Finally, it's given that ∠P and ∠S are congruent. That leaves us with the triangles having two angles and the side between them congruent. These are all corresponding parts too, because of the position of the triangles' vertices in the prove statement: $\triangle RPQ \cong \triangle RSO$.

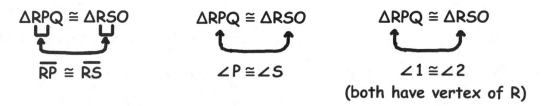

(both have vertex of R)

So in this example, instead of Side-Angle-Side, we have **Angle-Side-Angle** (or A.S.A.). Is that enough to prove that the two triangles are congruent? Yes it is. If you play around with a few triangles on your own, you'll find that whenever two angles and the included side (the side between them) are congruent, the entire triangles *must* be congruent. Instead of proving this rule, we'll accept it as a postulate.

Angle-Side-Angle Postulate

Postulate 10	If the vertices of two triangles can be paired so that two angles and the included side of one triangle are congruent to the corresponding parts of the second triangle, then the two triangles are congruent.

With the Angle-Side-Angle Postulate, we can prove in our example that $\triangle RPQ \cong \triangle RSO$.

Angle-Angle-Side

That gives us two shortcuts for proving triangles congruent: Side-Angle-Side (from the last lesson) and now Angle-Side-Angle. Let's look at another shortcut. As it turns out, when triangles have two corresponding angles and a side congruent, it doesn't matter where the side is located. Even if it's not between the two angles, the triangles must still be congruent. So our next shortcut is **Angle-Angle-Side** (or A.A.S.). Instead of accepting this as a postulate, we'll prove it informally.

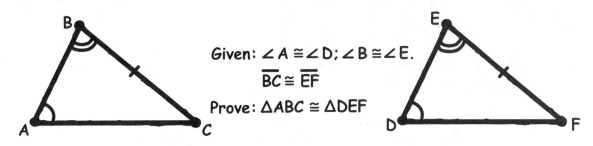

Given: $\angle A \cong \angle D$; $\angle B \cong \angle E$.
$\overline{BC} \cong \overline{EF}$

Prove: $\triangle ABC \cong \triangle DEF$

Since $\angle A \cong \angle D$ and $\angle B \cong \angle E$, it must be that $\angle C \cong \angle F$. (If two angles of one triangle are congruent to two angles of another triangle, then the third pair of angles are congruent.) Also, because $\overline{BC} \cong \overline{EF}$, by the Angle-Side-Angle Postulate, $\triangle ABC \cong \triangle DEF$.

Notice that we used A.S.A. to prove A.A.S., which is okay, because we've already accepted A.S.A. as a postulate. Here is A.A.S., our latest shortcut, written out formally.

Angle-Angle-Side Theorem

Theorem 19	If the vertices of two triangles can be paired so that two angles and the side opposite one of them in one triangle are congruent to the corresponding parts of the second triangle, then the two triangles are congruent.

They Always Work

One important thing to realize about all three of our shortcuts (S.A.S., A.S.A., and A.A.S.) is that they apply to *all* triangles no matter what their shape. The diagrams in our examples had specific shapes, but that was just because it's impossible to draw a diagram for every possible triangle. In the prove statement above (for A.S.A.), the information in the given statement didn't say anything about the length of the sides of the two triangles or the measures of their angles. That means the prove statement holds no matter what kinds of triangles are involved. This is what makes geometry proofs really powerful. With just one proof, you can show logically that something is true for an infinite number of figures of all different kinds.

Practice 34

a. Given congruent triangles in the diagram on the right, fill in the blank: $\overline{BC} \cong$ _____.

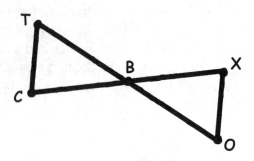

b. From the given statement below, tell the definition, property, postulate, or theorem that justifies the prove statement.

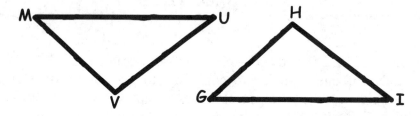

Given: $\angle V \cong \angle H$, $\angle U \cong \angle G$, $\overline{VM} \cong \overline{HI}$; Prove: $\triangle UVM \cong \triangle GHI$.

c. Tell whether the argument below is a valid or invalid deduction.

The ukulele player will perform an encore if the crowd applauds wildly. The crowd didn't applaud wildly. Therefore, the ukulele player must not have performed an encore.

d. If $z = 2x$ and $y = 2x$, find x.

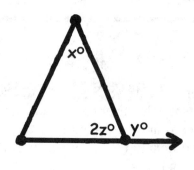

e. Do the proof below.

Given: $\overline{HD} \perp \overline{FH}$, $\overline{FP} \perp \overline{PD}$, $\angle 3 \cong \angle 4$;
Prove: $\triangle HDF \cong \triangle PFD$

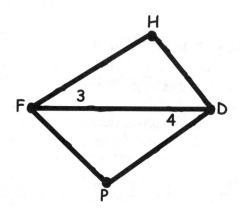

Problem Set 34

Tell whether each sentence below is True or False.

1. Whenever two angles and the included side (the side between them) are congruent, the entire triangles must be congruent.

2. If triangles have two angles and one side congruent but the side is not between the angles, then the triangles are not necessarily congruent.

Complete each sentence below by filling in the blanks.

3. A(n) _____ triangle has two congruent (equal) sides.

4. If two lines form _____ alternate exterior angles with a transversal, then the lines are parallel.

5. If the exterior sides of adjacent angles are perpendicular, the angles are _____.

6. If parallel lines are cut by a transversal, _____ angles on the same side of the transversal are _____.

Given $\triangle KLJ \cong \triangle RLP$ in the diagram on the right, fill in each of the blanks.

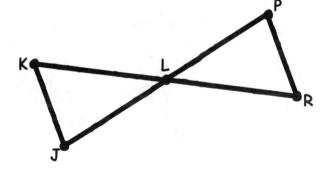

7. $\overline{KJ} \cong$ _____   8. $\angle J \cong$ _____

(a) 9. $\overline{LJ} \cong$ _____   10. $\angle R \cong$ _____

Complete each sentence below with *always*, *sometimes*, or *never*.

11. The measure of an exterior angle of a triangle _____ equals the sum of the measures of the two remote interior angles.

12. A right triangle is _____ equiangular.

From each given statement below, tell the definition, property, postulate, or theorem that justifies each prove statement.

13.   Given: $\overline{QW} \cong \overline{ST}$, $\overline{ST} \cong \overline{UV}$; Prove: $\overline{QW} \cong \overline{UV}$.

14.   Given: $\angle D \cong \angle Q$, $\angle C \cong \angle P$ (below); Prove: $\angle E \cong \angle N$

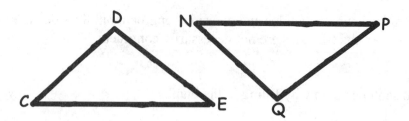

(b) 15.   Given: $\angle D \cong \angle Q$, $\angle C \cong \angle P$, $\overline{DE} \cong \overline{QN}$ (above); Prove: $\triangle CDE \cong \triangle PQN$.

Tell whether the arguments below are valid or invalid deductions.

16.   All of the mall Santas had fake beards. Walter was a mall Santa. Therefore, Walter had a fake beard.

(c) 17.   The telemarketers will stop calling if you put your name on the list. You did not put your name on the list. Therefore, the telemarketers will keep calling.

Answer each question below.

18.   Find x.

19.   If $y = 5x$ and $z = 4x$, find x.

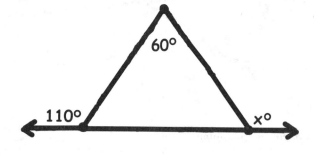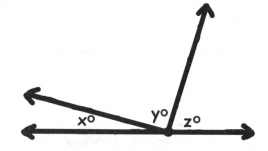

(d) 20.   If $z = 2x$ and $y = 3x$, find x.

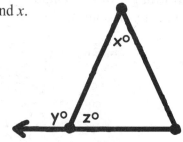

Answer each question below.

21. If Q-E-R, and if $QE = 8x + 3$, $QR = 64$, and $ER = 4x + 1$, then find ER.

22. $\angle A$ and $\angle D$ are supplementary. If $m\angle A = 9y - 19$ and $m\angle D = 3y - 5$, find $m\angle A$.

Do the proof below.

(e) 23. Given: $\overline{IG} \perp \overline{IK}$, $\overline{GM} \perp \overline{KM}$, $\angle 1 \cong \angle 2$;
Prove: $\triangle GKI \cong \triangle KGM$.

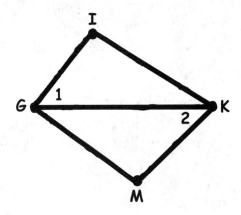

Lesson 35—Hypotenuse-Leg

So far, we've learned three shortcuts for proving that triangles are congruent: Side-Angle-Side, Angle-Side-Angle, and Angle-Angle-Side. That leaves Side-Side-Angle, which you may think is coming up next. A Side-Side-Angle shortcut would allow us to prove two triangles congruent even if the angle wasn't between the two sides.

This may surprise you, but S.S.A. usually doesn't work. In other words, most of the time, if we know that two sides and an angle are congruent, the angle has to be between the sides. So there's no S.S.A. rule that can be used on all kinds of different triangles.

A Special Case

There's one case, however, where a Side-Side-Angle rule (with the angle not between the two sides) will actually work. It's the case of two right triangles. Take a look at the example below.

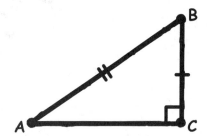 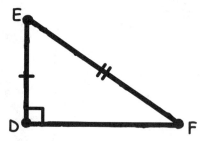

These right triangles have a hypotenuse and one leg
congruent (as well as the 90° angle).

See, we have two right triangles, which means that both have a 90° angle ($\angle C$ for $\triangle ABC$ and $\angle D$ for $\triangle DEF$). We've also shown on the diagram that the hypotenuse and one leg of each triangle are congruent: $\overline{AB} \cong \overline{FE}$ and $\overline{BC} \cong \overline{ED}$. That means the triangles have two sides and one angle congruent. And importantly, the angle is *not* between the two sides. So this is a Side-Side-Angle situation. As we said, normally S.S.A. can't be used. But in this case, since these are right triangles, S.S.A. will work. To satisfy yourself, do a few experiments with these triangles. Try to change one of the other sides or angles (that aren't congruent) and make the triangles not congruent. You won't be able to do it!

Only for Right Triangles

The main point is that we have another shortcut for proving triangles congruent. This one is called **Hypotenuse-Leg**, and it says that if the hypotenuse and one leg of two right triangles are congruent, then the entire triangles are congruent. Of course, since all right triangles have a 90° angle, the triangles will also have one pair of angles congruent. That's why this is a special case

216

of S.S.A. But it's very important to remember that this shortcut only works on right triangles. Instead of proving Hypotenuse-Leg, we'll accept it as a postulate. Here's the postulate written formally.

Hypotenuse-Leg Postulate

Postulate 11	If the vertices of two *right* triangles can be paired so that the hypotenuse and leg of one of them are congruent to the corresponding parts of the second *right* triangle, then the two *right* triangles are congruent.

Practice 35

From each given statement below, tell the definition, property, postulate, or theorem that justifies each prove statement.

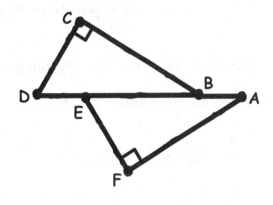

a. Given: $DE + EB = AB + EB$,
$DE + EB = DB$, and $AB + EB = AE$;
Prove: $DB = AE$

b. Given: $BD = AE$ and $CD = FE$;
Prove: $\triangle BCD \cong \triangle AFE$

c. If $\ell_1 \| \ell_2$, find x.

d. If $\ell \| m$ and $\overrightarrow{BC}$ bisects $\angle ABD$, find x.

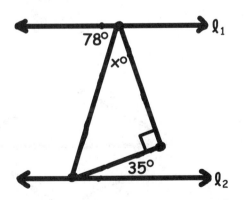

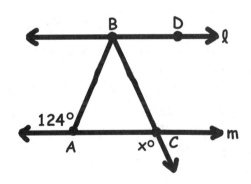

e. Do the proof below.

Given: $\overline{NL} \perp \overline{MO}$, $\overline{PQ} \perp \overline{MO}$,
$MN = PO$, $MQ = OL$;
Prove: $\triangle MLN \cong \triangle OQP$.

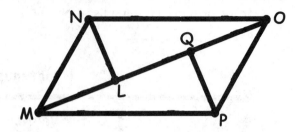

Problem Set 35

Tell whether each sentence below is True or False.

1. You can use a Side-Side-Angle shortcut to prove that all kinds of triangles are congruent.

2. As a special case of S.S.A., when two right triangles have a hypotenuse and one leg congruent (along with their 90° angles), then the entire triangles are congruent.

Complete each sentence below by filling in the blanks.

3. If parallel lines are cut by a transversal, corresponding angles are _____.

4. A _____ is a line that is perpendicular to a line segment and intersects the line segment at its midpoint.

5. A(n) _____ triangle has three congruent (equal) sides.

6. A(n) _____ triangle has all three angles with measure less than 90°.

Given $\triangle RQY \cong \triangle RTY$ in the diagram on the right, fill in each of the blanks.

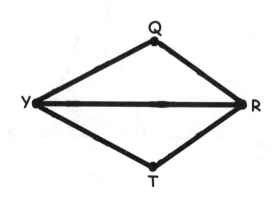

7. $\overline{QR} \cong$ _____

8. $\angle QYR \cong$ _____

9. $\overline{RY} \cong$ _____

From each given statement below, tell the definition, property, postulate, or theorem that justifies each prove statement.

10. Given: $AC = IG$;
    Prove: $AC + CI = IG + CI$

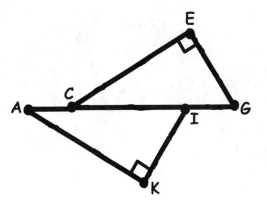

(a) 11. Given: $AC + CI = IG + CI$,
    $AC + CI = AI$, and $IG + CI = CG$;
    Prove: $AI = CG$

(b) 12. Given: ΔAKI and ΔCEG are right triangles, $AI = CG$, and $KI = EG$;
    Prove: $\Delta AKI \cong \Delta CEG$

From the diagram on the right, name a pair of lines that must be parallel if each statement below is true. If there are no lines that have to be parallel, write "none" for your answer.

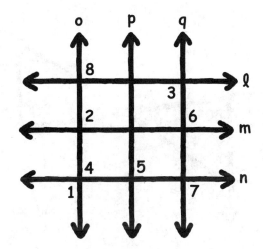

13. $\angle 2 \cong \angle 6$

14. $\angle 1 \cong \angle 8$

Find the measures of the angles of each triangle described below.

15. A right triangle with one angle measuring $45°$.

16. A triangle whose angles have measures of x, $\frac{1}{2}x$, and $\frac{1}{6}x$. What kind of triangle is it?

Answer each question below.

17. Find x and y.

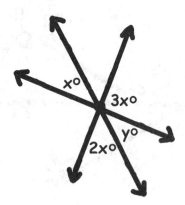

(c) 18. If $\ell_1 \parallel \ell_2$, find x.

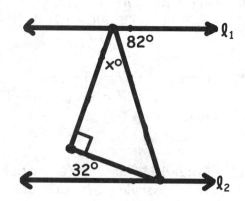

19. Find $x + y$.

(d) 20. If $\ell \parallel m$, and $\overrightarrow{DE}$ bisects $\angle CDF$, find y.

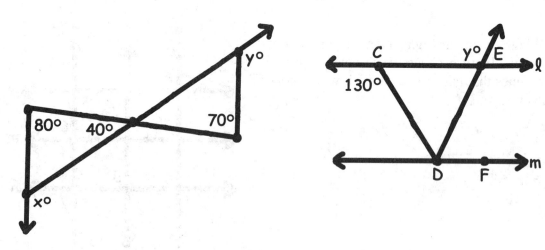

Write an equation to represent each question below; then solve the equation to get your answer.

21. The measure of an angle is $22°$ greater than its complement. Find the measure of the angle.

22. Two angles are supplementary. Twice the measure of the first angle minus 9 is equal to the measure of the second angle. Find the measures of both angles.

Do the proof below.

(e) 23.   Given: $\overline{HL} \perp \overline{GI}$, $\overline{JK} \perp \overline{GI}$,
          $GH = JI$, $GK = LI$;
          Prove: $\triangle GLH \cong \triangle IKJ$

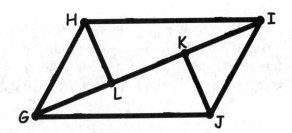

Complete the proof below by filling in the blanks.

24.

Given: $\overline{VU} \parallel \overline{QR}$, $\overline{VT} \parallel \overline{RS}$, QT = US;

Prove: $\triangle QRS \cong \triangle UVT$.

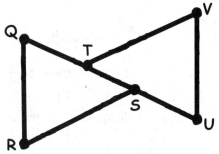

	Statements	Reasons
1.	$\overline{VU} \parallel \overline{QR}$	1. Given
2.	$\angle U \cong \angle Q$	2.
3.	QT + ST = QS and US + ST = UT	3. Betweenness of Points
4.	QT = US	4.
5.	QT + ST = US + ST	5.
6.	QS = UT	6.
7.		7. Given
8.	$\angle VTU \cong \angle QSR$	8.
9.		9.

Lesson 36—Side-Side-Side

We're continuing our work with shortcuts for proving triangles congruent. So far, we've covered Side-Angle-Side, Angle-Side-Angle, Angle-Angle-Side, and Hypotenuse-Leg. Our next (and last) shortcut is **Side-Side-Side** (S.S.S.). According to this shortcut, two triangles are congruent if all three of their corresponding sides are congruent. Here's an actual example.

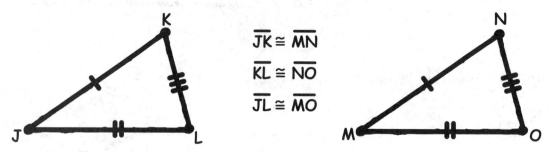

$$\overline{JK} \cong \overline{MN}$$
$$\overline{KL} \cong \overline{NO}$$
$$\overline{JL} \cong \overline{MO}$$

Since three corresponding sides are congruent, $\triangle JKL \cong \triangle MNO$.

Since all three corresponding sides of these two triangles are congruent, we know that $\triangle JKL \cong \triangle MNO$. This rule is true no matter what the shape of the two triangles. Instead of proving this rule, we'll accept it as a postulate.

Side-Side-Side Postulate

Postulate 12	If the vertices of two triangles can be paired so that three sides of one triangle are congruent to the corresponding sides of the second triangle, then the two triangles are congruent.

The Sturdy Eiffel Tower

Because of the Side-Side-Side postulate, when the lengths of a triangle's three sides are known, the triangle can have only one shape. If it could have a different shape, then the triangle wouldn't be congruent to some other triangle with sides of equal length. This fact is used a lot in construction. For example, the Eiffel Tower in Paris was built with triangle-shaped bracing. Triangles are used because they're more rigid than other shapes like rectangles.

Eiffel Tower

A triangular brace can't flatten when a lot of weight is placed on it. To flatten would mean that its shape is changing. The only way the triangular brace can give way is for its sides to bend or break. A rectangle, however, has four-sides. And there's no Side-Side-Side-Side Postulate for rectangles, which means that a rectangular brace can flatten when a lot of weight is placed upon it.

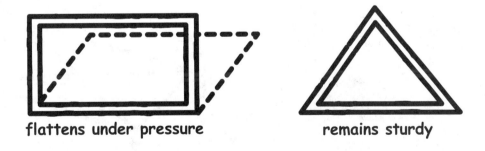

flattens under pressure   remains sturdy

A Quick Summary

Since S.S.S. is our last shortcut for proving congruent triangles, we should probably summarize all the shortcuts for you. There are five shortcuts in all, and four of them will work on triangles of any shape. The fifth one—Hypotenuse-Leg—will only work for right triangles.

Ways of Proving Triangles Congruent

Side-Angle-Side	Two corresponding sides and the angle between them are congruent.
Angle-Side-Angle	Two corresponding angles and the side between them are congruent.
Angle-Angle-Side	Two corresponding angles and a side opposite to one of them are congruent.
Side-Side-Side	Three corresponding sides are congruent.
Hypotenuse-Leg	The hypotenuse and one leg (corresponding) of *right* triangles are congruent.

Practice 36

a. From each given statement below, tell the definition, property, postulate, or theorem that justifies each prove statement.

Given: $\overline{AJ} \cong \overline{JF}$, $\overline{AH} \cong \overline{DF}$, $\overline{HJ} \cong \overline{JD}$;
Prove: $\triangle AJH \cong \triangle JFD$.

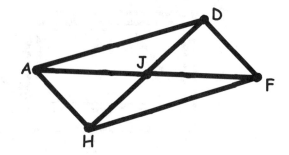

b. $\triangle ABC$ is equilateral and $AB = -x + 3y$, $BC = 4x - y$, and $AC = 11$. Find x and y.

c. Find *y*.

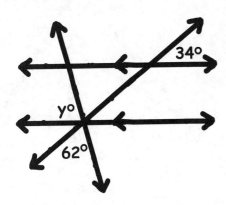

d. Find $m\angle M$ and $m\angle MRE$.

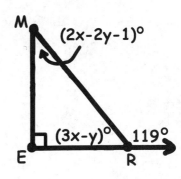

e. Do the proof below.

Given: $\overline{RS} \cong \overline{WU}$, *T* is the midpoint of $\overline{RW}$, $\overline{ST} \cong \overline{TV}$, $\overline{TU} \cong \overline{TV}$

Prove: $\triangle SRT \cong \triangle UWT$

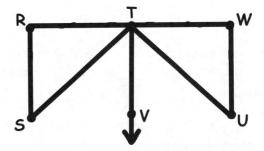

Problem Set 36

Tell whether each sentence below is True or False.

1. According to the Side-Side-Side shortcut, two triangles are congruent if all three of their corresponding sides are congruent.

2. Because of Side-Side-Side, triangles make stronger bracing (in construction) than rectangles.

Complete each sentence below by filling in the blanks.

3. If triangles have two corresponding angles and one corresponding side congruent but the side is not between the angles, then the triangles are _____.

4. The measure of an exterior angle of a triangle is _____ the sum of the measures of the _____ remote interior angles.

5. A scalene triangle has _____ congruent (equal) sides.

6. If parallel lines are cut by a transversal, alternate exterior angles are _____.

Given $\triangle TCG \cong \triangle FJG$ in the diagram on the right, fill in each of the blanks.

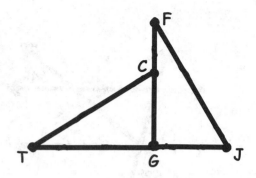

7. $\overline{CG} \cong$ _____

8. $\angle C \cong$ _____

9. $\overline{GF} \cong$ _____

Complete each sentence below with *always*, *sometimes*, or *never*.

10. If two angles are complementary, then the angles are _____ adjacent.

11. If triangles have two corresponding angles and the included side that are congruent, the triangles are _____ congruent.

From each given statement below, tell the definition, property, postulate, or theorem that justifies each prove statement.

12. Given: $\overline{LP} \cong \overline{NP}$, $\angle MLP \cong \angle ONP$,
    $\angle LMP \cong \angle NOP$;
    Prove: $\triangle LMP \cong \triangle NOP$

(a) 13. Given: $\overline{LP} \cong \overline{NP}$, $\overline{LO} \cong \overline{NM}$, $\overline{OP} \cong \overline{MP}$;
    Prove: $\triangle LPO \cong \triangle NPM$

14. Given: $\overline{MN} \parallel \overline{LO}$;
    Prove: $\angle OMN \cong \angle LOM$

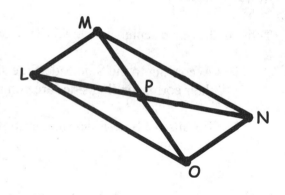

Answer each question below.

15. $\triangle DEF$ is a right triangle and $\angle E$ is a right angle. If $m\angle D = 8x - 1$ and $m\angle F = 5x$, find the measures of the angles of $\triangle DEF$.

(b) 16. $\triangle ABC$ is equilateral and $AB = 4x - y$, $BC = 2x + 3y$, and $AC = 7$. Find x and y.

Answer each question below.

17. Find *x*.

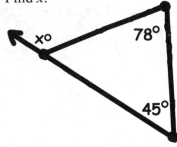

18. Find *y*.

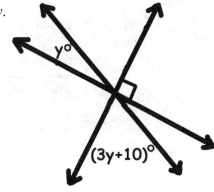

(c) 19. Find *x*.

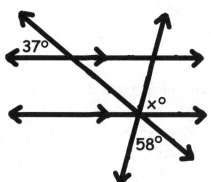

(d) 20. Find $m\angle P$ and $m\angle PQC$.

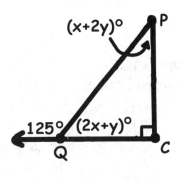

Write the converse of each statement below. Tell whether the converse is True or False.

21. If two angles are supplementary, then the sum of the measures of their angles is 180°.

22. If two angles are a linear pair, then they are supplementary.

Do each proof below.

23. Given: $\overline{AC}$ bisects $\angle BAD$
and $\angle BCD$.
Prove: $\triangle ABC \cong \triangle ADC$

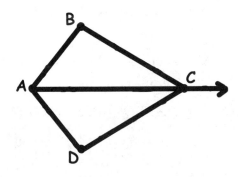

(e) 24. Given: $\overline{LK} \cong \overline{NP}$, *M* is the
midpoint of $\overline{KP}$,
$\overline{LM} \cong \overline{OM}$, $\overline{MN} \cong \overline{OM}$
Prove: $\triangle LKM \cong \triangle NPM$

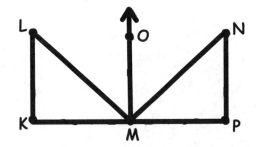

Lesson 37—Overlapping Triangles

We've been proving that triangles are congruent. Sometimes, though, the diagrams in a proof can be a little confusing. Take the proof below, for example.

Given: $\overline{RQ} \cong \overline{SQ}$, $\angle R \cong \angle S$.

Prove: $\triangle RQV \cong \triangle SQU$.

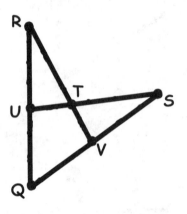

A Common Angle

We're supposed to prove that $\triangle RQV$ and $\triangle SQU$ are congruent. But notice that these are **overlapping triangles**, which just means that they are partially on top of each other. This makes it hard to see which sides and angles go with which triangle. Actually, $\angle Q$ is contained in both triangles. That makes $\angle Q$ a **common angle** of $\triangle RQV$ and $\triangle SQU$.

One way to figure out the angles and side contained in each triangle is to draw the diagram twice like this.

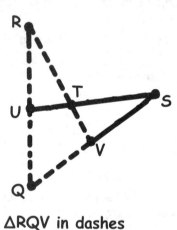

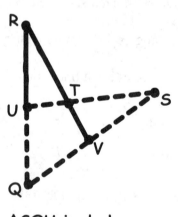

$\triangle RQV$ in dashes

$\triangle SQU$ in dashes

We've used dashed lines to show $\triangle RQV$ on the left and $\triangle SQU$ on the right. Now we can see clearly which sides and angles are contained in each triangle: $\triangle RQV$ has $\overline{RQ}$, $\overline{QV}$, $\overline{RV}$, and $\angle R$, $\angle Q$, $\angle TVQ$; $\triangle SQU$ has $\overline{SQ}$, $\overline{QU}$, $\overline{SU}$, and $\angle S$, $\angle Q$, $\angle TUQ$. Notice that $\angle Q$ is in both.

Next, let's go through the proof informally. We're given that $\overline{RQ} \cong \overline{SQ}$ and $\angle R \cong \angle S$. So we have one pair of congruent corresponding sides and one pair of congruent corresponding angles. Then, since $\angle Q$ is contained in both triangles, and $\angle Q$ is congruent to itself (by the Reflexive Property), we have another pair of corresponding angles that are congruent. Finally, because $\overline{RQ}$ and $\overline{SQ}$ are between the congruent angles, the triangles themselves have to be congruent by the A.S.A. Postulate.

A Common Side

Here's another example.

Given: $\overline{DE} \cong \overline{GF}$, $\overline{DE} \perp \overline{EF}$,
$\overline{GF} \perp \overline{EF}$,

Prove: $\triangle DEF \cong \triangle GFE$.

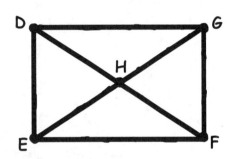

As you can see, $\triangle DEF$ and $\triangle GFE$ are overlapping triangles. This makes it tough to tell which sides and angles go with which triangle. Let's draw the diagram twice, and show one triangle in each with dashed lines, to make things clearer.

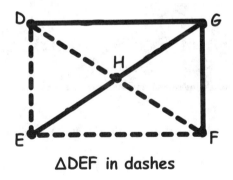

$\triangle DEF$ in dashes

$\triangle GFE$ in dashes

Now we can see clearly that both triangles contain the side $\overline{EF}$. So $\overline{EF}$ is a **common side** of $\triangle DEF$ and $\triangle GFE$.[6] Here are the other sides and angles: $\triangle DEF$ also has $\overline{DE}$, $\overline{DF}$, and $\angle EDF$, $\angle E$, $\angle DFE$; $\triangle GFE$ also has $\overline{GF}$, $\overline{GE}$, and $\angle EGF$, $\angle F$, $\angle GEF$.

From here, we can do the proof. We'll run through it informally. It's given that $\overline{DE} \cong \overline{GF}$, so that's one pair of corresponding sides that are congruent. Then, since $\overline{DE} \perp \overline{EF}$ and

---

[6] We've seen other cases of two triangles having a common side in previous lessons.

$\overline{GF} \perp \overline{EF}$ (also given), we know that $\angle E$ and $\angle F$ are right angles and congruent. That gives us one pair of congruent corresponding angles. Finally, the triangles have $\overline{EF}$ as a common side, so $\overline{EF} \cong \overline{EF}$ (by the Reflexive Property). If you look at the positions of these sides and angles, you'll see that the triangles themselves are congruent by S.A.S.

But the main point of these examples is to show you how to handle diagrams with overlapping triangles. The key is to keep straight in your head which sides and angles go with which triangle.

Practice 37

a. Given $\triangle DYI \cong \triangle IOD$ in the diagram on the right, fill in the blank: $\angle IDO \cong$ _____.

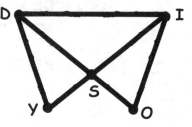

b. What is r in terms of p and q?

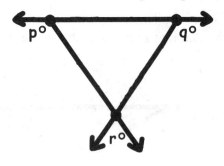

c. Find z.

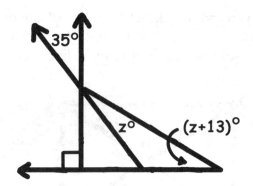

d. Write an equation to represent the question below; then solve the equation to get your answer.

The measure of an angle is 6 less than one third of its complement. Find the measure of the angle.

e. Do the proof below.

Given: $\triangle HJD$ is equilateral, F is the midpoint of $\overline{JD}$;
Prove: $\triangle DFH \cong \triangle JFH$

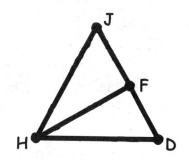

Problem Set 37

Tell whether each sentence below is True or False.

1. Triangles that are partially on top of each other are called overlapping triangles.

2. It's not possible for two triangles to share the same angle or the same side.

Complete each sentence below by filling in the blanks.

3. According to the Side-Angle-Side postulate, when _____ and the included _____ of a pair of triangles are congruent, the entire triangles must be congruent as well.

4. The longest side of a right triangle is called the _____ .

5. If two lines form _____ interior angles on the same side of a transversal, then the lines are parallel.

6. Pairs of vertical angles are _____ .

Given $\triangle LUR \cong \triangle RPL$ in the diagram on the right, fill in each of the blanks.

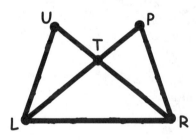

7. $\angle P \cong$ _____

8. $\overline{LR} \cong$ _____

(a) 9. $\angle PLR \cong$ _____

Find the measures of the missing sides of each triangle described below.

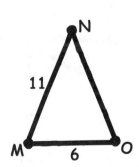

10. $\triangle MNO$ (as shown on the right) is isosceles and $\angle N$ is the vertex angle. Find $m\overline{NO}$.

11. $\triangle BVT$ is an equilateral triangle with $m\overline{BV} = x$. Find $m\overline{VT}$ and $m\overline{BT}$.

From each given statement below, tell the definition, property, postulate, or theorem that justifies each prove statement.

12. Given: $\triangle ABC$, $m\overline{AB} = 9$, and $m\overline{BC} = 9$; Prove: $\triangle ABC$ is isosceles.

13. Given: $\triangle JPW$ (on the right);
Prove: $m\angle J + m\angle W + m\angle JPW = 180$

14. Given: $\triangle JPW$ and $\overrightarrow{WR}$ (on the right);
Prove: $m\angle JPR = m\angle J + m\angle W$

Answer each question below.

15. Find x.

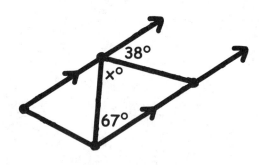

(b) 16. What is z in terms of x and y?

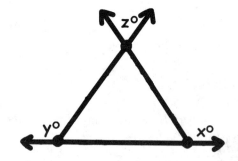

17. Find y.

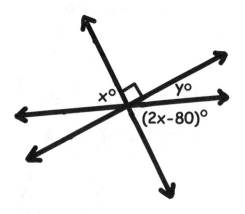

(c) 18. Find y.

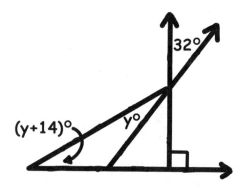

Answer each question below.

19. If $\overrightarrow{EF}$ - $\overrightarrow{EG}$ - $\overrightarrow{EH}$ and if $m\angle FEG = 17x + 1$, $m\angle GEH = 23$, and $m\angle FEH = 22x + 4$, then find $m\angle FEH$.

20. If line n bisects $\overline{AB}$ at point M, and if $AM = 9y + 2$ and $AB = 15y + 28$, then find MB.

Write an equation to represent each question below; then solve the equation to get your answer.

21. Two angles are a linear pair, and one has twice the measure of the other. Find the smaller angle's measure.

(d) 22. The measure of an angle is 6 greater than half the measure of its supplement. Find the measure of the angle.

Do each proof below.

23. Given: $\angle A \cong \angle E$, $\overline{AC} \cong \overline{EC}$.
Prove: $\triangle CAD \cong \triangle CEB$

(e) 24. Given: $\triangle GPK$ is equilateral; L is the midpoint of $\overline{GP}$.
Prove: $\triangle GLK \cong \triangle PLK$

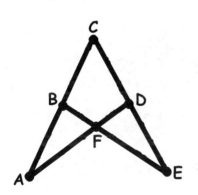

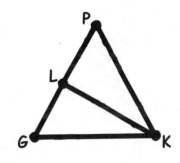

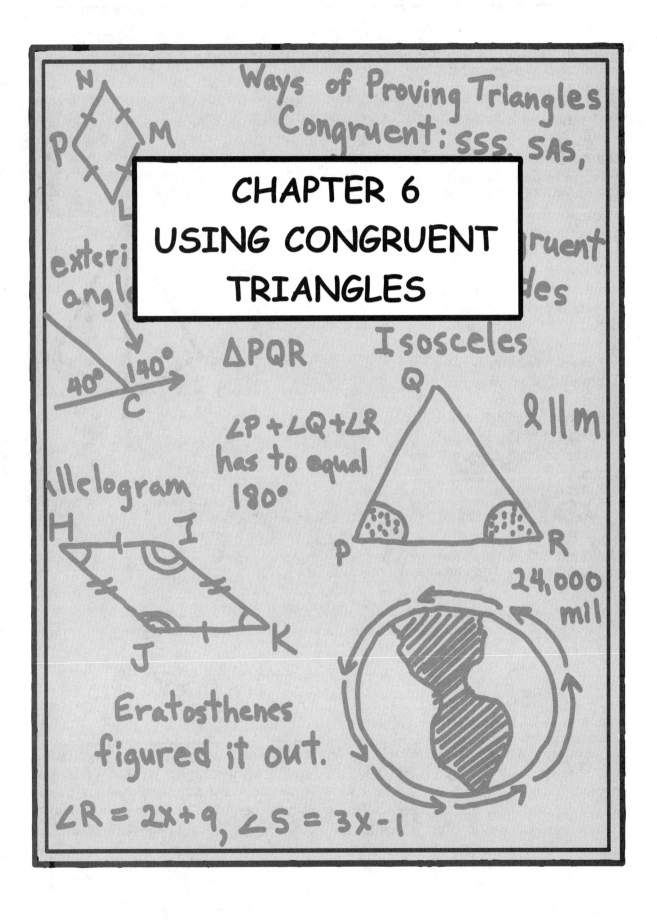

Ways of Proving Triangles Congruent: SSS, SAS,

CHAPTER 6
USING CONGRUENT
TRIANGLES

exteri... angl... ruent ...es

40° 140°
C

ΔPQR

Isosceles

ℓ ‖ m

∠P + ∠Q + ∠R has to equal 180°

...llelogram

H   I

J   K

P   R

24,000 mill

Eratosthenes figured it out.

∠R = 2x + 9, ∠S = 3x - 1

Lesson 38—Proving Corresponding Parts are Congruent

We spent the entire last chapter learning about triangles. In this chapter, we're going to use all of our rules on congruent triangles to prove other important things.

Proving Line Segments Congruent

First, let's learn to prove that two line segments are congruent. That may sound really easy. Why not just measure the line segments, you may be thinking. But remember this is geometry, and mathematicians aren't satisfied with mere measurements. Everything has to be proven deductively. So the process of proving line segments congruent is actually kind of complicated. To see how it works, let's go through an example shown on the right.

Given: $\overline{BP} \cong \overline{BV}$, $\angle PBC \cong \angle CBV$.

Prove: $\overline{PC} \cong \overline{VC}$

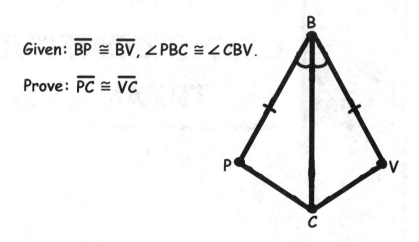

It's not at all obvious how we can show that $\overline{PC}$ is congruent to $\overline{VC}$. After all, we've not been given any information about the lengths of those line segments. We do, however, have enough information to prove that $\triangle BPC$ and $\triangle BVC$ are congruent. Even though it might seem like a waste of time, Here's an informal proof of that.

We're given that $\overline{BP} \cong \overline{BV}$ and $\angle PBC \cong \angle CBV$, so that's one pair of corresponding sides and one pair of corresponding angles that are congruent. Since $\overline{BC}$ is a common side of $\triangle BPC$ and $\triangle BVC$, $\overline{BC}$ is another congruent side for the triangles. Based on the positioning of those sides and angles, $\triangle BPC$ and $\triangle BVC$ are congruent by S.A.S.

How can this help us prove $\overline{PC} \cong \overline{VC}$? Well, think about it. If $\triangle BPC \cong \triangle BVC$, don't *all* of those triangles' sides and angles have to be congruent? Remember in our very first lesson on congruent triangles we said that if *all six* parts—three sides and three angles—of a pair of triangles are congruent, then the triangles themselves are congruent. Since that was a definition, its converse should also be true: If two triangles are congruent, then all six of their parts are congruent.[1] In other words, if $\triangle BPC \cong \triangle BVC$, then not only are $\overline{BP}$ and $\overline{BV}$ congruent, but all the other corresponding sides must be congruent as well. And that means $\overline{PC}$ must be congruent to $\overline{VC}$ (since they're corresponding sides). That's our method for proving line segments congruent.

C.P.C.T.C.

The reason we just gave to justify $\overline{PC} \cong \overline{VC}$ is called **Corresponding Parts of Congruent Triangles are Congruent** (or C.P.C.T.C. for short). It's really just the converse of the definition of congruent triangles, as we said. But since we're giving the converse a different name, we'll state it as a separate definition. Here's the converse written formally.

Converse of Definition of Congruent Triangles (C.P.C.T.C.)

Definition 39	If two triangles are congruent, then their vertices can be paired in a correspondence so that all pairs of corresponding angles are congruent and all pairs of corresponding sides are congruent.

To prove that line segments (or angles) are congruent using C.P.C.T.C., we first find two triangles that the line segments (or angles) are corresponding parts of. Next, we prove that the triangles themselves are congruent. Finally, we can conclude that the original line segments (or angles) are congruent. And the reason stated is C.P.C.T.C. Here are all the steps of the process summarized.

Proving Corresponding Parts of Congruent
Triangles Congruent (C.P.C.T.C.)

1.	Find a pair of triangles that contain the parts you're trying to prove are congruent and make sure the parts are corresponding.
2.	Prove that the two triangles are congruent.
3.	Then, by C.P.C.T.C., conclude that the corresponding parts must also be congruent.

---

[1] Remember, all good definitions are reversible, which means that the original statement of the definition and its converse should both be true.

Proving Angles Congruent

Since C.P.C.T.C. works for any of the parts (line segments or angles) of a pair of congruent triangles, we can also use the rule to prove that angles are congruent. Here's an example.

Given: $\overline{AE} \cong \overline{EG}$, $\overline{CA} \cong \overline{IG}$,

∠C and ∠I are right angles.

Prove: ∠A ≅ ∠G.

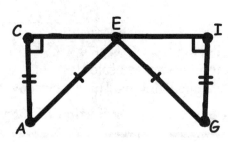

We're looking to prove that ∠*A* is congruent to ∠*G*, even though we don't know the measures of either angle. But notice that ∠*A* and ∠*G* are corresponding parts of two separate triangles: ∠*A* is an angle in Δ*ACE* and ∠*G* is an angle in Δ*GIE*. So if we can prove Δ*ACE* ≅ Δ*GIE*, then ∠*A* and ∠*G* will also have to be congruent by C.P.C.T.C. This time let's do the proof formally.

Statements	Reasons
1. ∠C and ∠I are right angles	1. Given
2. Δ*ACE* and Δ*GIE* are both right triangles.	2. Definition of a right triangle.
3. $\overline{AE} \cong \overline{EG}$, $\overline{CA} \cong \overline{IG}$	3. Given
4. Δ*ACE* ≅ Δ*GIE*	4. Hypotenuse-Leg
5. ∠A ≅ ∠G	5. C.P.C.T.C.

You see, congruent angles are proved with C.P.C.T.C. in very much the same way as congruent line segments.

Practice 38

a.   State which shortcut can be used to prove the pair of triangles on the right congruent. If no method applies, say "none."

b. From each given statement below, tell the definition, property, postulate, or theorem that justifies each prove statement.

Given: $\Delta FSD \cong \Delta DPF$ (below);
Prove: $\angle P \cong \angle S$

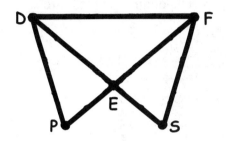

c. Find x, if $\overline{GF}$ bisects $\angle JFH$ and $\overline{GH}$ bisects $\angle FHK$.

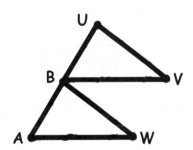

d. Tell whether the argument below is a valid or invalid deduction.

None of the preppies wore pinstriped overalls. Fowler wore pinstriped overalls, so he must not be a preppy.

e. Do the proof below.

Given: $\overline{UV} \parallel \overline{BW}$, $\overline{AW} \parallel \overline{BV}$, $\overline{AW} \cong \overline{BV}$;
Prove: $\Delta ABW \cong \Delta BUV$

Problem Set 38

Tell whether each sentence below is True or False.

1. If two triangles are congruent, then all six of their parts have to be congruent.

2. C.P.C.T.C. is a shortcut for proving that two angles are supplementary.

Complete each sentence below by filling in the blanks.

3. According to the _____ shortcut, two triangles are congruent if all three of their corresponding sides are congruent.

4. If two lines are parallel to a third line, then the lines are _____ to each other.

5. If two angles of a triangle are congruent to two angles of another triangle, then the remaining pair of angles are _____.

6. The sum of the measures of the angles of a triangle is _____.

Complete each sentence below with *always*, *sometimes*, or *never*.

7. If two lines are cut by a transversal, corresponding angles are _____ congruent.

8. If two angles are obtuse, then they are _____ supplementary.

From the diagram on the right, name a pair of lines that must be parallel if each statement below is true. If there are no lines that have to be parallel, write "none" for your answer.

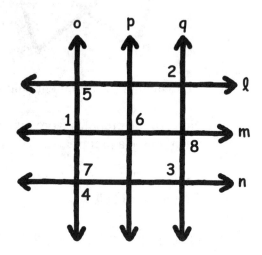

9. ∠4 ≅ ∠3

10. ∠7 and ∠5 are supplementary

State which shortcut can be used to prove each pair of triangles below congruent. If no method applies, say "none."

11. 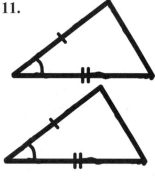　　**12.** 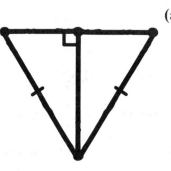　　**(a) 13.**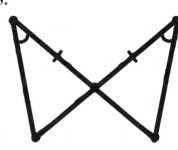

From each given statement below, tell the definition, property, postulate, or theorem that justifies each prove statement.

14. Given: $m\angle AOB = m\angle BOC$ (on the right);
Prove: $\overrightarrow{OB}$ bisects $\angle AOC$.

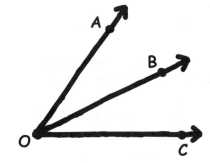

15. Given: $\triangle CDF \cong \triangle GDF$ (below);
Prove: $\overline{CF} \cong \overline{GF}$

(b) 16. Given: $\triangle AQC \cong \triangle CRA$ (below);
Prove: $\angle Q \cong \angle R$

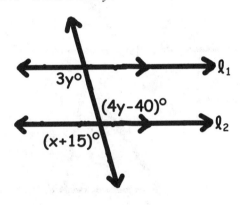

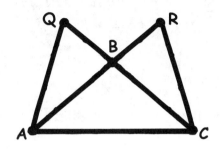

Answer each question below.

17. Find x and y.

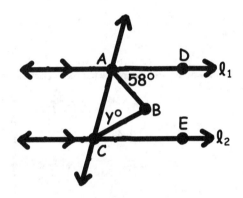

(c) 18. Find y, if $\overline{AB}$ bisects $\angle DAC$ and $\overline{CB}$ bisects $\angle ACE$.

19. Find x.

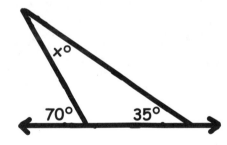

20. Find y.

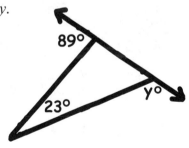

Tell whether the arguments below are valid or invalid deductions.

21. All of the flower girls are wearing ribbons in their hair. If Sarah is wearing ribbons in her hair, she must be a flower girl.

(d) 22. None of the Olympic divers did a belly flop last week. Dwayne did ten belly flops last week, so Dwayne must not be an Olympic diver.

Do the proof below.

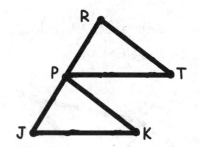

(e) 23. Given: $\overline{RT} \parallel \overline{PK}$, $\overline{JK} \parallel \overline{PT}$, $\overline{JK} \cong \overline{PT}$;
Prove: $\triangle JPK \cong \triangle PRT$.

Complete the proof below by filling in the blanks. This will become our Theorem 20.

24.

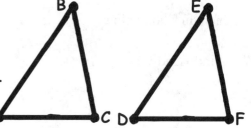

Given: $\triangle ABC \cong \triangle DEF$, $\triangle KLM \cong \triangle DEF$.

Prove: $\triangle ABC \cong \triangle KLM$.

Statements	Reasons
1. $\triangle ABC \cong \triangle DEF$, $\triangle KLM \cong \triangle DEF$	1.
2. $\overline{AB} \cong \overline{DE}$, $\overline{KL} \cong \overline{DE}$	2.
3. $\overline{AB} \cong \overline{KL}$	3.
4.	4. CPCTC
5. $\overline{BC} \cong \overline{LM}$	5.
6. $\overline{AC} \cong \overline{DF}$, $\overline{KM} \cong \overline{DF}$	6.
7.	7. Substitution
8. $\triangle ABC \cong \triangle KLM$	8.

Theorem 20	If two triangles are congruent to the same triangle, then they are congruent to each other.

Lesson 39—Proving Bisectors

In the last lesson, we learned the rule that "Corresponding Parts of Congruent Triangles are Congruent" (C.P.C.T.C.). And you may remember that we can use this rule to prove that line segments or angles inside triangles are congruent.

Proving a Segment Bisector

As it turns out, C.P.C.T.C. can also be used to prove quite a few other things. For example, with C.P.C.T.C. we can prove that a line is a segment bisector. A segment bisector, you'll recall, is just a line (or ray or line segment) that divides some line segment into two congruent segments (divides it in half, in other words). Here's an example of how to prove a segment bisector.

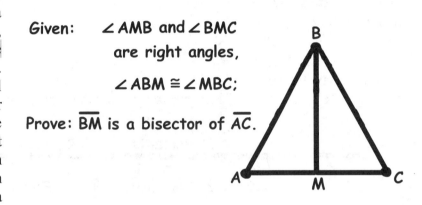

Given: ∠AMB and ∠BMC are right angles,

∠ABM ≅ ∠MBC;

Prove: $\overline{BM}$ is a bisector of $\overline{AC}$.

We're supposed to prove that $\overline{BM}$ bisects the bottom of $\triangle ABC$, which is the same as proving $\overline{AM} \cong \overline{MC}$. First, notice that $\triangle ABC$ actually contains two little triangles: $\triangle ABM$ and $\triangle CBM$. And, importantly, $\overline{AM}$ and $\overline{MC}$ are corresponding sides of those triangles. That means to do this proof we should first show that $\triangle ABM$ and $\triangle CBM$ are congruent. Then, by C.P.C.T.C., $\overline{AM}$ and $\overline{MC}$ will have to be congruent as well. We'll run through the steps informally.

> ∠AMB and ∠BMC are right angles (Given). And those are corresponding angles, so $\triangle ABM$ and $\triangle CBM$ have one pair of congruent angles. Also, ∠ABM ≅ ∠MBC (Given). That's another pair of congruent corresponding angles. $\overline{BM}$ is a common side to the two triangles, which means $\overline{BM}$ represents congruent corresponding sides. Then, $\triangle ABM \cong \triangle CBM$ by A.S.A. Finally, since $\overline{AM}$ and $\overline{MC}$ are corresponding sides of $\triangle ABM$ and $\triangle CBM$, $\overline{AM} \cong \overline{MC}$ by C.P.C.T.C. $\overline{BM}$ must therefore bisect $\overline{AC}$ (Definition of segment bisector).

So our method for proving a segment bisector is to show that the two sides of the segment being bisected are corresponding parts of congruent triangles (C.P.C.T.C.). That means those sides have to be congruent.

Proving an Angle Bisector

We can also prove an *angle* bisector with C.P.C.T.C. And the process is almost exactly the same as proving a segment bisector. Let's quickly run through an example of that (to the right). Here, we're supposed to prove that $\overline{MC}$ divides $\angle TCV$ into two equal halves. That's the same thing as proving $\angle TCM \cong \angle MCV$. This time, we'll show the proof formally.

Given: $\angle 1 \cong \angle 2$, $\overline{TM} \cong \overline{MV}$;

Prove: $\overline{MC}$ is a bisector of $\angle TCV$.

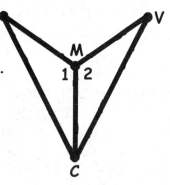

	Statements	Reasons
1.	$\angle 1 \cong \angle 2$, $\overline{TM} \cong \overline{MV}$;	1. Given
2.	$\overline{MC} \cong \overline{MC}$	2. Reflexive Property
3.	$\triangle TMC \cong \triangle VMC$	3. S.A.S.
4.	$\angle TCM \cong \angle MCV$	4. C.P.C.T.C.
5.	$\overline{MC}$ is a bisector of $\angle TCV$.	5. Definition of angle bisector

To prove an angle bisector, then, we show that the two parts of the (supposedly) bisected angle are corresponding parts of congruent triangles (C.P.C.T.C.), which makes the parts congruent.

Practice 39

   a.   State which shortcut can be used to prove the pair of triangles below congruent. If no method applies, say "none."

From each given statement below, tell the definition, property, postulate, or theorem that justifies each prove statement.

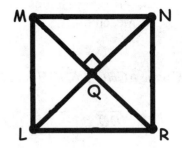

b. Given (on the right): $\triangle LMQ \cong \triangle NMQ$, $\overline{LQ} \cong \overline{NQ}$;
Prove: $\overline{MQ}$ is a segment bisector of $\overline{LN}$.

c. Given (on the right): $\triangle LQR \cong \triangle NQR$;
Prove: $\angle LRQ \cong \angle QRN$.

d. Find b in terms of a.

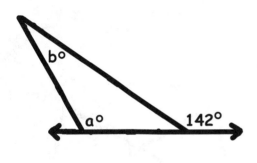

e. Do the proof below.
Given: $\angle B \cong \angle D$, $\overline{AB} \perp \overline{AE}$, $\overline{ED} \perp \overline{AE}$, $\overline{BC} \cong \overline{CD}$;
Prove: C is the midpoint of $\overline{AE}$.

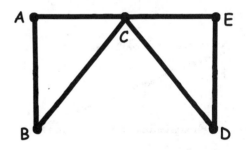

Problem Set 39

Tell whether each sentence below is True or False.

1. Using CPCTC, it's possible to prove that a line (or ray or line segment) bisects a line segment.

2. Using CPCTC, it's possible to prove that a line (or ray or line segment) bisects an angle.

Complete each sentence below by filling in the blanks.

3. If two angles in a linear pair have the same measure, then each is a _____.

4. According to the _____ postulate, when two angles and the included side of a pair of triangles are congruent, the entire triangles must be congruent as well.

5. The two congruent sides of an isosceles triangle are called _____.

6. If two triangles are _____ to the same triangle, then they are _____ to each other.

Given $\triangle CHQ \cong \triangle DQH$ in the diagram below, fill in each of the blanks.

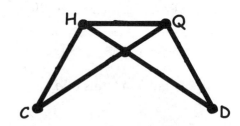

7. $\overline{DQ} \cong$ _____

8. $\angle HQC \cong$ _____

9. $\overline{HQ} \cong$ _____

10. $\angle DQH \cong$ _____

State which shortcut can be used to prove each pair of triangles below congruent. If no method applies, say "none."

11.

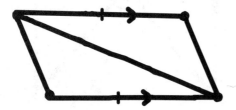

(a) 12.

From each given statement below, tell the definition, property, postulate, or theorem that justifies each prove statement.

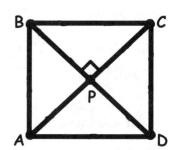

13. Given (on the right): $\triangle ABP \cong \triangle CBP$; Prove: $\overline{AP} \cong \overline{PC}$.

(b) 14. Given: $\overline{AP} \cong \overline{PC}$ (on the right); Prove: $\overline{BP}$ is a segment bisector of $\overline{AC}$.

(c) 15. Given (on the right): $\triangle APD \cong \triangle CPD$; Prove: $\angle ADP \cong \angle CDP$.

16. Given (on the right): $\angle ADP \cong \angle CDP$; Prove: $\overline{PD}$ is an angle bisector of $\angle ADC$.

Answer each question below.

17. Find *y*.

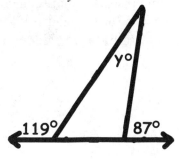

18. Find *x*.

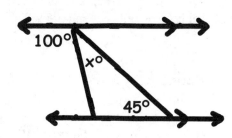

19. Find *x*.

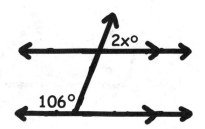

(d) 20. Find *y* in terms of *x*.

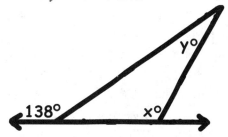

Write an equation to represent each question below; then solve the equation to get your answer.

21. An angle is three times its supplement. Find the measure of the angle.

22. An angle is equal to one-fifth its complement. Find the angle's measure.

Do each proof below.

23. Given: $\overline{AO} \cong \overline{CO}$, $\overline{AB} \cong \overline{CB}$;
  Prove: $\overline{BO}$ bisects $\angle ABC$.

(e) 24. Given: $\angle F \cong \angle J$, $\overline{FD} \perp \overline{DH}$, $\overline{JH} \perp \overline{DH}$,
  $\overline{FG} \cong \overline{JG}$;
  Prove: *G* is the midpoint of $\overline{DH}$.

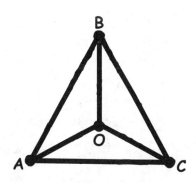

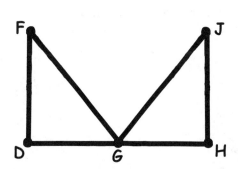

Lesson 40—Proving Lines Parallel or Perpendicular

In the last lesson, we learned how to prove that a particular line bisects a line segment or angle. We used the "Corresponding Parts of Congruent Triangles are Congruent" rule (C.P.C.T.C.). As it turns out, we can also use C.P.C.T.C. to prove that two lines are parallel.

Proving Parallel Lines

Let's go through an example shown on the right. Here we need to prove that $\overline{AB}$ and $\overline{CD}$ are parallel. If we're going to use C.P.C.T.C., $\overline{AB}$ and $\overline{CD}$ should be parts of triangles that can be proven congruent. You can see from the diagram that $\overline{AB}$ is part of $\triangle ABE$ and $\overline{CD}$ is part of $\triangle CDF$. What's more, those triangles look like they might be congruent. Let's try to prove it.

Given: $\overline{BE} \parallel \overline{FD}$, $\overline{BE} \cong \overline{FD}$,
$\overline{CE} \cong \overline{AF}$;

Prove: $\overline{AB} \parallel \overline{CD}$.

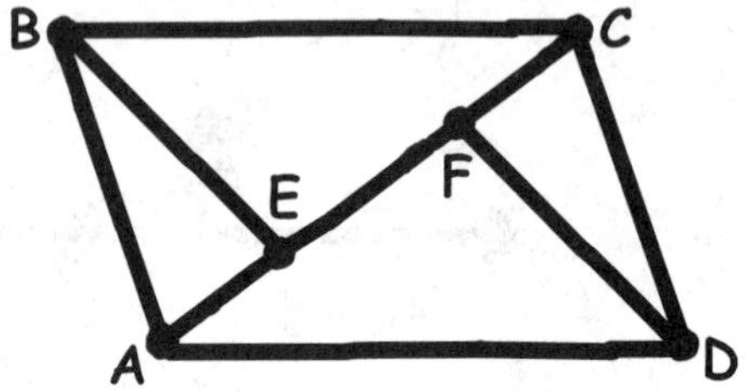

We're given that $\overline{BE} \cong \overline{DF}$. So that's one pair of corresponding sides that are congruent. Since $\overline{BE}$ and $\overline{DF}$ are also parallel (given), we can conclude that $\angle BEA$ and $\angle CFD$ are congruent (they're alternate exterior angles). That's one pair of congruent corresponding angles. We're also given that $\overline{CE} \cong \overline{AF}$. Even though they aren't sides of $\triangle ABE$ and $\triangle CDF$, watch what we can do. Since $AE + EF = AF$ and $CF + EF = CE$ (Betweenness of Points) and $CE = AF$, we can substitute to get $AE + EF = CF + EF$. Now we just subtract EF from both sides: $AE = CF$ (or $\overline{AE} \cong \overline{CF}$). These are corresponding sides of $\triangle ABE$ and $\triangle CDF$ and so now we have three corresponding parts that are congruent. Therefore, $\triangle ABE \cong \triangle CDF$ by S.A.S.

That's not the end of the proof, because we're trying to prove $\overline{AB} \parallel \overline{CD}$. But now that we know $\triangle ABE \cong \triangle CDF$, the process is fairly simple. $\angle BAE$ and $\angle DCF$ are congruent by C.P.C.T.C. And since they're congruent, $\overline{AB}$ has to be parallel to $\overline{CD}$. (If two lines form alternate interior angles with a transversal, then the lines are parallel.) That finishes our proof.

248

Proving Lines Perpendicular

In addition to proving lines parallel, with C.P.C.T.C. we can also prove that lines are perpendicular. Let's quickly run through an example of that.

Given: $\overline{AB} \cong \overline{AC}$,

$\overline{AP}$ is a bisector of $\overline{BC}$;

Prove: $\overline{AP} \perp \overline{BC}$.

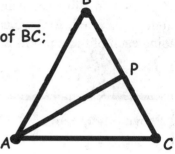

To show that $\overline{AP}$ and $\overline{BC}$ are perpendicular, we need to prove that the lines form right angles. The main steps are to first prove that $\triangle APB$ and $\triangle APC$ are congruent. Once that's done, we can conclude that $\angle APB$ and $\angle APC$ are congruent (by C.P.C.T.C.). But since $\angle APB$ and $\angle APC$ are also a linear pair, they have to be right angles. (If two angles in a linear pair are congruent, then each is a right angle.) Finally, we can conclude that $\overline{AP}$ and $\overline{BC}$ are perpendicular. (Definition of perpendicular lines) Here's the formal proof.

Statements	Reasons
1. $\overline{AB} \cong \overline{AC}$, $\overline{AP}$ is a bisector of $\overline{BC}$.	1. Given
2. $\overline{PB} \cong \overline{PC}$	2. Definition of segment bisector
3. $\overline{AP} \cong \overline{AP}$	3. Reflexive Property
4. $\triangle APB \cong \triangle APC$	4. S.S.S.
5. $\angle APB \cong \angle APC$	5. C.P.C.T.C.
6. $\angle APB$ and $\angle APC$ are a linear pair.	6. Definition of linear pair
7. $\angle APB$ and $\angle APC$ are right angles.	7. If two angles in a linear pair are congruent, then each is a right angle.
8. $\overline{AP} \perp \overline{BC}$	8. Definition of perpendicular lines

A Recap

We've covered a lot of ground in the last three lessons. The main point, though, has been that congruent triangles can be used to prove other things. Specifically, with C.P.C.T.C. we can prove that two line segments or angles are congruent. We can also prove that a segment or an angle is bisected. And we can prove that lines are parallel or perpendicular. The main steps for doing each of these proofs are recapped below.

Things that can be Proven with C.P.C.T.C.

Proving segments or angles ≅	Show triangles are congruent. Prove segments or angles contained in the triangles are congruent by C.P.C.T.C.
Proving segment or angle bisector	Show triangles are congruent. Parts of bisecting segment or angle are contained in triangles. Prove that those parts are congruent by C.P.C.T.C., which proves the bisector.
Proving lines parallel	Show triangles are congruent. Angles contained in triangles are alternate interior, corresponding, or alternate exterior angles of lines. Prove those angles are congruent by C.P.C.T.C. Lines then have to be parallel.
Proving lines perpendicular	Show triangles are congruent. Angles contained in triangles and formed by the lines are a linear pair. Prove those angles are congruent by C.P.C.T.C. Angles then have to be right angles and lines must be perpendicular.

Practice 40

From each given statement below, tell the definition, property, postulate, or theorem that justifies the prove statement.

a. Given: $\triangle ABD \cong \triangle CDB$ (below);
Prove: $\angle ADB \cong \angle CBD$

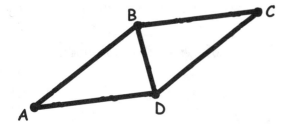

b. Given: $\angle SUR \cong \angle TUR$ (below),
$\angle SUR$ and $\angle TUR$ are a linear pair;
Prove: $\angle SUR$ and $\angle TUR$ are right angles.

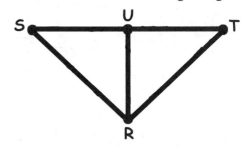

c. Find x and y.

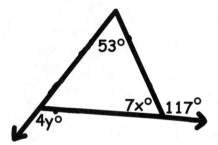

d. Find x and y.

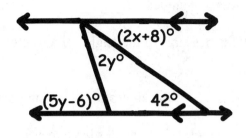

e. Do the proof below.

Given: $\overline{JG} \parallel \overline{KM}$, $\overline{JG} \cong \overline{KM}$, $\overline{HJ} \cong \overline{JK}$;
Prove: $\overline{HG} \parallel \overline{JM}$.

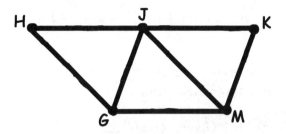

Problem Set 40

Tell whether each sentence below is True or False.

1. C.P.C.T.C. can be used to show that two lines are parallel.

2. C.P.C.T.C. can be used to show that two lines are perpendicular.

Complete each sentence below by filling in the blanks.

3. If two triangles are congruent, then their vertices can be paired in a correspondence so that all pairs of _____ are congruent and all pairs of _____ are congruent.

4. According to the _____ theorem, when two angles and the side opposite one of them in a triangle are congruent to the corresponding parts of a second triangle, then the two triangles are congruent.

5. If parallel lines are cut by a transversal, _____ angles on the same side of the transversal are _____.

6. A(n) _____ triangle has three congruent (equal) sides.

Complete each sentence below with *always*, *sometimes*, or *never*.

7. Adjacent angles are _____ complementary.

8. The measures of the angles of a triangle _____ add to 180°.

Find the measures of the angles of each triangle described below.

9. A triangle whose angles have measures of x, $3x$, and $3x + 5$. What kind of triangle is it?

10. A triangle with angles measuring 110° and 45°. What kind of triangle is it?

From each given statement below, tell the definition, property, postulate, or theorem that justifies each prove statement.

(a) 11. Given: $\triangle DEG \cong \triangle FGE$;
    Prove: $\angle DGE \cong \angle FEG$

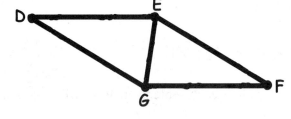

12. Given: $\angle DGE \cong \angle FEG$;
    Prove: $\overline{DG} \parallel \overline{EF}$

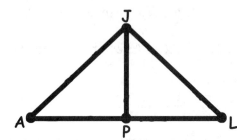

(b) 13. Given: $\angle APJ \cong \angle LPJ$ (on the right),
    $\angle APJ$ and $\angle LPJ$ are a linear pair;
    Prove: $\angle APJ$ and $\angle LPJ$ are right angles.

State which shortcut can be used to prove each pair of triangles below congruent. If no method applies, say "none."

14.

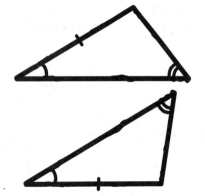

15.

252

Answer each question below.

16. Find x.

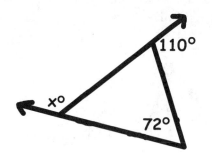

(c) 17. Find x and y.

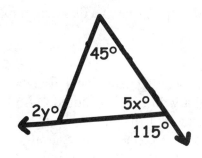

18. Find x and y.

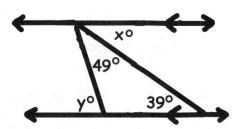

(d) 19. Find x and y.

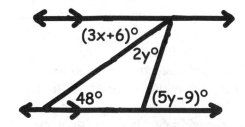

Write the converse of each statement below. Tell whether the converse is True or False.

20. If a triangle is obtuse, then it has one angle that is less than 90°.

21. If all three corresponding angles and all three corresponding sides of two triangles are congruent, then the triangles are congruent.

Do each proof below.

22. Given: $\overline{MT} \cong \overline{LT}$, $\overline{OT}$ is a bisector of $\angle MTL$;
Prove: $\overline{OT} \perp \overline{LM}$

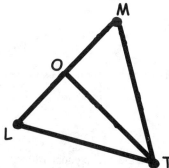

(e) 23. Given: $\overline{BE} \parallel \overline{CD}$, $\overline{BE} \cong \overline{CD}$,
$\overline{AE} \cong \overline{ED}$;
Prove: $\overline{AB} \parallel \overline{CE}$

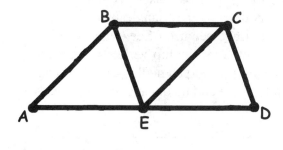

Lesson 41—Altitudes and Medians of Triangles

Quite a few lessons ago we learned about auxiliary lines. These are just extra lines that sometimes need to be drawn in a diagram to make it easier to do a proof.[2]

Altitudes

Well, one line segment that's used a lot as an auxiliary line is an altitude. An **altitude** of a triangle is a line segment that runs from one vertex of the triangle straight to the other side. Importantly, an altitude is always perpendicular to that other side. An example is shown on the right. See, this altitude starts at the top vertex and then makes a right angle with the bottom of the triangle. An altitude is like a measure of a triangle's height, because it measures the distance between the extreme tip of the triangle—the top vertex, in this case—and the opposite side. We also could have drawn an altitude starting from either of the other vertices, though. That means every triangle actually has three altitudes.

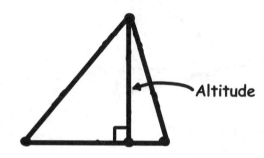

Perpendicular segment from one vertex to other side

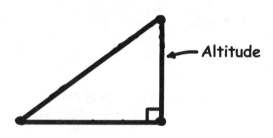

Altitude of a right triangle runs along one leg.

Another important point is that an altitude doesn't always lie inside the triangle. In a right triangle, for instance, an altitude can lie right on top of one of the triangle's legs. Notice the altitude in the triangle on the left is exactly the same as the vertical leg of the right triangle.

In some triangles an altitude can actually lie outside the triangle entirely (on the right). In those cases, we have to extend the bottom of the triangle in order to draw the altitude segment. See, when we draw a segment from the top vertex straight down, so that it's perpendicular to the triangle's bottom, we end up outside the triangle itself.

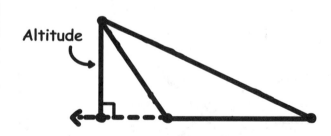

Altitude

---

[2] We used an auxiliary line to prove that the measures of the angles of any triangle add to equal 180° .

To summarize, then, an altitude can be inside a triangle, on top of one side, or even completely outside the triangle. But an altitude always starts at one vertex and makes a right angle with the opposite side. Here's the formal definition.

Definition 40	An *altitude* of a triangle is a segment drawn from any vertex of the triangle, perpendicular to the opposite side, extended outside the triangle if necessary.

Medians

Another line that's frequently drawn with triangles is a median (on the right). A **median** is a line segment that starts at one vertex of a triangle and then goes to the midpoint of the opposite side. Notice that the median is not perpendicular to the bottom of the triangle. That's because it has to go to the midpoint of that bottom side. And since the triangle is tilted to the left, the median ends up with a bit of a slant. In fact, the more tilted the triangle, the greater the slant the median will have. Here are a couple of other examples.

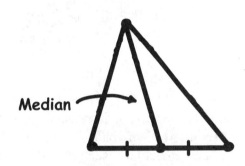

A segment from one vertex to the midpoint of the other side.

 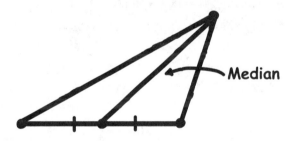

Medians can have different slants.

Since a median can start at any vertex, every triangle actually has three medians. (It's like an altitude in that way.) And a really interesting fact is that the three medians always intersect at a single point, no matter what the shape of the triangle.

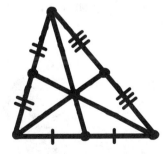

There are three medians, and they all intersect at a single point.

Here's the formal definition of a median.

Definition 41	A *median* of a triangle is a segment drawn from any vertex of the triangle to the midpoint of the opposite side.

Altitude and Median in One

Even though a median doesn't have to be perpendicular to the opposite side, sometimes it actually is. Take the triangle on the right, for example. $\overline{BM}$ is an altitude, since it's perpendicular to $\overline{AC}$. But $\overline{BM}$ is also a median of the triangle, because it intersects $\overline{AC}$ at its midpoint (point M). Way back in Lesson 20 we defined a "perpendicular bisector" as a line that is perpendicular to a line segment and intersects the line segment at its midpoint (Definition 22). That's what $\overline{BM}$ does here, which is why it's actually a perpendicular bisector. In fact, any altitude and median combined into one is a perpendicular bisector.

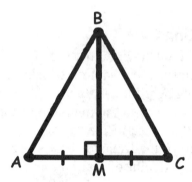

$\overline{BM}$ is both an altitude and a median (perpendicular bisector)

Practice 41

a. If $\overline{TQ} \perp \overline{RS}$, then $\overline{TQ}$ is a(n) _____ of $\triangle RST$.

b. Draw $\triangle RST$ showing all three of its medians.

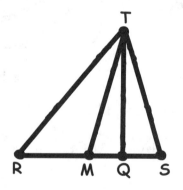

c. Find x, y, and z.

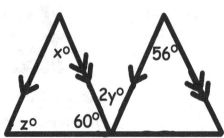

d. Write an equation to represent the question below; then solve the equation to get your answer.

Two angles are supplementary. The measure of one is 20% of the measure of the other. Find the measures of *both* angles.

e. Do the proof below.

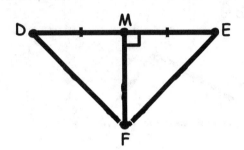

Given: $\overline{MF}$ is the perpendicular bisector of $\overline{DE}$.

Prove: $\overline{FD} \cong \overline{FE}$

Problem Set 41

Tell whether each sentence below is True or False.

1. An altitude of a triangle is a segment drawn from any vertex of the triangle to the midpoint of the opposite side.

2. A median of a triangle is a segment drawn from any vertex of the triangle, perpendicular to the opposite side, extended outside the triangle if necessary.

Complete each sentence below by filling in the blanks.

3. Every triangle has _____ altitudes and _____ medians.

4. A segment that is both an altitude and a median of a triangle is a _____ .

5. According to the _____ shortcut, two triangles are congruent if all three of their corresponding sides are congruent.

6. The measure of an exterior angle of a triangle is equal to the _____ of the measures of the two _____ interior angles.

Answer each question below.

7. If M is the midpoint of $\overline{AC}$, then $\overline{BM}$ is a(n) _____ of $\triangle ABC$.

(a) 8. If $\overline{BP} \perp \overline{AC}$, then $\overline{BP}$ is a(n) _____ of $\triangle ABC$.

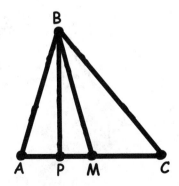

257

(b) 9. Draw $\triangle ABC$ showing all three of its medians.

10. Draw $\triangle ABC$ showing all three of its altitudes.

State which shortcut can be used to prove each pair of triangles below congruent. If no method applies, say "none."

11.

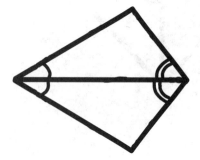

12.

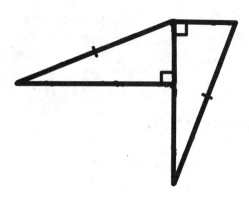

From each given statement below, tell the definition, property, postulate, or theorem that justifies each prove statement.

13. Given: $\triangle GHK$ (on the right);
Prove: $m\angle 1 = m\angle 2 + m\angle 3$.

14. Given: $\triangle GHK$ (on the right);
Prove: $m\angle 1 + m\angle 4 = 180$.

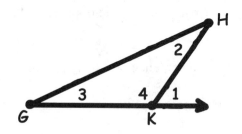

Answer each question below.

15. Find x and y.

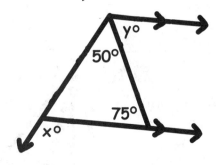

(c) 16. Find x, y, and z.

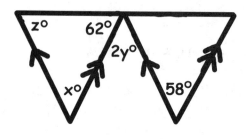

17. Find x and y.

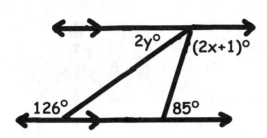

18. Find x and y.

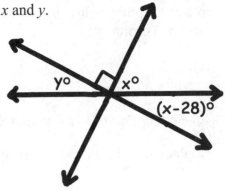

Tell whether the arguments below are valid or invalid deductions.

19. Every one of the ragamuffins has holes in his socks. If Lenny is a ragamuffin, then he must have holes in his socks.

20. None of the mailmen wanted to pet the Doberman. If Henry did not want to pet the Doberman then he must be a mailman.

Write an equation to represent each question below; then solve the equation to get your answer.

21. Two angles are complementary. The measure of one is 50% of the measure of the other. Find the measures of *both* angles.

(d) 22. Two angles are supplementary. The measure of one is 80% of the measure of the other. Find the measures of *both* angles.

Do the proof below. It will become our Theorem 21.

(e) 23. Given: $\overline{BX}$ is the perpendicular bisector of $\overline{AC}$.
Prove: $\overline{AB} \cong \overline{BC}$

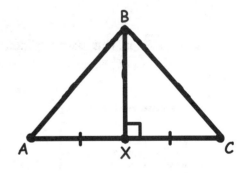

Theorem 21	If a point lies on the perpendicular bisector of a segment, then the point is equidistant from the endpoints of the segment.

259

Complete the proof below by filling in the blanks. It will become our Theorem 22 (and the converse of Theorem 21).

24.

Given: Point B is equidistant from points A and C.

Prove: B is on the perpendicular bisector of $\overline{AC}$.

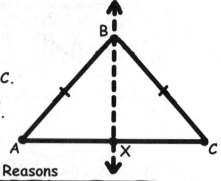

	Statements		Reasons
1.	$\overline{AB} \cong \overline{BC}$	1.	Given
2.	Draw median $\overline{BX}$, $\overline{AX} \cong \overline{XC}$	2.	Definition of median
3.	$\overline{BX} \cong \overline{BX}$	3.	
4.	$\triangle ABX \cong \triangle CBX$	4.	
5.		5.	C.P.C.T.C.
6.	∠BXA and ∠BXC are a linear pair.	6.	
7.	∠BXA and ∠BXC are right angles.	7.	
8.		8.	Definition of perpendicular lines
9.	$\overline{BX}$ is the perpendicular bisector of $\overline{AC}$.	9.	Definition of perpendicular bisector

Theorem 22	If a point is equidistant from the endpoints of a segment, then the point lies on the perpendicular bisector of the segment.

Lesson 42—Base Angles of an Isosceles Triangle

So far in this chapter, we've proven a lot of different things using C.P.C.T.C. Now we're going to use C.P.C.T.C., along with an auxiliary line, to prove a really interesting fact about isosceles triangles (with two congruent sides). It turns out that for all isosceles triangles, the angles opposite each of the congruent sides are always congruent. Let's go through the proof shown on the right This is an isosceles triangle, because $\overline{DE}$ and $\overline{EF}$ are congruent. And, as you can see, the angles opposite those two sides are

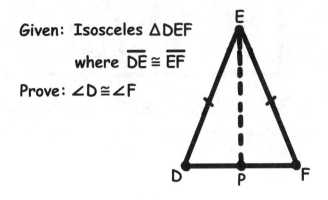

Given: Isosceles $\triangle DEF$

where $\overline{DE} \cong \overline{EF}$

Prove: $\angle D \cong \angle F$

$\angle D$ and $\angle F$. Also notice $\overline{EP}$. We've drawn that auxiliary segment so that it bisects $\angle DEF$. With C.P.C.T.C. and a few other steps, we can prove $\angle D \cong \angle F$. Here's the complete proof. [3]

Statements	Reasons
1. Isosceles $\triangle DEF$, $\overline{DE} \cong \overline{EF}$	1. Given
2. Draw $\overline{EP}$ so that it bisects $\angle DEF$.	2. An angle has exactly one bisector.
3. $\angle DEP \cong \angle FEP$	3. Definition of angle bisector
4. $\overline{EP} \cong \overline{EP}$	4. Reflexive Property
5. $\triangle DEP \cong \triangle FEP$	5. S.A.S.
6. $\angle D \cong \angle F$	6. C.P.C.T.C.

This is a very important theorem because it holds true for *any* isosceles triangle, no matter what its shape. The angles opposite the congruent sides have to be congruent. Here's the theorem stated officially.

---

[3] The reason for step 2 means that there's just one bisector of $\angle DEF$. In other words, $\overline{EP}$ is "determined."

Base Angles Theorem

Theorem 23	If two sides of a triangle are congruent (equal), then the angles opposite those sides are congruent (equal).

The theorem is called the **Base Angles Theorem**, because the third side of an isosceles triangle (not the two congruent sides) is the triangle's "base" ($\overline{DF}$ in our diagram), and the opposite angles are always next to the base. Some books call it the "Isosceles Triangle Theorem."

A Corollary

There's a corollary that goes with the Base Angles Theorem. It says that any equilateral triangle (with three congruent sides) is also an equiangular triangle. In other words, if the three sides of a triangle are congruent, then the three angles have to be congruent as well. Here's the informal proof, followed by an official statement of the corollary.

$\triangle ABC$ is equilateral (Given) which means $\overline{BC} \cong \overline{AB}$ and $\overline{AC} \cong \overline{AB}$ (Definition of equilateral triangle). It follows that $\angle A \cong \angle C$ and $\angle B \cong \angle C$ (Base Angle Theorem). By the transitive property, $\angle A \cong \angle B$. Therefore, $\triangle ABC$ is equiangular (Definition of equiangular triangle).

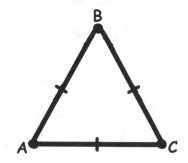

Corollary 23.1	If a triangle is equilateral, then it is also equiangular.

Practice 42

a. Find the measures of the angles of a triangle whose angles are in the ratio of $3: 4: 11$. What kind of triangle is it?

b. Find the measures of the angles of an isosceles triangle with a vertex angle of $40°$.

c. Find *y*.

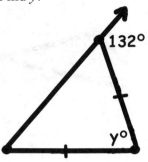

132°

y°

d. Find *y*.

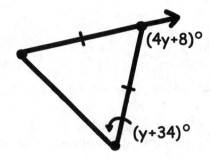

(4y+8)°

(y+34)°

e. Do the proof below.

Given: $\overline{PN} \cong \overline{PK}$; $\angle 3 \cong \angle 4$; $\overline{NM} \cong \overline{LK}$
Prove: $\overline{MO} \cong \overline{LQ}$

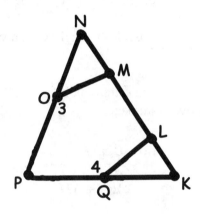

Problem Set 42

Tell whether each sentence below is True or False.

1. The Base Angles Theorem only pertains to isosceles triangles.

2. According to the Base Angles Theorem, if two sides of a triangle are congruent (equal), then the angles opposite those sides are congruent (equal).

Complete each sentence below by filling in the blanks.

3. If a triangle is equilateral, then it is also _____.

4. A(n) _____ of a triangle is a segment drawn from any vertex of the triangle to the midpoint of the opposite side.

5. A(n) _____ of a triangle is a segment drawn from any vertex of the triangle, perpendicular to the opposite side, extended outside the triangle if necessary.

6. If the exterior sides of adjacent angles are perpendicular, the angles are _____.

Given congruent triangles in the diagram below, fill in each of the blanks.

7. $\angle CEB \cong$ _____

8. $\overline{BC} \cong$ _____

9. $\triangle ECF \cong$ _____

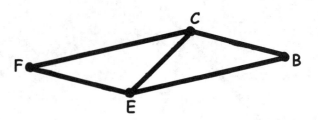

Find the measures of the angles of each triangle described below.

(a) 10. A triangle whose angles have measures in the ratio 1: 5: 6. What kind of triangle is it?

(b) 11. An isosceles triangle with a vertex angle of 50°.

From each given statement below, tell the definition, property, postulate, or theorem that justifies each prove statement.

12. Given: $\overline{AB} \cong \overline{TP}$, $\angle A \cong \angle T$,
    $\quad\quad \angle ABP \cong \angle TPU$ (on the right);
    Prove: $\triangle APB \cong \triangle TUP$

13. Given: $\triangle APB \cong \triangle TUP$ (on the right);
    Prove: $\overline{BP} \cong \overline{PU}$

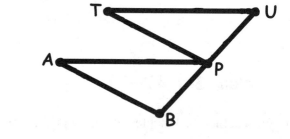

14. Given: $\angle SRK \cong \angle YRK$ (on the right);
    Prove: $\angle SRK$ and $\angle YRK$ are right
    $\quad\quad$ angles.

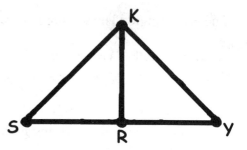

State which shortcut can be used to prove each pair of triangles below congruent. If no method applies, say "none."

15.

16.

Answer each question below.

17. Find *x*.

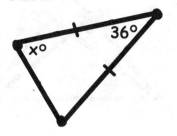

(c) 18. Find *x*.

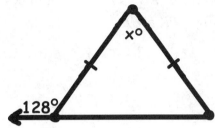

19. Find *x* and *y*.

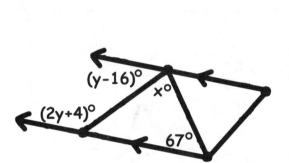

(d) 20. Find *y*.

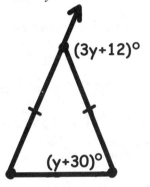

Draw a Venn diagram to represent each set of conditional statements below.

21. All of the true bodybuilders have a plan for improving their ankle strength. Seth is a true bodybuilder. Therefore, Seth has a plan for improving his ankle strength.

22. Every TV anchorwoman owns a back-up can of hair spray. Linda does not own a back-up can of hair spray. Therefore, Linda is not a TV anchorwoman.

Do each proof below. Number 23 will become our Theorem 24.

23. Given: $\triangle PEG$, $\overline{EP} \cong \overline{EG}$, altitudes $\overline{PK}$ and $\overline{GH}$
     Prove: $\overline{PK} \cong \overline{GH}$

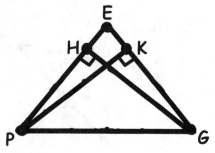

Theorem 24	The altitudes extending to the legs of an isosceles triangle are congruent (equal).

(e) 24. Given: $\overline{DF} \cong \overline{AF}$; $\angle 1 \cong \angle 2$; $\overline{DC} \cong \overline{AB}$
     Prove: $\overline{CE} \cong \overline{BG}$

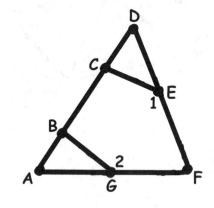

Lesson 43—Proving That a Triangle is Isosceles

In the last lesson, we proved the Base Angles Theorem, which says that for any isosceles triangle the angles opposite the two congruent sides are also congruent. In this lesson, we're going to prove the converse of the Base Angles Theorem, which turns out to be true as well.

Converse of the Base Angles Theorem

Here is the Base Angles Theorem again: If two sides of a triangle are congruent (equal), then the angles opposite those sides are congruent (equal). And here's its converse. If two angles of a triangle are congruent (equal), then the sides opposite those angles are congruent (equal). Notice all we did was reverse the premise and the conclusion. Now we'll show the formal proof of the converse. It uses C.P.C.T.C. (like the Base Angles Theorem) and also involves an auxiliary line.

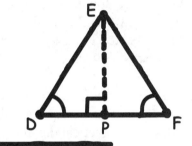

Given: ∠D ≅ ∠F   Prove: $\overline{DE} \cong \overline{EF}$

Statements	Reasons
1. ∠D ≅ ∠F	1. Given
2. Draw $\overline{EP}$ as an altitude of △DEF.	2. Through a given point not on a line, there exists exactly one perpendicular to the given line.
3. $\overline{EP} \perp \overline{DF}$	3. Definition of altitude
4. ∠DPE and ∠EPF are right angles.	4. Perpendicular lines form right angles.
5. ∠DPE ≅ ∠EPF	5. All right angles are congruent.
6. $\overline{EP} \cong \overline{EP}$	6. Reflexive
7. △DEP ≅ △FEP	7. A. A. S.
8. $\overline{DE} \cong \overline{EF}$	8. C.P.C.T.C.

Here is the new theorem stated officially.

Converse of Base Angles Theorem

Theorem 25	If two angles of a triangle are congruent (equal), then the sides opposite those angles are congruent (equal).

Proving a Triangle is Isosceles

The really important thing about the Converse of Base Angles Theorem is that it can be used to prove that a triangle is isosceles. If we know that two of a triangle's angles are congruent, then we know automatically (by this theorem) that the two sides opposite those angles have to be congruent as well. But when two sides of a triangle are congruent, that makes the triangle isosceles. The key thing to remember is that it's always the sides *opposite* the congruent angles that must be congruent.

So now we have the Base Angles Theorem and its converse which tells us that when two sides of a triangle are congruent, the two opposite angles are congruent and vice versa. These are two of the most practical theorems in geometry.

Another Corollary

You remember that the Base Angles Theorem had a corollary (Corollary 23.1): If a triangle is equilateral, it is also equiangular. Or, to use plain language, when a triangle's three sides are congruent, its three angles also must be congruent.

Well, it turns out that this corollary has a converse that's also true: If a triangle is equiangular, then it also must be equilateral. In other words, when all three angles of a triangle are congruent, all three of its sides must be congruent as well. Here is the official version of this corollary, along with an informal proof.

ΔDEF is equiangular (Given) which means $\angle D \cong \angle F$ and $\angle E \cong \angle F$. It follows that $\overline{EF} \cong \overline{DE}$ and $\overline{DF} \cong \overline{DE}$ (Converse of Base Angle Theorem). By the transitive property, $\overline{EF} \cong \overline{DF}$. Therefore, ΔDEF is equilateral (Definition of equilateral triangle).

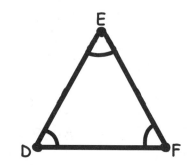

Corollary 25.1	If a triangle is equiangular, then it is also equilateral.

So now whenever you see an equilateral triangle, you'll automatically know that its angles also have to be congruent. And whenever you see an equiangular triangle, you'll automatically know that its sides have to be congruent.

Practice 43

a. From the given statement below, tell the definition, property, postulate, or theorem that justifies the prove statement.

Given: $\triangle AEI$ and $\angle I \cong \angle E$ (on the right);
Prove: $\overline{AE} \cong \overline{AI}$.

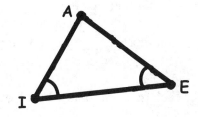

b. Find z.

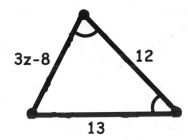

c. Find x.

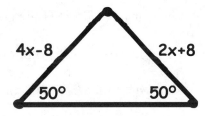

d. Write an equation to represent the question below; then solve the equation to get your answer.

Two angles are a linear pair. One third the measure of the first plus 12 is equal to the measure of the second. What are the measures of *both* angles?

e. Do the proof below.

Given: $\overline{AB} \cong \overline{BC}$; $\overline{JC}$ and $\overline{KA}$ are medians of $\triangle ABC$
Prove: $\overline{JC} \cong \overline{KA}$

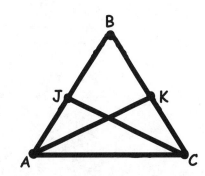

269

Problem Set 43

Tell whether each sentence below is True or False.

1. According to the Converse Base Angles Theorem, if two angles of a triangle are congruent (equal), then the opposite sides are congruent (equal).

2. The Converse Base Angles Theorem can be used to prove that a triangle is isosceles.

Complete each sentence below by filling in the blanks.

3. The measure of each angle of an equiangular triangle is _____.

4. A segment that's both an altitude and a median of a triangle is a _____.

5. According to the _____ shortcut, if the hypotenuse and one leg of one _____ triangle are congruent to the hypotenuse and the corresponding leg of another _____ triangle, then the triangles are congruent.

Answer each question below based on the accompanying diagram.

6. Which angle of $\triangle PED$ is opposite to $\overline{PE}$?

7. Which angles of $\triangle PED$ are congruent?

8. Which side of $\triangle ETD$ is opposite $\angle T$?

9. Which sides of $\triangle ETD$ are congruent?

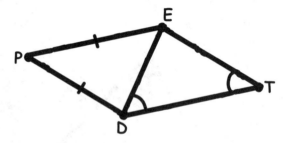

Draw each line segment described below.

10. Draw the altitude of $\triangle ABC$ from vertex B.

11. Draw the median of $\triangle ABC$ from vertex A.

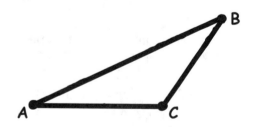

From each given statement below, tell the definition, property, postulate, or theorem that justifies each prove statement.

12. Given: $\triangle KLR$ (below) and $\overline{KL} \cong \overline{LR}$; **(a) 13.** Given: $\triangle FGH$ (below), $\angle F \cong \angle H$
Prove: $\angle K \cong \angle R$ Prove: $\overline{FG} \cong \overline{GH}$

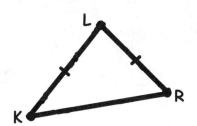
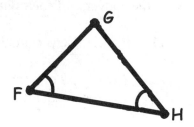

14. Given: $\triangle ABC \cong \triangle DEF$ and $\triangle ABC \cong \triangle RST$; Prove: $\triangle DEF \cong \triangle RST$.

Answer each question below.

15. Find x and y. **16.** Find x and y.

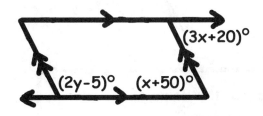
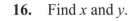
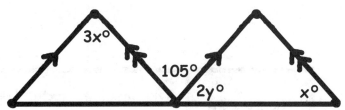

(b) 17. Find y. **(c) 18.** Find x.

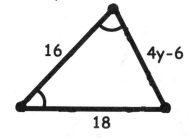
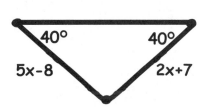

Write an equation to represent each question below; then solve the equation to get your answer.

19. An angle has four times the measure of its complement. What is the measure of the angle?

(d) 20. Two angles are a linear pair. Half the measure of the first plus 9 is equal to the measure of the second. What is the measure of *both* angles?

Write the converse of each statement below. Tell whether the converse is True or False.

21. If a triangle is equilateral, then it is also equiangular.

22. If two sides of a triangle are congruent (equal), then the angles opposite those sides are congruent (equal).

Do each proof below. Number 23 will become our Theorem 26.

(e) 23. Given: $\overline{WT} \cong \overline{TU}$; $\overline{RU}$ and $\overline{SW}$ are medians of $\triangle WTU$
Prove: $\overline{RU} \cong \overline{SW}$

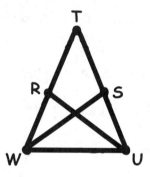

Theorem 26	The medians extending to the legs of an isosceles triangle are congruent (equal).

24. Given: $\overline{PS} \cong \overline{QS}$, $\overline{DP} \cong \overline{LQ}$
Prove: $\triangle DSL$ is isosceles

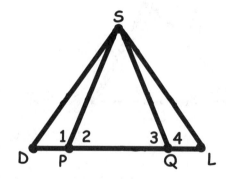

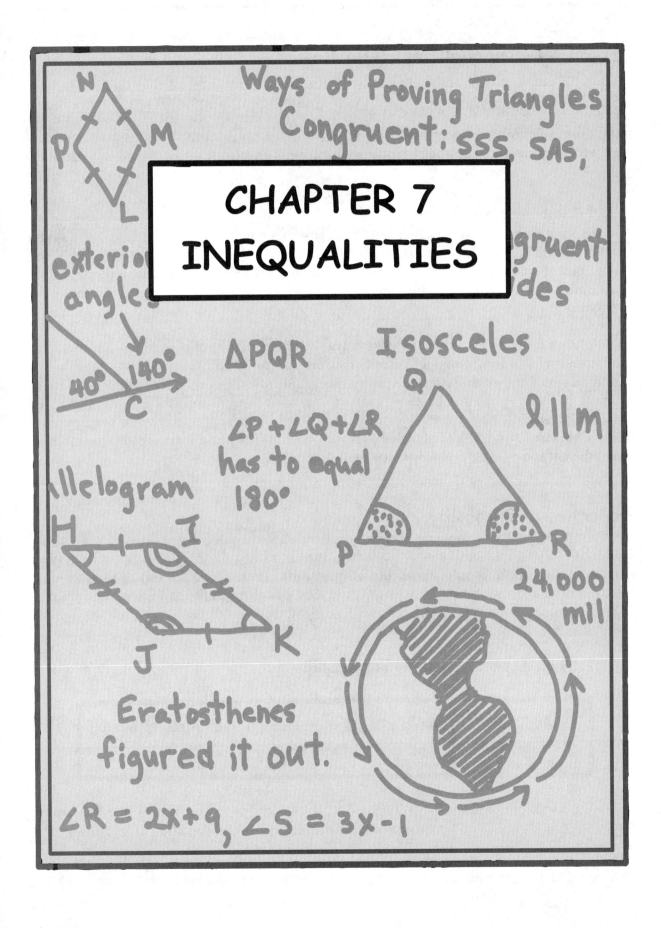

Ways of Proving Triangles Congruent: SSS, SAS,

CHAPTER 7
INEQUALITIES

exterior
angles

40° 140°
C

ΔPQR

Isosceles

∠P + ∠Q + ∠R
has to equal
180°

gruent
des

ℓ ‖ m

24,000
mil

allelogram

Eratosthenes
figured it out.

∠R = 2x + 9, ∠S = 3x - 1

Lesson 44—Inequalities: The Basics

So far in this book, we've seen lots of examples where two segments or two angles are congruent to each other. But it's also possible for a pair of segments or angles to be of different sizes. That requires not a congruence or an equality but an **inequality**. For this entire chapter, then, we'll concentrate on geometry problems involving inequalities.

A Lot Like Algebra

The first point to make is that inequalities in geometry work in much the same way as they do in algebra. The symbol $>$ means "greater than" and the symbol $<$ means "less than." The pointed end of the symbol is always in the direction of the smaller quantity, and the open end is in the direction of the larger quantity. So $7 > 3$ means "7 is greater than 3," and $2 < 9$ means "2 is less than 9."

Another related point is that, just like equations, inequalities can contain x's. For example, $x \geq 7$ means that "some quantity x is greater than or equal to 7." Unlike an equation, though, lots of different numbers will solve this inequality. The number 8 will work. But so will 9, 10, 11 and numbers all the way up. In fact, every number 7 or above (even fractions and decimals) will make the left side of $x \geq 7$ greater than the right side and solve the inequality. The number 7 is a solution because $\geq$ is a "greater than or equal to" symbol (not just a plain greater than). Seven makes the left and right sides equal, which is allowed.

Properties of Inequality

You know that when solving algebra equations and when doing geometry proofs we use properties, such as the addition and subtraction properties and the multiplication and division properties. Well, there are also **properties of inequality**. These properties can be used to solve inequalities with x's, such as $-4x + 3 < 19$. And they can also be applied to line segments and angles in geometry, which is mostly how we'll be using them in this book. Let's run through the major properties of inequality.

The first is the **addition property of inequality**.[1]

Addition Property	If a > b, then a + c > b + c. Also, if a > b and c > d, then a + c > b + d.

Here are a couple of examples. If $5 > 3$, then $5 + 2 > 3 + 2$ or $7 > 5$. And if $5 > 3$ and $9 > 4$, then $5 + 9 > 3 + 4$ or $14 > 7$. You have to be careful when adding two inequalities, as with $a > b$ and

---

[1] Even though all these properties are stated using "greater than" symbols, they also apply with "less than" symbols.

$c > d$. For this to work, the inequality symbols have to be in the same direction in both of the inequalities. If we had $a > b$ and $c < d$ (c is "less than" d), then $a + b > c + d$ is not necessarily true. Watch out for that.

The **subtraction property of inequality** works pretty much the same way as the addition property.

Subtraction Property	If a > b, then a - c > b - c.

Here's a simple example of this one: If $16 > 12$, then $16 - 7 > 12 - 7$ or $9 > 5$.

Next comes the **multiplication property of inequality**.

Multiplication Property	If a > b and c > 0, then ac > bc.

Notice that c has to be greater than 0 for ac to be greater than bc. This is one of the big differences between properties of equality and properties of inequality. Let's take an actual example: $5 > 3$. When we multiply both sides of $5 > 3$ by a positive number, everything works fine.

$$5(2) > 3(2)$$

$$10 > 6$$

But watch what happens when we multiply both sides of $5 > 3$ by a negative number.

$$5(-2) > 3(-2)$$

$$-10 < -6$$

Since -10 is less than -6, the inequality symbol has to be flipped after multiplying by -2. That wasn't just a fluke. As it turns out, we always have to flip the inequality symbol when multiplying both sides of an inequality by a negative number. That's the reason for $c > 0$ in the box above. If c were less than 0 (a negative number), then ac would not be greater than bc after multiplying both sides. Instead ac would be less than bc.

Now let's move on to the **division property of inequality**. Here's the formal rule.

Division Property	If a > b and c > 0, then $\frac{a}{c} > \frac{b}{c}$.

And notice that c has to be greater than 0 again. The reason is that division works the same way as multiplication when inequalities are involved. If we divide both sides by a positive number, nothing has to be done to the inequality symbol. Let's take the example $20 > 8$.

$$\frac{20}{4} > \frac{8}{4}$$

$$5 > 2$$

But if we divide both sides by a negative number, the inequality symbol has to be flipped.

$$\frac{20}{-4} > \frac{8}{-4}$$

$$-5 < -2$$

There's also a **substitution property of inequality** and a **transitive property of inequality**.

Substitution Property	If a = b, then a can be substituted for b in any inequality.

Transitive Property	If a > b and b > c, then a > c.

Here's a simple example of the substitution property. Let's say we have the little equation $x = 11$ and the inequality $11 > 9$. Since x and 11 are equal, we can substitute to get $x > 9$, which also has to be true. To show the transitive property, we'll use an all number example: if $8 > 3$ and $3 > 1$, then $8 > 1$.

There's also a property of inequality based on the Betweenness of Points and Betweenness of Rays concepts. This property is usually called the **Whole Greater than Its Part Property**. Here it is stated formally.

Whole Greater than Its Part	If c = a + b and b > 0, then c > a.

It's easier to show this property using angles and line segments rather than numbers. Look at the diagram on the right. From Betweenness of Rays, we know that $m\angle AOB + m\angle BOC = m\angle AOC$. It's also true that $m\angle BOC > 0$, since every angle has a measure that's greater than 0. By the "Whole is Greater than Its Part" property, then, we can conclude that $m\angle AOC > m\angle BOC$. In other words, the entire angle AOC is greater than one of its parts, BOC.

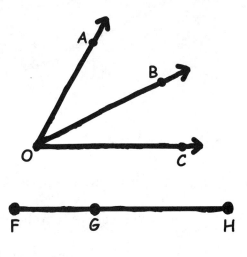

Take a line segment shown on the right for example. From Betweenness of Points, $FG + GH = FH$. And since $GH > 0$, $FH > FG$. Once again, the entire segment (FH) is greater than one of its parts (FG).

Practice 44

a. Based on the appearance of the diagram, complete the inequality below:

$m\angle JKL$ _____ $m\angle MKP$

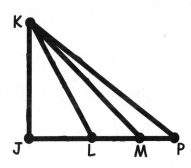

b. Solve the inequality $-8x - 9 \geq -33$.

c. From the given statement below, tell the definition, property, postulate, or theorem that justifies the prove statement.

Given: $\overrightarrow{QU} - \overrightarrow{QF} - \overrightarrow{QX}$;
Prove: $m\angle UQX > m\angle UQF$.

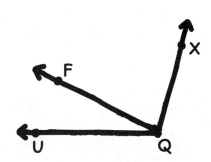

277

d. Find z.

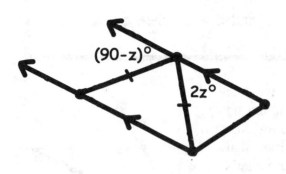

e. Do the proof below.

Given: $\overline{FB} \cong \overline{FE}$, $\overline{FB} \perp \overline{AC}$, $\overline{FE} \perp \overline{AD}$,

F is the midpoint of $\overline{CD}$.

Prove: $\triangle CAD$ is isosceles.

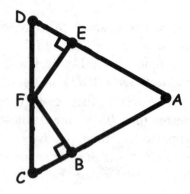

Problem Set 44

Tell whether each sentence below is True or False.

1. Inequalities are used exclusively in algebra.

2. There are properties of inequality, and these are very similar to the properties of equality used in geometry proofs.

Complete each sentence below by filling in the blanks. If the sentence is a property, name the property.

3. When _____ or _____ both sides of an inequality by a negative number, the inequality symbol must be flipped.

4. If $a > b$ and $b > c$, then _____.

5. If $a > b$, then $a + c > b + c$. Also, if $a > b$ and $c > d$, then _____.

6. According to the _____, if two sides of a triangle are congruent (equal), then the angles opposite those sides are congruent (equal).

Based on the appearance of the diagram, complete each of the inequalities below.

7. OC ____ AD

(a) 8. $m\angle DBA$ ____ $m\angle OBC$

9. $m\angle CBA$ ____ $m\angle OBA$

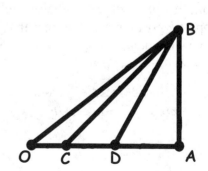

Solve each inequality below. Show your steps and give a reason for each one.

10. $5x + 14 \leq 29$ **(b) 11.** $-6x - 7 \geq -19$

Find the measures of the angles of each triangle described below.

12. A triangle whose angles have measures in the ratio 2: 3: 4. What kind of triangle is it?

13. An isosceles triangle with a vertex angle of $110°$.

From each given statement below, tell the definition, property, postulate, or theorem that justifies each prove statement.

14. Given: $TY > AG$; Prove: $TY - HJ > AG - HJ$

15. Given: $m\angle L < m\angle N$; Prove: $\dfrac{1}{2}m\angle L < \dfrac{1}{2}m\angle N$

(c) 16. Given: $\overrightarrow{PD}$ - $\overrightarrow{PE}$ - $\overrightarrow{PF}$; Prove: $m\angle DPF > m\angle EPF$

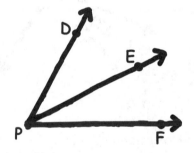

State which shortcut can be used to prove each pair of triangles below congruent. If no method applies, say "none."

17.

18.

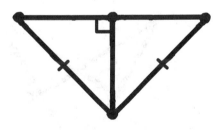

Answer each question below.

19. Find x.

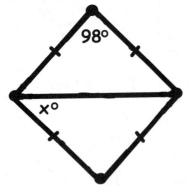

(d) 20. Find y.

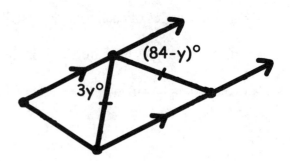

21. Find x and y.

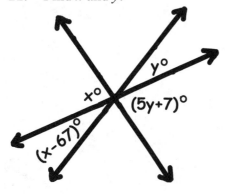

22. Find x and y.

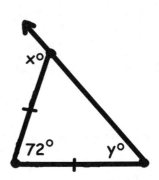

Do each proof below.

23. Given: $\angle D \cong \angle H$, $\overline{DF} \cong \overline{HF}$
Prove: $\overline{DG} \cong \overline{HE}$

(e) 24. Given: $\overline{YS} \cong \overline{YU}$, $\overline{YS} \perp \overline{RT}$, $\overline{YU} \perp \overline{RV}$,
Y is the midpoint of $\overline{TV}$.
Prove: $\triangle TRV$ is isosceles.

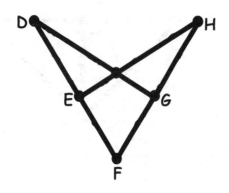

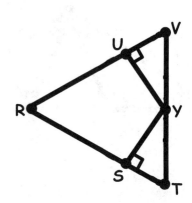

Lesson 45—Triangle Side Inequality

In this chapter we're learning how inequalities are used in geometry. Probably the most basic geometry inequality involves the three sides of a triangle. We'll explain the concept with a real world example. Let's say we're in Texas and we want to travel from Dallas to Houston.

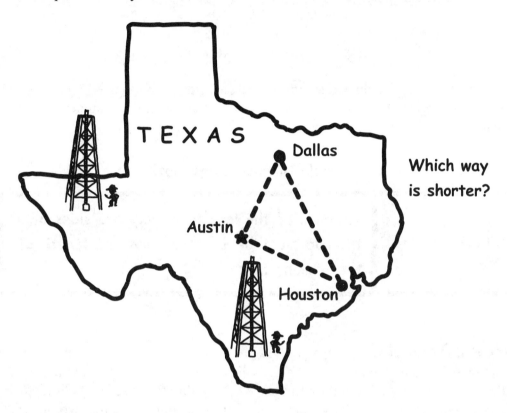

Which way is shorter?

Is it shorter to go straight from Dallas to Houston or to go through Austin first? The answer is obvious. Since the shortest distance between two points is a straight line, we want to go from Dallas straight to Houston—no detours through Austin. But notice that the lines between the cities make a triangle. What we're really saying is that the lengths of the two left sides of the triangle added together ($BA + AC$) are greater than the length of the side on the right (BC).

Going through $\overline{BA}$ and $\overline{AC}$ is longer.

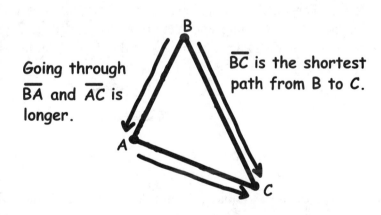

$\overline{BC}$ is the shortest path from B to C.

This relationship can be shown as an inequality.

$$BA + AC > BC$$

Instead of going from B to C, if we wanted to go between any other two vertices of the triangle, the same principle would apply.

$$AC + CB > AB$$

$$AB + BC > AC$$

The general rule is that the combined lengths of any two sides of a triangle will always be greater than the length of the remaining side, no matter what the shape of the triangle. We'll accept this as a postulate. Here it is stated officially.

Triangle Inequality Postulate

Postulate 13	The sum of the lengths of any two sides of a triangle must be greater than the length of the remaining side.

Can It be a Triangle?

Sometimes the side lengths of a triangle will be given without showing a diagram of the triangle itself. For instance, we might be given $\triangle ABC$ with side lengths $AB = 3$, $BC = 4$, and $AC = 9$. But look closely at those numbers. Can you find anything wrong with them? Remember, the sum of the lengths of any two sides of a triangle must always be greater than the length of the remaining side. Yet $AB + BC$ is equal to 7, and that's less than AC, which equals 9. If we tried to construct a triangle with these side lengths it just wouldn't work.

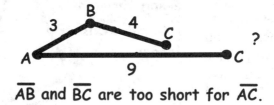

$\overline{AB}$ and $\overline{BC}$ are too short for $\overline{AC}$.

See, there's no way that $\overline{AB}$ and $\overline{BC}$ can extend the entire length of $\overline{AC}$, even if both sides were perfectly horizontal (and then we wouldn't have a triangle anymore). So side lengths of $AB = 3$, $BC = 4$, and $AC = 9$ just don't make sense for a triangle.

Using the Triangle Inequality Postulate, it's easy to tell whether three side lengths can make a triangle. If any two sides always add up to be greater than the remaining side, then you've got a triangle. If the sum of any two sides falls short (and is less than the length of the remaining side), then those three sides can't possibly make a triangle.

Practice 45

a. Tell whether the following numbers can represent the side lengths of a triangle: 5, 6, 3.

b. From the given statement below, tell the definition, property, postulate, or theorem that justifies the prove statement.

Given: $\triangle RST$; Prove: $RS + RT > ST$

c. Find x, if $\overline{ML}$ bisects $\angle NLK$ and $\overline{MK}$ bisects $\angle PKL$ (shown on the right).

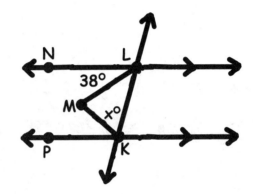

d. Write an equation to represent the question below; then solve the equation to get your answer.

Two angles are supplementary. One angle measures 20 more than 3 times the other. Find the measures of *both* angles.

e. Do the proof below.

Given: $\overline{TR} \cong \overline{TS}$, $\overline{AT}$ bisects $\angle RTS$
(Shown on the right)
Prove: $\triangle RUA \cong \triangle SUA$

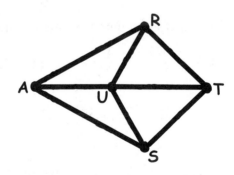

Problem Set 45

Tell whether each sentence below is True or False.

1. The sum of the lengths of any two sides of a triangle must be greater than the length of the remaining side.

2. The Triangle Inequality Postulate pertains to the angles of any triangle.

Complete each sentence below by filling in the blanks. If the sentence is a property, name the property.

3. According to the _____, if two angles of a triangle are congruent (equal), then the opposite sides are congruent (equal).

4. If _____ and $c > 0$, then $\dfrac{a}{c} > \dfrac{b}{c}$.

5. A(n) _____ of a triangle is a segment drawn from any vertex of the triangle to the midpoint of the opposite side.

Based on the appearance of the diagram below, complete each of the following inequalities.

6. WS ____ WQ

7. $m\angle QSW$ ____ $m\angle WQS$

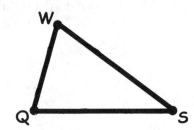

Solve each inequality below. Show your steps and give a reason for each one.

8. $12y - 2 < 82$

9. $-\dfrac{1}{2}x + 5 > 13$

Tell whether each set of numbers below can represent the side lengths of a triangle.

(a) 10. 9, 7, 4

11. 6, 3, 10

12. 5, 8, 11

From each given statement below, tell the definition, property, postulate, or theorem that justifies each prove statement.

13. Given: *A-D-S* (shown on the right);
    Prove: $AD < AS$

(b) 14. Given: $\triangle JHK$; Prove: $JH + JK > HK$

State which shortcut can be used to prove each pair of triangles below congruent. If no method applies, say "none."

15.

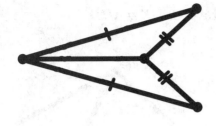

16.

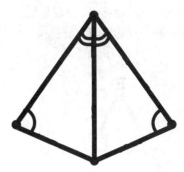

Answer each question below.

17. Find *x*.

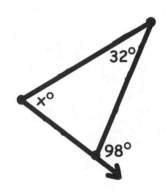

(c) 18. Find *y*, if $\overline{BC}$ bisects $\angle ABD$ and $\overline{AC}$ bisects $\angle BAE$.

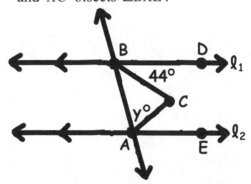

19. Find *x* and *y*.

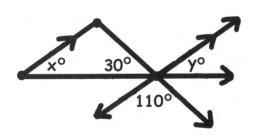

20. Find *x* and *y*.

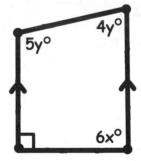

Write an equation to represent each question below; then solve the equation to get your answer.

21. An angle's measure is 22° greater than its complement. Find the measure of the angle.

(d) 22. Two angles are supplementary. One angle measures 10 more than 9 times the other. Find the measure of *both* angles.

Do each proof below.

23. Given: $\overline{EA} \cong \overline{EU}$, $\overline{AU} \parallel \overline{IO}$
Prove: $\triangle IEO$ is isosceles.

(e) 24. Given: $\overline{FG} \cong \overline{FH}$, $\overline{FK}$ bisects $\angle HFG$.
Prove: $\triangle GJK \cong \triangle HJK$

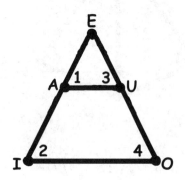

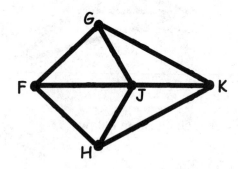

Lesson 46—Exterior Angle Inequality Theorem

Continuing our work with inequalities, let's look at another triangle.

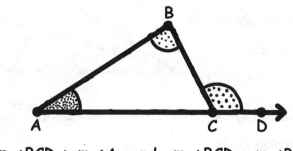

$$m\angle BCD > m\angle A \quad \text{and} \quad m\angle BCD > m\angle B$$

One side of $\triangle ABC$ is extended so that an exterior angle ($\angle BCD$) is showing. And according to the Exterior Angle of a Triangle Theorem (which we hope you remember), any exterior angle must have a measure that equals the sum of the measures of the two remote interior angles. That means $m\angle BCD = m\angle A + m\angle B$.

But there's another relationship between an exterior angle and the remote interior angles of a triangle. This one involves inequalities. As it turns out, an exterior angle of a triangle is always greater than either one of the remote interior angles taken individually. In symbols, $m\angle BCD > m\angle A$ and $m\angle BCD > m\angle B$. These inequalities hold true for any triangle, no matter what its shape, and for any of the triangle's exterior angles. Here's another example.

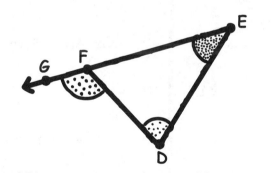

$$m\angle GFD > m\angle D \quad \text{and} \quad m\angle GFD > m\angle E$$

This new rule is called the **Exterior Angle Inequality Theorem.** Despite the fancy name, it's really just common sense. After all, if an exterior angle equals the sum of both remote interior angles, then it has to be greater than either one individually.

Obvious or not, the Exterior Angle Inequality Theorem is still a separate rule that has to be proven deductively. So here's a formal proof (which is surprisingly long and complicated).

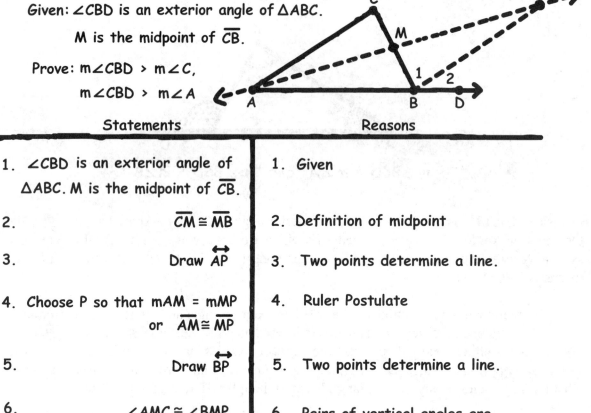

Given: ∠CBD is an exterior angle of △ABC.

M is the midpoint of $\overline{CB}$.

Prove: m∠CBD > m∠C,

m∠CBD > m∠A

Statements	Reasons
1. ∠CBD is an exterior angle of △ABC. M is the midpoint of $\overline{CB}$.	1. Given
2. $\overline{CM} \cong \overline{MB}$	2. Definition of midpoint
3. Draw $\overleftrightarrow{AP}$	3. Two points determine a line.
4. Choose P so that mAM = mMP or $\overline{AM} \cong \overline{MP}$	4. Ruler Postulate
5. Draw $\overleftrightarrow{BP}$	5. Two points determine a line.
6. ∠AMC ≅ ∠BMP	6. Pairs of vertical angles are congruent.
7. △ACM ≅ △PBM	7. Side-Angle-Side
8. ∠C ≅ ∠1	8. C.P.C.T.C.
9. m∠CBD = m∠1 + m∠2	9. Betweenness of Rays
10. m∠CBD > m∠1	10. Whole Greater than Its Parts
11. m∠CBD > m∠C	11. Substitution

This proves the first part of the theorem. We won't show the second part (that $m\angle CBD > m\angle A$), because the steps are almost exactly the same. Here is an official statement of the Exterior Angle Inequality Theorem.

Exterior Angle Inequality Theorem

Theorem 27	The measure of an exterior angle of a triangle is greater than the measure of either of the remote interior angles.

Practice 46

a. From the given statement below, tell the definition, property, postulate, or theorem that justifies the prove statement.

Given: $\triangle RST$ (on the right);
Prove: $m\angle PTS > m\angle R$

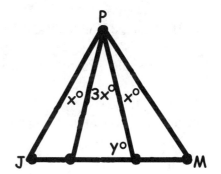

b. Find x and y.

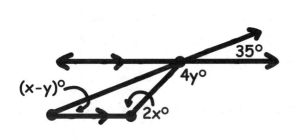

c. Find y in the equilateral triangle JPM.

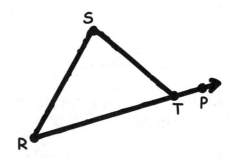

d. $\triangle STU$ is isosceles and the length of base $\overline{SU}$ is 9. Find the other two side lengths if $ST = 4y - 3$ and $TU = 2y + 5$.

e. Do the proof below.

Given: $\overline{GH} \parallel \overline{IJ}$, $\overline{GH} \cong \overline{IJ}$, $\overline{GK} \cong \overline{IL}$
Prove: $\angle IHK \cong \angle GJL$

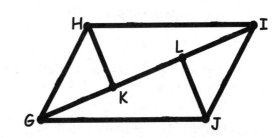

Problem Set 46

Tell whether each sentence below is True or False.

1. According to the Exterior Angle of a Triangle Theorem, any exterior angle has a measure that equals the sum of the measures of the two remote interior angles.

2. According to the Exterior Angle Inequality Theorem, an exterior angle of a triangle is always greater than either one of the remote interior angles.

Complete each sentence below by filling in the blanks.

3. The _____ of the lengths of any two sides of a triangle must be _____ the length of the remaining side.

4. If two angles of a triangle are congruent to two angles of another triangle, then the remaining pair of angles are _____.

5. A triangle is equilateral iff it is _____.

Complete each sentence below with *always*, *sometimes*, or *never*.

6. If a triangle is isosceles, then its base angles are _____ congruent.

7. If a triangle is isosceles, then it is _____ scalene.

Tell whether each set of numbers below can represent the side lengths of a triangle.

8. 2, 13, 8

9. 3, 4, 5

Find the measures of the angles of each triangle described below.

10. An isosceles obtuse triangle with one angle measuring $20°$.

11. An isosceles right triangle.

From each given statement below, tell the definition, property, postulate, or theorem that justifies each prove statement.

12. Given: M is the midpoint of $\overline{TC}$.; Prove: $\overline{TM} \cong \overline{MC}$

13. Given: $\triangle UKS$ and $\angle U \cong \angle S$;
Prove: $\overline{UK} \cong \overline{KS}$

(a) 14. Given: $\triangle DWV$ (on the right);
Prove: $m\angle CDW > m\angle V$

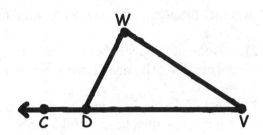

Answer each question below.

15. Find x and y.

(b) 16. Find x and y.

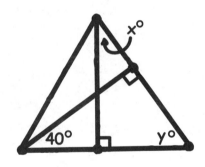

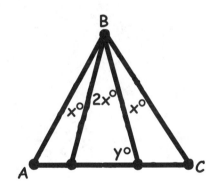

17. Find x and y.

(c) 18. Find x and y in equilateral triangle ABC.

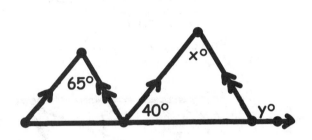

Answer each question below.

19. Find $m\angle H$ and $m\angle K$ if the two angles are complementary and if $m\angle H = 2x - 1$ and $m\angle K = 8x - 9$.

(d) 20. $\triangle DEF$ is isosceles and the length of base $\overline{DF}$ is 8. Find the other two side lengths if $DE = 5z - 4$ and $EF = 3z + 2$.

Tell whether the arguments below are valid or invalid deductions.

21. None of the apple bobbers was at risk of drowning. Naomi was not at risk of drowning. Therefore, she must have been an apple bobber.

22. All of the certified magicians can pull a rabbit out of a hat. If Antonio is a certified magician, then he can pull a rabbit out of a hat.

Do each proof below.

23. Given: $\overline{BA} \perp \overline{PA}$, $\overline{CD} \perp \overline{PD}$,
Point P is the midpoint of $\overline{BC}$.
Prove: $\overline{BC}$ bisects $\overline{AD}$.

(e) 24. Given: $\overline{AB} \parallel \overline{CD}$, $\overline{AB} \cong \overline{CD}$,
$\overline{AE} \cong \overline{CF}$
Prove: $\angle CBE \cong \angle ADF$

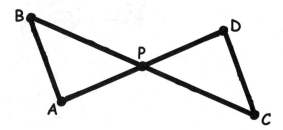

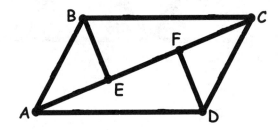

Lesson 47—Indirect Proofs

We've done quite a lot of proofs in this book, and every one has been different. In one way, though, all of our proofs have been the same. Specifically, they've all started with a given statement and then proceeded directly—one deduction after another—to the prove statement. This kind of proof is called a "direct proof," as you may remember.

A Process of Elimination

But some things can't easily be proven with a direct proof. For such cases, there is another method of proof that can be used. It's called an indirect proof. To show you how an indirect proof works, let's go through an example. The direct way to do the proof on the right would be to start with the given statement, $\overline{AB} \cong \overline{DB}$, then prove something from that, followed by something else, and so on, until we finally

Given: $\overline{AB} \cong \overline{DB}$

Prove: $\overline{AB}$ is not $\cong$ to $\overline{BC}$.

get to the statement "$\overline{AB}$ is not congruent to $\overline{BC}$." But in an **indirect proof**, instead of heading directly to "$\overline{AB}$ is not congruent to $\overline{BC}$," we first eliminate all of the other possibilities. There are only two possibilities here. Either $\overline{AB}$ is *not* congruent to $\overline{BC}$ or $\overline{AB}$ *is* congruent to $\overline{BC}$. So what we do is eliminate the possibility that $\overline{AB} \cong \overline{BC}$. After that, the only logical conclusion is that $\overline{AB}$ is *not* congruent to $\overline{BC}$. To start off the proof, then, we write down the given statement and list the two possibilities.

Statements	Reasons
1. $\overline{AB} \cong \overline{DB}$	1. Given
2. Either $\overline{AB}$ is not $\cong$ to $\overline{BC}$ or $\overline{AB} \cong \overline{BC}$.	2. A statement is either true or false.

Notice the reason for the second step: "A statement is either true or false." That just means that there are no other possibilities besides these.

The next step of the proof may seem strange. We're going to assume $\overline{AB} \cong \overline{BC}$, which is the opposite (or "negation") of what we're trying to prove. (It's also the second of our two possibilities.) Since there's no reason for this assumption, we just include it as part of step 2.

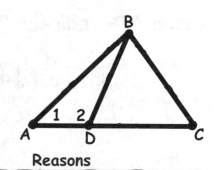

Given: $\overline{AB} \cong \overline{DB}$

Prove: $\overline{AB}$ is not $\cong$ to $\overline{BC}$.

Statements	Reasons
1. $\overline{AB} \cong \overline{DB}$	1. Given
2. Either $\overline{AB}$ is not $\cong$ to $\overline{BC}$ or $\overline{AB} \cong \overline{BC}$. Assume $\overline{AB} \cong \overline{BC}$.	2. A statement is either true or false.

Now we're going to do a couple more steps, and watch what happens.

3. $\angle 1 \cong \angle C, \angle 1 \cong \angle 2$	3. Base Angles Theorem
4. $\angle 2 \cong \angle C$	4. Transitive (Substitution)

We end up with $\angle 2 \cong \angle C$, which, if you study the diagram, doesn't make sense. These two angles can't possibly be congruent, because $\angle 2$ is an exterior angle of $\triangle DBC$ and $\angle C$ is a remote interior angle. According to the Exterior Angle Inequality Theorem, an exterior angle must always be greater than either of the remote interior angles. So step 4 contradicts a known theorem of geometry. Since our logic was correct, the assumption that $\overline{AB} \cong \overline{BC}$ must be wrong. But remember, there are only two possibilities: either $\overline{AB}$ is *not* congruent to $\overline{BC}$ or $\overline{AB} \cong \overline{BC}$. We've just shown that the second possibility is wrong, so by a process of elimination, the first possibility, $\overline{AB}$ is *not* congruent to $\overline{BC}$, must be right. And that finishes the proof! Here's the way the last step should be written down.

5. $\overline{AB}$ is not $\cong$ to $\overline{BC}$	5. Statement 4 contradicts the Exterior Angle Inequality Theorem. By elimination, statement 5 must be true.

As our example shows, in an indirect proof the key step is to assume that the other possibility—the negation of the prove statement—is true. Then, after a few steps, we should get a contradiction, which shows that the prove statement has to be true.

In our example, there were only two possibilities: either $\overline{AB}$ is *not* congruent to $\overline{BC}$ or $\overline{AB} \cong \overline{BC}$. In some indirect proofs, there are more than two possibilities. For instance, if we were trying to prove that $\angle A$ and $\angle B$ are congruent, there would actually be three possibilities: $\angle A \cong \angle B$, $m\angle A > m\angle B$, and $m\angle A < m\angle B$. To do the proof, we would have to assume $m\angle A > m\angle B$ and get a contradiction. Then we would have to assume that $m\angle A < m\angle B$ and get another contradiction. Only then would all of the other possibilities be eliminated, leaving $\angle A \cong \angle B$ as the only remaining option. So indirect proofs can sometimes get pretty messy.

Even though its method is different, an indirect proof uses deductive reasoning just like a direct proof. That means both styles of proof are perfectly acceptable in geometry (or in any area of mathematics). In some cases the direct method is easier, and in other cases the indirect method is the better way. You may have noticed that in our example we prove that two segments are *not* congruent, which is a little unusual. An indirect proof is often the easiest way to prove that one thing is not congruent to another. That's why we've waited until the chapter on inequalities (where things are unequal instead of equal) to show you the indirect method.

Summarizing the Steps

To wrap up this lesson, let's summarize the major steps for doing an indirect proof.

Steps for Doing an Indirect Proof

1.	List all of the other possibilities in addition to the thing you're trying to prove.
2.	Assume that the other possibility(ies), besides the one you want to prove, are true.
3.	Do some more steps until you get a contradiction with the given statement or with a known fact of geometry.
4.	Since the other possibility(ies) are false, by a process of elimination, the prove statement must be true.

Practice 47

a. The lengths of two sides of a triangle are 6 and 10. Tell the lengths that the third side must be greater than and less than.

b. Find y in terms of x.

c. Find y in terms of x.

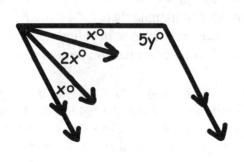

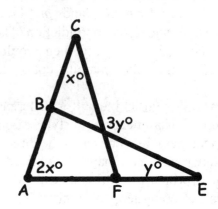

d. Two angles are supplementary. The measure of one angle is 3.5 times the measure of the other angle. Find the measures of *both* angles.

e. Use the indirect method to do the proof below.

Given: $\overline{KM} \perp \overline{NL}$, $\angle 3$ is not $\cong$ to $\angle 4$.
Prove: $\overline{KM}$ is not the median to side $\overline{NL}$.

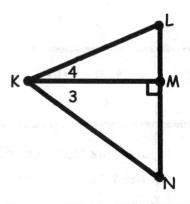

Problem Set 47

Tell whether each sentence below is True or False.

1. In an indirect proof, instead of proving the desired theorem directly, we first eliminate all of the other possibilities.

2. A direct proof uses deductive reasoning, but an indirect proof uses inductive reasoning.

Complete each sentence below by filling in the blanks. If the sentence is a property, name the property.

3. According to the _____, if two sides of a triangle are congruent (equal), then the angles opposite those sides are congruent (equal).

4. According to the _____, an exterior angle of a triangle is always greater than either one of the remote interior angles.

5. If _____, then a can be substituted for b in any inequality.

The lengths of two sides of a triangle are given. Tell the lengths that the third side must be greater than and less than.

(a) 6. 15, 13

7. 5, 18

Solve each inequality below. Show your steps and give a reason for each one.

8. $2x + 4 \leq -7x + 22$

9. $y - 1 \geq 5y$

From each given statement below, tell the definition, property, postulate, or theorem that justifies each prove statement.

10. Given: $\triangle UIO$; Prove: $UO < UI + IO$

11. Given: $\triangle UIO$; Prove: $m\angle I < m\angle IOE$

12. Given: $\triangle UIO$;
Prove: $m\angle IOE = m\angle U + m\angle I$

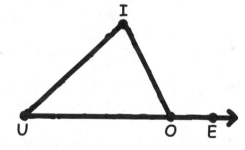

State which shortcut can be used to prove each pair of triangles below congruent. If no method applies, say "none."

13.

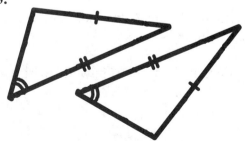

14.

297

Answer each question below.

15. Find x and y.

(b) 16. Find y in terms of x.

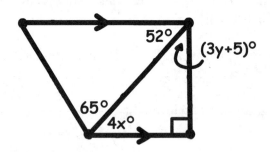

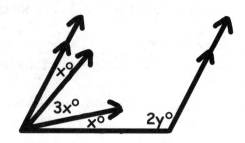

17. Find y.

(c) 18. Find y in terms of z.

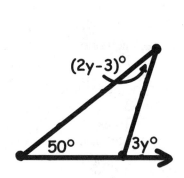

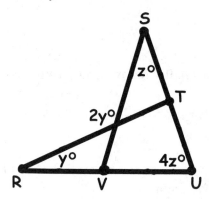

Write an equation to represent each question below; then solve the equation to get your answer.

19. The exterior sides of two adjacent angles make a right angle. The first angle has a measure that is 3 more than half of the second. What is the measure of *both* angles?

(d) 20. Two angles are supplementary. The measure of one angle is 1.5 times the measure of the other angle. Find the measures of *both* angles.

Draw a Venn diagram to represent each set of conditional statements below.

21. All chimney sweeps think black is their best color. Marianne does not think black is her best color. Therefore, Marianne must not be a chimney sweep.

22. Anthony is a drum major. And since all drum majors know how to twirl a baton, Anthony must know how to twirl a baton.

Do each proof below. Use the indirect method on 24.

23. Given: $\overline{EF} \cong \overline{GF}$;
Prove: $m\angle 3 > m\angle 1$

(e) 24. Given: $\overline{DB} \perp \overline{AC}$, $\angle 1$ is not $\cong$ to $\angle 2$
Prove: $\overline{DB}$ is not the median to side $\overline{AC}$.

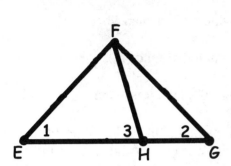

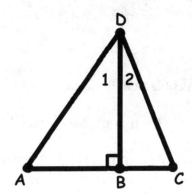

Lesson 48—More on Logic

We've been learning about logic throughout this book. That's one of the main reasons for studying geometry. One thing logic teaches you, though, is to be very careful about making any changes to a statement. Even a slight change can alter a statement's entire meaning. Here's an example.

If a triangle is acute, then it has one angle which is less than 90°.

This statement is true, but watch what happens when we switch it around.

If a triangle has one angle which is less than 90°, then it is acute.

The second statement is false. Just because a triangle has one angle that's less than 90° doesn't mean that the other two angles are also that small. All we did was change the order of the phrases and our statement went from true to false.

You may remember that the second statement is called the **converse** of the first. We write the converse by switching the order of the premise and the conclusion in the original statement. Using the letter a for the original premise and the letter b for the original conclusion, it looks like this.[2]

Original Statement
If a, then b

Converse
If b, then a

Our example shows that a statement and its converse don't both have to be true (although they may be).

Inverse Statements

As it turns out, there are other ways of changing a statement besides making it into its converse. We can also change a statement to its **inverse**. That's done by adding a "not" to both the premise and the conclusion. Let's go back to our original statement about the acute triangle.

If a triangle is acute, then it has one angle which is less than 90°.

The inverse looks like this.

If a triangle is *not* acute, then it does *not* have one angle which is
less than 90°.

---

[2] As you may remember from Chapter 1, we can also write the statements using arrows. The original statement is $a \rightarrow b$ and the converse is $b \rightarrow a$.

Even though the original statement is true, the inverse is false, because even if it's not acute, a triangle does have to have one angle less than 90° (in fact, it has to have two angles under 90°). Using the letters a and b, here is how an original statement compares to its inverse.[3]

Original Statement   Inverse

If a, then b If not a, then not b

By the way, adding a "not" to something, is called taking a "negation." We are taking the negative of it, in other words. We can also take the negation of a statement that already contains a not. We just take the not away. For example, the negation of the clause "If a triangle is not acute" is "If a triangle is acute."

Contrapositive Statements

Another way to change a statement is to make it into its **contrapositive**. To do that, we switch the positions of the premise and conclusion, then take the negation of each. Here it is with a's and b's.[4]

Original Statement   Contrapositive

If a, then b If not b, then not a

To make sure you understand, let's take the contrapositive of our original statement about the acute triangle.

> If a triangle is acute, then it has one angle which is less than 90°.

We change "is acute" to "is not acute" and "has one angle" to "does not have one angle." Then we switch the order of the premise and conclusion.

> If a triangle does not have one angle which is less than 90°, then it is not acute.

This is the contrapositive of the original.

Equivalent Statements

One interesting thing about the last example is that the original statement was true, and so was the contrapositive. (There's no way a triangle can be acute if it doesn't have one angle under 90°.) That was no coincidence. It turns out that if any statement is true, its contrapositive has to be true as well. The reason is that the two statements are "logically equivalent," which is just saying that they're logically the same. An easy way to see this is to look at a couple of Venn Diagrams, one (below left) representing the original statement and another (below right) representing the contrapositive.

---

[3] Using arrows, the original statement is shown as $a \rightarrow b$ and the inverse as not $a \rightarrow$ not b.

[4] Using arrows, the original statement is shown as $a \rightarrow b$ and the contrapositive as not $b \rightarrow$ not a.

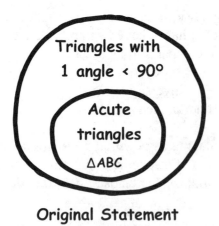

Original Statement

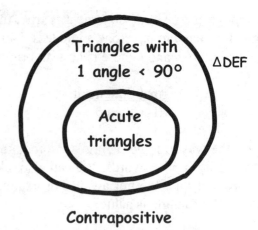

Contrapositive

Notice both diagrams are exactly the same. Only the position of the specific triangle is different. On the left, $\triangle ABC$ is acute, so it's inside the little circle. And since $\triangle ABC$ is also inside the big circle, it must have one angle less than $90°$. On the right, $\triangle DEF$ does *not* have one angle that's less than $90°$, so it's outside the big circle. That means $\triangle DEF$ can't possibly be inside the little circle, which is why it's also *not* acute. Basically, the original statement is saying that when a triangle is inside the little circle, it must also be inside the big circle. The contrapositive is saying that when a triangle is outside the big circle, it can't possibly be inside the little one. If one of the statements is true, the other one must be true too. Or if one is false, the other must also be false.

Not only is a statement always logically equivalent to its contrapositive, but a converse is also always logically equivalent to its inverse. In other words, if the converse is true, the inverse must be true. Or if the converse is false, the inverse must also be false. We'll rewrite the converse and inverse statements from above.

Converse: If a triangle has one angle which is less than $90°$, then it is acute.

Inverse: If a triangle is *not* acute, then it does *not* have one angle which is less than $90°$.

Here are the Venn diagrams to represent these two.

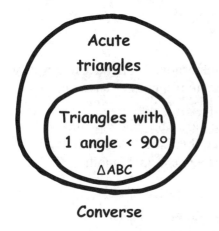

Converse

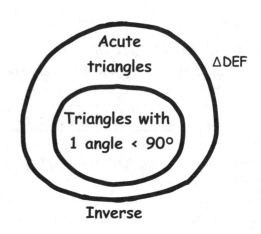

Inverse

On the left, $\triangle ABC$ is inside the little circle, so it has to also be inside the big one. On the right, $\triangle DEF$ is not in the big circle, which is why it's not in the little circle either. So the converse and inverse are actually saying the same thing. In our acute triangle example, of course, both the converse and inverse are false.

You may be wondering why it's necessary to know about all these different kinds of statements. Well, as we said earlier, one reason is so you can avoid accidentally changing a statement and giving it a different meaning. One slip like that can blow an entire proof. However, another reason is that it's sometimes easier to prove a statement when it's written in a certain way. For instance, it might be easier to prove something in the form "if not b, then not a" rather than when it's in the form "if a, then b." But if you understand that the first statement is the contrapositive of the second, then you can go ahead and prove "If not b, then not a" and from that conclude that "if a, then b" is also true (since the two statements are logically equivalent). That can be a big help.

To finish up the lesson, let's summarize all the different kinds of statements and how they relate logically.

Types of Logical Statements

Logically equivalent {	Statement	If a, then b.
	Contrapositive	If not b, then not a.
Logically equivalent {	Converse	If b, then a.
	Inverse	If not a, then not b.

Practice 48

a. Tell whether the statement below is the converse, inverse, or contrapositive of the following statement: If two angles are right angles, then they are congruent.

If two angles are not congruent, then they are not right angles.

b. Write the converse, inverse, and contrapositive of the true statement below. Tell whether your answer is true or false.

If a triangle is equiangular, then it has one angle measuring $60°$.

c. Find $a + b$.

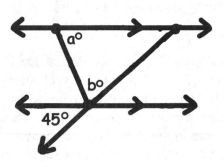

d. Find a.

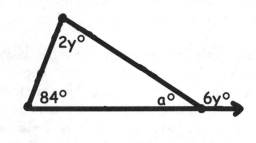

e. Use the indirect method to do the proof below.

Given: $\angle 3 \cong \angle 4$
Prove: $KL \neq JK$

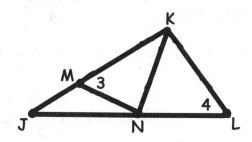

Problem Set 48

Tell whether each sentence below is true or false.

1. A statement is always logically equivalent to its contrapositive.

2. The converse of a statement is always logically equivalent to the inverse of the statement.

Complete each sentence below by filling in the blanks. If the sentence is a property, name the property.

3. If the original statement is in the form "If a, then b," then the inverse is in the form _____.

4. If the original statement is in the form "If a, then b," then the contrapositive is in the form _____.

5. The acute angles of a right triangle are _____.

6. If _____ and $c > 0$, then $ac > bc$.

The lengths of two sides of a triangle are given. Tell the lengths that the third side must be greater than and less than.

7. 4, 1

8. 9, 19

Tell whether each statement below is the converse, inverse, or contrapositive of the following statement: If two angles are vertical angles, then they are congruent.

9. If two angles are not vertical angles, then they are not congruent.

10. If two angles are congruent, then they are vertical angles.

(a) 11. If two angles are not congruent, then they are not vertical angles.

Write the converse, inverse, and contrapositive of each true statement below. Tell whether your answer is true or false.

12. If Jane lives in Los Angeles, then she lives in California.

(b) 13. If two angles are a linear pair, then they are supplementary.

Find the measures of the angles of each triangle described below.

14. A triangle whose angles have measures in the ratio 6: 11: 19. What kind of triangle is it?

15. A right triangle where one of the two acute angles measures 5 times the other.

From each given statement below, tell the definition, property, postulate, or theorem that justifies each prove statement.

16. Given: $\ell_1 \| \ell_2$; Prove: $\angle 1 \cong \angle 5$

17. Given: $\ell_1 \| \ell_2$; Prove: $\angle 1 \cong \angle 4$

18. Given: $\angle 3$ and $\angle 4$ are supplementary; Prove: $\ell_1 \| \ell_2$

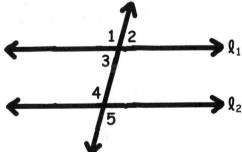

Answer each question below.

19.   Find $w + x + y + z$.

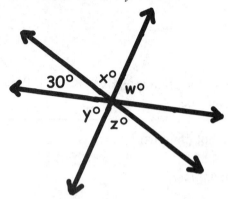

(c) 20.   Find $s + t$.

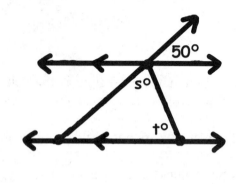

21.   Find x in terms of y.

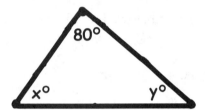

(d) 22.   Find b.

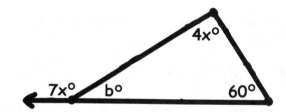

Do each proof below. Use the indirect method on 24.

23.   Given: G is between H and E
Prove: $m\angle HGD > m\angle F$

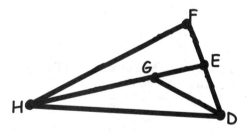

(e) 24.   Given: $\angle 1 \cong \angle 2$
Prove: $RS \neq ST$

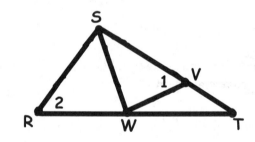

Lesson 49—Unequal Sides, Unequal Angles

In the last chapter, we learned about the Base Angles Theorem, which says that in a triangle with two congruent sides (an isosceles triangle), the angles opposite those sides are congruent (on the top right). But what do you think is the relationship between the angles when the two sides of the triangle are *not* congruent? Since this is a chapter on inequalities, we should cover a case like that.

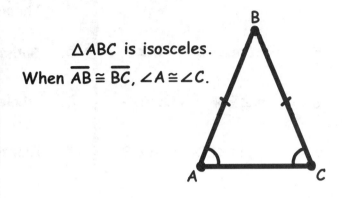

$\triangle ABC$ is isosceles.
When $\overline{AB} \cong \overline{BC}$, $\angle A \cong \angle C$.

In $\triangle DEF$ on the right, $\overline{DE}$ and $\overline{EF}$ are not congruent, and the two opposite angles are $\angle EDF$ and $\angle F$. From the diagram on the bottom right, $m\angle EDF$ appears to be greater than $m\angle F$. But by now you know that appearances don't count in geometry. We need to prove that $m\angle EDF > m\angle F$ to be sure. As part

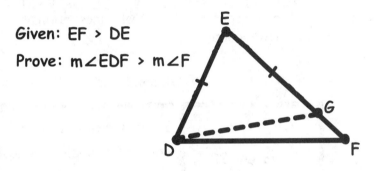

Given: EF > DE
Prove: $m\angle EDF > m\angle F$

of the proof, we have drawn a line segment from point D to side EF. And the segment is positioned so that $DE = EG$. Here's the formal proof.

Statements	Reasons
1. EF > DE	1. Given
2. Draw $\overline{DG}$ such that DE = EG	2. Two points determine a line.
3. $m\angle EDG = m\angle EGD$	3. Base Angles Theorem

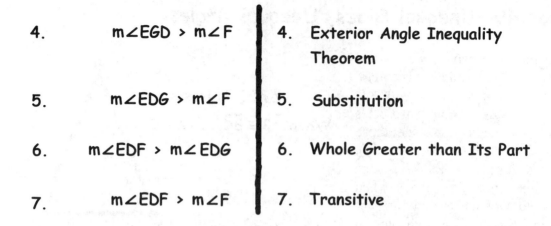

We should make a couple of points about this proof. First, not only does it show that the angles opposite the incongruent (unequal) sides are not congruent, it also shows that the angle opposite the longer side is greater than the angle opposite the shorter side. Second, this proof covers *any* triangle with two incongruent (unequal) sides, no matter what its specific shape.[5] That gives us an important new theorem.

If Unequal Sides, then Unequal Angles

Theorem 28	If two sides of a triangle are not congruent, then the angles opposite those sides are not congruent, and the greater angle is opposite the longer side.

Theorem 28 makes a lot of sense when you think about it. If when the sides are congruent, the opposite angles are congruent, then when the sides are not congruent, the opposite angles shouldn't be congruent either. And the longer side has the greater opposite angle, because that angle has to open up more to make room for that longer side (look at the diagram again).

The Converse Too

We've proved that if two sides of a triangle are not congruent, then the opposite angles are not congruent (and the greater angle is opposite the longer side) But what about the converse of Theorem 28? When a triangle has incongruent (unequal) angles, do the opposite sides have to be incongruent (unequal)? And does the greater angle have to be opposite the longer side?

---

[5] The proof never mentions any specific measures for the sides or angles of the triangle. That's why it covers all different possibilities.

Remember, just because a statement is true, doesn't necessarily mean its converse is true as well. The only way to be sure about the converse of Theorem 28 is to prove it deductively. We'll use the statements and diagram on the right for the proof. This is going to be an indirect proof. And the interesting thing about it is that there are actually three possibilities. Either

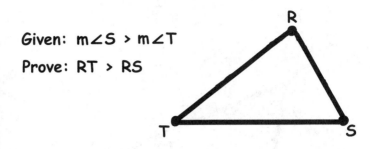

Given: m∠S > m∠T

Prove: RT > RS

$RT > RS$ (which is what we're trying to prove) or $RT = RS$ or $RT < RS$. To do the prove indirectly, we need to assume $RT = RS$ and get a contradiction, then assume $RT < RS$ and get another contradiction. That will eliminate the other two possibilities, leaving $RT > RS$ as the only conclusion. We'll show the steps of the proof informally, followed by the official theorem.

Either $RT > RS$ or RT is not $> RS$. If RT is not greater than RS, it could be equal to RS or less than RS. First, let's assume that $RT = RS$. Then $m∠S = m∠T$ (Base Angles Theorem). But that contradicts the given statement that $m∠S > m∠T$. Next, assume that $RT < RS$. Then $m∠S < m∠T$ (If Unequal Sides, then Unequal Angles). That too contradicts the given statement, $m∠S > m∠T$. So by elimination $RT > RS$.

If Unequal Angles, then Unequal Sides

Theorem 29	**If two angles of a triangle are not congruent, then the sides opposite those angles are not congruent, and the longer side is opposite the greater angle.**

Practice 49

a. Tell whether the statement below is the converse, inverse, or contrapositive of the following statement: If a triangle has two sides with a length of 5, then it is not a scalene triangle.

If a triangle does not have two sides with a length of 5, then it is a scalene triangle.

b. Write the converse, inverse, and contrapositive of the false statement below. Tell whether your answer is true or false.

If a figure is a polygon, then it is a square.

c. In $\triangle JKQ$ (below), $m\angle K = 55$ and $m\angle Q = 28$. Is $\overline{JQ}$ or $\overline{KJ}$ longer?

d. From the given statement below, tell the definition, property, postulate, or theorem that justifies the prove statement.

Given: $m\angle WPB > m\angle BWP$;
Prove: $WB > PB$

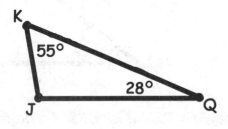

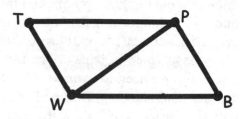

e. Use the indirect method to do the proof below.

Given: $KN = PN$
Prove: $PM \neq MO$

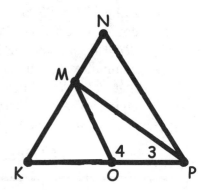

Problem Set 49

Tell whether each sentence below is true or false.

1. If two sides of a triangle are unequal, then the angles opposite those sides are unequal.

2. When two sides of a triangle are unequal, the angle opposite the longer side is greater than the angle opposite the shorter side.

Complete each sentence below by filling in the blanks.

3. _____ are a pair of nonadjacent angles formed by intersecting lines.

4. If the original statement is in the form "If a, then b," then the converse is in the form _____.

5. A(n) _____ of a triangle is a segment drawn from any vertex of the triangle, perpendicular to the opposite side, extended outside the triangle if necessary.

Complete each sentence below with *always*, *sometimes*, or *never*.

6. If the two angles of a linear pair are congruent, they are _____ right angles.

7. The angles of a scalene triangle are _____ congruent.

Tell whether each statement below is the converse, inverse, or contrapositive of the following statement: If a triangle has an angle measuring 100°, then it is not an acute triangle.

8. If a triangle is not an acute triangle, then it has an angle measuring 100°.

(a) 9. If a triangle does not have an angle measuring 100°, then it is an acute triangle.

Write the converse, inverse, and contrapositive of each false statement below. Tell whether your answer is true or false.

10. If James lives in Florida, then he lives in Miami.

(b) 11. If a figure is a polygon, then it is a triangle.

Answer each question below.

12. In $\triangle ABC$ (below), $m\overline{AB} = 6$ and $m\overline{BC} = 9$. Is $\angle A$ or $\angle C$ greater?

(c) 13. In $\triangle DEF$ (below), $m\angle D = 30$ and $m\angle E = 60$. Is $\overline{EF}$ or $\overline{DF}$ longer?

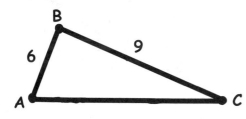

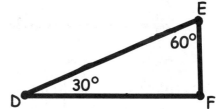

From each given statement below, tell the definition, property, postulate, or theorem that justifies each prove statement.

14. Given: $\triangle GKS \cong \triangle DSK$; Prove: $\angle G \cong \angle D$

15. Given: $KS > GK$; Prove: $m\angle G > m\angle GSK$

(d) 16. Given: $m\angle SDK > m\angle SKD$;
Prove: $KS > DS$

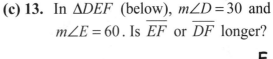

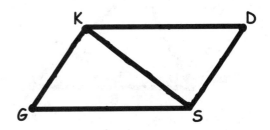

311

State which shortcut can be used to prove each pair of triangles below congruent. If no method applies, say "none."

17.

18.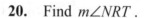

Answer each question below.

19. If $\ell_1 \parallel \ell_2$, find $p+q$.

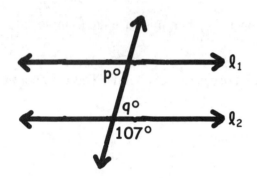

20. Find $m\angle NRT$.

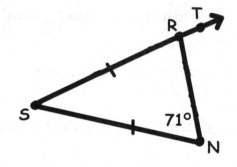

21. If $2a = b$, find c in terms of a.

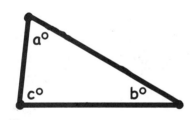

22. Find x.

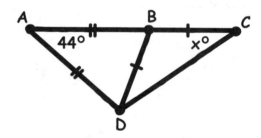

Do each proof below. Use the indirect method on 24.

23. Given: $m\angle 5 = m\angle 6$ (below)
Prove: $EC > AE$

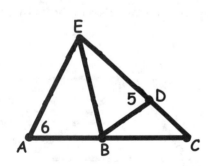

(e) 24. Given: $AB = CB$ (below)
Prove: $AD \neq DE$

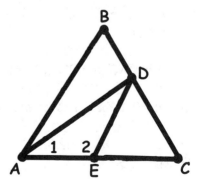

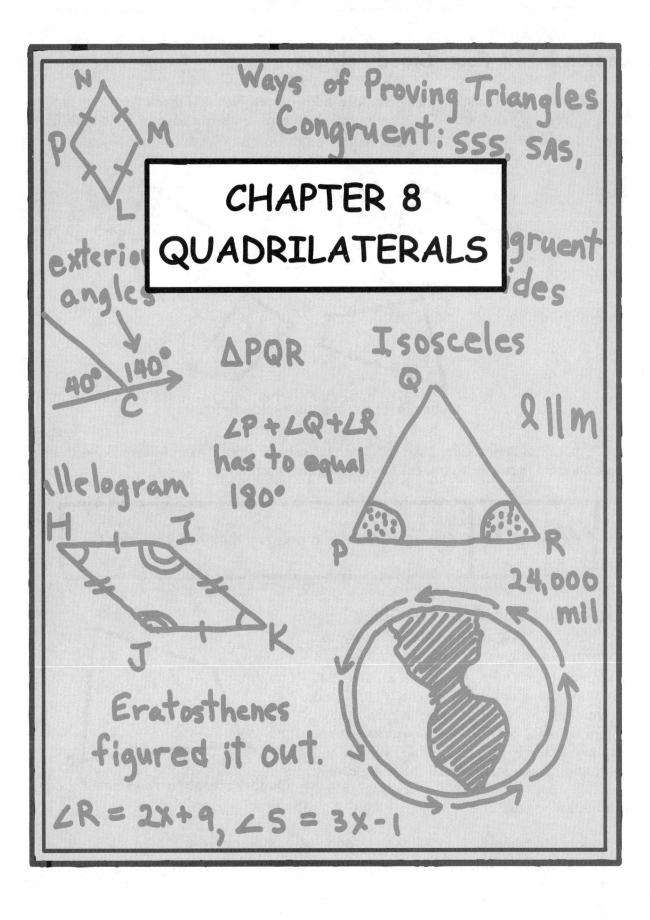

Ways of Proving Triangles Congruent: SSS, SAS,

**CHAPTER 8
QUADRILATERALS**

gruent ides

exterior angles

40° 140°
C

ΔPQR

∠P + ∠Q + ∠R has to equal 180°

Isosceles
Q

ℓ ‖ m

P   R

llelogram

H   I

J   K

24,000 mil

Eratosthenes figured it out.

∠R = 2x + 9, ∠S = 3x - 1

Lesson 50—A Four-Sided Polygon

We've studied triangles, which are three-sided figures. Now it's time to move up to four-sided figures or **quadrilaterals**, as they're called. Quadrilaterals can have all sorts of different shapes (just like triangles). Below are a few examples of quadrilaterals of various shapes.

Quadrilaterals are four-sided figures.

Notice that all of these figures have four line segments for sides. That's what qualifies them as quadrilaterals.[1] Here's the formal definition of a quadrilateral.

Definition 42	A *quadrilateral* is a polygon that has four sides.

Consecutive and Opposite Sides

Now let's look at a quadrilateral, shown on the right, in a little more detail. The four sides of quadrilateral $ABCD$ are $\overline{AB}$, $\overline{BC}$, $\overline{CD}$, and $\overline{DA}$. $ABCD$ also has four vertices—points A, B, C, and D—and four interior angles (one at each vertex): $\angle A$, $\angle B$, $\angle C$, and $\angle D$. So a quadrilateral not only has four sides, it also has four vertices and four angles. This is really similar to a triangle, only a triangle has just three of everything (sides, vertices, and angles).

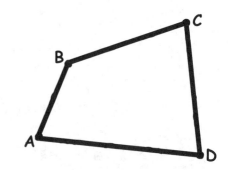

Quadrilateral: a four-sided figure

---

[1] All of the quadrilaterals shown are convex, but there are also concave quadrilaterals. In this book, however, we'll only study the convex kind.

Certain pairs of sides of a quadrilateral have special names. In quadrilateral *ABCD*, shown on the right, $\overline{AB}$ and $\overline{BC}$ are called **consecutive sides**, since they're right next to each other. And consecutive sides are always connected by a vertex. Sides $\overline{AB}$ and $\overline{BC}$ are connected by vertex *B*. Sides $\overline{BC}$ and $\overline{CD}$ are also

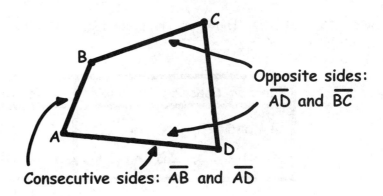

Opposite sides: $\overline{AD}$ and $\overline{BC}$

Consecutive sides: $\overline{AB}$ and $\overline{AD}$

consecutive sides, and they're connected by vertex *C*. The remaining pairs of consecutive sides are $\overline{CD}$ and $\overline{DA}$ (connected by vertex *D*) and $\overline{AD}$ and $\overline{AB}$ (connected by vertex *A*).

Sides $\overline{AB}$ and $\overline{CD}$ are not considered consecutive sides, because they're not right next to each other (and so not connected by a vertex). They're actually on opposite sides of the quadrilateral, which is why $\overline{AB}$ and $\overline{CD}$ are called **opposite sides**. There's one other pair of opposite sides in quadrilateral *ABCD*: $\overline{AD}$ and $\overline{BC}$.

Here's a complete list of all the pairs of consecutive sides and opposite sides of quadrilateral *ABCD*.

Pairs of Consecutive Sides	Pairs of Opposite Sides
$\overline{AB}$ and $\overline{BC}$, $\overline{BC}$ and $\overline{CD}$ $\overline{CD}$ and $\overline{DA}$, $\overline{DA}$ and $\overline{AB}$	$\overline{AB}$ and $\overline{CD}$, $\overline{AD}$ and $\overline{BC}$

Consecutive and Opposite Angles

Certain pairs of angles in a quadrilateral also have names. And the words "consecutive" and "opposite" are used here too. **Consecutive angles** are angles that are located right next to each other. The technical way of saying it is that their vertices are "adjacent." In quadrilateral *ABCD* (on the right), the consecutive angles are $\angle A$ and $\angle B$, $\angle B$ and $\angle C$, $\angle C$ and $\angle D$, and $\angle A$ and $\angle D$. **Opposite angles** are angles that are located at alternate vertices. That just means that their vertices are one apart from each other. In quadrilateral *ABCD*, the pairs of opposite angles are $\angle A$ and $\angle C$

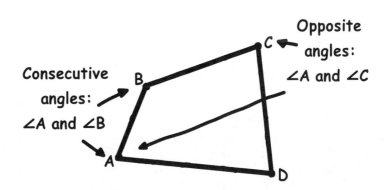

Consecutive angles: $\angle A$ and $\angle B$

Opposite angles: $\angle A$ and $\angle C$

and $\angle B$ and $\angle D$. Here's a complete list of all the consecutive and opposite angles in quadrilateral $ABCD$.

Pairs of Consecutive Angles	Pairs of Opposite Angles
$\angle A$ and $\angle B$, $\angle B$ and $\angle C$, $\angle C$ and $\angle D$, $\angle D$ and $\angle A$	$\angle A$ and $\angle C$, $\angle B$ and $\angle D$

Diagonals

There's one more pair of lines within a quadrilateral that you should know. These are actually extra or "auxiliary" line segments that can be drawn between a pair of opposite vertices. These segments are called **diagonals**. Every quadrilateral has two diagonals, each one connecting a pair of opposite vertices.

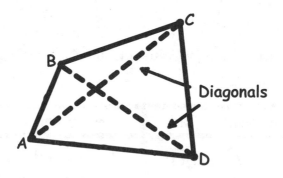

Adding Up the Angles

Now that we've learned a few basic facts about quadrilaterals, let's do our first quadrilateral theorem. You already know that the angles of any triangle, no matter what its shape, add to 180°. Well, it turns out that the angles of any quadrilateral—again, no matter what its shape—add to 360°. Here is the formal proof. And an official statement of the theorem is below that.

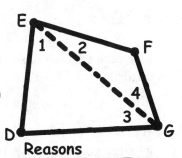

Given: Quadrilateral DEFG

Prove: m∠D + m∠FED + m∠F + m∠FGD = 360

Statements	Reasons
1. Quadrilateral DEFG	1. Given
2. Draw diagonal $\overline{EG}$.	2. Two points determine a line.
3. m∠1 + m∠3 + m∠D = 180 and m∠2 + m∠4 + m∠F = 180	3. The sum of the measures of the angles of a triangle is 180.
4. m∠1 + m∠3 + m∠D + m∠2 + m∠4 + m∠F = 360	4. Addition Property
5. m∠1 + m∠2 = m∠FED and m∠3 + m∠4 = m∠FGD	5. Betweenness of Rays
6. m∠FED + m∠D + m∠FGD + m∠F = 360	6. Substitution

Theorem 30	The sum of the measures of the angles of a quadrilateral is 360.

Practice 50

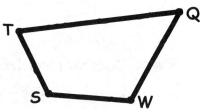

a. List each of the consecutive and opposite sides of quadrilateral *STQW*.

b. Write the converse, inverse, and contrapositive of the true statement below. Tell whether your answer is true or false.

If an angle is obtuse, then it has a measure of greater than 90° (and less than 180°).

c. In $\triangle JKM$, $KM > JK$ and $JM < JK$. Which is the largest angle of the triangle?

d. Find *x*.

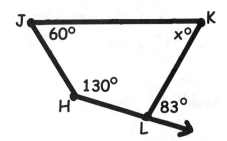

e. Do the proof below.
Given: $\triangle ABC$ is equilateral;
Point *Q* is any point on $\overline{AB}$.
Prove: $CQ < AC$, $CQ < BC$, $CQ < AB$

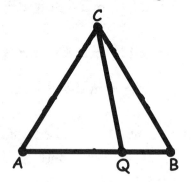

Problem Set 50

Tell whether each sentence below is true or false.

1. A quadrilateral is a polygon that has four sides.

2. The sum of the measures of the angles of a quadrilateral is 180.

Complete each sentence below by filling in the blanks.

3. _____ sides of a quadrilateral are sides that are connected by a vertex.

4. _____ angles of a quadrilateral are angles that are located at alternate vertices.

5. The converse of a statement is always logically equivalent to the _____ of that statement.

6. If two sides of a triangle are not congruent, then the angles opposite those sides are _____, and the _____ angle is opposite the _____ side.

Answer each question below.

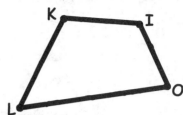

(a) 7. List each of the consecutive and opposite sides of quadrilateral *LKIO*.

8. List each of the consecutive and opposite angles of quadrilateral *LKIO*.

The lengths of two sides of a triangle are given. Tell the lengths that the third side must be greater than and less than.

9. 5, 14

10. 45, 65

Tell whether each statement below is the converse, inverse, or contrapositive of the following statement: If two sides of a triangle are congruent, then the angles opposite those sides are congruent.

11. If two angles of a triangle are not congruent, then the sides opposite those angles are not congruent.

12. If two sides of a triangle are not congruent, then the angles opposite those sides are not congruent.

Write the converse, inverse, and contrapositive of each true statement below. Tell whether your answer is true or false.

(b) 13. If an angle is acute, then it has a measure of less than $90°$.

14. If two angles are the acute angles of a right triangle, then they are complementary.

Answer each question below.

15. In $\triangle ABC$, $m\angle A = 49$ and $m\angle B = 18$. Is $\overline{BC}$ or $\overline{AC}$ longer?

(c) 16. In $\triangle RST$, $ST > RS$ and $RT < RS$. Which is the greatest angle of $\triangle RST$?

From each given statement below, tell the definition, property, postulate, or theorem that justifies each prove statement.

17. Given: $\triangle UYB$ (on the right);
Prove: $m\angle YBV = m\angle U + m\angle Y$

18. Given: $UY > YB$ (on the right);
Prove: $m\angle YBU > m\angle U$

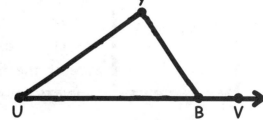

319

Answer each question below.

19. Find x.

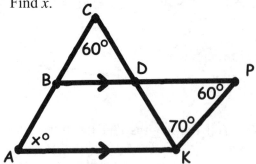

(d) 20. Find y.

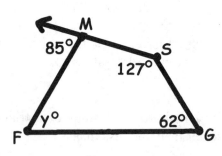

Write an equation to represent each question below; then solve the equation to get your answer.

21. In $\triangle ABC$, $m\angle A = 120$ and $m\angle B$ is twice $m\angle C$. Find $m\angle B$ and $m\angle C$.

22. Two angles are supplementary. The measure of one angle is one-third the measure of the other. Find the measures of *both* angles.

Do each proof below. Number 24 will become our Theorem 31.

23. Given: $EU = UT$
Prove: $EU > UR$

(e) 24. Given: $\triangle JKL$ is equilateral;
Point P is any point on $\overline{JL}$.
Prove: $KP < JK$, $KP < KL$, $KP < JL$

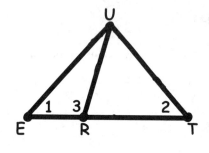

Theorem 31	The length of a line segment drawn from any vertex of an equilateral triangle to a point on the opposite side is less than the length of any side of the triangle.

Lesson 51—Trapezoids

You already know that there are special kinds of triangles, such as equilateral triangles, isosceles triangles, and right triangles. As it turns out, there are also special kinds of quadrilaterals. One special quadrilateral is a **trapezoid**. This is just a quadrilateral where one pair of its sides are parallel. Here's a picture.

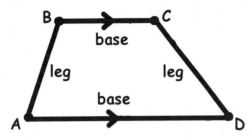

A trapezoid has one pair of sides that are parallel.

Parts of a Trapezoid

The parallel sides are $\overline{AD}$ and $\overline{BC}$. These sides are called the **bases** of the trapezoid. The two nonparallel sides, $\overline{AB}$ and $\overline{CD}$, are the trapezoid's **legs**. And the angles where each base connects to the trapezoid are called **base angles**. So $\angle A$ and $\angle D$ is the lower pair of base angles and $\angle B$ and $\angle C$ is the upper pair. Here is the formal definition of a trapezoid.

Definition 43	A *trapezoid* is a quadrilateral which has exactly one pair of parallel sides. The parallel sides are called *bases* and the nonparallel sides are called *legs*.

Altitudes, Median, and Diagonals

A trapezoid also has extra (auxiliary) lines that can be drawn in. For example, an **altitude** of a trapezoid is a perpendicular line segment drawn from any point on one of the bases (the parallel sides) to the opposite base. One interesting thing about a trapezoid is that it has an infinite number of altitudes. That's because it's possible to draw a perpendicular line from any point on one

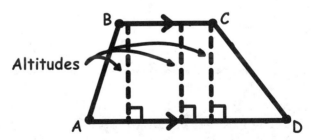

A trapezoid has an infinite number of altitudes.

base to the other base (see right). As you may remember, the altitudes of a triangle work differently. In a triangle, an altitude has to start from a vertex, which is why a triangle has just three altitudes.

The **median** of a trapezoid is the line segment that joins the midpoints of the legs (the nonparallel sides). A trapezoid has only one median, since there's just one segment that will go between the midpoints of both legs. By contrast, a median of a triangle has one endpoint at a vertex. And that's why a triangle has three medians.

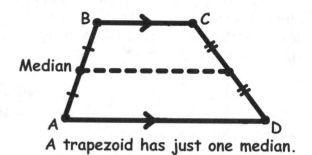

A trapezoid has just one median.

The last auxiliary lines are **diagonals**. These are segments that run diagonally between the pairs of opposite vertices of the trapezoid. As you can see from the diagram on the middle right, a trapezoid has two diagonals.

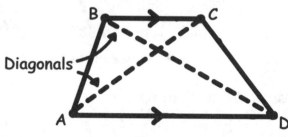

A trapezoid has two diagonals.

Isosceles Trapezoids

Just as there are isosceles triangles that have two sides congruent, there are also **isosceles trapezoids,** where the two legs are congruent. Trapezoid *DEFG* is isosceles, because the legs $\overline{DE}$ and $\overline{GF}$ are congruent, as you can see in the bottom right diagram. Here's the definition of an isosceles trapezoid.

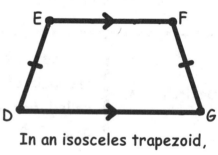

In an isosceles trapezoid, the legs are congruent.

Definition 44	An *isosceles trapezoid* is a trapezoid that has both legs congruent (equal).

There are two theorems about isosceles trapezoids that we should introduce. The first one says that in all isosceles trapezoids, the lower base angles are congruent and the upper base angles are congruent. Here's an informal proof of this theorem.

Given: Isosceles trapezoid DEFG

Prove: ∠D ≅ ∠G and ∠DEF ≅ ∠GFE

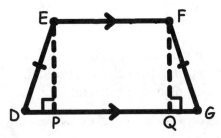

$\overline{EP}$ and $\overline{FQ}$ are altitudes, so $\angle EPD$ and $\angle FQG$ are right angles and congruent. And $\overline{EP} \cong \overline{FQ}$ (the distance between parallel lines is always the same). Then, $\triangle DEP \cong \triangle GFQ$ (Hypotenuse-Leg). So $\angle D \cong \angle G$ (C.P.C.T.C). Since $\overline{EF} \parallel \overline{DG}$, $\angle D$ and $\angle DEF$ as well as $\angle G$ and $\angle GFE$ are supplementary (If two parallel lines are cut by a transversal, then interior angles on the same side of the transversal are supplementary.) Therefore, $\angle DEF \cong \angle GFE$ (Two angles supplementary to congruent angles are congruent).

Theorem 32	The lower (and upper) base angles of an isosceles trapezoid are congruent (equal).

The second theorem on isosceles trapezoids pertains to the diagonals. It turns out that when a trapezoid is isosceles (the legs are congruent), the diagonals have to be congruent. Here's an informal proof of this theorem.

Given: Isosceles trapezoid DEFG

Prove: $\overline{DF} \cong \overline{EG}$

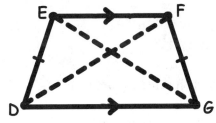

$\overline{DF}$ and $\overline{EG}$ are diagonals. $\overline{DE} \cong \overline{FG}$ (Definition of isosceles trapezoid). Also, $\overline{DG} \cong \overline{DG}$ (Reflexive). $\angle EDG \cong \angle FGD$ (Theorem 32). Overlapping triangles $\triangle DEG$ and $\triangle GFD$ are congruent (S.A.S.). Therefore, $\overline{DF} \cong \overline{EG}$ (C.P.C.T.C.).

Theorem 33	The diagonals of an isosceles trapezoid are congruent (equal).

Practice 51

a. Tell whether the figure below is a trapezoid, isosceles trapezoid, or just a plain quadrilateral.

b. Draw one of the altitudes, both diagonals, and the median of the trapezoid below.

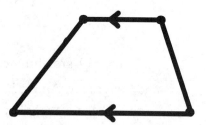

c. Write the converse, inverse, and contrapositive of the true statement below. Tell whether your answer is true or false.

If two lines are not perpendicular, then they do not intersect to form right angles.

d. Find *y*.

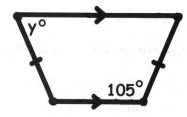

e. Do the proof below.
Given: Trapezoid *ABCD*, *KL = KM* ,
        AL = MD, *BM = CL*
Prove: Trapezoid *ABCD* is isosceles.

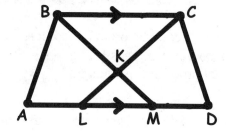

Problem Set 51

Tell whether each sentence below is true or false.

1. A trapezoid is a quadrilateral with only three sides.

2. In an isosceles trapezoid the two legs are congruent.

Complete each sentence below by filling in the blanks.

3. The two parallel sides of a trapezoid are called its _____.

4. The diagonals of an isosceles trapezoid are _____.

5. A statement is always logically equivalent to its _____.

Tell whether each figure below is a trapezoid, isosceles trapezoid, or just a plain quadrilateral.

6.   **(a) 7.**   **8.**

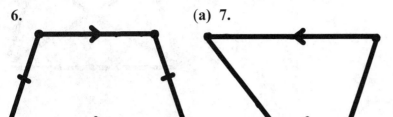
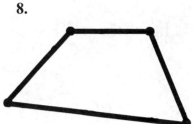

Draw one of the altitudes, both diagonals, and the median of each trapezoid below.

(b) 9.   **10.**

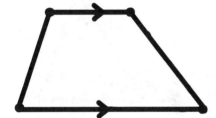
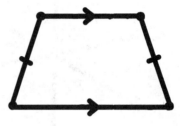

Write the converse, inverse, and contrapositive of each true statement below. Tell whether your answer is true or false.

(c) 11. If a triangle is not equilateral, then it is not equiangular.

12. If a polygon has four sides, then it is a quadrilateral.

Answer each question below.

13. In $\triangle WRP$, $m\overline{WR} = 7$ and $m\overline{WP} = 5$. Is $\angle P$ or $\angle R$ smaller?

14. In $\triangle ABC$, $m\angle C = 55$ and $m\angle B = 45$. Is $\overline{AC}$ or $\overline{AB}$ shorter?

15. In $\triangle JFR$, $JF > JR$ and $FR > JR$. Which is the smallest angle of $\triangle JFR$?

From each given statement below, tell the definition, property, postulate, or theorem that justifies each prove statement.

16. Given: $\angle 1 \cong \angle 4$, $\angle 4$ and $\angle 5$ are supplementary, $\angle 1$ and $\angle 6$ are supplementary;
Prove: $\angle 5 \cong \angle 6$.

17. Given: Trapezoid *CVBN* (on the right);
Prove: $\overline{VB} \parallel \overline{CN}$

18. Given: Isosceles trapezoid *CVBN* (on the right);
Prove: $\overline{VN} \cong \overline{BC}$.

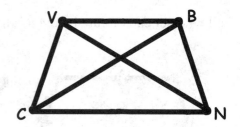

Answer each question below.

19. Find *y*.

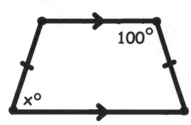

20. If $x = 2z$ and $y = 3z$, find *z*.

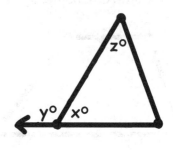

(d) 21. Find *x*.

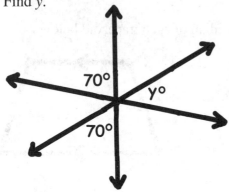

22. If $DU = 7$, find *SH*.

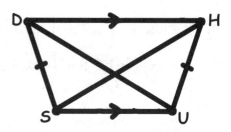

Do each proof below. Use the indirect method on 23.

23. Given: $\triangle ABC$ is not isosceles;
AB does not equal *BC*
AC does not equal *AB*
$\angle 1 \cong \angle 2$;
Prove: *AP* does not equal *PC*

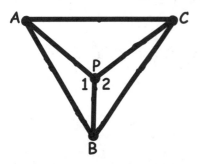

(e) 24. Given: Trapezoid *RSTU*, $VP = VQ$,
$RP = UQ$, $SQ = TP$;
Prove: Trapezoid *RSTU* is isosceles.

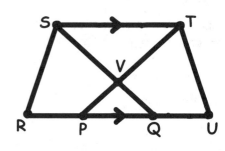

Lesson 52—Parallelograms

In the last lesson, we learned about trapezoids, which are special quadrilaterals that have one pair of parallel sides. Now we're going to talk about parallelograms, which are another type of special quadrilateral. **Parallelograms** actually have two pairs of parallel sides. Here's an example.

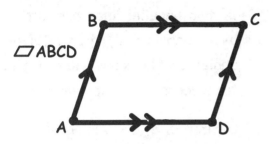

□ ABCD

A parallelogram has two pairs
of sides that are parallel.

As you can see from the diagram on the left, *ABCD* the upper and lower sides ($\overline{AD}$ and $\overline{BC}$) are parallel, and so are the left and right sides ($\overline{AB}$ and $\overline{CD}$). That's why *ABCD* qualifies as a parallelogram. By the way, notice the slanted box next to *ABCD*. This is the symbol for a parallelogram. So we use a little parallelogram for a parallelogram symbol, just as we use a little triangle for a triangle symbol ($\triangle ABC$, for instance). Here's the formal definition of a parallelogram.

Definition 45	A *parallelogram* is a quadrilateral that has both pairs of opposite sides parallel.

Consecutive Angles are Supplementary

There are several important things that all parallelograms, no matter what their shape, have in common (besides the fact that both pairs of opposite sides are parallel). The first is that the consecutive angles (angles that are right next to each other) are supplementary. Here's a proof of this theorem.

Given: □ ABCD

Prove: ∠A and ∠B, ∠C and ∠D,
  ∠B and ∠C, ∠D and ∠A
  are supplementary.

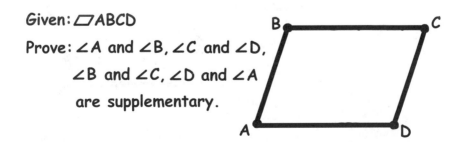

Statements	Reasons
1. ☐ABCD	1. Given
2. $\overline{BC} \parallel \overline{AD}$	2. Definition of parallelogram
3. ∠A and ∠B are supplementary. ∠C and ∠D are supplementary.	3. If two parallel lines are cut by a transversal, then interior angles on the same side of the transversal are supplementary.
4. $\overline{AB} \parallel \overline{CD}$	4. Definition of parallelogram
5. ∠B and ∠C are supplementary. ∠D and ∠A are supplementary.	5. same as number 3

Theorem 34	If a quadrilateral is a parallelogram, then pairs of consecutive angles are supplementary.

Opposite Angles are Congruent

Something else that's true for all parallelograms is that their opposite angles are congruent. Those are the angles located at alternate (every other) vertices. Here's the proof of this theorem.

Given: ☐ABCD

Prove: ∠A ≅ ∠C and ∠B ≅ ∠D

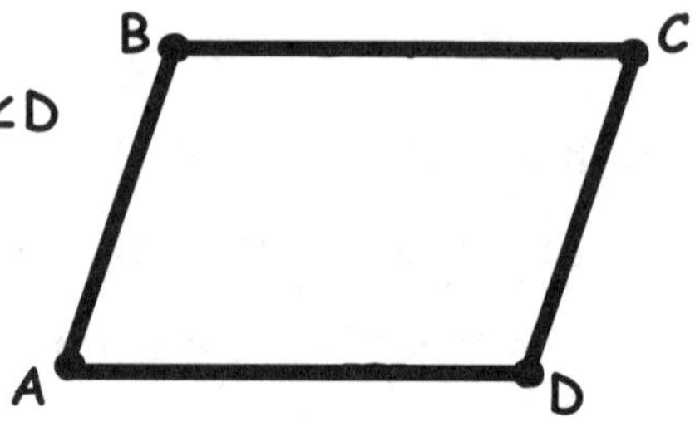

Statements	Reasons
1. $\square$ABCD	1. Given
2. ∠A and ∠D are supplementary. ∠D and ∠C are supplementary.	2. Consecutive pairs of angles of a parallelogram are supplementary.
3. ∠A ≅ ∠C	3. If two angles are supplementary to the same angle, then they are congruent.
4. ∠B and ∠C are supplementary. ∠C and ∠D are supplementary.	4. Consecutive pairs of angles of a parallelogram are supplementary.
5. ∠B ≅ ∠D	5. If two angles are supplementary to the same angle, then they are congruent.

Theorem 35	If a quadrilateral is a parallelogram, then both pairs of opposite angles are congruent (equal).

So to summarize, a parallelogram is a special quadrilateral that has both pairs of opposite sides parallel. And in all parallelograms the consecutive angles (the ones next to each other) are supplementary, and the opposite angles are congruent. If you experiment by drawing different shaped parallelograms (making sure that opposite sides are always parallel), you'll find that there's no way to draw a parallelogram without these angle relationships holding true.

Practice 52

a. In $\triangle RWE$, $m\angle R = 50$ and the measure of the exterior angle at W is 125. Which is the longest side of the triangle?

b. In $\triangle DEF$, $\angle F$ is obtuse. Which is the longest side of the triangle?

c. From the given statement below, tell the definition, property, postulate, or theorem that justifies the prove statement.

Given: Parallelogram *AEIO*;
Prove: $\angle E \cong \angle O$ and $\angle A \cong \angle I$

d. Find *x* in parallelogram *ARTV*.

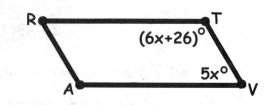

e. Do the proof below.

Given: Parallelogram *MNOP*, *MP* > *OP*
Prove: *m*$\angle NMO$ > *m*$\angle OMP$

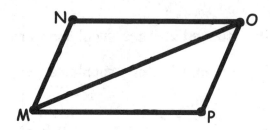

Problem Set 52

Tell whether each sentence below is True or False.

1. A parallelogram is a quadrilateral that has both pairs of opposite sides parallel.

2. Consecutive pairs of angles of a parallelogram are congruent.

Complete each sentence below by filling in the blanks.

3. The lower (and upper) _____ of an isosceles trapezoid are congruent.

4. _____ pairs of angles of a parallelogram are supplementary.

5. The sum of the measures of the angles of any quadrilateral is _____.

Answer each question below.

6. List each of the consecutive and opposite sides of quadrilateral *DPRT*.

7. List each of the consecutive and opposite angles of quadrilateral *DPRT*.

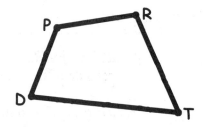

Complete each sentence below with *always*, *sometimes*, or *never*.

8. A trapezoid is _____ a quadrilateral.

9. A trapezoid is _____ isosceles.

Tell whether each statement below is the converse, inverse, or contrapositive of the following statement: If a quadrilateral is a parallelogram, then both pairs of its opposite sides are parallel.

10. If a quadrilateral is not a parallelogram, then both pairs of its opposite sides are not parallel.

11. If both pairs of opposite sides of a quadrilateral are parallel, then the quadrilateral is a parallelogram.

Answer each question below.

(a) 12. In $\triangle JFR$, $m\angle J = 35$ and the measure of the exterior angle at F is 115. Which is the longest side of the triangle?

13. In $\triangle MBV$, $m\angle M < m\angle V$ and $m\angle B > m\angle V$. Which is the largest angle of the triangle?

(b) 14. In $\triangle ABC$, $\angle A$ is obtuse. Which is the longest side of the triangle?

From each given statement below, tell the definition, property, postulate, or theorem that justifies each prove statement.

15. Given: $\overline{CK} \cong \overline{YJ}$, $\angle K$ and $\angle J$ **(c) 16.** Given: Parallelogram $WGHX$
         are right angles, $\angle K \cong \angle J$;   Prove: $\angle G \cong \angle X$ and $\angle W \cong \angle H$
     Prove: $\triangle CKY \cong \triangle YJC$

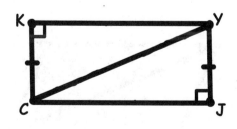

Find the measures of the angles of each triangle described below.

17. An isosceles triangle with a vertex angle of $42°$.

18. A triangle whose angles have measures in the ratio $3: 4: 5$. What kind of triangle is it?

Answer each question below.

19. Find z.

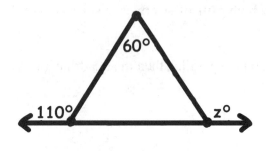

20. If $a = 69$, find e.

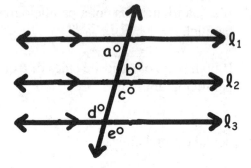

21. Find y in isosceles trapezoid *UMNI*

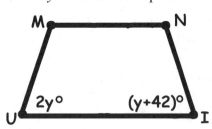

(d) 22. Find x in parallelogram *DLER*.

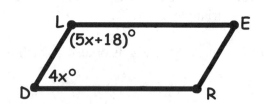

Do each proof below.

23. Given: *ABCD* and *AFGH* are
   parallelograms.
  Prove: $\angle G \cong \angle C$

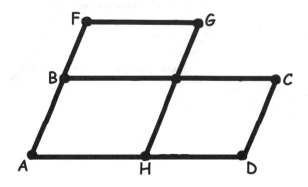

(e) 24. Given: Parallelogram *DFGJ*,
    $DJ > DF$
   Prove: $m\angle GJF > m\angle DJF$

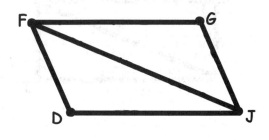

Lesson 53—Congruent Sides and Bisecting Diagonals

In the previous lesson, we covered two important theorems about parallelograms. As it turns out, there are two more parallelogram theorems that we should show you. The first one says that, in addition to being parallel, both pairs of sides of a parallelogram are also congruent. To see for yourself, take a close look at the opposite sides of the different parallelograms below.

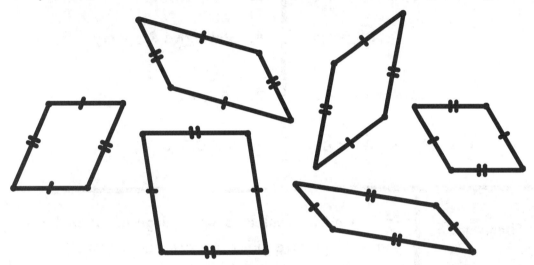

For any parallelogram, opposite pairs of sides are always congruent.

Proving Opposite Sides Congruent

In all these parallelograms, the pairs of opposite sides are congruent. Of course, in geometry it's not enough to say that the opposite sides *appear* to be congruent. We have to prove it deductively. So here's a proof of this new theorem.

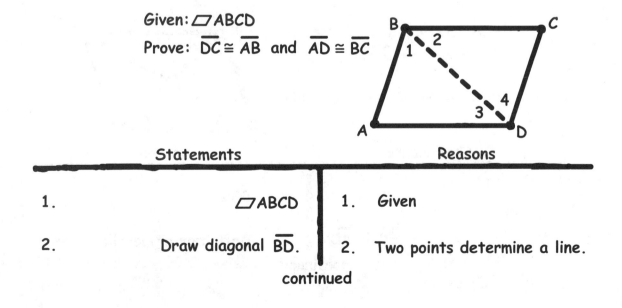

Given: ▱ABCD

Prove: $\overline{DC} \cong \overline{AB}$ and $\overline{AD} \cong \overline{BC}$

Statements	Reasons
1. ▱ABCD	1. Given
2. Draw diagonal $\overline{BD}$.	2. Two points determine a line.

continued

Statements	Reasons
3. ∠2 ≅ ∠3 and ∠1 ≅ ∠4	3. If two parallel lines are cut by a transversal, then their alternate interior angles are congruent.
4. $\overline{DB} \cong \overline{DB}$	4. Reflexive Property
5. △DCB ≅ △BAD	5. A.S.A.
6. $\overline{DC} \cong \overline{AB}$ and $\overline{AD} \cong \overline{BC}$	6. C.P.C.T.C.

Theorem 36	If a quadrilateral is a parallelogram, then both pairs of opposite sides are congruent (equal).

Proving Bisecting Diagonals

The next new theorem says that the two diagonals of any parallelogram bisect each other. That just means that each diagonal cuts the other one exactly in half. As always, this theorem has to be proved deductively. Here's the formal proof.

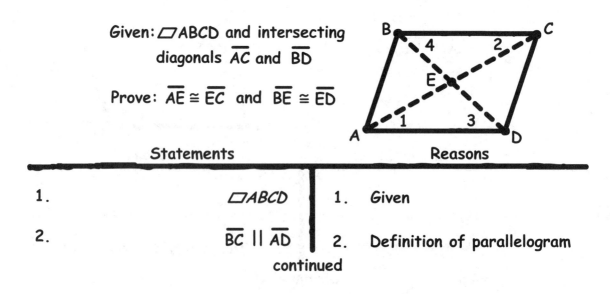

Given: ▱ABCD and intersecting diagonals $\overline{AC}$ and $\overline{BD}$

Prove: $\overline{AE} \cong \overline{EC}$ and $\overline{BE} \cong \overline{ED}$

Statements	Reasons
1. ▱ABCD	1. Given
2. $\overline{BC} \parallel \overline{AD}$	2. Definition of parallelogram

continued

334

	Statements		Reasons
3.	$\angle 1 \cong \angle 2$ and $\angle 3 \cong \angle 4$	3.	If two parallel lines are cut by a transversal, then their alternate interior angles are congruent.
4.	$\overline{AD} \cong \overline{BC}$	4.	Opposite sides of a parallalogram are congruent.
5.	$\triangle BEC \cong \triangle DEA$	5.	A.S.A.
6.	$\overline{AE} \cong \overline{EC}$ and $\overline{BE} \cong \overline{ED}$	6.	C.P.C.T.C.

Theorem 37	If a quadrilateral is a parallelogram, then the diagonals bisect each other.

We've covered a lot of ground in the last two lessons. So let's summarize all of the facts that we've learned about parallelograms. Whatever its specific shape, any parallelogram has to have the following five characteristics.

In any Parallelogram

1.	Both pairs of opposite sides are parallel (definition).
2.	Pairs of consecutive angles are supplementary (Theorem 34).
3.	Both pairs of opposite angles are congruent (Theorem 35).

In any Parallelogram (continued)

4.	Both pairs of opposite sides are congruent (Theorem 36).
5.	The diagonals bisect each other (Theorem 37).

Practice 53

a. In right triangle CSD, altitude $\overline{CF}$ is drawn to hypotenuse $\overline{SD}$. What is the longest side of $\triangle CFD$?

b. In $\overline{FL}$ (below), $FG = 5$, $JL = 4$, and $FL = 12$. What is the distance from F to the midpoint of $\overline{GJ}$?

c. From the given statement below, tell the definition, property, postulate, or theorem that justifies the prove statement.

Given: Parallelogram $ABCD$ (below);
Prove: $\overline{AP} \cong \overline{PC}$ and $\overline{BP} \cong \overline{PD}$.

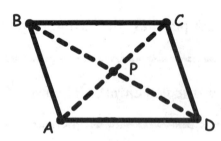

d. In parallelogram $CFHI$, $FP = 3y - 5$ and $PI = y - 3$, find y.

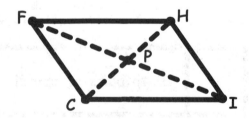

e. Do the proof below.

Given: Parallelogram $DEFG$, $\overline{DH} \cong \overline{FI}$
Prove: $\angle DEH \cong \angle FGI$

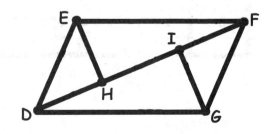

Problem Set 53

Tell whether each sentence below is true or false.

1. Both pairs of opposite sides of a parallelogram are congruent.

2. The diagonals of a parallelogram bisect each other.

Complete each sentence below by filling in the blanks.

3. A _____ is a quadrilateral that has one pair of opposite sides parallel.

4. A _____ is a quadrilateral that has both pairs of opposite sides parallel.

5. The diagonals of an isosceles trapezoid are _____.

Tell whether each figure below is a trapezoid, isosceles trapezoid, parallelogram, or just a plain quadrilateral.

6.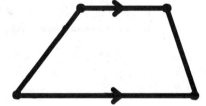

7.

8.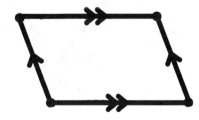

9.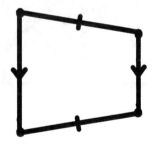

Write the converse, inverse, and contrapositive of each true statement below. Tell whether your answer is true or false.

10. If a figure is a parallelogram, then it is a quadrilateral.

11. If a figure is not a quadrilateral, then it is not a trapezoid.

Answer each question below.

(a) 12. In right triangle *BNP*, altitude $\overline{BC}$ is drawn to hypotenuse $\overline{NP}$. What is the longest side of $\triangle BCP$?

13. In $\triangle QPT$, $m\angle T = 20$ and the measure of the exterior angle at *P* is 118. Which is the longest side of the triangle?

(b) 14. In $\overline{AD}$ (below), $AB = 3$, $CD = 4$, and $AD = 10$. What is the distance from *D* to the midpoint of $\overline{BC}$?

From each given statement below, tell the definition, property, postulate, or theorem that justifies each prove statement.

15. Given: Parallelogram *GIWH* (on the right)
Prove: $\overline{GI} \cong \overline{HW}$ and $\overline{GH} \cong \overline{IW}$.

(c) 16. Given: Parallelogram *GIWH* (on the right)
Prove: $\overline{GO} \cong \overline{OW}$ and $\overline{IO} \cong \overline{OH}$.

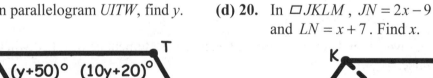

Answer each question below.

17. Find $p + q$.

18. Find *x*.

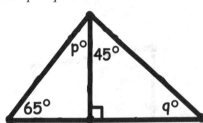

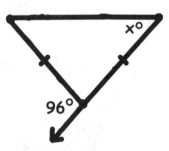

19. In parallelogram *UITW*, find *y*.

(d) 20. In $\square JKLM$, $JN = 2x - 9$ and $LN = x + 7$. Find *x*.

338

Write an equation to represent each question below; then solve the equation to get your answer.

21. In $\triangle DEF$, $m\angle D = 80$ and $m\angle E$ is three times $m\angle F$. Find $m\angle E$ and $m\angle F$.

22. Two angles are complementary. The measure of one angle is 6 greater than twice the other. Find the measures of *both* angles.

Do the proof below.

23. Given: $\overline{AB} \cong \overline{BC}$, $\overline{BM}$ is an altitude of $\triangle ABC$.

Prove: Point M is the midpoint of $\overline{AC}$.

(e) 24. Given: Parallelogram $SPQT$, $\overline{PK} \cong \overline{TL}$

Prove: $\angle PSK \cong \angle TQL$

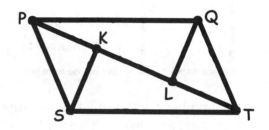

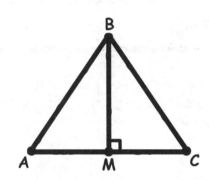

Lesson 54—Proving that it's a Parallelogram: Part 1

So far, we've started out with a parallelogram and then proved some fact that was true about it. But how do we prove that a figure is a parallelogram in the first place? In the next couple of lessons, we'll learn several methods for proving that a quadrilateral is actually a parallelogram.

According to its definition, a parallelogram has both pairs of opposite sides parallel. Therefore, one way to prove that a quadrilateral is a parallelogram is just to show that both pairs of its opposite sides are actually parallel.

Method 1: Use definition of parallelogram

> If both pairs of opposite sides are parallel, then a quadrilateral is a parallelogram.

The only problem with using the definition of a parallelogram (Method 1, as we'll call it) is that it sometimes takes awhile. That's why we're also going to show you some other methods—two more in this lesson and two in the next—that can be faster in some cases.

Both Pairs of Opposite Angles Congruent

Method 2 for proving that a quadrilateral is a parallelogram is to show that both pairs of opposite angles are congruent. If Method 2 sounds familiar, it's because it's actually the converse of Theorem 35 (from the last lesson). Remember, Theorem 35 says that if we already have a parallelogram, then both pairs of opposite angles have to be congruent. The converse just reverses the logic (which is what converses always do) by saying that if we know the pairs of opposite angles of a plain quadrilateral are congruent, then that quadrilateral is really a parallelogram. Here's the official version of Theorem 35 again.

> If a quadrilateral is a parallelogram, then pairs of opposite angles
> of a quadrilateral are congruent (equal).

Now to get the converse, we just change "if a, then b" to "if b, then a":

> If pairs of opposite angles of a quadrilateral are congruent (equal),
> then the quadrilateral is a parallelogram.

Before actually using this converse, we have to prove it. That's because the converse of a true statement doesn't necessarily have to be true (as we hope you understand by now). So here's the proof followed by the official theorem.

Given: In ABCD, m∠A = m∠C,
m∠B = m∠D

Prove: ABCD is a parallelogram

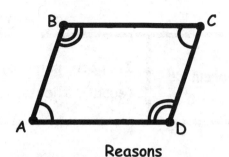

Statements	Reasons
1. In ABCD, m∠A = m∠C, m∠B = m∠D	1. Given
2. ∠A + ∠B + ∠C + ∠D = 360	2. The sum of the measures of the angles of a quadrilateral is 360.
3. ∠A + ∠D + ∠A + ∠D = 360 or 2∠A + 2∠D = 360	3. Substitution
4. ∠A + ∠D = 180	4. Division Property
5. ∠A and ∠D are supplementary.	5. Definition of supplementary angles
6. $\overline{AB} \parallel \overline{CD}$	6. If two lines form supplementary interior angles on the same side of the transversal, then the lines are parallel.
7. ∠A + ∠B = 180	7. Substitution
8. ∠A and ∠B are supplementary.	8. Definition of supplementary angles
9. $\overline{BC} \parallel \overline{AD}$	9. same as number 6
10. ABCD is a parallelogram	10. Definition of parallelogram

Method 2

Theorem 38	If both pairs of opposite angles are congruent (equal), then a quadrilateral is a parallelogram.

Both Pairs of Opposite Sides are Congruent

Method 3 for proving that a quadrilateral is a parallelogram is to show that both pairs of opposite *sides* are congruent. This is the converse of Theorem 36. Here's the proof and the official version of the new theorem.

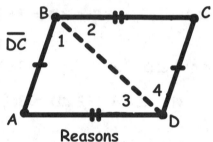

Given: In ABCD, $\overline{AD} \cong \overline{BC}$ and $\overline{AB} \cong \overline{DC}$

Prove: ABCD is a parallelogram

	Statements		Reasons
1.	In ABCD, $\overline{AD} \cong \overline{BC}$ and $\overline{AB} \cong \overline{DC}$	1.	Given
2.	Draw $\overline{BD}$	2.	Two points determine a line.
3.	$\overline{BD} \cong \overline{BD}$	3.	Reflexive Property
4.	$\triangle ABD \cong \triangle CDB$	4.	S.S.S.
5.	$\angle 2 \cong \angle 3, \angle 1 \cong \angle 4$	5.	C.P.C.T.C.
6.	$\overline{AB} \parallel \overline{CD}, \overline{BC} \parallel \overline{AD}$	6.	If two lines form congruent alternate interior angles with a transversal, then the lines are parallel.
7.	ABCD is a parallelogram	7.	Definition of parallelogram

Method 3

Theorem 39	If both pairs of opposite sides are congruent (equal), then a quadrilateral is a parallelogram.

Both Theorem 38 and 39 are sometimes easier to use, when proving a quadrilateral is a parallelogram, than having to show that the opposite sides are parallel. So use these whenever they seem better to you.

Practice 54

Tell whether each figure below is a trapezoid, isosceles trapezoid, parallelogram, or just a plain quadrilateral.

a.

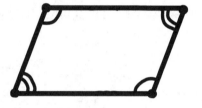

b.

c. From the given statement below, tell the definition, property, postulate, or theorem that justifies the prove statement.

Given: Quadrilateral $ABCD$ (on the right), $\overline{AB} \cong \overline{CD}$, $\overline{AD} \cong \overline{BC}$;
Prove: $ABCD$ is a parallelogram.

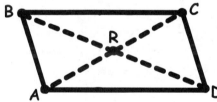

d. Find $m\angle EKD$.

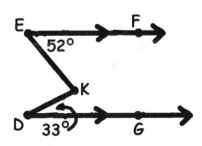

e. Do the proof below.
Given: Isosceles trapezoid $MNPQ$,
$\angle QSP \cong \angle QPS$
Prove: $MNSQ$ is a parallelogram.

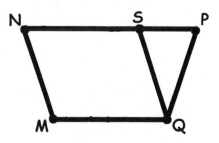

Problem Set 54

Tell whether each sentence below is true or false.

1. If both pairs of opposite sides are congruent, then a quadrilateral is a parallelogram.

2. If both pairs of opposite angles are congruent, then a quadrilateral is a parallelogram.

Complete each sentence below by filling in the blanks.

3. If a quadrilateral is a parallelogram, then _____ angles are supplementary.

4. The _____ of a parallelogram bisect each other.

5. The sum of the measures of the angles of any quadrilateral is _____.

Tell whether each figure below is a trapezoid, isosceles trapezoid, parallelogram, or just a plain quadrilateral.

6.

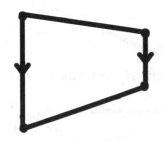

(a) 7.

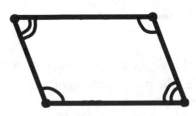

8.

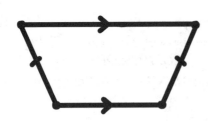

(b) 9.

Complete each sentence below with *always*, *sometimes*, or *never*.

10. The lower base angles of a trapezoid are _____ congruent.

11. Pairs of consecutive angles of a parallelogram are _____ congruent.

Tell whether each statement below is the converse, inverse, or contrapositive of the following statement: If a quadrilateral is a parallelogram, then pairs of its consecutive angles are supplementary.

12. If pairs of its consecutive angles are not supplementary, then a quadrilateral is not a parallelogram.

13. If pairs of its consecutive angles are supplementary, then a quadrilateral is a parallelogram.

Answer each question below.

14. In $\triangle GHJ$, $m\angle H = 110$, $m\angle J = 40$ and I is the point on $\overline{GJ}$ that makes $\overline{HI}$ bisect $\angle GHJ$. What is the longest side of $\triangle HIJ$?

15. In $\triangle EAO$, $EA = 7$, $AO = 4$ and $EO = 9$. Which is the largest angle of the triangle?

From each given statement below, tell the definition, property, postulate, or theorem that justifies each prove statement.

(c) 16. Given: Quadrilateral $LPQV$ (on the right),
$\overline{PL} \cong \overline{QV}$, $\overline{LV} \cong \overline{PQ}$;
Prove: $LPQV$ is a parallelogram.

17. Given: Quadrilateral $LPQV$ (above),
$\angle PLV \cong \angle PQV$, $\angle LPQ \cong \angle QVL$;
Prove: $LPQV$ is a parallelogram.

18. Given: Parallelogram $LPQV$ (above); Prove: $\overline{PM} \cong \overline{MV}$, $\overline{LM} \cong \overline{MQ}$.

Answer each question below.

19. Find $a + b$.

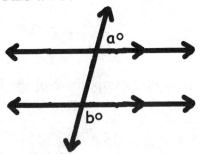

20. In parallelogram $RWCV$, find y.

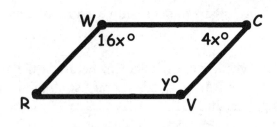

21. In isosceles trapezoid $ACEG$, find x.

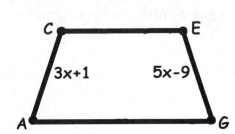

(d) 22. Find $m\angle TQR$.

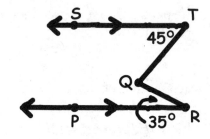

Do each proof below.

23. Given: Isosceles trapezoid $PQST$
Prove: $\triangle QSU$ is isosceles.

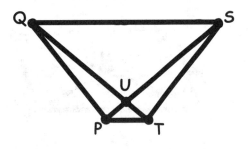

(e) 24. Given: Isosceles trapezoid $EFGH$,
$\angle FEJ \cong \angle FJE$
Prove: $FJGH$ is a parallelogram.

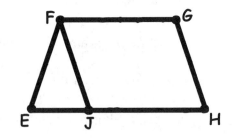

Lesson 55—Proving that it's a Parallelogram: Part 2

In Lesson 54, we learned several methods for proving that a quadrilateral is a parallelogram. We still have two methods to go, so let's do those now.

One Pair both Parallel and Congruent

According to our next method (Method 4), we can prove a quadrilateral is a parallelogram by showing that just one pair of opposite sides is both parallel and congruent. As an example, take a look at the quadrilateral on the right. If we know that $\overline{AB} \parallel \overline{CD}$ *and* $\overline{AB} \cong \overline{CD}$ (we need both), that's enough to prove that quadrilateral *ABCD* is a parallelogram. We could also do the proof by showing that $\overline{AD}$ and $\overline{BC}$ are both parallel and congruent. So either pair of opposite sides will work, as long as they're *both* parallel and congruent. As always, this new rule has to be proved deductively before we can use it. Here's an informal proof, followed by the official version of the theorem.

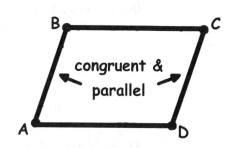

If $\overline{AB} \parallel \overline{CD}$ *and* $\overline{AB} \cong \overline{CD}$, then ABCD is a parallelogram.

Given: In ABCD, $\overline{AB} \parallel \overline{CD}$
and $\overline{AB} \cong \overline{CD}$

Prove: ABCD is a parallelogram.

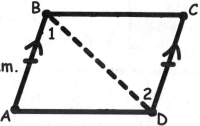

Draw $\overline{DB}$. Since $\overline{AB} \parallel \overline{CD}$, $\angle 1 \cong \angle 2$ (alternate interior angles are congruent.) Also, $\overline{AB} \cong \overline{CD}$ (Given) and $\overline{BD} \cong \overline{BD}$ (Reflexive). So $\triangle ABD \cong \triangle CDB$ (S.A.S.). Also, $\overline{BC} \cong \overline{AD}$ (C.P.C.T.C.). Therefore, *ABCD* is a parallelogram (A parallelogram has both pairs of opposite sides congruent.)

Method 4

Theorem 40	If one pair of opposite sides is both parallel and congruent (equal), then a quadrilateral is a parallelogram.

Bisecting Diagonals

The last method for proving that a quadrilateral is a parallelogram is to show that the diagonals bisect each other. This is the converse of Theorem 37 from a couple of lessons ago. Here's an informal proof of Method 5, which will become our Theorem 41.

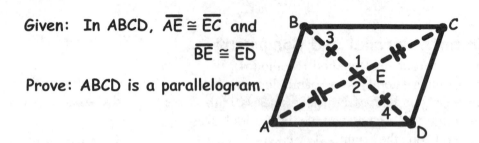

Given: In ABCD, $\overline{AE} \cong \overline{EC}$ and
$\overline{BE} \cong \overline{ED}$

Prove: ABCD is a parallelogram.

$\overline{AE} \cong \overline{EC}$ and $\overline{BE} \cong \overline{ED}$ (Given). $\angle 1 \cong \angle 2$ (Pairs of vertical angles are congruent.) $\triangle BEC \cong \triangle DEA$ (S.A.S.) So $\overline{AD} \cong \overline{BC}$ (C.P.C.T.C.). Also, $\angle 3 \cong \angle 4$ (C.P.C.T.C.), which means that $\overline{AD} \parallel \overline{BC}$ (alternate interior angles are congruent). Therefore, ABCD is a parallelogram (A parallelogram has one pair of sides both parallel and congruent.)

Method 5

Theorem 41	If the diagonals bisect each other, then a quadrilateral is a parallelogram.

A Summary of Five Methods

In the previous two lessons, we covered a total of five methods for proving that a quadrilateral is a parallelogram. And interestingly, most of these methods are just converses of some theorem that we had learned previously about parallelograms. For instance, we learned that in all parallelograms both pairs of opposite sides are congruent. But then our Method 3 for proving that a quadrilateral is a parallelogram is to show that both pairs of opposite sides are congruent. So even though converses of true statements don't have to be true, in the case of parallelograms, most of them are. Here's a summary of our five methods for proving that a quadrilateral is a parallelogram.

Five Methods for Proving a Quadrilateral is a Parallelogram

1.	Both pairs of opposite sides are parallel (definition).
2.	Both pairs of opposite angles are congruent (Theorem 38).
3.	Both pairs of opposite sides are congruent (Theorem 39).
4.	One pair of opposite sides is both parallel and congruent (Theorem 40).
5.	The diagonals bisect each other (Theorem 41).

Practice 55

a. From the given statement below, tell the definition, property, postulate, or theorem that justifies the prove statement.

Given: Quadrilateral $ABCD$ (on the right),
$\overline{AD} \parallel \overline{BC}$, $\overline{AD} \cong \overline{BC}$;
Prove: $ABCD$ is a parallelogram.

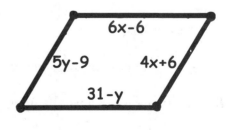

b. Find p, q, r, and s.

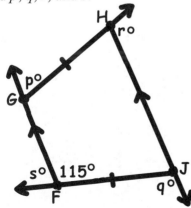

c. In the parallelogram below, find x and y.

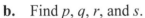

6x-6

5y-9   4x+6

31-y

d. Two angles are supplementary. The measure of one angle is 6 less than 20% of the other. Find the measures of *both* angles.

e. Do the proof below.

Given: $\triangle KJL \cong \triangle MNL$;
$\qquad$ N is the midpoint of $\overline{MO}$.
Prove: *KJON* is a parallelogram.

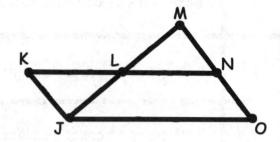

Problem Set 55

Tell whether each sentence below is true or false.

1. If one pair of opposite angles is both congruent and acute, then a quadrilateral is a parallelogram.

2. If the diagonals are congruent, then a quadrilateral is a parallelogram.

Complete each sentence below by filling in the blanks.

3. If both pairs of _____ sides are congruent, then a quadrilateral is a parallelogram.

4. If both pairs of _____ angles are congruent, then a quadrilateral is a parallelogram.

5. A _____ is a quadrilateral that has one pair of opposite sides parallel.

6. The two parallel sides of a trapezoid are called its _____.

Write the converse, inverse, and contrapositive of each false statement below. Tell whether your answer is true or false.

7. If a figure is a polygon, then it is a quadrilateral.

8. If a figure is not a parallelogram, then it is not a polygon.

Answer each question below.

9. In $\triangle CDS$, $CD = 16$, $CS = 12$ and $DS = 8$. Which is the smallest angle of the triangle?

10. In $\triangle KLQ$, $KL > LQ$ and $KL < KQ$. Which is the smallest angle of $\triangle KLQ$?

11. In right triangle WRT, $m\angle W = 50$ and $\angle R$ is a right angle. What is the shortest side of $\triangle WRT$?

State which shortcut can be used to prove each pair of triangles below congruent. If no method applies, say "none."

12.

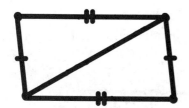

13.

From each given statement below, tell the definition, property, postulate, or theorem that justifies each prove statement.

(a) 14. Given: Quadrilateral $RSTU$ (on the right), $\overline{RS} \parallel \overline{UT}$, $\overline{RS} \cong \overline{UT}$;
Prove: $RSTU$ is a parallelogram.

15. Given: Quadrilateral $RSTU$ (on the right), $\overline{SP} \cong \overline{UP}$, $\overline{RP} \cong \overline{PT}$;
Prove: $RSTU$ is a parallelogram.

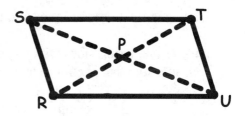

16. Given: Quadrilateral $RSTU$ (above), $\overline{RS} \cong \overline{UT}$, $\overline{ST} \cong \overline{RU}$; Prove: $\triangle RST \cong \triangle TUR$.

Answer each question below.

17. Find x.

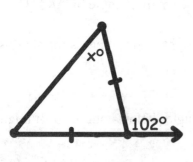

(b) 18. Find u, x, y, and z.

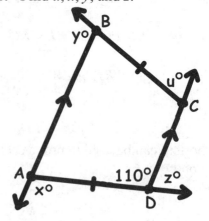

19. In the parallelogram below, find x, y, and z.

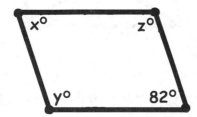

(c) 20. In the parallelogram below, find x and y.

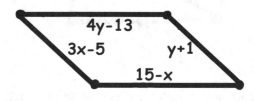

Write an equation to represent each question below; then solve the equation to get your answer.

21. The exterior sides of two adjacent angles make a right angle. The first angle has a measure that is 6 more than half of the second. What are the measures of *both* angles?

(d) 22. Two angles are supplementary. The measure of one angle is 5 greater than 40% of the other. Find the measures of *both* angles.

Do the proof below.

(e) 23. Given: $\triangle BCD \cong \triangle EFD$,

B is the midpoint of $\overline{AC}$.
Prove: $ABEF$ is a parallelogram.

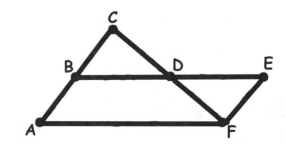

352

Fill in the blanks of the proof below. This will become our Theorem 42.

24. Given: $\triangle ABC$, D is the midpoint of $\overline{AB}$ and E is the midpoint of $\overline{AC}$.

Prove: $\overline{DE} \parallel \overline{BC}$ and $DE = \dfrac{1}{2} BC$.

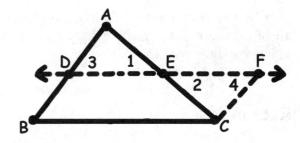

(1) Draw $\overleftrightarrow{DE}$. (Two points determine a line.)

(2) Choose point F on $\overrightarrow{DE}$ so that $EF = DE$. (Ruler Postulate).

(3) Draw $\overline{CF}$. (Two points determine a line.)

(4) $AE = EC$ (_____)

(5) $\angle 1 \cong \angle 2$ (_____)

(6) $\triangle ADE \cong \triangle CFE$ (_____)

(7) $BD = DA$ (Definition of midpoint)

(8) $DA = CF$ (C.P.C.T.C.)

(9) $BD = CF$ (_____)

(10) $\angle 3 \cong \angle 4$ (_____)

(11) $\overline{BD} \parallel \overline{CF}$ (or $\overline{BA} \parallel \overline{CF}$) (If two lines form congruent alternate interior angles with a transversal, then the lines are parallel.)

(12) $BCFD$ is a parallelogram (_____)

(13) $\overline{DE} \parallel \overline{BC}$ (or $\overline{DF} \parallel \overline{BC}$) and $DF = BC$ (_____)

(14) $DE = \dfrac{1}{2} DF$ (Definition of midpoint)

(15) $DE = \dfrac{1}{2} BC$ (Substitution)

Theorem 42	The line segment joining the midpoints of two sides of a triangle is parallel to the third side and is one-half its length.

Lesson 56—Rectangles, Rhombuses, and Squares

We've been learning about parallelograms. And by now you've probably realized that not all of them are alike. That's why we need to spend a little time learning about several special kinds of parallelograms.

Rectangles

The first is a **rectangle**. You may have never thought of a rectangle as a parallelogram. But it is, because both pairs of its opposite sides are parallel. What's "special" about a rectangle, though, is that all four of its angles are congruent (rather than just opposite angles, like most parallelograms). So we could say that a rectangle is an "equiangular parallelogram." A picture of a rectangle is shown on the right. Since the angles of any quadrilateral add to equal 360, each angle of a rectangle has to be a right angle (90°). This fact is in the official definition of a rectangle.

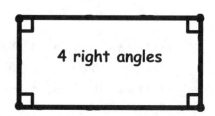

4 right angles

A rectangle is a parallelogram
with all four angles congruent.

Definition 46	A *rectangle* is a parallelogram with four right angles.

Of course, rectangles can have lots of different shapes. But whether they're tall or short, fat or skinny, they all have four right angles. That's what separates rectangles from other parallelograms.

Rhombuses

There's another special parallelogram that you probably haven't heard of. It's called a rhombus. A **rhombus** is a parallelogram where all four of its sides are congruent (unlike most parallelograms that just have opposite sides congruent). A rhombus has the shape of a diamond, as you can see on the right. Notice the little marks on the sides. Those show that all four sides are the same length. Here's the official definition of a rhombus.

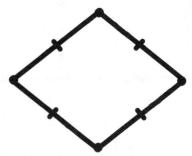

A rhombus is a parallelogram with
all four sides congruent.

Definition 47	A *rhombus* is a parallelogram with four congruent sides.

Rhombuses can also have different shapes (like rectangles). But every rhombus basically looks like a diamond. Some rhombuses are turned to one side, however, which can make the diamond a little harder to recognize. Here are a few more rhombus examples.

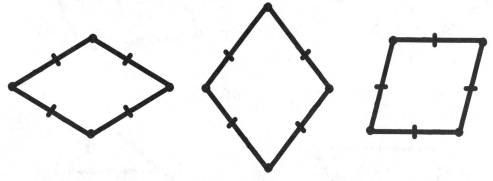

Three rhombuses with different shapes.

Squares

The simplest and most famous special parallelogram of all is the square. As you already know, a **square** has both four congruent (and right) angles and four congruent sides. So a square actually qualifies as both a rectangle and a rhombus. Here's the official definition of a square.

Definition 48	A *square* is a parallelogram with four congruent sides and four congruent (right) angles.

Even though you already know what a square looks like, we'll include a picture of one on the right. One interesting thing about squares is that they are all exactly the same shape. That's because there's no way for a parallelogram to have four congruent sides and four right angles without being shaped as a square.

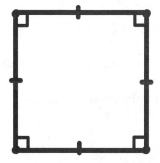

A square is a parallelogram with four congruent sides and four congruent angles.

Practice 56

Tell whether the figure below is a trapezoid, isosceles trapezoid, parallelogram, rectangle, rhombus, square, or just a plain quadrilateral.

a.

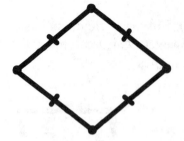

b.

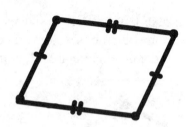

c. In $\square ABCD$, find b in terms of a and c.

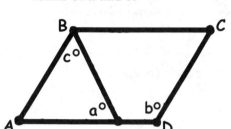

d. Find y.

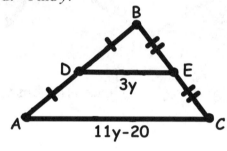

e. Do the proof below.

Given: $ABCD$ is a rhombus.
$\overline{BE} \cong \overline{CF}$; $\overline{CE} \cong \overline{FD}$
Prove: $ABCD$ is a square.

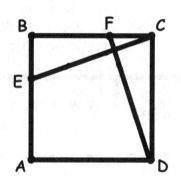

Problem Set 56

Tell whether each sentence below is true or false.

1. A rectangle is a parallelogram with four congruent (and right) angles.

2. A rhombus is a parallelogram with four congruent sides.

Complete each sentence below by filling in the blanks.

3. The line segment joining the midpoints of two sides of a triangle is _____ to the third side and _____ its length.

4. If the diagonals _____, then a quadrilateral is a parallelogram.

5. A _____ is a parallelogram with four congruent (and right) angles and four congruent sides.

Tell whether each figure below is a trapezoid, isosceles trapezoid, parallelogram, rectangle, rhombus, square, or just a plain quadrilateral.

6. 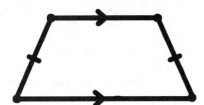   **7.**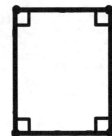

(a) **8.**    **(b)** **9.**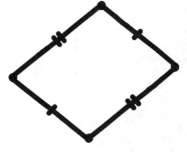

Complete each sentence below with *always*, *sometimes*, or *never*.

10. A rhombus is _____ a parallelogram.

11. A rectangle _____ has acute angles.

12. A parallelogram is _____ a square.

Tell whether each statement below is the converse, inverse, or contrapositive of the following statement: If a parallelogram is a rectangle, then its angles are all congruent.

13. If the angles of a parallelogram are all congruent, then it is a rectangle.

14. If a parallelogram is not a rectangle, then its angles are not all congruent.

Find the measures of the angles of each triangle described below.

15. A triangle whose angles have measures in the ratio 1: 2: 6.

16. A right triangle where one of the two acute angles measures 2 times the other.

Answer each question below.

17. In $\triangle DFG$, $FG < DG$ and $DF > DG$. Which is the smallest angle of $\triangle DFG$?

18. In $\triangle ABC$, $m\angle A = 35$ and the measure of the exterior angle at C is 100. Which is the longest side of the triangle?

Answer each question below.

19. In square *HJKR*, find *b*.

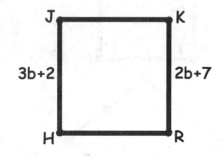

(c) 20. In $\square STUV$, find *y* in terms of *x* and *z*.

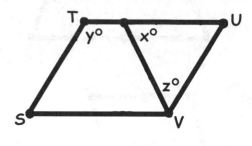

21. Find *g*.

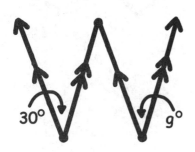

(d) 22. Find *x*.

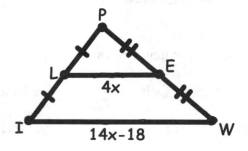

Do each proof below.

23. Given: Rectangle *DEFG*,
        T is the midpoint of $\overline{EF}$.
    Prove: $\triangle DTG$ is isosceles.

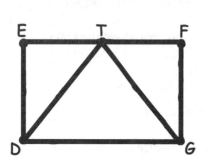

(e) 24. Given: *JKLM* is a rhombus.
        $\overline{KP} \cong \overline{JQ}$, $\overline{LP} \cong \overline{KQ}$
    Prove: *JKLM* is a square.

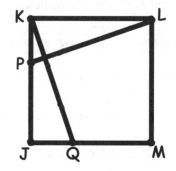

Lesson 57—The Big Picture

In this last lesson of the chapter, we're going to cover two new theorems on diagonals, and then we'll step back to look at "the big picture." That means we're going to see how all of the quadrilaterals are related to one another.

Diagonals of a Rectangle

Our first diagonals theorem is about rectangles. Since a rectangle is a parallelogram, we already know that one of its diagonals bisects the other.[2] But in a rectangle, not only do the diagonals bisect each other, but they are also congruent. That makes sense when you look a picture (see below). Since a rectangle is straight, the diagonals are the same length. In a plain parallelogram, which is slanted to one side, one diagonal is longer than the other. Here's an informal proof of this new theorem.

Given: Rectangle ABCD

Prove: $\overline{AC} \cong \overline{BD}$

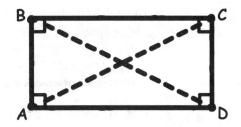

$\angle DAB$ and $\angle ADC$ are right angles (Definition of rectangle). $\angle DAB \cong \angle ADC$ (All right angles are congruent.) $\overline{AB} \cong \overline{CD}$ (A rectangle/parallelogram has both pairs of opposite sides congruent.) $\overline{AD} \cong \overline{AD}$ (Reflexive). Therefore, $\triangle DAB \cong \triangle ADC$ (S.A.S.) and $\overline{AC} \cong \overline{BD}$ (C.P.C.T.C.)

Theorem 43	The diagonals of a rectangle are congruent.

Diagonals of a Rhombus

The next theorem is about the diagonals of a rhombus. They bisect each other, of course, since a rhombus is just a special kind of parallelogram. But the diagonals also happen to be perpendicular to each other. Here's an informal proof of this one.

---

[2] Remember, Theorem 37 says that if a quadrilateral is a parallelogram, then the diagonals bisect each other.

Given: Rhombus LMNT, diagonals

$\overline{MT}$ and $\overline{LN}$ intersect at P.

Prove: $\overline{LN} \perp \overline{MT}$

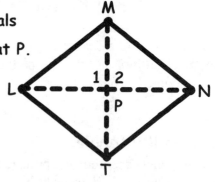

$\overline{LM} \cong \overline{MN}$ (Definition of rhombus). $\overline{LP} \cong \overline{PN}$ (The diagonals of a rhombus/parallelogram bisect each other.) $\overline{MP} \cong \overline{MP}$ (Reflexive). That means $\triangle LMP \cong \triangle NMP$ (S.S.S.). Therefore, $\angle 1 \cong \angle 2$ (C.P.C.T.C.) $\angle 1$ and $\angle 2$ are right angles. (If two angles in a linear pair are congruent, then they are right angles.). So, $\overline{LN} \perp \overline{MT}$ (Perpendicular lines intersect to form right angles.)

Theorem 44	The diagonals of a rhombus are perpendicular to each other.

Putting it All Together

Now let's look at how all of the different quadrilaterals that we've studied in this chapter are related. There are two basic types of quadrilaterals: trapezoids and parallelograms. Trapezoids have just one pair of opposite sides that are parallel. Parallelograms have two pairs of opposite sides that are parallel. There's only one type of special trapezoid: the isosceles trapezoid, which has two congruent legs.

However, as we saw in the last lesson, there are three special types of parallelograms: rectangles, rhombuses, and squares. A rectangle has four congruent (and right) angles. A rhombus has four congruent sides. A square is actually both a rectangle and rhombus, because its sides and its angles are all congruent. The diagram on the next page may help you memorize all of this.

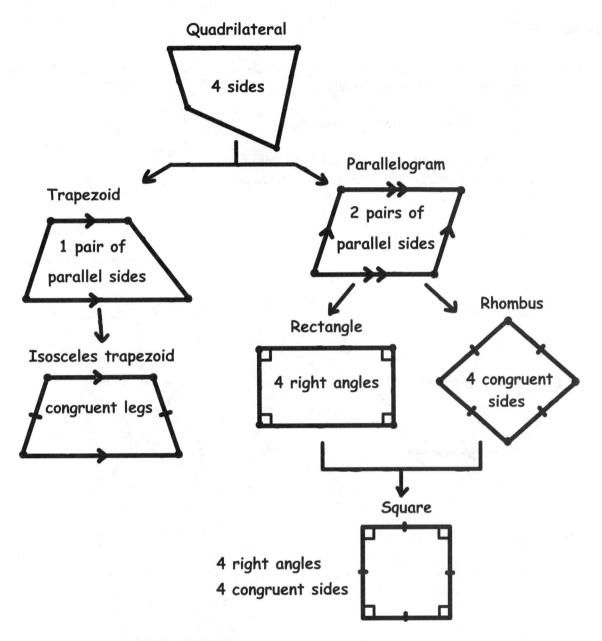

One important thing to understand about this diagram is that every figure has all the characteristics or "properties" as the ones above it, plus all of its own unique properties. So, for example, a rectangle has all the properties of a parallelogram and of a plain quadrilateral: It has opposite sides parallel and, it has four sides (like any quadrilateral). Similarly, an isosceles trapezoid has all the properties of a plain trapezoid and of a quadrilateral. A square, since it's at the very bottom has all the properties of a rectangle, a rhombus, a parallelogram, and a plain quadrilateral. This means that if you are doing a proof with a rectangle, then you can use any theorems on rectangles plus theorems for parallelograms or quadrilaterals. All of those apply too. And the same goes for all the other figures. You can use theorems for all the figures that are above them in this diagram.

Practice 57

a. Write the converse, inverse, and contrapositive of the true statement below. Tell whether your answer is true or false.

If a figure is a square, then it is a rectangle.

b. From each given statement below, tell the definition, property, postulate, or theorem that justifies each prove statement.

Given: Rhombus $ALNM$ (on the right);
Prove: $\overline{AN} \perp \overline{LM}$.

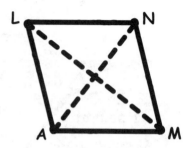

c. Find a, b, and c.

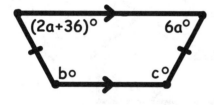

d. In rhombus $ABCD$, $m\angle BEC = 4x + 2$, $m\angle BAD = 3x + 19$. Find $m\angle ADC$.

e. Do the proof below.

Given: Rhombus $LKJN$
Prove: $\angle 1 \cong \angle 2$, $\angle 3 \cong \angle 4$

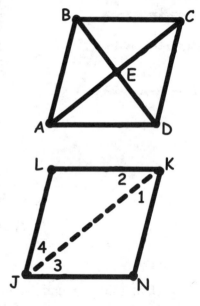

Problem Set 57

Tell whether each sentence below is True or False.

1. The diagonals of a parallelogram are congruent.

2. The diagonals of a rhombus are perpendicular to each other.

Complete each sentence below by filling in the blanks.

3. A _____ is a parallelogram with four congruent (and right) angles.

4. A _____ is a parallelogram with four congruent sides.

5. A _____ is a quadrilateral that has one pair of opposite sides parallel.

6. If both pairs of _____ sides are congruent, then a quadrilateral is a parallelogram.

Tell whether each figure below is a trapezoid, isosceles trapezoid, parallelogram, rectangle, rhombus, square, or just a plain quadrilateral.

7.

8.

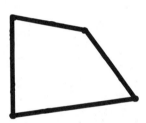

9.

Write the converse, inverse, and contrapositive of each true statement below. Tell whether your answer is true or false.

10. If a figure is not a parallelogram, then it is not a rectangle.

(a) 11. If a figure is a square, then it is a rhombus.

Answer each question below.

12. In $\overline{RU}$ (below), $RS = 5$, $RU = 16$, and $TU = 4$. What is the distance from R to the midpoint of $\overline{ST}$?

13. In $\triangle ABC$, $AB = 6.2$, $AC = 9.5$ and $BC = 5.1$. Which is the smallest angle of the triangle?

363

From each given statement below, tell the definition, property, postulate, or theorem that justifies each prove statement.

14. Given: Rectangle *HDSK* (below);   **(b) 15.** Given: Rhombus *BRYT* (below);
Prove: $\overline{HS} \cong \overline{DK}$.   Prove: $\overline{BY} \perp \overline{RT}$.

   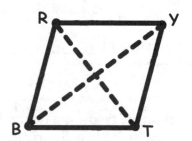

16.   Given: $\triangle GHJ$, $\overline{GH} \cong \overline{HJ}$; Prove: $\angle G \cong \angle J$

Answer each question below.

17.   If $\overline{AC} \parallel \overline{DE}$, find *x*.   **18.**   In $\square SDFL$, find $m\angle S$ and $m\angle D$.

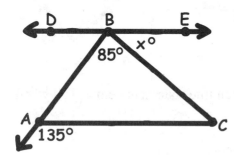   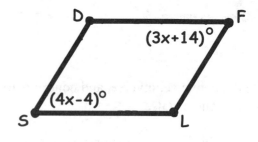

(c) 19.   Find *x*, *y*, and *z*.   **(d) 20.**   In rhombus *DFIP*, $m\angle FOI = 4x + 10$
and $m\angle FDP = 3x + 4$. Find $m\angle DPI$.

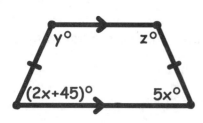   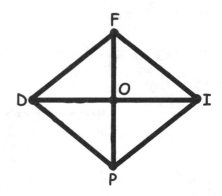

Write an equation to represent each question below; then solve the equation to get your answer.

21. In $\triangle ABC$, $m\angle C = 60$ and $m\angle A$ is two times $m\angle B$. Find $m\angle A$ and $m\angle B$.

22. Two angles are complementary. The measure of one angle is 80% of the other. Find the measures of *both* angles.

Do each proof below. Number 24 will become our Theorem 45.

23. Given: Rectangle $ATPZ$, $\overline{TV} \cong \overline{BZ}$
  Prove: $\overline{AV} \cong \overline{PB}$

(e) 24. Given: Rhombus $ABCD$
  Prove: $\angle 1 \cong \angle 2$, $\angle 3 \cong \angle 4$

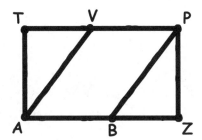
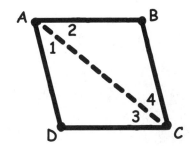

Theorem 45	The diagonals of a rhombus bisect the angles at the vertices which they join.

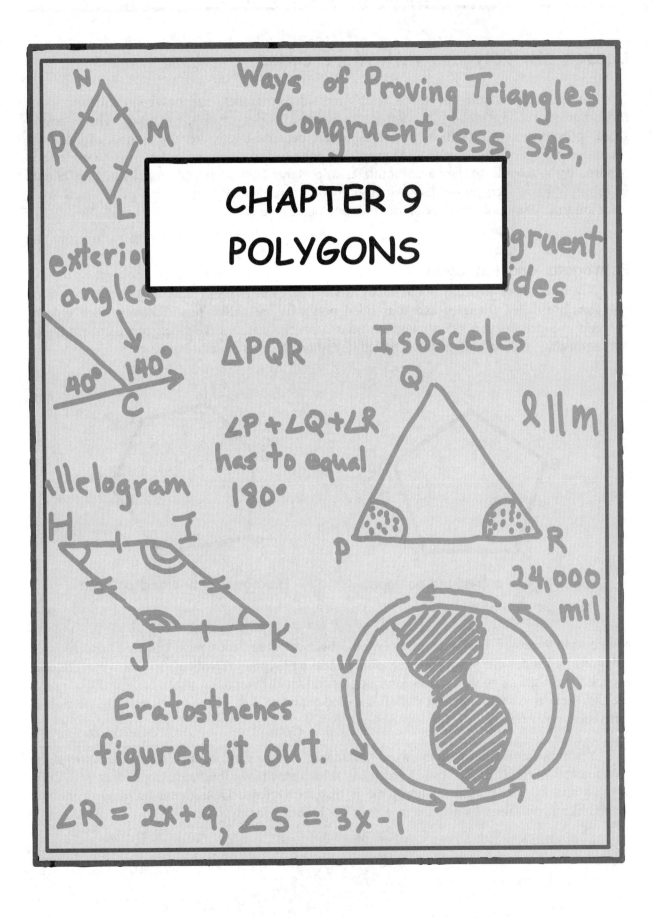

Ways of Proving Triangles Congruent: SSS, SAS,

**CHAPTER 9
POLYGONS**

exterior angles

congruent sides

△PQR

Isosceles

$\ell \parallel m$

40° 140°
C

∠P + ∠Q + ∠R
has to equal
180°

Parallelogram

Eratosthenes
figured it out.

24,000
mil

∠R = 2x + 9, ∠S = 3x - 1

Lesson 58—Polygons with More Sides

So far, we've studied polygons with three sides (triangles) and polygons with four-sides (quadrilaterals). There are also polygons with 5 sides, 6 sides, 7 sides, and on up. These "many-sided" polygons, as we'll call them, can be tough, because the greater the number of sides, the more complicated things become. Many-sided polygons are not as common as triangles and quadrilaterals, though, so they aren't quite as important. That's why, in this chapter, we'll only learn a few basic facts about many-sided polygons. And actually, every one of the facts we'll learn are true for all polygons, even triangles and quadrilaterals.

Pentagons and Hexagons

The first thing to learn about many-sided polygons is their names. Just as three-sided polygons are called triangles and four-sided polygons are called quadrilaterals, each type of polygon (5-sided ones, 6-sided ones, etc.) has a special name. Five-sided polygons are called **pentagons**, and 6-sided polygons are called **hexagons**. Here is a picture of each.

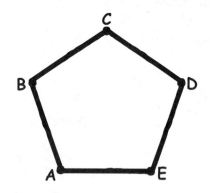

Pentagon: a 5-sided polygon

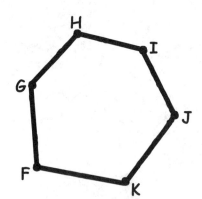

Hexagon: a 6-sided polygon

Notice that these are both convex polygons, because their sides push outward. (Remember, polygons with sides that "cave" in are called concave polygons.)[1] Notice also that we put a letter at each vertex, the same way we do for triangles and quadrilaterals. And the names of the figures use those letters. So the figure on the left is called pentagon *ABCDE* and the figure on the right is called hexagon *FGHIJK*.

You may be familiar with the word "pentagon," by the way, because that's the name of the headquarters of the U.S. Defense Department, which was hit in the tragic September 11th, 2001 terrorist attacks. The reason for the name is that the Defense Department building is literally shaped like a pentagon. It's also the largest office building in the world.

---

[1] We won't study concave many-sided polygons.

Here's an overhead view of the Pentagon building. Notice the similarity in shape between it and our pentagon *ABCDE*.

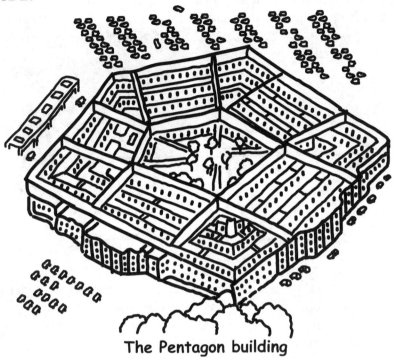

The Pentagon building

Up to Ten Sides

Now let's move to polygons with even more sides. A 7-sided polygon is called a **heptagon**, an 8-sided polygon is called an **octagon**, a 9-sided polygon is called a **nonagon**. Finally, a 10-sided polygon is called a **decagon**. There are names for polygons with an even greater number of sides, but since they're not used much, we'll stop at 10. We don't have room to show you a picture of every one of these new polygons either. We'll just show an octagon (which is fairly common) and a decagon.

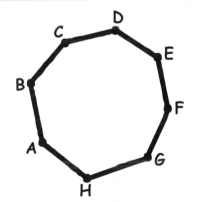

Octagon: an 8-sided polygon

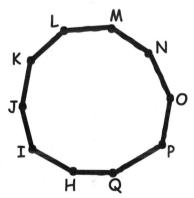

Decagon: a 10-sided polygon

These are also both convex polygons. And notice that the number of angles equals the number of sides in each of these cases as well. The octagon has 8 angles and the decagon has 10 angles.

Even More Diagonals

Many-sided polygons have diagonals, just as triangles and quadrilaterals do. In fact, the more sides a polygon has, the greater its number of diagonals. That's because a polygon has a diagonal running between every two non-consecutive vertices. Here are the pentagon and hexagon from above with their diagonals drawn in.

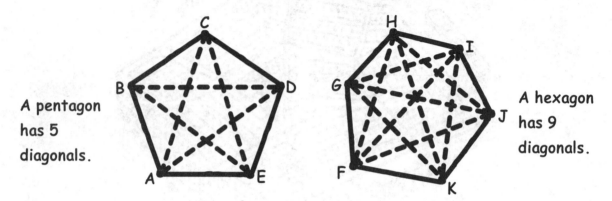

A pentagon has 5 diagonals.

A hexagon has 9 diagonals.

From our examples, you can see that the number of diagonals does not always equal the number of sides of the polygon. That's obvious from our work with triangles and quadrilaterals: a triangle, which has 3 sides, doesn't have any diagonals at all (It has no non-consecutive vertices to connect). And a quadrilateral, with 4 sides, has only 2 diagonals. Actually, as the number of sides of a polygon goes up, the number of diagonals goes up even faster.[2] To finish this lesson, we'll show you a table of all the polygon names from the 3-sided triangle to the 10-sided decagon.

Number of Sides	Name of Polygon
3	Triangle
4	Quadrilateral
5	Pentagon
6	Hexagon
7	Heptagon
8	Octagon
9	Nonagon
10	Decagon

---

[2] There's a way to calculate the number of diagonals in any polygon. If the polygon has N sides, then the number of its diagonals (D) can be found with this equation: $D = \dfrac{1}{2}N(N-3)$.

Practice 58

a. Name the type of polygon below and whether it's convex or concave.

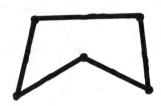

b. Draw all of the diagonals in the polygon below. Tell how many diagonals there are.

c. In rectangle *DLMV*, find *x* and *y*.

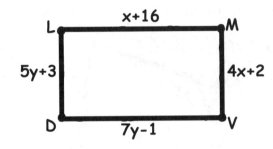

d. Find $a + b + c$.

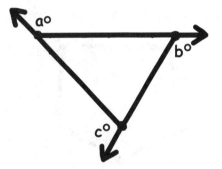

e. Do the proof below.

Given: Parallelogram *AECF*, $\overline{BE} \cong \overline{DF}$;
Prove: *ABCD* is a parallelogram.

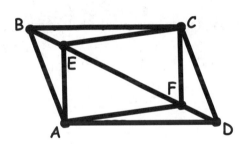

Problem Set 58

Tell whether each sentence below is True or False.

1. A polygon can have a maximum of 8 sides.

2. The number of angles of a polygon is equal to the number of its sides.

Complete each sentence below by filling in the blanks.

3. A 5-sided polygon is called a _____, and a 6-sided polygon is called a _____.

4. The _____ of a rhombus bisect the angles at the vertices which they join.

5. A _____ is a parallelogram with four congruent (and right) angles and four congruent sides.

Name the type of each polygon below and tell whether it's convex or concave.

6.

(a) 7.

8.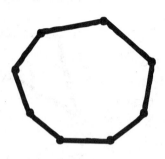

Draw all of the diagonals in each polygon below and tell how many diagonals there are.

(b) 9.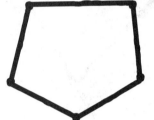

10.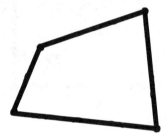

Complete each sentence below with *always*, *sometimes*, or *never*.

11. A parallelogram is _____ a rhombus.

12. A square is _____ a rectangle.

Tell whether each statement below is the converse, inverse, or contrapositive of the following statement: If a figure is a polygon with 10 sides, then it is a decagon.

13. If a figure is not a decagon, then it is not a polygon with 10 sides.

14. If a figure is not a polygon with 10 sides, then it is not a decagon.

Answer each question below.

15. In $\triangle TYK$, $TY > TK$ and $YK < TK$. If one of the angles in $\triangle TYK$ is obtuse, which angle is it?

16. In $\triangle PLW$, $m\angle L = 104$ and the measure of the exterior angle at P is 143. Which is the shortest side of the triangle?

From each given statement below, tell the definition, property, postulate, or theorem that justifies each prove statement.

17. Given: $\overline{AE} \cong \overline{IO}$, $\overline{AO} \cong \overline{EI}$; (on the right)
Prove: $AEIO$ is a parallelogram.

18. Given: Parallelogram $AEIO$ (on the right);
Prove: $\angle A \cong \angle I$, $\angle E \cong \angle O$.

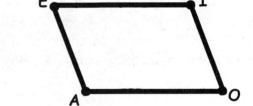

Answer each question below.

19. Find x.

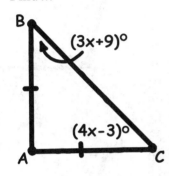

(c) 20. In rectangle $CDGH$, find x and y.

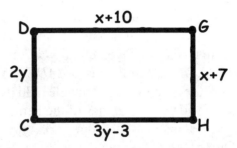

21. In square $WXYZ$, find p and q.

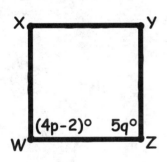

(d) 22. Find $r + s + t$.

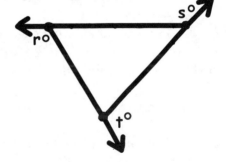

Do each proof below.

23. Given: Rhombus $TCBV$,
$\overline{CU} \perp \overline{BV}$, $\overline{CS} \perp \overline{TV}$
Prove: $\overline{CU} \cong \overline{CS}$

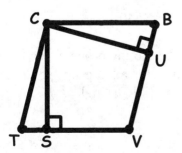

(e) 24. Given: Parallelogram $RJTI$,
$\overline{EI} \cong \overline{SJ}$
Prove: $ERST$ is a parallelogram.

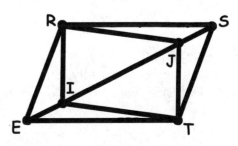

Lesson 59—Adding Up the Angles of any Polygon

So far, we've been talking mostly about the sides of a polygon. But now we're going to shift to the angles of a polygon. You already know that the sum of the angles of any triangle is 180°, and the sum of the angles of any quadrilateral is 360°. But what about the sum of the angles of any pentagon or hexagon, or of polygons with even more sides?

Splitting it into Triangles

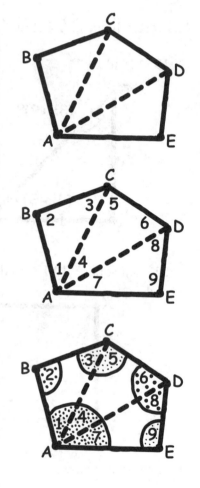

In this lesson, we'll show you a method for calculating the sum of the angles of *any* polygon, no matter how many sides it has. To see how the method works, take a look at the pentagon on the top right. Notice that we've drawn in two diagonals starting from vertex A. We could have drawn the diagonals from any one of the other vertices. It wouldn't have mattered. The important thing is that these diagonals divide the pentagon into three triangles: $\triangle ABC$, $\triangle ACD$, and $\triangle ADE$. And since we already know that the angles of a triangle add to 180°, we can now calculate the sum of the angles of the pentagon. All we have to do is add up the angles of the three triangles. The grand total will equal the angles of the pentagon. First, the angles of the three triangles are numbered and indicated in the middle right diagram. Now, we just add up the three angles of $\triangle ABC$.

$$m\angle 1 + m\angle 2 + m\angle 3 = 180$$

Next, we do the same thing for $\triangle ACD$ and $\triangle ADE$.

$$m\angle 4 + m\angle 5 + m\angle 6 = 180 \qquad m\angle 7 + m\angle 8 + m\angle 9 = 180$$

If you look carefully at the diagram on the bottom right, you'll see that $m\angle A$ equals $m\angle 1 + m\angle 4 + m\angle 7$, $m\angle B$ equals $m\angle 2$, $m\angle C$ equals $m\angle 3 + m\angle 5$, $m\angle D$ equals $m\angle 6 + m\angle 8$, and $m\angle E$ equals $m\angle 9$. By adding angles 1 through 9, we are really adding angles A through E, which is what we want.

$$m\angle 1 + m\angle 2 + m\angle 3 + m\angle 4 + m\angle 5 + m\angle 6 + m\angle 7 + m\angle 8 + m\angle 9 = 540$$

$$m\angle A + m\angle B + m\angle C + m\angle D + m\angle E = 540$$

So the sum of the angles of any pentagon is 540°. And the key to the process was to divide the pentagon into triangles. Basically, this is the way the method for adding up the angles of any polygon works. Using diagonals, we divide up the polygon into little triangles.

Hexagons and Octagons Too

Now let's quickly go through the same process on a hexagon and on an octagon. At first, you might think that we would need a separate theorem to prove each one of these. Using diagonals, we can divide the hexagon into four triangles, as shown in the top right diagram. The angles of each triangle add to 180°, of course. And so to calculate the total number of angles of the hexagon, we just add up all the angles of the four triangles:

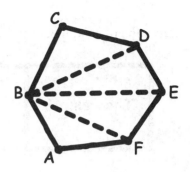

$$180 + 180 + 180 + 180 = 720$$

The angles of a hexagon add to equal 720°.

We'll do one last example. This one is an octagon (bottom right). As you can see, we end up with six triangles this time. To calculate the sum of the angles of the octagon, all we have to do is add up the angles in those six triangles.

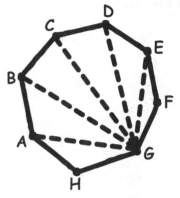

$$180 + 180 + 180 + 180 + 180 + 180 = 1,080$$

The angles of an octagon add to equal 1,080°.

Our three examples show a pattern. Think about it. We divided the 5-sided pentagon into 3 triangles. That's two fewer triangles than sides. We divided the 6-sided hexagon into 4 triangles. That's two fewer triangles than sides again. And then in the last example, we divided the 8-sided octagon into 6 triangles. Once more, there are two fewer triangles than sides.

Using the Equation

Generally, we can divide a polygon with n sides into $n - 2$ triangles. Then, to calculate the sum of the angles of the polygon, we multiply the number of triangles, which is $n - 2$, by 180. So to figure out the sum of the angles of any polygon, we just use the equation below.

$$S = 180(n - 2)$$

The variable S stands for the sum of the angles of the polygon, and n is the number of sides of the polygon.

Let's use this equation to figure out the sum of the angles of a 10-sided polygon, which is a decagon. All we do is put 10 in for n and calculate the value of the right side.

$$S = 180(10 - 2)$$
$$S = 180(8)$$

$$S = 1,440$$

Here's the official theorem for our new method.

Theorem 46	The sum of the measures of the interior angles of a polygon with n sides is 180(n-2).

Practice 59

a. Find the sum of the angles of the polygon below.

b. From the given statement below, tell the definition, property, postulate, or theorem that justifies the prove statement.

Given: Rhombus *BCIJ* (below);
Prove: $\angle 1 \cong \angle 2$ and $\angle 3 \cong \angle 4$.

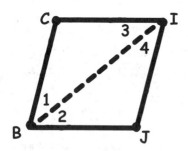

c. Find *y*.

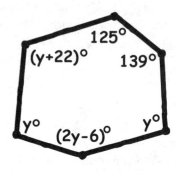

d. Write an equation to represent each question below; then solve the equation to get your answer.

Two angles are a linear pair. The measure of one angle is 5 more than $\frac{3}{4}$ the other.

Find the measures of *both* angles.

e. Do the proof below.

Given: Quadrilateral *FGHI*, $\overline{GF} \parallel \overline{HK}$,
  and $\overline{GF} \cong \overline{HK}$;
Prove: *FGHI* is a trapezoid.

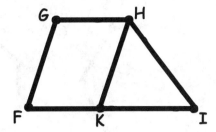

Problem Set 59

Tell whether each sentence below is True or False.

1. The sum of the measures of the interior angles of a polygon with *n* sides is $180(n-2)$.

2. The sum of the measures of the interior angles of a hexagon is 360.

Complete each sentence below by filling in the blanks.

3. A 7-sided polygon is called a _____, and a 10-sided polygon is called a
   _____.

4. If a quadrilateral is a parallelogram, then _____ angles are supplementary.

5. The nonparallel sides of a trapezoid are called its _____.

Tell whether each figure below is a trapezoid, isosceles trapezoid, parallelogram, rectangle, rhombus, square, or just a plain quadrilateral.

6.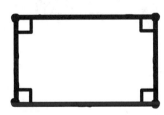

7.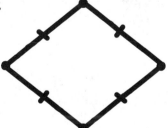

8.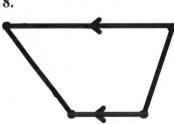

Find the sum of the angles of each polygon below.

9. 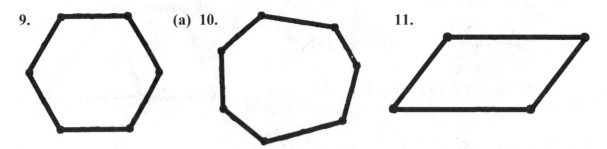 **(a) 10.** **11.**

Write the converse, inverse, and contrapositive of each true statement below. Tell whether your answer is true or false.

12. If a figure is a nonagon, then it is a polygon.

13. If a figure is a square, then it has four congruent sides.

Find the measures of the angles of each triangle described below.

14. An isosceles triangle with one angle measuring $94°$.

15. A triangle whose angles have measures in the ratio $5: 7: 8$.

From each given statement below, tell the definition, property, postulate, or theorem that justifies each prove statement.

16. Given: Rhombus $ADFH$; Prove: $\overline{AD} \cong \overline{DF}$

(b) 17. Given: Rhombus $ADFH$;
    Prove: $\angle 1 \cong \angle 2$ and $\angle 3 \cong \angle 4$

Answer each question below.

18. Find $m\overline{TU}$. **19.** Find $x + y + z$.

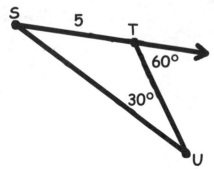

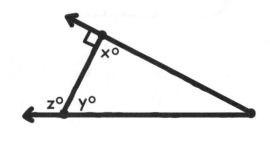

(c) 20. Find x.

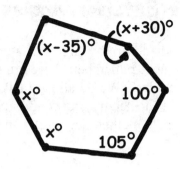

Write an equation to represent each question below; then solve the equation to get your answer.

21. Two angles are complementary. The measure of one angle is $\frac{1}{5}$ of the other. Find the measures of *both* angles.

(d) 22. Two angles are a linear pair. The measure of one angle is 5 more than $\frac{2}{3}$ the other. Find the measures of *both* angles.

Do each proof below.

23. Given: $\angle B \cong \angle D$ and $\angle A \cong \angle C$;
Prove: $\overline{AB} \cong \overline{DC}$

(e) 24. Given: Quadrilateral *LPRS*,
$\overline{PT} \parallel \overline{RS}$, and $\overline{PT} \cong \overline{RS}$;
Prove: *LPRS* is a trapezoid.

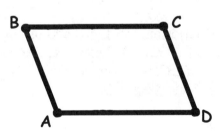

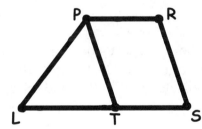

Lesson 60—Adding Up the Exterior Angles

In the last lesson, we learned how to add up the angles of a polygon. The angles we were adding were actually inside the polygon, and, remember, those are called "interior" angles. But every polygon also has several exterior angles. (We've already talked about the exterior angles of triangles.) So in this lesson we're going to learn how to add up all the exterior angles of a polygon. And once again, we'll learn a single method that works on any polygon, no matter how many sides it has.

Adding Up the Exterior Angles

Let's start with a quadrilateral as shown on the right. In addition to the four interior angles, quadrilateral $ABCD$ also has four exterior angles: $\angle 1$, $\angle 2$, $\angle 3$, and $\angle 4$.[3] And, as we've already learned, those interior angles add to equal 360. But how do we find the sum of the four exterior angles? Well, look closely at the diagram. Each exterior angle makes a linear pair with the interior angle at the same vertex. For example, $\angle 2$ and $\angle ABC$ are a linear pair, and so are $\angle 3$ and $\angle BCD$. The other two linear pairs are $\angle 4$ and $\angle CDA$ and $\angle 1$ and $\angle BAD$. Also, since a linear pair always must add to $180°$, the following must be true.

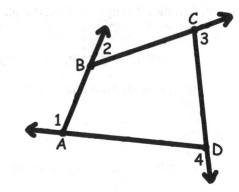

$\angle 1$, $\angle 2$, $\angle 3$, and $\angle 4$ are exterior angles of quadrilateral ABCD.

$$m\angle 1 + m\angle BAD = 180 \qquad m\angle 2 + m\angle ABC = 180$$

$$m\angle 3 + m\angle BCD = 180 \qquad m\angle 4 + m\angle CDA = 180$$

Now, here's how we can figure out the sum of the exterior angles. If we add up all 8 of the angles above, the total comes out to $180 + 180 + 180 + 180$ or 720. But we already know that the interior angles—$m\angle BAD$, $m\angle ABC$, $m\angle BCD$, and $m\angle CDA$—have a sum of $360°$, So subtracting 360 from 720 should leave us with the sum of the exterior angles.

Total of exterior angles $=$ Total of all 8 angles $-$ Total of interior angles

$$x \quad = \quad 720 \quad - \quad 360$$

$$x = 360$$

The four exterior angles add up to $360°$.

---

[3] There are actually 8 exterior angles, because we could extend both sides at every vertex. But we usually only show one exterior angle at each vertex.

Always 360 Degrees

We said that our method for adding exterior angles would work on any polygon. So how do we add the exterior angles on a pentagon, a hexagon, or the others? Well, it's a whole lot easier than you might think, because, as it turns out, the exterior angles of a polygon always add to equal 360, no matter how many sides the polygon has.

That probably seems strange. How can the 10 exterior angles of a decagon add to equal the same number (360°) as the 3 exterior angles of a triangle? Shouldn't the total be bigger, the greater the number of exterior angles? Actually, no. The reason is that the greater the number of sides that a polygon has, the smaller each exterior angle becomes. To show you, let's compare the exterior angles of a triangle, with only 3 sides, to those of a decagon, with 10 sides.

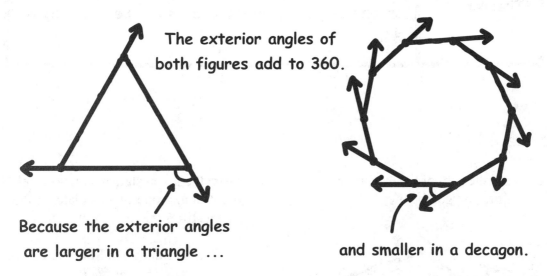

The exterior angles of both figures add to 360.

Because the exterior angles are larger in a triangle ...

and smaller in a decagon.

Notice that the exterior angles of the triangle are quite big; each one is actually greater than 90°. But the exterior angles of the decagon are really small. So that's how the total comes out the same for each figure.

Here's an informal proof showing that the sum of the exterior angles of a polygon is always 360. First of all, we learned from the last lesson that for a polygon with n sides, the interior angles add up to equal $180(n-2)$. Second, the total number of angles—both interior and exterior—of a polygon always equals $180n$. That's because a polygon has just as many interior angles as it does sides. And at every angle, there's an interior and an exterior angle that make up a linear pair, with each linear pair adding to 180. So 180 times n is the total of all the interior and exterior angles of the polygon. Finally, we can put these two expressions into the equation from above to get this.

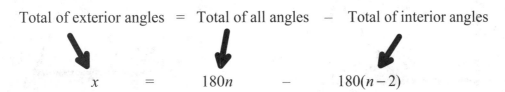

Total of exterior angles = Total of all angles − Total of interior angles

$$x = 180n - 180(n-2)$$

From here, we just simplify the right side by distributing and combining like terms.

$$x = 180n - 180n + 360$$

$$x = 360$$

This proves that no matter how many sides the polygon has (*n* could have been anything), the exterior angles have to add to equal 360. Here's the official theorem.

Theorem 47	The sum of the measures of the exterior angles of any polygon (one exterior angle per vertex) is 360.

Practice 60

a. Find the sum of the exterior angles of the polygon below.

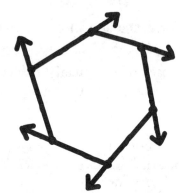

b. From the given statement below, tell the definition, property, postulate, or theorem that justifies the prove statement.

Given: Parallelogram *STVW* and
       $m\angle STP > m\angle TSP$
Prove: $SP > TP$.

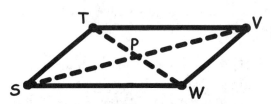

c. In rectangle *ERPL*, find $a + b$ in terms of *c*.

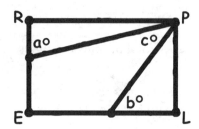

d. If $LP = 9$, find *MP*.

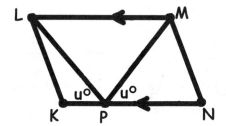

e. Do the proof below.
Given: Rectangle $ABCD$, $\overline{BP} \cong \overline{CP}$
Prove: $\overline{AL} \cong \overline{DM}$

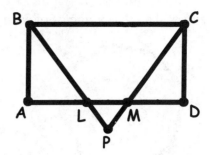

Problem Set 60

Tell whether each sentence below is True or False.

1. The interior angles of any polygon always add to equal $180°$.

2. The exterior angles of any polygon always add to equal $360°$.

Complete each sentence below by filling in the blanks.

3. A 4-sided polygon is called a _____, and a 9-sided polygon is called a _____.

4. The diagonals of a rectangle are _____.

5. According to the _____, if two sides of a triangle are congruent (equal), then the angles opposite those sides are congruent (equal).

Name each polygon below.

6.

7.

Find the sum of the interior angles of each polygon below.

8.

9.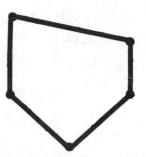

Find the sum of the exterior angles of each polygon below.

10.

(a) 11.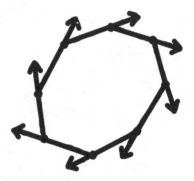

Complete each sentence below with *always*, *sometimes*, or *never*.

12. A trapezoid is _____ a parallelogram.

13. A pentagon is _____ an octagon.

Tell whether each statement below is the converse, inverse, or contrapositive of the following statement: If a figure is a rectangle, then its diagonals are congruent.

14. If a figure has diagonals that are congruent, then the figure is a rectangle.

15. If a figure is not a rectangle, then its diagonals are not congruent.

Answer each question below.

16. In $\overline{AZ}$ (below), $AJ = 9$, $AZ = 25$, and $JQ = 10$. What is the distance from Z to the midpoint of $\overline{AJ}$?

17. In $\triangle FGH$, $GH = 9\frac{2}{3}$, $FH = 7$ and $FG = 9\frac{1}{2}$. Which is the largest angle of the triangle?

From each given statement below, tell the definition, property, postulate, or theorem that justifies each prove statement.

18. Given: Parallelogram $ABCD$ (on the right);
     Prove: $\overline{AO} \cong \overline{CO}$

(b) 19. Given: Parallelogram $ABCD$ (on the right)
     and $m\angle ABO < m\angle BAO$;
     Prove: $BO > AO$

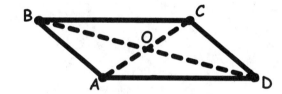

Answer each question below.

20. Find $r + s$.

(c) 21. In rectangle $ABCD$, find $x + y$ in terms of z.

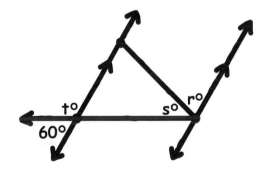

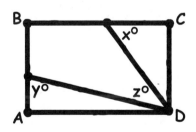

(d) 22. If $ED = 7$, find EA.

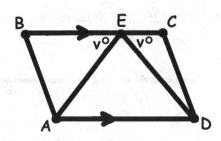

Do each proof below.

23. Given: $HIJK$ is a rectangle;
           $HIKL$ is a parallelogram.

Prove: $\triangle HJL$ is isosceles.

(e) 24. Given: Rectangle $QPRS$,
           $\overline{QU} \cong \overline{SU}$.

Prove: $\overline{PV} \cong \overline{RT}$.

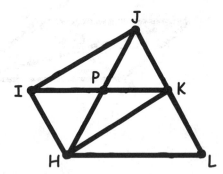

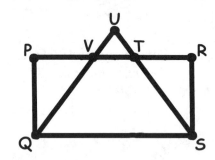

Lesson 61—Regular Polygons

So far in this chapter, we've seen a lot of different polygons. Most of them were kind of "lopsided," because their sides were different lengths and their angles were different. For instance, here's a lopsided pentagon on the top right.

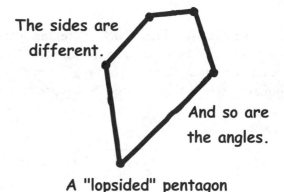

The sides are different.

And so are the angles.

A "lopsided" pentagon

Pretty Polygons

Not all polygons are lopsided, though. In some of them, every side is congruent and every interior angle is congruent. These are called **regular polygons**. A regular pentagon is shown on the bottom right. Notice that the sides of the pentagon are all the same. And if you measure the angles with a protractor, they'll all come out the same as well (making allowances for a not-so-perfect artist).

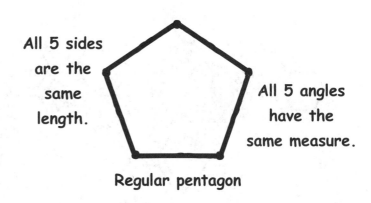

All 5 sides are the same length.

All 5 angles have the same measure.

Regular pentagon

Most people would say that the regular pentagon is prettier then the ordinary one. That's because the human eye tends to prefer shapes that are balanced.[4] The U.S. Defense Department building that we talked about a few lessons ago is actually a regular pentagon. Go back and look at the picture, and you can see for yourself. Here's the official definition of a regular polygon.

Definition 49	A *regular polygon* is a convex polygon that is both equilateral and equiangular.

Well-Known Regular Polygons

There is a regular polygon version of every type of polygon that we've studied. The simplest regular polygon is the equilateral triangle (where all 3 sides are congruent). Since an equilateral triangle is also equiangular (all 3 interior angles are also congruent), it qualifies as a regular polygon. Probably the most common regular polygon, though, is the square. It has 4

---

[4] Technically, a regular polygon looks balanced because it's "cyclic." That means you can draw a circle around the polygon, with every vertex lying on that circle.

congruent sides and 4 congruent interior angles, so the square is the 4-sided version of a regular polygon.

We've already talked about the regular pentagon, so we'll skip to the regular hexagon. A regular hexagon—with 6 congruent sides and 6 congruent interior angles—is common in nature. The outer edge of a snowflake is a regular hexagon shape, for example.[5] The little compartments in a honeycomb are also shaped like regular hexagons, as you can see from the picture.

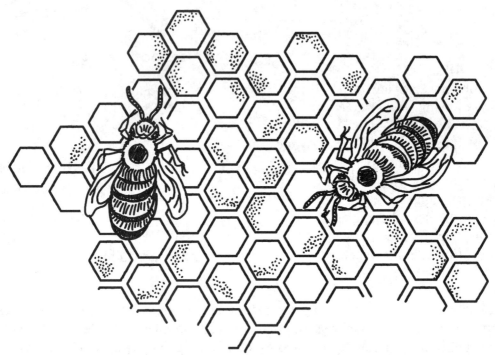

A honeycomb is made up of regular hexagons.

Another well-known regular polygon is the regular octagon, which is the shape of most stop signs on roads (on the right).

A stop sign is a regular octagon

Finding each Interior Angle

It's easy to calculate the measure of each interior angle of a regular polygon. The first step is to figure out the sum of all the interior angles. Remember, that sum is equal to $180(n-2)$, where n is the number of sides of the polygon. Then, since the

---

[5] You may have heard that no two snowflakes are alike. But that's because the design on the inside of each snowflake is different. The outer edge is a regular hexagon.

angles of a regular polygon are all congruent, we divide that sum by the number of angles, n. That gives us the equation below.

$$\text{Measure of each interior angle of a regular polygon} = \frac{180(n-2)}{n}$$

And the neat thing is that this equation works no matter how many sides the regular polygon has. Here's the official theorem.

Theorem 48	The measure of each interior angle of a regular polygon is $\dfrac{180(n-2)}{n}$, where n is the number of sides of the regular polygon.

To show you how to use this equation, let's calculate the measure of each angle of the regular pentagon on the right. A pentagon has 5 sides, so $n = 5$. Now we just put 5 in for n in the right side of our equation to get this.

$$\frac{180(5-2)}{5}$$

What's the measure of each angle?

?

Regular pentagon

Simplifying gives us 108°. So each of the 5 angles of our regular pentagon measures 108°. And that makes sense, because adding 108° five times, gives us 540°, which is the sum of all the interior angles of any pentagon.

Finding each Exterior Angle

Now that we know how to calculate the measure of each of the interior angles of a regular polygon, it's really easy to calculate the measure of each exterior angle. Look at the pentagon on the right. Each exterior angle is supplementary to the interior angle that's next to it (because they make a linear pair). So each exterior angle

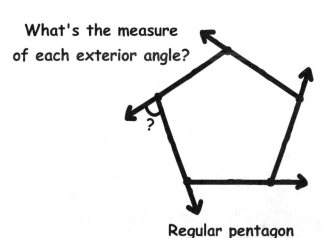

What's the measure of each exterior angle?

?

Regular pentagon

is equal to 180 minus the measure of each interior angle.

Measure of each exterior angle = 180 – measure of each interior angle

So since the interior angles of a pentagon are all 108°, each exterior angle has to be 180 – 108 or 72°.

There's also another way to find each exterior angle. We learned in the last lesson that the sum of all the exterior angles of any polygon (even those that aren't regular) is 360°. Since there's an exterior angle for every side of the polygon, all we have to do is divide 360 by n (the number of sides).

$$\text{Measure of each exterior angle} = \frac{360}{n}$$

Either method will work on any *regular* polygon. But if the polygon is not regular, neither method will work, because the exterior angles won't all be the same.

Practice 61

a. Name the polygon below and tell whether it is regular.

b. Name the regular polygon below and find the measures of the interior angle and exterior angle indicated

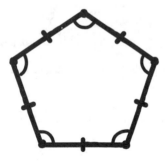

c. If $f = 25$ and $e = \frac{2}{3} m\angle JKL$, find e.

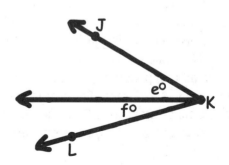

d. Write an equation to represent the question below; then solve the equation to get your answer.

Two angles are complementary. The measure of one angle is 150% of the other. Find the measures of *both* angles.

e. Do the proof below.

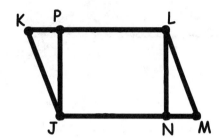

Given: *JKLM* is a parallelogram.
$\overline{JP} \perp \overline{KL}$, $\overline{LN} \perp \overline{JM}$
Prove: $\triangle KJP \cong \triangle MLN$

Problem Set 61

Tell whether each sentence below is True or False.

1. A regular polygon is a polygon where every one of its sides is congruent and every one of its interior angles is congruent.

2. Every parallelogram is a regular polygon.

Complete each sentence below by filling in the blanks.

3. The measure of each interior angle of a regular polygon equals _____, where *n* is the number of sides of the polygon.

4. The measure of each exterior angle of a regular polygon equals _____ or _____.

5. The diagonals of a _____ are perpendicular to each other.

Name each polygon below and tell whether it is regular.

6.

7.

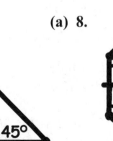

(a) 8.

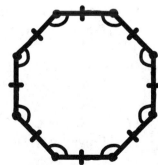

Find the sum of the interior angles and the sum of the exterior angles for each polygon below.

9.

10.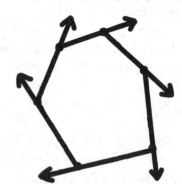

Name each regular polygon below and find the measure of the interior angle and exterior angle indicated.

11.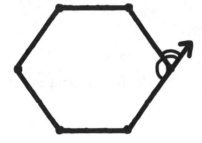

(b) 12.

Write the converse, inverse, and contrapositive of each true statement below. Tell whether your answer is true or false.

13. If a quadrilateral is a parallelogram, then both pairs of its opposite angles are congruent.

14. If the diagonals of a quadrilateral bisect each other, then a quadrilateral is a parallelogram.

From each given statement below, tell the definition, property, postulate, or theorem that justifies each prove statement.

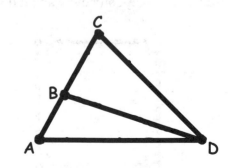

15. Given: $\triangle ADC$ and $\overline{AD}$ - $\overline{BD}$ - $\overline{CD}$ (on the right);
Prove: $\angle ADC > \angle ADB$

16. Given: $AB < AD$ (on the right);
Prove: $m\angle ABD > m\angle ADB$

17. Given: $m\angle A = 60$, $m\angle ABD = 100$ (on the right);
Prove: $m\angle ADB = 20$

Answer each question below.

18. Find *y*.

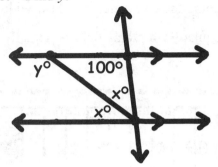

19. Find $a+b+c+d$.

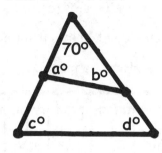

(c) 20. If $s = 24$ and $r = \dfrac{3}{5} m\angle AOC$, find *r*.

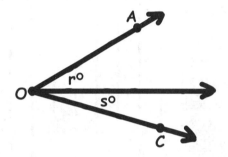

Write an equation to represent each question below; then solve the equation to get your answer.

21. In $\triangle FGH$, $m\angle F = 30$ and $m\angle G$ is four times $m\angle H$. Find $m\angle G$ and $m\angle H$. What kind of triangle is $\triangle FGH$?

(d) 22. Two angles are complementary. The measure of one angle is 125% of the other. Find the measures of *both* angles.

Do each proof below.

23. Given: $\overline{LQ} \cong \overline{PQ}$, $\angle L \cong \angle HQP$,

        LQ is not parallel to *PH*

Prove: *PLQH* is a trapezoid.

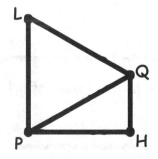

(e) 24. Given: *ABCD* is a parallelogram.

        $\overline{BE} \perp \overline{AD}$, $\overline{FD} \perp \overline{BC}$

Prove: $\triangle ABE \cong \triangle CDF$

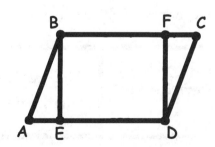

Lesson 62—Perimeter of a Polygon

A football field is 120 yards (or 360 feet) long including the end zones. But how wide is it? A lot of football fans don't know. It turns out that a regulation football field is actually $53\frac{1}{3}$ yards (160 feet) wide. Here's a picture.

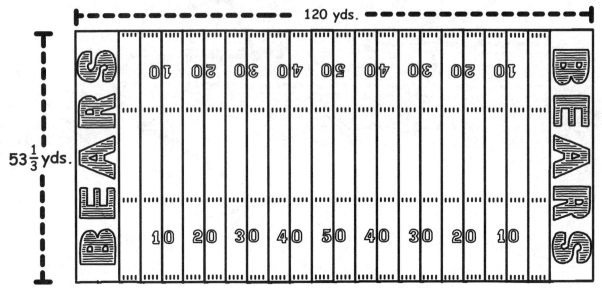

Given that information, it's easy to figure out the distance around the football field. All we have to do is add the lengths of the four sides. Doing the addition in feet gives us this.

$$360 + 360 + 160 + 160 = 1,040$$

The length all the way around a figure is called its **perimeter**. Therefore, the perimeter of a football field is 1,040 feet.

It's possible to find the perimeter of any polygon in much the same way as our football field example. All we have to do is add up the lengths of all the polygon's sides. So for any polygon with side lengths of a, b, c, d, etc., the perimeter (P) can be calculated as follows.

$$P = a + b + c + d + ...$$

Here is the formal definition of the perimeter of a polygon.

Definition 50	The *perimeter* of a polygon is the sum of the lengths of its sides.

Special Perimeters

Most ordinary polygons have sides of different lengths, as you know. But special polygons often have some sides that are the same, which makes the perimeter calculation a little simpler. Actually, a football field is a special polygon, because it's a rectangle with opposite sides equal (on the right). That means to calculate the perimeter of a football field or any rectangle, instead of adding up all four sides separately, we can just multiply the length by 2 and the width by 2, then add those totals.

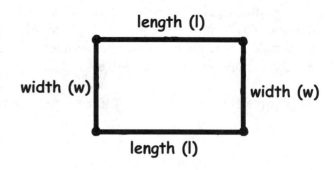

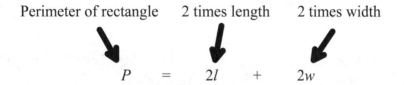

$$P \quad = \quad 2l \quad + \quad 2w$$

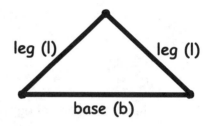

Another special polygon is an isosceles triangle (on the right). Since the two legs of any isosceles triangle have to be the same length, the perimeter can be calculated by multiplying the length of the legs by 2 and then adding that length to the base (the third side). Here's that equation.

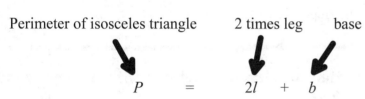

$$P \quad = \quad 2l \quad + \quad b$$

There are also other special cases. Since any parallelogram (not just a rectangle) has opposite sides equal, we can calculate the perimeter of a parallelogram using the same shortcut method as we do with a rectangle.

Perimeters of Regular Polygons

Of all the special polygons, the easiest ones to do a perimeter calculation on are the regular polygons. Remember, in a regular polygon every side has exactly the same length. Take an equilateral triangle on the right as an example. Its 3 sides have the same length, so to calculate the perimeter we can just multiply that side length by 3.

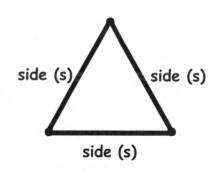

Perimeter of equilateral triangle   3 times side length

$$P \quad = \quad 3s$$

Another regular polygon is a square shown on the right. That's just an "equilateral quadrilateral." The simplest way to calculate the perimeter of a square is to multiply its side length by 4.

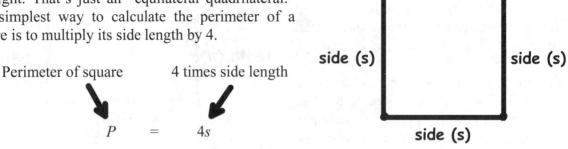

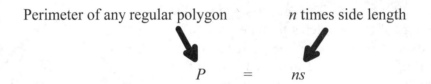

Perimeter of square ‎ ‎ ‎ ‎ 4 times side length

$$P = 4s$$

Going on up, the perimeter of a regular pentagon, which has 5 equal sides, can be calculated by multiplying its side length by 5. And a regular hexagon's perimeter is found by multiplying its side length by 6.

By now you should be seeing the pattern. To calculate the perimeter of any regular polygon, we just multiply its side length by the number of sides.

Perimeter of any regular polygon ‎ ‎ ‎ ‎ *n* times side length

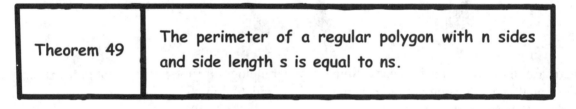

$$P = ns$$

We'll include this as one of our theorems. Here it is written officially.

Theorem 49	The perimeter of a regular polygon with n sides and side length s is equal to ns.

Of course, if you forget this perimeter equation or any of the other shorter methods for figuring out perimeters, you can always do it the long way, by adding up every side of your figure individually.

Practice 62

a. Find the perimeter of a rectangle with length measuring 7 and width measuring 11.

b. Find the perimeter of a regular hexagon with sides measuring 12.

c. Find $a+b$.

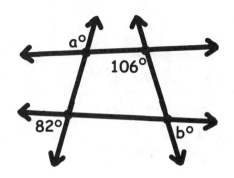

d. How much smaller is the perimeter of square *LMNO* than the perimeter of rectangle *JKMN*?

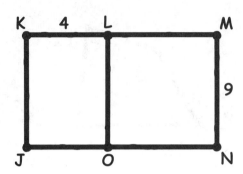

e. Do the proof below.

Given: Quadrilateral *STUR*;
$\overline{SU}$ and $\overline{TL}$ bisect each other; $\overline{SR} \cong \overline{TU}$
Prove: $\angle R \cong \angle RUT$

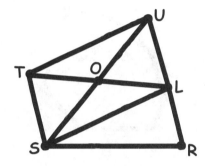

Problem Set 62

Tell whether each sentence below is True or False.

1. The perimeter of a polygon is the sum of the lengths of its sides.

2. The perimeter (*P*) of a regular polygon with *n* sides and side length *s* can be found with the equation $P = ns$.

Complete each sentence below by filling in the blanks.

3. A _____ is a polygon where every one of its sides is congruent and every one of its interior angles is congruent.

4. The sum of the measures of the interior angles of a polygon with *n* sides is _____ .

5. The sum of the measures of the interior angles of a(n) _____ is 900.

Tell whether each figure below is a trapezoid, isosceles trapezoid, parallelogram, rectangle, rhombus, square, or just a plain quadrilateral.

6.

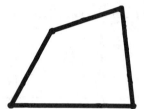

7.

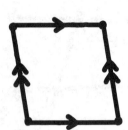

Find the sum of the interior angles of each polygon below.

8.

9.

Find the perimeter of each polygon described below.

(a) 10. A rectangle with length measuring 9 and width measuring 6.

11. A square with sides measuring 6.5.

(b) 12. A regular octagon with sides measuring 13.

Find the measures of the angles of each triangle described below.

13. A triangle whose angles have measures in the ratio 6: 8: 10. What kind of triangle is it?

14. An equilateral triangle.

Complete each sentence below with *always*, *sometimes*, or *never*.

15. A polygon is _____ a regular polygon.

16. The measures of the exterior angles of a polygon _____ have a sum of 360.

Answer each question below.

17. In $\triangle CDF$, $m\angle C < m\angle D$ and $m\angle C > m\angle F$. Which is the shortest side of the triangle?

18. In $\triangle ABC$, $m\angle B = 100$, $m\angle C = 50$ and P is the point on $\overline{AB}$ that makes $\overline{PC}$ bisect $\angle ACB$. What is the longest side of $\triangle ACP$?

From each given statement below, tell the definition, property, postulate, or theorem that justifies each prove statement.

19. Given: Parallelogram $ADGK$
Prove: $\angle A$ and $\angle K$ are supplementary.

20. Given: Parallelogram $ADGK$
Prove: $\overline{AD} \cong \overline{GK}$

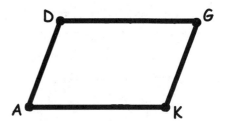

Answer each question below.

(c) 21. Find $x + y$.

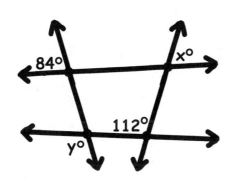

(d) 22. How much smaller is the perimeter of square $ABCF$ than the perimeter of rectangle $ABDE$?

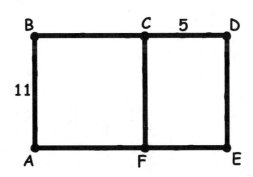

Do each proof below.

23. Given: $\overline{RV} \cong \overline{ST}$; $\angle RTS \cong \angle TRV$
     Prove: *RSTV* is a parallelogram.

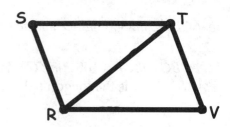

(e) 24. Given: Quadrilateral *DJKL*;
          $\overline{JL}$ and $\overline{FK}$ bisect each other;
          $\overline{JK} \cong \overline{DL}$
     Prove: $\angle D \cong \angle DJK$

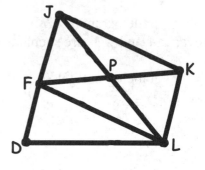

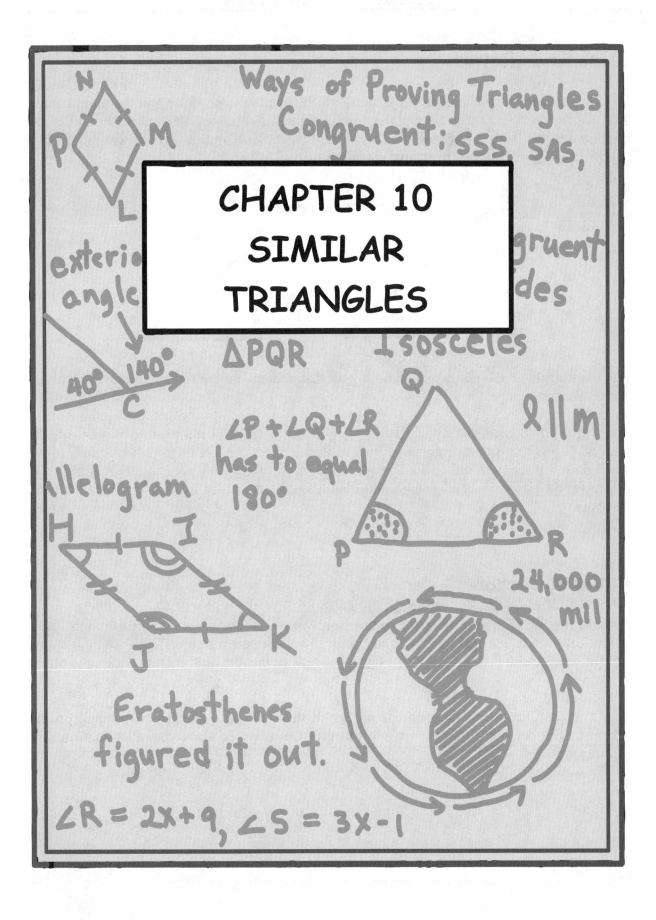

Ways of Proving Triangles
Congruent: SSS, SAS,

CHAPTER 10
SIMILAR
TRIANGLES

N

P   M

L

exterior
angle

40° 140°
    C

ΔPQR

gruent
des

Isosceles
Q

ℓ || m

∠P + ∠Q + ∠R
has to equal
180°

P   R

24,000
mil

Parallelogram

H   I

J   K

Eratosthenes
figured it out.

∠R = 2x + 9, ∠S = 3x - 1

Lesson 63—Ratios

We've learned about congruent figures, which have the same shape and the same size. In this chapter, we're going to learn about similar figures. We talked about these briefly at the beginning of the book. To refresh your memory, though, **similar figures** have the same shape but are of a different size. Here are two similar triangles.

Similar Triangles

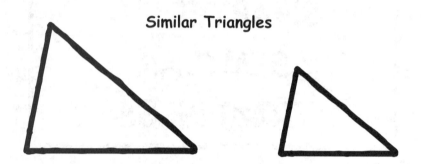

See, the triangle on the left is quite a bit bigger than the one on the right. But they both have exactly the same shape.

All of our theorems on similar figures will be for triangles. That's because triangles are the simplest polygons.[1] Similar figures with more than 3 sides can get pretty complicated, so we won't do too much with those. But to understand much of anything about similar figures, you first have to know some details about ratios and proportions, which is what Lessons 63 and 64 are about.

A Way to Compare

What if we wanted to compare two quantities, like the numbers 40 and 20? There are basically two methods for making the comparison. We could subtract one number from the other to get 20, which tells us that the first quantity is 20 greater than the second. Or we could divide the two numbers: 40 divided by 20 gives 2, which tells us that the first quantity is twice as big as the second.

You may think that the methods are about the same. But actually, depending on the circumstances, one method often works better than the other. To show you, let's go through a quick example.

---

[1] That's also why we only studied congruent triangles and not congruent quadrilaterals, pentagons, etc.

The City Park Association is planning a picnic for kids 12 years and younger. Maggie Clarkson, the coordinator, wants to have a fairly even balance between boys and girls at the picnic. What if Maggie is told that 20 more boys than girls have signed up? Are the boys and girls in a fairly even balance?

With the information that there are 20 more boys signed up, can Maggie tell whether the boys and girls are in balance? Not really. What if only 40 kids in total are signed up for the picnic? That would be 30 boys and 10 girls, which isn't at all balanced, because that's three times as many boys as girls. But what if 820 kids are signed up? With 20 more boys than girls that comes out to 420 boys and 400 girls. That's actually a very even balance. So subtracting the boys and girls to get a difference of 20 isn't a good method of comparison in this case. It doesn't give Maggie the information she needs.

Maggie would be better off doing the comparison by dividing. Let's say that 820 kids (420 boys and 400 girls) are actually signed up for the picnic. Dividing boys by girls gives us $\frac{420}{400}$, which comes out to 1.05. Since 1.05 is close to 1, that means the number of boys and girls are close together. Dividing tells Maggie what she wants to know.

When two numbers are compared by dividing them, the result is called a **ratio**. You've worked with ratios for years. In fact, we've already done a lot of problems involving ratios in this book. But our example shows that the real advantage of a ratio is in comparing quantities. A ratio of near 1 means that the quantities are in close balance. A ratio of much greater than or less than 1 means that the quantities are out of balance.

Saying it Right

Mathematicians insist that ratios should be spoken in a certain way. In answering our picnic question, for example, we could say that "the ratio of boys to girls is 420 to 400." But since fractions are simpler when fully reduced, $\frac{420}{400}$ should really be rewritten as $\frac{21}{20}$. So it would be better to state it this way: "the ratio of boys to girls is 21 to 20." This just means that for every 21 boys, there are 20 girls signed up for the picnic. Of course, it's also okay to change the fraction to a decimal, which is what we did when calculating the ratio as 1.05. And, as a decimal, the ratio could also be referred to as "1.05 to 1." As you know, ratios are also sometimes written not with a fraction bar, but with a colon. So $\frac{21}{20}$ could also be written as $21:20$. The colon means exactly the same thing as a fraction bar.[2]

Another important thing to remember when working with ratios is that the order in which we state the quantities being compared matters a lot. If we say "the ratio of boys to girls is 21 to 20," that means that boys divided by girls equals $\frac{21}{20}$. It does *not* mean that girls divided by boys is $\frac{21}{20}$. The ratio of girls to boys is actually $\frac{20}{21}$ or $20:21$. Whatever is stated first goes on the top of the fraction (or before the colon). And whatever is stated second goes on the bottom of the fraction (or after the colon). Here is the formal definition of a ratio.

Definition 51	The *ratio* of two numbers a and b ($b \neq 0$) is the quotient of the numbers. It's written as $\frac{a}{b}$ or $a : b$.

Practice 63

a. Tell whether the pair of ratios $56:16$, $7:2$ is equal.

b. Find the measures of the angles of the triangle described below.

An isosceles triangle where the ratio of the vertex angle to one of the base angles is $4:1$.

---

[2] We can also show three numbers in a ratio. An example is 3:4:5. In fact, we've already done quite a few problems with ratios that have three numbers.

c. Find x and y (as shown in the figure).

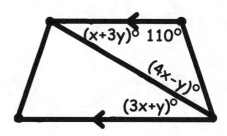

d. Write an equation to represent the question below; then solve the equation to get your answer.

In $\triangle GEF$, $m\angle G = 40$ and $m\angle E$ is three times $m\angle F$. Find $m\angle E$ and $m\angle F$.

e. Do the proof below.

Given: Regular hexagon $OPQRST$
with diagonals $\overline{PR}$ and $\overline{TR}$
Prove: $\overline{PR} \cong \overline{TR}$

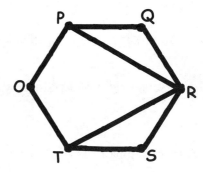

Problem Set 63

Tell whether each sentence below is True or False.

1. Similar figures have the same shape but are of a different size.

2. When two numbers are compared by dividing them, the result is called a ratio.

Complete each sentence below by filling in the blanks.

3. The measure of each interior angle of a regular polygon equals _____, where n is the number of sides of the polygon.

4. A _____ is a quadrilateral that has one pair of opposite sides parallel.

5. The line segment joining the midpoints of two sides of a triangle is _____ to the third side and _____ its length.

Name each regular polygon below and find the measure of the interior angle indicated.

6.

7.

Find the perimeter of each polygon described below.

8. A regular pentagon with sides measuring 42.

9. A rectangle with length measuring $8\frac{1}{2}$ and width measuring $5\frac{1}{3}$.

Tell whether each pair of ratios is equal.

10. $\frac{5}{7}, \frac{20}{28}$ **(a) 11.** $54:18, 9:3$ **12.** 39 to 68, 68 to 39

Find the measures of the angles of each triangle described below.

13. A right triangle where one of the acute angles is 3.5 times the other.

(b) 14. An isosceles triangle where the ratio of the vertex angle to one of the base angles is $1:2$.

Tell whether each statement below is the converse, inverse, or contrapositive of the following statement: If a figure is a rhombus, then all four of its sides are congruent.

15. If a figure does not have all four of its sides congruent, then the figure is not a rhombus.

16. If a figure has all four of its sides congruent, then the figure is a rhombus.

From each given statement below, tell the definition, property, postulate, or theorem that justifies each prove statement.

17. Given: Quadrilateral *NMPR* (on the right),
$\overline{NR} \parallel \overline{MP}$, $\overline{NR} \cong \overline{MP}$;
Prove: *NMPR* is a parallelogram.

18. Given: Parallelogram *NMPR*; Prove: $\angle N \cong \angle P$

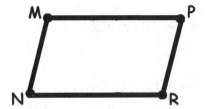

Answer each question below.

(c) 19. Find *x* and *y*.

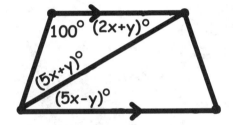

20. Find $w+u$.

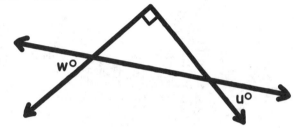

Write an equation to represent each question below; then solve the equation to get your answer.

21. Two angles are a linear pair. If one angle is half of a right angle, find the measures of *both* angles.

(d) 22. In $\triangle SDR$, $m\angle S = 50$ and $m\angle D$ is four times $m\angle R$. Find $m\angle D$ and $m\angle R$.

Do each proof below.

23. Given: Trapezoid *ABCE* with bases
$\overline{AE}$ and $\overline{BC}$, $\overline{AD} \cong \overline{BC}$
Prove: *ABCD* is a parallelogram.

(e) 24. Given: Regular octagon *ABCDEFGH*
with diagonals $\overline{HF}$ and $\overline{DF}$
Prove: $\overline{HF} \cong \overline{DF}$

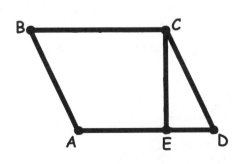

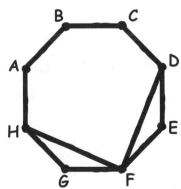

Lesson 64—Proportions

In the last lesson we covered ratios, which can be used to compare two quantities. We also said that ratios are important when working with similar figures. And we'll get to that very soon. But we mentioned proportions as well in the last lesson. What about them?

Two Equal Ratios

A **proportion**, as it turns out, is just two ratios set equal to each other. To show a simple way that a proportion might be used, let's go back to our picnic example.

The City Park Association picnic was a big success (with 820 kids attending), and Maggie Clarkson, the coordinator, is already planning another picnic for next year. If 525 boys have signed up, how many girls must be at next year's picnic for the ratio of boys to girls to be the same as it was last year?

Last year the picnic had 420 boys and 400 girls, for a ratio of $\dfrac{420}{400}$ or $\dfrac{21}{20}$. To answer our question, all we have to do is create an equation that sets $\dfrac{21}{20}$ equal to another ratio for next year.

$$\frac{\text{Boys next year}}{\text{Girls next year}} = \frac{21}{20}$$

This is a proportion, because it has two ratios that are equal. The next step is to finish the equation by putting 525 in for "Boys next year." (Maggie already knows that 525 boys have signed up.) And since the number of girls is unknown, that should be represented by an x.

$$\frac{525}{x} = \frac{21}{20}$$

From here, we can clear the fractions by multiplying both sides by the lowest common denominator, which is $20x$.

$$20x \cdot \frac{525}{x} = 20x \cdot \frac{21}{20}$$

Next, we simplify on the left and right.

$$10,500 = 21x$$

Finally, we divide both sides by 21.

$$500 = x$$

Maggie needs 500 girls at the picnic for the ratio of boys to girls to be the same as last year.

This is one way that proportions are used: to find a missing number when two sets of quantities are supposed to have the same ratio. We just create an equation by setting the two ratios equal to each other, and make x the thing we're trying to find. Here's the formal definition of a proportion. And notice that the ratios on both sides can also be written with colons.

Definition 52	A *proportion* is an equation which states that two ratios are equal to each other. It's written as $\frac{a}{b} = \frac{c}{d}$ or as $a : b = c : d$. $(b \neq 0, d \neq 0)$

Means and Extremes

Mathematicians use a few technical words when talking about proportions that you should be aware of. To explain these, look at the proportion below.

$$\frac{a}{b} = \frac{c}{d}$$

The numbers in the b and c positions are called the **means**, while the numbers in the a and d positions are called the **extremes**. The formal definitions are as follows.

Definition 53	In the proportion $\dfrac{a}{b} = \dfrac{c}{d}$, b and c are referred to as the *means* of the proportion, and a and d are referred to as the *extremes* of the proportion.

Here's where the names "means" and "extremes" come from. When a proportion is written with colons instead of fractions, the extremes end up on the "extreme" outside of the equation. On the right, the proportion $\dfrac{a}{b} = \dfrac{c}{d}$ is written with colons, and you can see that the extremes, a and d, are on the outside.

The extremes are on the outside.

$$a : b = c : d$$

The means are on the inside.

Geometric Mean

The means are always on the inside, which might make you wonder why it's not "insides and extremes." But the origin of the name "means" is a little more complicated. "Mean" is actually another word for average, like when you calculate your grade average. A normal average is called an "arithmetic mean." However, in a proportion where both of the means equal the same number, that number is called a "geometric mean." As an example, look at the proportion below.

$$\frac{18}{6} = \frac{6}{2}$$

The numbers in the b and c positions (which are the means) are both 6. So 6 is called the geometric mean of 18 and 2. And the word "mean" comes from the fact that when the means positions have the same number, that number turns out to be the geometric mean of the two numbers in the extremes position. (Even when b and c are different, we still call them the means.) Here's the formal definition of geometric mean.

Definition 54	If $\dfrac{a}{b} = \dfrac{b}{c}$, then b is the *geometric mean* of a and c (where a, b, and c are positive).

Interestingly, the geometric mean of two numbers can be calculated without setting up a proportion. We know that an *arithmetic* mean of two numbers (a normal average, in other words) is calculated by adding the two numbers and dividing by 2. For instance, to average the two test scores 76 and 62, we add the numbers to get 138. Then we divide 138 by 2 to get an arithmetic mean of 69. To calculate a geometric mean of two numbers, we *multiply* the numbers and take the *square root* of that result. So to get the geometric mean of 18 and 2 (which we already know is 6), we first multiply: $18 \cdot 2 = 36$. Then instead of dividing the result by 2, we find its square root: $\sqrt{36} = 6$.

Cross-Multiplying

Another interesting thing about the means and extremes of a proportion is that they can be used to rewrite the proportion in a simpler form with just one step. All we have to do is multiply the means and multiply the extremes and then set those two totals equal to each other, like on the right. This is the same equation as before, but now it's in a simpler form. Sometimes it's easier to work with a proportion when it's written as two multiplications, instead of as two fractions.

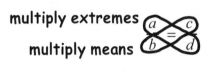

$$ad = bc$$

Of course, we could have gotten the same result by clearing the fractions in the original equation. Multiplying both sides of $\dfrac{a}{b} = \dfrac{c}{d}$ by the lowest common denominator, which is bd, we get:

$$bd \cdot \frac{a}{b} = bd \cdot \frac{c}{d}.$$

Then, simplifying on both sides gives us

$$ad = bc.$$

See, we end up with the same result. Multiplying the means and the extremes is just a shortcut for clearing the fractions in a proportion. This technique is also called **cross-multiplying**.[3] You may have already heard of it. But here's the formal theorem for cross-multiplying.

Theorem 50	In a proportion, the product of the means is equal to the product of the extremes.

---

[3] You have to be careful when cross-multiplying, though. It doesn't work if there's anything else other than the fractions on each side of the equation. In other words, you can't cross-multiply in an equation like $\dfrac{a}{b} = \dfrac{c}{d} + e$.

Flipping it Over

We should make one last point about proportions in this long (and tough!) lesson. If you flip a proportion over, the two sides will still be equal. To show what we mean, take a look at the proportion below.

$$\frac{3}{12} = \frac{1}{4}$$

This qualifies as a proportion, because the fractions on both sides are equal. Now watch what happens when we flip both of the fractions over.

$$\frac{12}{3} = \frac{4}{1}$$

Since $\frac{12}{3}$ is the same as 4, the two sides are still equal.

It shouldn't surprise you that a proportion can be flipped over like this. In our picnic example, instead of using the ratios of boys to girls for the two years, we could have used the ratios of girls to boys just as easily. That would have given us this.

$$\frac{\text{Girls next year}}{\text{Boys next year}} = \frac{20}{21}$$

$$\frac{x}{525} = \frac{20}{21}$$

The solution to this equation is still 500, which we know is the correct number of girls.

So when setting up your own proportions, you're free to choose which quantity goes on top and which goes on bottom. But be careful. If you put girls on top and boys on bottom in one ratio, you have to be sure and put girls on top and boys on bottom in the other ratio as well. They have to match.

Practice 64

a. Find the perimeter of the polygon on the right.

b. Find the geometric mean of 9 and 36.

c. Solve for y in the proportion $\frac{y}{7} = \frac{114}{42}$.

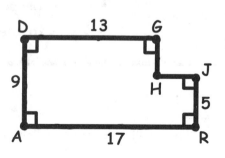

d. Write a proportion to represent the question below; then solve the proportion to get your answer.

The ratio of lip synchers to real singers was 8 to 9. If there were 234 real singers, how many lip synchers were there?

e. Do the proof below.

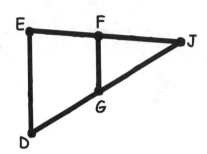

Given: F is the midpoint of $\overline{EJ}$ and
       G is the midpoint of $\overline{DJ}$;
       $m\angle FGJ > m\angle J$
Prove: $EJ > DE$

Problem Set 64

Tell whether each sentence below is True or False.

1. A proportion is a ratio that is fully reduced.

2. In the proportion $\dfrac{a}{b} = \dfrac{c}{d}$, a and d are the means and b and c are the extremes.

Complete each sentence below by filling in the blanks.

3. When the means positions in a proportion have the same number, that number is the _____ of the two numbers in the extremes position.

4. To _____ in a proportion, you multiply the means and the extremes and set the totals equal to each other.

5. A _____ is a parallelogram with four congruent sides.

Find the sum of the interior angles of each polygon below.

6.

7.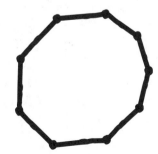

Find the perimeter of each polygon below.

8. Find the perimeter of *ABCDEFG*, if *ABCDFG* is a regular hexagon and $\triangle DFE$ is equilateral.

(a) 9. Find the perimeter of *JKLMNP*.

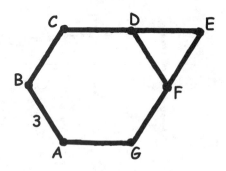

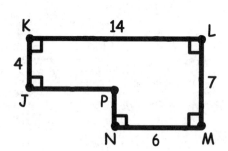

Name the means and extremes in each proportion below.

10. $\dfrac{3}{4} = \dfrac{24}{32}$

11. $\dfrac{s}{t} = \dfrac{u}{v}$

Find the geometric mean of each pair of numbers below.

12. Find the geometric mean of 4 and 16, if $\dfrac{4}{8} = \dfrac{8}{16}$.

(b) 13. Find the geometric mean of 5 and 20.

Solve for the unknown in each proportion below by cross-multiplying.

14. $\dfrac{65}{x} = \dfrac{130}{14}$

(c) 15. $\dfrac{99}{72} = \dfrac{y}{8}$

Answer each question below.

16. In $\triangle ABC$, $AC = 5.4$, $BC = 6.1$ and $AB = 6.3$. Which is the smallest angle of $\triangle ABC$?

17. In $\triangle XYZ$, $XY < YZ$ and $XZ < YZ$. Which is the largest angle of $\triangle XYZ$?

Answer each question below.

18. Find x.

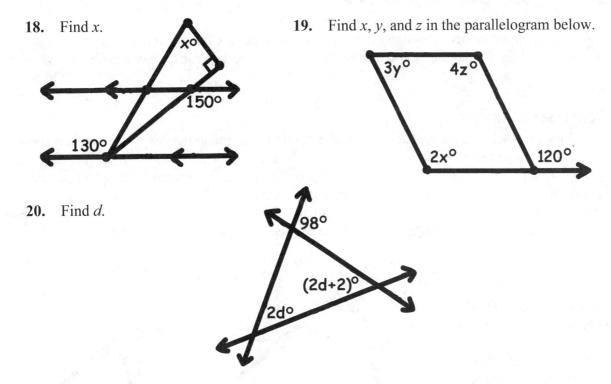

19. Find x, y, and z in the parallelogram below.

20. Find d.

Write a proportion to represent each question below; then solve the proportion to get your answer.

21. The ratio of the two legs of a right triangle is 3 to 4. If the short leg has a measure of 9, what is the measure of the long leg?

(d) 22. Chip & Dip magazine's ratio of men to women subscribers is 5 to 8. If Chip & Dip magazine has 75,000 women subscribers (at least that's how many they claim to have) how many men subscribers does it have?

Do each proof below.

23. Given: $\overline{AB} \cong \overline{DC}$, $\overline{AD} \cong \overline{BC}$

Prove: $\angle A$ and $\angle B$ are supplementary.

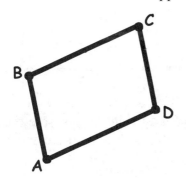

(e) 24. Given: P is the midpoint of $\overline{CL}$ and V is the midpoint of $\overline{CT}$; $m\angle PVC > m\angle C$

Prove: $CL > LT$

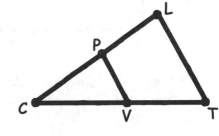

Lesson 65—Similar Figures

Now that we've been through ratios and proportions, it's finally time to get into the details of similar figures. Remember, these are figures that have the same shape but a different size.

Congruent Angles

First, we need to give a more precise definition of similar figures (since mathematicians insist on being precise). The mathematical definition for **similar figures** is that their corresponding angles must be congruent *and* the lengths of their corresponding sides must be in proportion (or "proportional," as it's also called). This is why we spent so much time on proportions in the last lesson. Let's analyze that definition more closely, though. The first part means that the only way two figures can have the same shape is if all their matching angles are congruent. Take a look at the two similar triangles on the right. See, all three pairs of corresponding angles are congruent: $\angle A \cong \angle D$, $\angle B \cong \angle E$, and $\angle C \cong \angle F$. And that's what gives $\triangle ABC$ and $\triangle DEF$ the same shape. If we were to make $\angle A$ smaller, then $\triangle ABC$ would end up shorter and have a different shape than $\triangle DEF$.

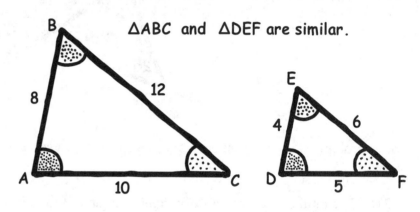

$\triangle ABC$ and $\triangle DEF$ are similar.

But congruent corresponding angles are not always enough to cause two figures to be similar. As an example, look at these rectangles below.

Rectangles ABCD and EFGH are *not* similar.

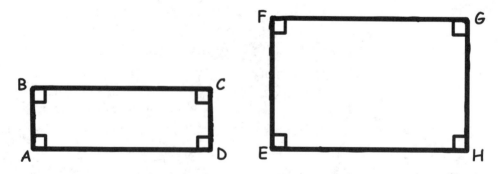

Even though all their angles are congruent (because they're all right angles), the rectangles are obviously not the same shape: Rectangle *ABCD* is quite a bit thinner than rectangle *EFGH*, so they can't be similar.

Proportional Sides

That's where the other part of our definition comes in: the lengths of the similar figures' corresponding sides must also be in proportion. That means if we divide any two corresponding sides of similar figures, we will always get the same answer. Let's do the calculation on the two triangles introduced at the beginning of the lesson, which we know are similar. See, when we divide corresponding sides AB and

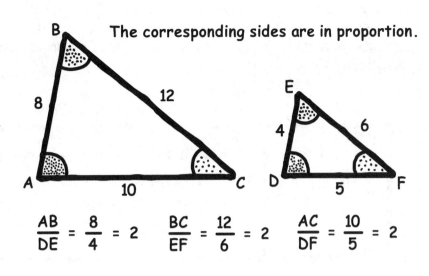

The corresponding sides are in proportion.

$$\frac{AB}{DE} = \frac{8}{4} = 2 \qquad \frac{BC}{EF} = \frac{12}{6} = 2 \qquad \frac{AC}{DF} = \frac{10}{5} = 2$$

DE, that gives us the ratio $\frac{8}{4}$, which reduces to $\frac{2}{1}$ or just 2. But then when we divide another

pair of corresponding sides, BC and EF, even though those sides have different lengths, the ratio

ends up equaling 2 as well: $\frac{BC}{EF} = \frac{12}{6} = \frac{2}{1} = 2$. And the same thing happens when we divide the

third pair of corresponding sides, AC and DF: $\frac{AC}{DF} = \frac{10}{5} = \frac{2}{1} = 2$. That's what it means to say

that the corresponding sides are "in proportion." We can set up a proportion with any two corresponding pairs of sides, and the fractions in the proportion are guaranteed to be equal.

$$\frac{AB}{DE} = \frac{BC}{EF} \qquad\qquad \frac{AB}{DE} = \frac{AC}{DF} \qquad\qquad \frac{BC}{EF} = \frac{AC}{DF}$$

The other interesting thing about these proportions is that it doesn't matter which triangle goes on top and which goes on bottom. In our calculations above, we always put the big triangle's side on top. But we could have just as easily flipped everything over. Here are the ratios with the small triangle's side on top in every fraction.

$$\frac{DE}{AB} = \frac{4}{8} = \frac{1}{2} \qquad\qquad \frac{EF}{BC} = \frac{6}{12} = \frac{1}{2} \qquad\qquad \frac{DF}{AC} = \frac{5}{10} = \frac{1}{2}$$

The answer is the same for every ratio. Only instead of 2, it's $\frac{1}{2}$. So when setting up a ratio or

proportion with similar figures, you can put either figure's sides on top. Just make sure you're consistent. If you put the big figure's side on top in one ratio, you have to put big over small in the other ratios as well.

The main point is that when the sides of two figures are in proportion, the figures have to be the same shape (as long as corresponding angles are also congruent). And the reason is that each pair of matching sides of the big and small figures will compare in size in exactly the same way. In our triangles, for instance, each side of the big triangle is twice as long as each side of the small triangle. If all of the ratios had come out to equal 3, then each side of the big triangle would have been three times as long as each side of the small triangle. Here's the definition of similar figures written formally.[4]

Definition of Similar Figures

Definition 55	If the vertices of two polygons can be paired so that corresponding angles are congruent and the lengths of corresponding sides are in proportion, then the polygons are similar.

The Symbol for Similar Figures

It's important not to confuse similar figures with *congruent* figures. Remember, congruent figures are the same shape and the same size. Speaking mathematically, their corresponding angles are congruent and their corresponding sides are congruent. But with similar figures, since their sizes are different, the corresponding sides are not the same length. Our big triangle, remember, had sides that were twice as long as the small triangle's sides. So always be aware of whether you're working with similar figures or congruent figures and don't mix the two up.

One way to keep track of this is to pay close attention to symbols. The symbol for congruent figures is " $\cong$," as you know. It turns out that the symbol for similar figures is just "~". There's no equal sign on the bottom. So to show that triangles *ABC* and *DEF* are similar, we write $\triangle ABC \sim \triangle DEF$.

As with congruent figures, the order of the vertices is very important. When writing $\triangle ABC \sim \triangle DEF$, we mean that $\angle A$ corresponds with $\angle D$ (because they're both listed first), that $\angle B$ corresponds with $\angle E$ (because they're both listed second), and that $\angle C$ corresponds with $\angle F$ (since they're both listed last).

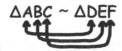

ΔABC ~ ΔDEF

∠A ≅ ∠D   ∠B ≅ ∠E   ∠C ≅ ∠F

These angles go together.

---

[4] Instead of similar "figures," the definition is for similar "polygons." Those are just figures with sides that are straight lines. We won't be doing any theorems on similar figures with curved sides.

The order of the vertices also tells us which sides are corresponding. Sides *AB* and *DE* go together (because their vertices are first and second), sides *BC* and *EF* go together (since their vertices are second and third), and sides *AC* and *DF* go together (since their vertices are first and third).

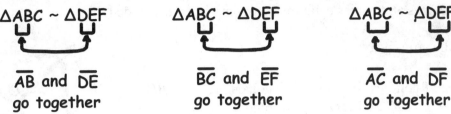

△ABC ~ △DEF	△ABC ~ △DEF	△ABC ~ △DEF
$\overline{AB}$ and $\overline{DE}$ go together	$\overline{BC}$ and $\overline{EF}$ go together	$\overline{AC}$ and $\overline{DF}$ go together

Since each pair of corresponding sides is in proportion with each other pair, we know automatically that *AB* divided by *DE* has to equal *BC* divided by *EF*, and so on.

$$\frac{AB}{DE} = \frac{BC}{EF} = \frac{AC}{DF}$$

Practice 65

a. Find the perimeter of the figure on the right in terms of *r* and *s*.

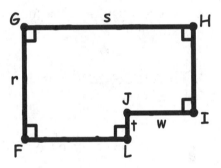

b. By cross-multiplying, solve for *g* in terms of the other variables in $\dfrac{b}{g} = \dfrac{u}{v}$.

c. Use proportions to tell whether △*RTV* and △*STU* on the right are similar.

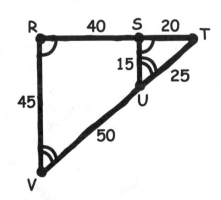

d. Write a proportion to represent each question below; then solve the proportion to get your answer.

The ratio of dogs to ponies at the Annual Dog and Pony Show was $3:4$. If there were 7,000 dogs and ponies combined, how many dogs attended?

e. Do the proof below.

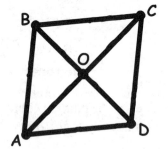

Given: Rhombus $ABCD$ with diagonals $\overline{AC}$ and $\overline{BD}$
Prove: $\angle OBC$ and $\angle OCB$ are complementary.

Problem Set 65

Tell whether each sentence below is True or False.

1. Similar figures have congruent corresponding angles and the lengths of their corresponding sides are in proportion.

2. If every pair of corresponding angles of two rectangles is congruent, then the rectangles are similar.

3. If $\triangle ABC \sim \triangle DEF$, then $\dfrac{DE}{AB} = \dfrac{EF}{BC}$.

Complete each sentence below by filling in the blanks.

4. If the ratio of all the corresponding sides of two similar figures is equal to 2, then the big figure's sides are always _____ as long as the small figure's sides.

5. A _____ is two ratios that are set equal to each other.

Tell whether each figure below is a trapezoid, isosceles trapezoid, parallelogram, rectangle, rhombus, square, or just a plain quadrilateral.

6.

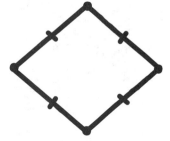

7.

Find the perimeter of each polygon below.

8.

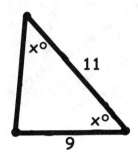

(a) 9. State the perimeter in terms of u and v.

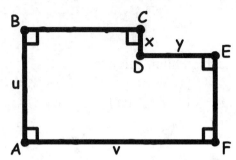

Tell whether each pair of ratios below is in proportion.

10. $\dfrac{5}{7}$ and $\dfrac{20}{21}$

11. $12:9$ and $3:4$

Find the geometric mean of each pair of numbers below.

12. Find the geometric mean of 7 and 28, if $\dfrac{7}{14} = \dfrac{14}{28}$.

13. Find the geometric mean of 6 and 11.

Solve in each proportion below by cross-multiplying.

14. $\dfrac{x}{60} = \dfrac{4}{5}$

(b) 15. Solve for q in terms of the other variables in $\dfrac{p}{q} = \dfrac{s}{t}$.

Use proportions to tell whether each pair of figures below is similar.

16.

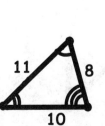

17.

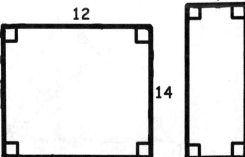

421

(c) 18. $\triangle ABE$ and $\triangle ACD$

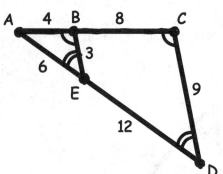

Answer each question below.

19. If $\ell_1 \parallel \ell_2 \parallel \ell_3$, find $s + u$.

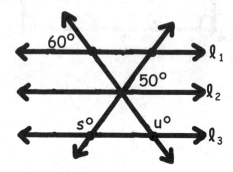

20. Find x.

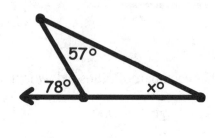

Write a proportion to represent each question below; then solve the proportion to get your answer.

21. The ratio of the width to the length of a rectangle is 2 to 5. If the width is 32, then what is the perimeter of the rectangle?

(d) 22. The ratio of annoying telemarketing calls to deceptive junk mails was 2:3. If there were 5,000 annoying telemarketing calls and deceptive junk mails combined, how many annoying telemarketing calls were there?

Do each proof below.

23. Given: $\overline{GI}$ and $\overline{FH}$ are altitudes to $\overline{DH}$ and $\overline{DG}$; $\angle HGF \cong \angle IHG$
Prove: $\overline{GI} \cong \overline{FH}$

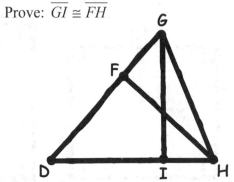

(e) 24. Given: Rhombus $RTUV$ with diagonals $\overline{RU}$ and $\overline{TV}$
Prove: $\angle QTU$ and $\angle QUT$ are complementary.

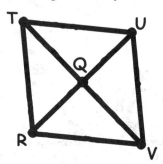

Lesson 66—Similar Figures in the Real World

Similar figures are used all the time in the real world. One simple case is a floor plan, which is just a drawing that shows the arrangement of all the furniture in a room. Here's an example of how an interior decorator might work with a floor plan.

Sally Bartholomew is redecorating a living room. Along one wall, she wants to put a big couch that is $3\frac{1}{2}$ feet wide and 7 feet long.

If, on the floor plan, the couch has a length of 1 inch, what is the width of the couch on the floor plan?

Obviously, the floor plan drawing (on the right) is much smaller than the actual living room. But if the floor plan is drawn properly, every object on the floor plan should be the exact same shape as every object in the actual living room. In other words, the real couch (or at least the space the couch takes up on the floor) and the drawing of the couch should be similar figures.

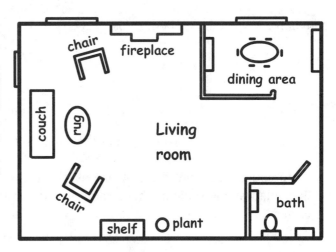

Matching the Units

So how do we figure out the width of the couch in the floor plan? Remember, in similar figures the ratios of the corresponding sides are always equal. That means the width of the drawing of the couch divided by the width of the real couch should be equal to the length of the drawing of the couch divided by the length of the real couch.

$$\frac{\text{width of drawing of couch}}{\text{width of real couch}} = \frac{\text{length of drawing of couch}}{\text{length of real couch}}$$

Before putting in the numbers, we have to make sure that each ratio has numbers that have the same units. In other words, if one number in a ratio is in feet, the other number should also be in feet. Or if one number is in inches, the other number should also be in inches. Right now, the measurements for the real couch are in feet and those for the drawing of the couch are in inches. So let's convert the width of $3\frac{1}{2}$ feet into inches by multiplying by 12. That gives us 42 inches.

Let's also convert the length of 7 feet into inches by multiplying it by 12 to get 84 inches. The length of the drawing is already in inches (1 inch). So with all the units matched up, we can put the numbers in the proportion to get this.

$$\frac{x}{42} = \frac{1}{84}$$

The remaining unknown is the width of the drawing. That's what we're trying to find, so we have represented that by an x.

Solving the Proportion

Now we can solve the proportion as usual. The first step is to cross-multiply.

$$84x = 42$$

From here, we just divide both sides by 84.

$$x = 0.5$$

We end up with a width of 0.5. And since all the units are in inches, that means 0.5 inches (or $\frac{1}{2}$ inch). That's how wide the drawing of the couch should be in the floor plan.

We could figure out the dimensions of the drawings of all the other pieces of furniture in the floor plan by the same method. Each drawing must be similar to the real piece of furniture it represents.[5]

---

[5] Technically, it's the floor space that the piece of furniture takes up that is similar to its drawing. The actual piece of furniture is three dimensional, and so it can't be similar to a two dimensional drawing on paper.

Maps Too

There are lots of other cases where similar figures are used in the real world. Another common use is on a map. For example, the map on the right shows several states in the middle of the United States. Each state on the map should have the same shape as the actual state that it represents. That means the width of Colorado on the map divided by the width of the actual state of Colorado should equal the length of Colorado on the map divided by Colorado's actual length. The same goes for each of the other states. It's fairly easy to calculate ratios for Colorado, because it has a rectangular shape. Some of the other states—like Missouri or Illinois—would be a lot tougher. The underlying concept, though, is the same as in our floor plan example: the ratios of corresponding sides of similar figures are equal.

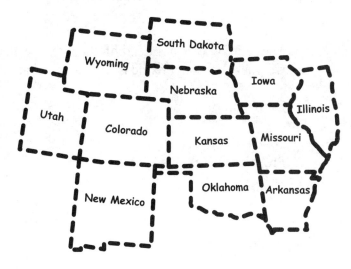

Practice 66

a. Use proportions to tell whether the pair of figures on the right is similar.

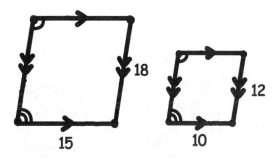

b. Calculate the ratio below.

A basketball hoop is 10 feet high and a basketball is 9.39 inches in diameter. Calculate the ratio of the hoop's height to the basketball's height, in inches. (Write your answer as a decimal rounded to 2 places.)

c. If *ABCDEFGH* is a regular octagon, find *a*.

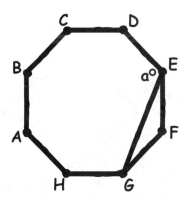

d. Write a proportion to represent the question below; then solve the proportion to get your answer.

The ratio by weight of carbon dioxide to water in a chemical reactor is $5:4$. If the weight of carbon dioxide is 25 grams, what is the weight of water?

e. Do the proof below.

Given: Rhombus *FGHI*
Prove: $\triangle FJH$ is isosceles.

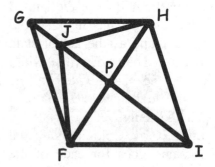

Problem Set 66

Tell whether each sentence below is True or False.

1. If a baby is 18 inches long and the baby's father is 6 feet tall, then the ratio of the baby's length to the father's height is $\dfrac{18}{6}$ (which reduces to 3).

2. When using ratios on real-world problems, it's never important to match up the units.

Complete each sentence below by filling in the blanks.

3. _____ have congruent corresponding angles and the lengths of their corresponding sides are in proportion.

4. A _____ is a polygon where every one of its sides is congruent and every one of its interior angles is congruent.

5. If $\dfrac{a}{b}=\dfrac{b}{c}$, then b is the _____ of a and c (where a, b, c are positive).

Name each polygon below and tell whether it is regular.

6.

7.

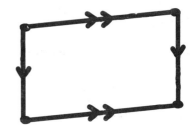

Use proportions to tell whether each pair of figures below is similar.

8.

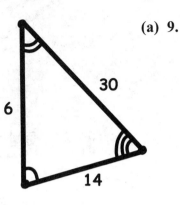

(a) 9.

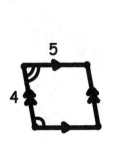

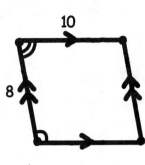

Complete each sentence below with *always*, *sometimes*, or *never*.

10. Two similar triangles _____ have congruent corresponding angles.

11. The two ratios in a proportion _____ have the same value.

Calculate each ratio below.

12. The 4-year-old was able to broad jump a distance of 24 inches. The 24-year-old was able to broad jump a distance of 14 feet. Calculate the ratio of the 4-year-old's jump to the 24-year-old's jump, in feet.

(b) 13. The roof of a house is 12 feet high and the first step of the house is 5 inches high. Calculate the ratio of the roof's height to the first step's height in inches. (Write your answer as a decimal.)

Solve in each proportion below by cross-multiplying.

14. $\dfrac{20}{60} = \dfrac{4}{r}$

15. Solve for b in terms of the other variables in $\dfrac{b}{t} = \dfrac{m}{v}$.

From each given statement below, tell the definition, property, postulate, or theorem that justifies each prove statement.

16. Given: $\angle A$ is supplementary to $\angle C$ and $\angle B$ is supplementary to $\angle C$
Prove: $\angle A \cong \angle B$

427

17.   Given $\triangle BNV$ (on the right) and $m\angle B > m\angle V$
      Prove: $NV > BN$

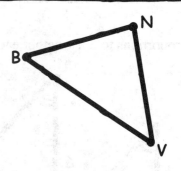

Answer each question below.

18.   Find x.

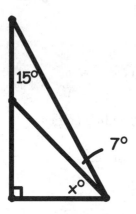

19.   Find y.

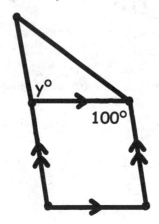

(c) 20.   Find z if $ABCDEF$ is a regular hexagon.

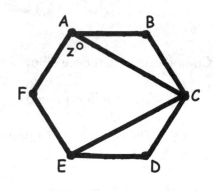

Write a proportion to represent each question below; then solve the proportion to get your answer.

21.   The drawing of a dining room on a floor plan measures 10 inches wide and 20 inches long. If the actual dining room has a length of 50 feet, what is its width?

(d) 22.   The ratio by mass of hydrogen to oxygen in a chemical reactor is $1:8$. If the mass of oxygen is 64 grams, what is the mass of hydrogen?

Do each proof below.

23.   Given: $RS = TU$; $\angle VTR \cong \angle WSU$; $\angle VRT \cong \angle WUS$;
      Prove: $\triangle RVT \cong \triangle UWS$

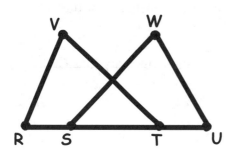

(e) 24.   Given: Rhombus $ABCD$
      Prove: $\triangle DPB$ is isosceles.

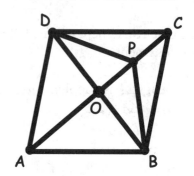

Lesson 67—Splitting a Triangle... Not in the Middle

If you remember back to the chapter on quadrilaterals, we did a theorem involving a line that runs through the midpoints of two sides of a triangle and that is parallel to the third side. On the right is an example of such a situation. See, since P and Q are the midpoints of the left and right sides, each side divides into two equal segments: $BP = AP$ and $BQ = QC$.

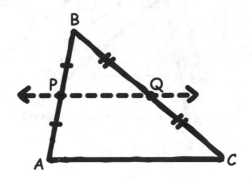

BP = AP, BQ = QC, and $\overline{PQ}$ || $\overline{AC}$.

Sides Divided Proportionally

In some cases, instead of going through the midpoints of the two sides of the triangle, the line runs a little higher or a little lower. In the diagram on the right, for example, $\overline{PQ}$ is still parallel to $\overline{AC}$, but P and Q aren't the midpoints of the other two sides. That means BP and AP aren't equal and neither are BQ and QC.

$\overline{PQ}$ || $\overline{AC}$ and $\dfrac{BP}{AP} = \dfrac{BQ}{QC}$

But here's the interesting thing. Those line segments are still related to each other. As it turns out, the ratio of BP to AP and the ratio of BQ to QC are in proportion. In other words, those ratios are equal: $\dfrac{BP}{AP} = \dfrac{BQ}{QC}$. And what's amazing is that this relationship holds true no matter what the position of $\overline{PQ}$, as long as $\overline{PQ}$ is parallel to $\overline{AC}$.

What makes this rule really useful, though, is that it can be further extended. Not only are the ratios of the two small segments in proportion, but the ratios of each small segment to the entire side are in proportion as well.

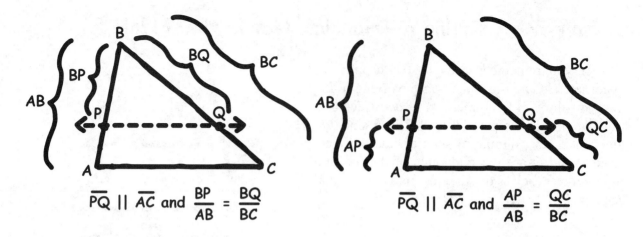

$$\overline{PQ} \parallel \overline{AC} \text{ and } \frac{BP}{AB} = \frac{BQ}{BC}$$

$$\overline{PQ} \parallel \overline{AC} \text{ and } \frac{AP}{AB} = \frac{QC}{BC}$$

You can see above (left) that the ratio of the upper small segment, BP, to the entire left side, AB, is equal to the ratio of the upper small segment, BQ, to the entire right side, BC. That gives us the proportion $\frac{BP}{AB} = \frac{BQ}{BC}$. The ratios of the lower small segments to each entire side are also equal: $\frac{AP}{AB} = \frac{QC}{BC}$ (as shown above right).

Now, since proportions can be flipped over and still be true, every one of these triangle proportions can be flipped over as well. For example, instead of $\frac{BP}{AP} = \frac{BQ}{QC}$, we could also write $\frac{AP}{BP} = \frac{QC}{BC}$. And instead of $\frac{BP}{AB} = \frac{BQ}{BC}$, we could write $\frac{AB}{BP} = \frac{BC}{BQ}$, and so on. So this really is a very broad and useful rule. Instead of proving it, though, we'll just accept the rule as a postulate.

Postulate 14	If a line is parallel to one side of a triangle and intersects the other two sides, then the line divides those sides proportionally.

Converse Too

Basically, Postulate 14 says that *if* a parallel line intersects two lines of a triangle, *then* the line divides those sides proportionally. But is the converse of Postulate 14 true? The converse says that if a line divides two sides of a triangle proportionally, then that line has to be parallel to the third side. As it turns out, the converse is true as well. So we have both Postulate 14 and its converse to work with. The converse (Postulate 15) is stated formally below.

Postulate 15	If a line intersects two sides of a triangle and divides those sides proportionally, then the line is parallel to the third side.

Here's a quick example of how Postulate 15 might be used. In $\triangle ABC$, $\overrightarrow{PQ}$ divides the two sides into segments AP, PB and segments AQ and QC. To figure out whether $\overrightarrow{PQ}$ is parallel to $\overline{BC}$, we just have to show that the ratios of the small segments are in proportion. Dividing AP and PB, we get $\dfrac{AP}{PB} = \dfrac{15}{3} = 5$. Then, dividing AQ and QC, we get $\dfrac{AQ}{QC} = \dfrac{10}{2} = 5$. The ratios are in proportion (equal), so $\overrightarrow{PQ}$ is parallel to $\overline{BC}$.

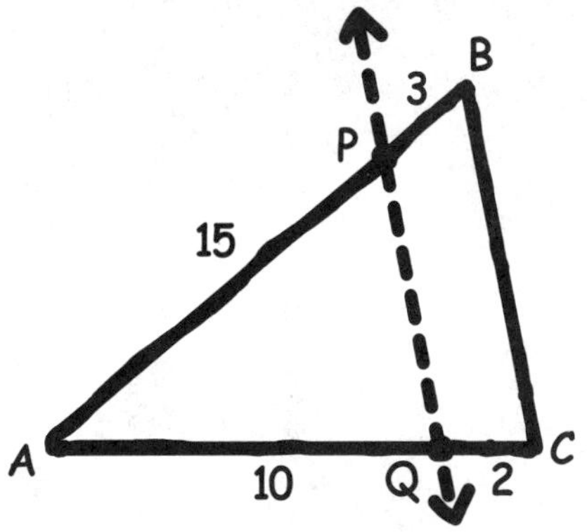

Notice also that we could have used any of the other ratio combinations to prove the same thing. For instance, we could have divided PB by AP and QC by AQ: $\dfrac{PB}{AP} = \dfrac{3}{15} = \dfrac{1}{5}$ and $\dfrac{QC}{AQ} = \dfrac{2}{10} = \dfrac{1}{5}$. Or we could have divided AP by AB and AQ by AC: $\dfrac{AP}{AB} = \dfrac{15}{18} = \dfrac{5}{6}$ and $\dfrac{AQ}{AC} = \dfrac{10}{12} = \dfrac{5}{6}$. You see in both cases, the two ratios come out the same. So it doesn't matter which ratios you use. Just be consistent.

$$\frac{AP}{PB} = \frac{15}{3} = 5 \text{ and } \frac{AQ}{QC} = \frac{10}{2} = 5,$$

$$\text{therefore } \overleftrightarrow{PQ} \parallel \overline{BC}.$$

Practice 67

a. Based on the diagram below, complete the proportion $\dfrac{?}{MQ} = \dfrac{KV}{UV}$.

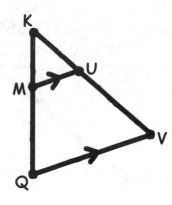

b. In the triangle below, find the ratios $\dfrac{HJ}{HP}$ and $\dfrac{IJ}{IK}$. Do the ratios indicate that the sides are divided proportionally?

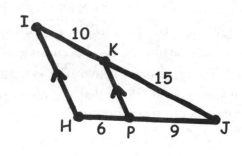

c. Find the perimeter of the polygon below in terms of x and y.

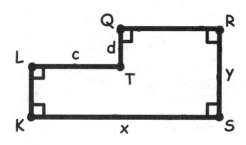

d. If *PRST* is a rhombus, find x.

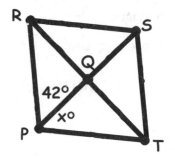

e. Do the proof below.

Given: $\triangle MCA$ and rectangle $BCDN$

Prove: $\dfrac{DM}{DC} = \dfrac{BC}{AB}$

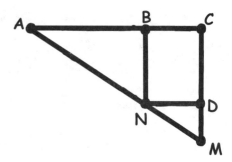

Problem Set 67

Tell whether each sentence below is True or False.

1. If a line is parallel to one side of a triangle and intersects the other two sides, then the line divides those sides proportionally.

2. If a line intersects two sides of a triangle and divides those sides proportionally, then the line is parallel to the third side.

Complete each sentence below by filling in the blanks.

3. The sum of the measures of the interior angles of a polygon with n sides is
_____.

4. The diagonals of a rectangle are _____.

5. If two sides of a triangle are not congruent, then the angles opposite those sides are _____, and the _____ angle is opposite the _____ side.

Name each regular polygon below and find the measure of the interior angle indicated.

6.

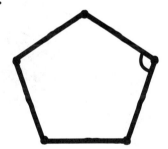

7.

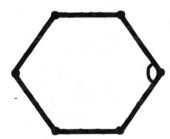

Based on the diagram, complete each proportion below.

8. $\dfrac{LS}{SP} = \dfrac{?}{TR}$

(a) 9. $\dfrac{?}{LS} = \dfrac{LR}{LT}$

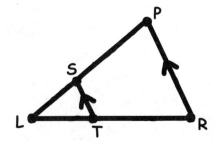

In the triangle below, find each of the ratios indicated. Do the ratios show that the sides are divided proportionally?

10. $\dfrac{EC}{BE}$ and $\dfrac{OA}{BO}$

(b) 11. $\dfrac{BA}{OA}$ and $\dfrac{BC}{EC}$

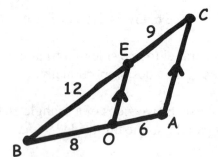

Find the perimeter of each polygon below.

(c) 12. State the perimeter in terms of a and b.

13. State the perimeter of $\triangle ABC$.

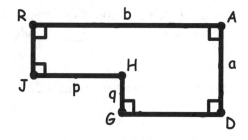

Solve in each proportion below by cross-multiplying.

14. Solve for x in $\dfrac{12+x}{x} = \dfrac{4}{3}$.

15. Solve for y in terms of m in $\dfrac{y}{m} = \dfrac{1}{3}$.

Answer each question below.

16. In $\triangle ABC$, $AB < BC$ and $BC < CA$. Which is the smallest angle of $\triangle ABC$?

17. In $\triangle XYZ$, $YZ = 13$, $XZ = 3$ and $XY = 8$. Which is the largest angle of $\triangle XYZ$?

Answer each question below.

18. Find *x*.

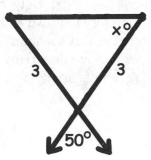

(d) 19. If *ABCD* is a rhombus, find *y*.

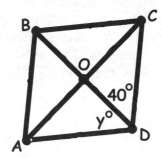

20. Find *x*.

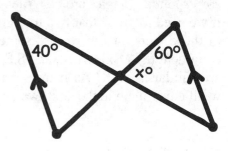

Write an equation to represent each question below; then solve the equation to get your answer.

21. In $\triangle FGH$, $m\angle F$ is twice as large as $m\angle G$ and $m\angle G$ is three times $m\angle H$. Find $m\angle G$.

22. Two angles are supplementary. The measure of one angle is 20 less than $\frac{1}{3}$ of the other. Find the measures of *both* angles.

Do each proof below.

23. Given: *B* is the midpoint of $\overline{AC}$ and

D is the midpoint of $\overline{CE}$;

$m\angle E > m\angle A$

Prove: $AB > ED$

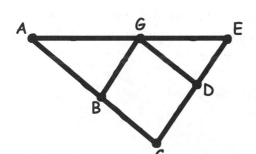

(e) 24. Given: $\triangle DHF$ and rectangle *EJHP*

Prove: $\dfrac{FJ}{JH} = \dfrac{HP}{PD}$

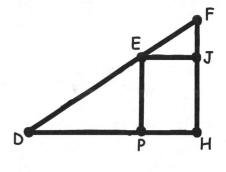

Lesson 68—Angle-Angle Similarity

We've learned that in similar triangles (triangles with the same shape), the three pairs of corresponding angles are congruent and the three corresponding sides are proportional. But what if we need to prove that two triangles are similar in the first place? Is it necessary to prove all six of those facts, or can we use some shortcuts? We have shortcuts for proving that triangles are congruent (S.A.S., A.A.S., and S.S.S., for example). Why not shortcuts for proving that triangles are similar as well? As it turns out, there are three shortcuts for proving similar triangles, and we'll cover them in the next two lessons.[6]

Just Two Pairs of Angles

To start our explanation of the first shortcut, take a look at the diagram below.

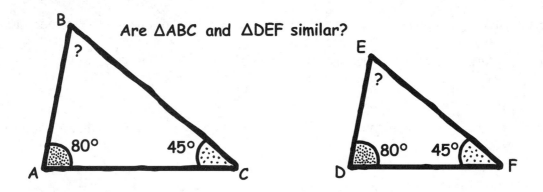

We need to figure out whether $\triangle ABC$ and $\triangle DEF$ are similar. All we know is that two pairs of their corresponding angles are congruent: $\angle A \cong \angle D$ and $\angle C \cong \angle F$. You might think that's not enough information to tell whether the triangles are similar, but it is. Here's why. Since the three angles of any triangle must add to equal $180°$, the third pair of angles must also be the same. Specifically, $\angle B$ and $\angle E$ must both equal $55°$. That tells us that all three pairs of corresponding angles are congruent. And with all three angle pairs congruent, the triangles must have the same shape (be similar).

To show you why, let's conduct a little experiment. Right now, our triangles are exactly the same shape. But let's see if we can change the shape of the smaller triangle without changing any of its angles. We'll move $\overline{EF}$ down a bit and see what happens.

---

[6] We won't learn any shortcuts for similar figures with greater than 3 sides, because the situation gets quite a bit more complicated as the number of sides goes up.

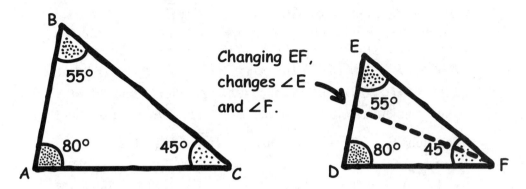

We can't change the shape of a triangle without changing an angle.

Notice two of the triangle's angles, $\angle E$ and $\angle F$, have been changed as a result of moving $\overline{EF}$. And that changes the shape of the entire triangle. This is always what happens, because the three angles of a triangle determine its shape. If any of the angles change, the shape changes. That's why any two triangles with three pairs of congruent angles must be similar.[7] But, remember, when triangles have two congruent angles, the third pair of angles has to be congruent as well. Our first shortcut for proving similar triangles, then, is just to prove that two pairs of their angles are congruent. That's all it takes. This shortcut is called **Angle-Angle Similarity** (A.A. Similarity).

Proving It

After coming this far in geometry, you know that an "experiment" with a couple of triangles is not enough to prove a new theorem. We need to prove Angle-Angle Similarity deductively. An informal proof of A.A. Similarity is shown below, followed by a formal statement of the theorem.

Given: $\angle H \cong \angle K, \angle I \cong \angle L,$

Prove: $\triangle HIJ \sim \triangle KLM$

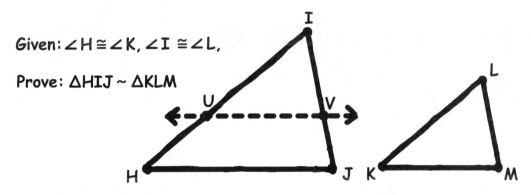

Since two pairs of angles of $\triangle HIJ$ and $\triangle KLM$ are congruent, the third pair must also be congruent: $\angle J \cong \angle M$. The next step is to

---

[7] For figures with more than three sides, such as quadrilaterals, having every pair of angles congruent is not a guarantee that the figures are similar. Remember, the example from a few lessons ago of the two rectangles? Their angles were all congruent, but the rectangles still weren't the same shape.

choose points U and V on $\triangle HIJ$ so that $\overline{UI} \cong \overline{KL}$ and $\overline{IV} \cong \overline{LM}$. Next, we draw a line through U and V. (Two points determine a line.) Since $\angle I \cong \angle L$, $\triangle UIV \cong \triangle KLM$ (S.A.S.). That means $\angle IUV \cong \angle K$ (C.P.C.T.C.) But since $\angle H \cong \angle K$, by substitution $\angle IUV \cong \angle H$. So $\overline{UV} \parallel \overline{HJ}$. Since a line parallel to one side of a triangle and intersecting the other two sides divides those sides proportionally, $\dfrac{UI}{HI} = \dfrac{IV}{IJ}$. Because $\overline{UI} \cong \overline{KL}$ and $\overline{IV} \cong \overline{LM}$, it's also true by substitution that $\dfrac{KL}{HI} = \dfrac{LM}{IJ}$. By going through the same process, we can show that $\dfrac{KL}{HI} = \dfrac{KM}{HJ}$. Therefore, $\dfrac{KL}{HI} = \dfrac{LM}{IJ} = \dfrac{KM}{HJ}$.

Angle-Angle Similarity Theorem (AA Similarity)

Theorem 51	If two angles of one triangle are congruent to two angles of another triangle, then the triangles are similar.

Practice 68

a. In the triangle on the right, find the ratios $\dfrac{BP}{PC}$ and $\dfrac{AM}{MC}$. Do the ratios show that $\overline{AB} \parallel \overline{PM}$?

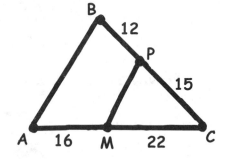

b. Calculate the ratio of 420 centimeters to 21 meters. Write your answer in the form $a:b$, with a and b fully reduced.

c. Tell whether $\triangle PQR$ and $\triangle SVR$ (on the right) are similar.

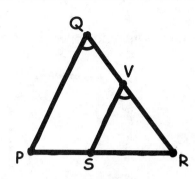

d. Write a proportion to represent the question below; then solve the proportion to get your answer.

There were 16 women at the countdown to the pre-game Super Bowl party. If the ratio of women to total people in attendance was $4:13$, how many men were there?

e. Do the proof below.

Given: $\triangle ABC$ with altitudes $\overline{AK}$ and $\overline{CJ}$
Prove: $\triangle JOA \sim \triangle KOC$

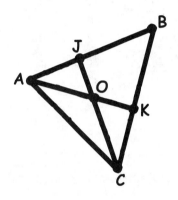

Problem Set 68

Tell whether each sentence below is True or False.

1. If two angles of one triangle are congruent to two angles of another triangle, then the triangles are similar.

2. It is not possible to change the shape of a triangle without changing at least one of its angles.

Complete each sentence below by filling in the blanks.

3. According to the _____, if two sides of a triangle are congruent (equal), then the angles opposite those sides are congruent (equal).

4. If a quadrilateral is a parallelogram, then _____ angles are supplementary.

5. The _____ of a rhombus bisect the angles at the vertices which they join.

Find the sum of the interior angles of each polygon below.

6.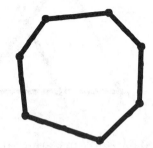

7.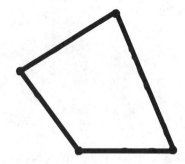

In the triangle below, find each of the ratios indicated. Do the ratios show that the sides are divided proportionally?

8. $\dfrac{BW}{WC}$ and $\dfrac{AT}{TC}$

9. $\dfrac{BC}{BW}$ and $\dfrac{AC}{AT}$

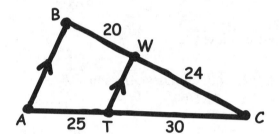

In the triangle below, find each of the ratios indicated. Do the ratios show that $\overline{IE} \parallel \overline{GH}$?

10. $\dfrac{GI}{FG}$ and $\dfrac{HE}{FH}$

(a) 11. $\dfrac{FI}{IG}$ and $\dfrac{FE}{EH}$

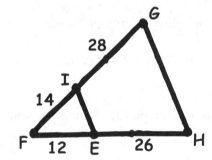

Find the geometric mean of each pair of numbers below.

12. Find the geometric mean of 4 and 64.

13. Find the geometric mean of 7 and 63.

Calculate each ratio below.

14. The height of the proposed new church auditorium is 56 feet. The height of the architect's model of the auditorium is only 14 inches. Calculate the ratio of the height of the architect's model to the height of the actual auditorium, in inches. Write your answer in the form $a:b$, with a and b fully reduced.

(b) 15. Calculate the ratio of 750 milliliters to 1.5 liters. Write your answer in the form $a:b$, with a and b fully reduced.

Tell whether each pair of figures below is similar.

16.

17.

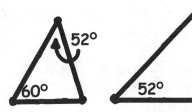

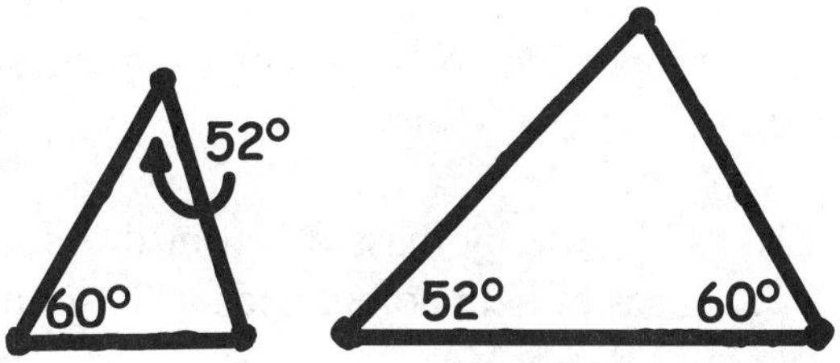

(c) 18. $\triangle ABC$ and $\triangle ADE$

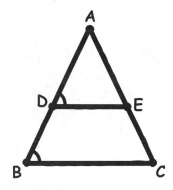

Answer each question below.

19. Find *x*.

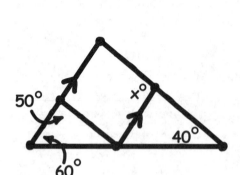

20. If $\ell_1 \parallel \ell_2 \parallel \ell_3$, find *y*.

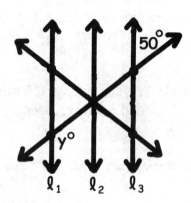

Write a proportion to represent each question below; then solve the proportion to get your answer.

21. The ratio by mass of sulfur dioxide to oxygen in a chemical reactor is $5:3$. If the total mass of both compounds is 72 grams, what is the mass of oxygen?

(d) 22. There were 21 boys at the birthday party. If the ratio of boys to total partygoers was $7:15$, how many girls were there?

Do each proof below.

23. Given: $\overline{AC} \cong \overline{CE}$, $\overline{RZ} \perp \overline{AE}$, $\overline{LV} \perp \overline{AE}$
Prove: $\triangle RZE \sim \triangle LVA$

(e) 24. Given: $\triangle PRD$ with altitudes $\overline{LD}$ and $\overline{PS}$
Prove: $\triangle LEP \sim \triangle SED$

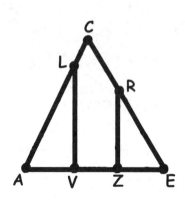

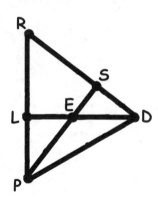

Lesson 69—Side-Angle-Side and Side-Side-Side Similarity

In the last lesson, we learned about Angle-Angle Similarity (A.A. Similarity), which is a shortcut for proving that two triangles are similar. Remember, in A.A. Similarity, we have to show that any two pairs of corresponding angles are congruent. That's enough to prove that triangles are similar. There are actually two more shortcuts for proving similar triangles. And even though these aren't as popular as AA Similarity, in some cases, they're the only way to do a proof. So in this lesson, we'll cover the last two shortcuts.

Side-Angle-Side Similarity

The next shortcut is Side-Angle Side Similarity (S.A.S. Similarity). To show you how this one works, look at the diagram on the right.

We have two triangles, $\triangle PQR$ and $\triangle TVW$, and, as you can see, one pair of their corresponding angles are congruent ($\angle P \cong \angle T$). Since the triangles are of different sizes, none of the sides are congruent. But since ratios are used a lot in similar triangles, let's compare

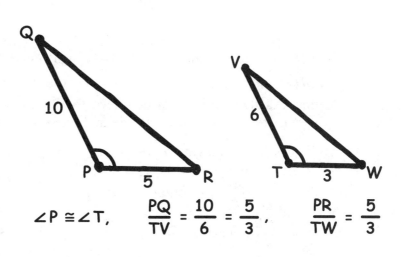

$$\angle P \cong \angle T, \quad \frac{PQ}{TV} = \frac{10}{6} = \frac{5}{3}, \quad \frac{PR}{TW} = \frac{5}{3}$$

the ratios of the two pairs of corresponding sides that connect to the congruent angles ($\overline{PQ}$, $\overline{TV}$ and $\overline{PR}$, $\overline{TW}$). And since we're doing a comparison, we should make sure that each ratio is fully reduced.

$$\frac{PQ}{TV} = \frac{10}{6} \text{ or } \frac{5}{3}, \text{ and } \frac{PR}{TW} = \frac{5}{3}$$

It turns out that $\dfrac{PQ}{TV}$ equals $\dfrac{PR}{TW}$. So our two triangles have not just one pair of congruent angles, but also two pairs of corresponding sides that are proportional. That's enough information to prove that $\triangle PQR$ and $\triangle TVW$ are similar ($\triangle PQR \sim \triangle TVW$). This is how the Side-Angle-Side Similarity shortcut works. One pair of angles has to be congruent, and the two pairs of sides connected to those angles have to be proportional (their ratios should be equal).

A lot of people confuse the Side-Angle-Side Similarity shortcut with the Side-Angle-Side *congruent* triangles shortcut. But the two are actually totally different. S.A.S. Similarity is used only on similar triangles (triangles with the same shape but a different size), while plain S.A.S. is used only on congruent triangles. In S.A.S. Similarity, the two pairs of sides are proportional; in plain S.A.S., the two sides are congruent. Below is a deductive proof of S.A.S. Similarity, followed by an official statement of the theorem.

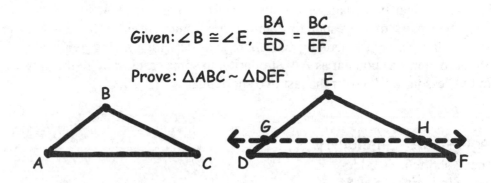

$$\text{Given: } \angle B \cong \angle E, \quad \frac{BA}{ED} = \frac{BC}{EF}$$

$$\text{Prove: } \triangle ABC \sim \triangle DEF$$

First, we choose point G on $\overline{ED}$ so that $\overline{EG} \cong \overline{BA}$. Next, we draw $\overline{GH}$ through G so that $\overline{GH} \parallel \overline{DF}$. (Through a given point not on a line, exactly one line may be drawn parallel to that line.) Since a line parallel to one side of a triangle and intersecting the other two sides divides those sides proportionally, $\dfrac{EG}{ED} = \dfrac{EH}{EF}$. But since $\overline{EG} \cong \overline{BA}$,

then $\dfrac{BA}{ED} = \dfrac{EH}{EF}$ (substitution). It's given that $\dfrac{BA}{ED} = \dfrac{BC}{EF}$. Therefore,

$\dfrac{BC}{EF} = \dfrac{EH}{EF}$ (substitution). Multiplying both sides of $\dfrac{BC}{EF} = \dfrac{EH}{EF}$ by EF

gives $BC = EH$ (or $\overline{BC} \cong \overline{EH}$). By the S.A.S. congruent triangles shortcut, $\triangle ABC \cong \triangle GEH$. That means $\angle A \cong \angle EGH$ (C.P.C.T.C.) Also, $\angle D \cong \angle EGH$ (If two parallel lines are cut by a transversal, then their corresponding angles are congruent.) But then $\angle A \cong \angle D$ (Transitive). Since $\angle A$ and $\angle D$ are another pair of congruent angles (along with $\angle B$ and $\angle E$), then $\triangle ABC \sim \triangle DEF$ (A.A. Similarity).

Side-Angle-Side Similarity Theorem (S.A.S. Similarity)

Theorem 52	If a pair of corresponding angles of two triangles are congruent and the sides including those angles are proportional, then the triangles are similar.

Side-Side-Side Similarity

The next (and last) shortcut for proving similar triangles is **Side-Side-Side Similarity** (S.S.S. Similarity). As you might expect from its name, this shortcut has nothing to do with angles. To use S.S.S. Similarity, we need to show that all three pairs of corresponding sides of the triangles are proportional. That's done by making three ratios (one for each pair of sides) and showing that all three are equal.

S.S.S. Similarity is also often confused with the Side-Side-Side shortcut for congruent triangles. Just remember that S.S.S. Similarity is for similar triangles, and so the sides aren't supposed to be congruent; they are supposed to be proportional. Here's a quick example of S.S.S. Similarity in action.

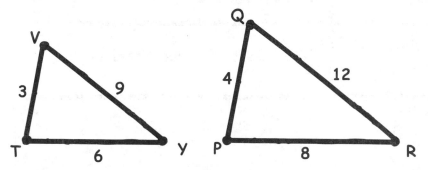

See, we have two triangles, and no information about their angles. We're given only the lengths of all three sides. That means S.S.S. Similarity is the only method that might work. The first step is to create three ratios, one for each pair of sides. And since we want to show that the ratios are equal, we should make sure they're all fully reduced.

$$\frac{VT}{QP} = \frac{3}{4} \qquad\qquad \frac{TY}{PR} = \frac{6}{8} = \frac{3}{4} \qquad\qquad \frac{VY}{QR} = \frac{9}{12} = \frac{3}{4}$$

Every ratio equals $\frac{3}{4}$. That means, according to S.S.S. Similarity, the two triangles are similar.

We're not going to prove S.S.S. Similarity deductively, because it's not used very much and we don't have room to show the proof. So we'll accept this shortcut as a postulate. Here is the official statement.

Side-Side-Side Similarity Postulate (S.S.S. Similarity)

Postulate 16	If all three pairs of corresponding sides of both triangles are proportional, then the triangles are similar.

That gives us three shortcuts for proving similar triangles: A.A. Similarity (which is by far the most popular), S.A.S. Similarity, and S.S.S. Similarity. Here are the rules for using all three.

Three Methods for Proving Similar Triangles

Angle-Angle Similarity	Two pairs of congruent angles
Side-Angle-Side Similarity	One pair of congruent angles and two pairs of proportional sides.
Side-Side-Side Similarity	Three pairs of proportional sides.

Practice 69

a. In the triangle, the missing length x can be found with several different proportions. Complete the possible proportion below and find x.

$$\frac{x}{21} = \frac{10}{?}$$

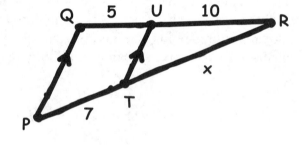

b. State which shortcut can be used to prove that the pair of triangles below are similar. If no method applies, say "none."

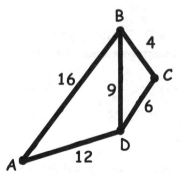

c. If $\overline{AC} \cong \overline{AD}$ and $\overline{BC} \cong \overline{BD}$, find x.

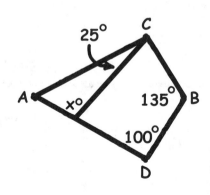

d. The measures of a pair of consecutive angles of a parallelogram have a ratio of $4:11$. Find the measure of each angle of the parallelogram.

e. Given: $\triangle ABC \sim \triangle PLM$, $\triangle ABC \sim \triangle XYZ$
Prove: $\triangle PLM \sim \triangle XYZ$

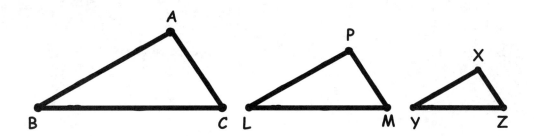

Problem Set 69

Tell whether each sentence below is True or False.

1. For the Side-Angle-Side Similarity shortcut, one pair of angles has to be congruent, and the two pairs of sides connected to those angles have to be proportional.

2. For the Side-Side-Side Similarity shortcut, all three pairs of corresponding sides of the triangles have to be proportional.

Complete each sentence below by filling in the blanks.

3. A _____ is a polygon where every one of its sides is congruent and every one of its interior angles is congruent.

4. The lower (and upper) base angles of a(n) _____ are congruent.

5. According to the _____, an exterior angle of a triangle is always greater than either one of the remote interior angles.

Tell whether each statement below is the converse, inverse, or contrapositive of the following statement: If two triangles are similar, then their corresponding sides are proportional.

6. If two triangles are not similar, then their corresponding sides are not proportional.

7. If the corresponding sides of two triangles are not proportional, then the triangles are not similar.

In the triangle, the missing length x can be found with several different proportions. Complete the possible proportions below, and find x for each.

8. $\dfrac{15}{?} = \dfrac{20}{x}$

(a) 9. $\dfrac{x}{32} = \dfrac{9}{?}$

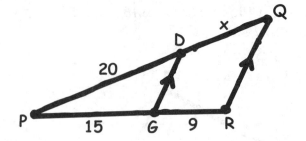

Solve in each proportion below by cross-multiplying.

10. Solve for p in $\dfrac{p-4}{p} = \dfrac{5}{7}$.

11. Solve for k in $\dfrac{k-3}{2} = \dfrac{k+1}{5}$.

Find the perimeter of each polygon below.

12. A rhombus with sides measuring 7.25 inches.

13. A regular hexagon with sides measuring $10\dfrac{1}{2}$ centimeters.

From each given statement below, tell the definition, property, postulate, or theorem that justifies each prove statement.

14. Given: $\triangle STU$ (on the right)
Prove: $m\angle S + m\angle T = m\angle TUV$

15. Given: $m\angle S < m\angle U$ (on the right)
Prove: $ST > TU$

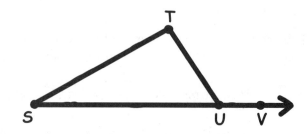

State which shortcut can be used to prove that each pair of triangles below are similar. If no method applies, say "none."

16.

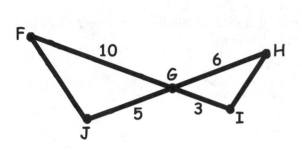

(b) 17.

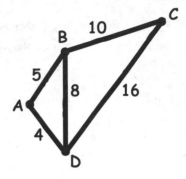

18.

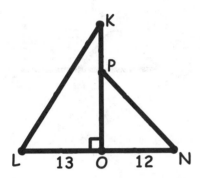

Answer each question below.

19. Find x.

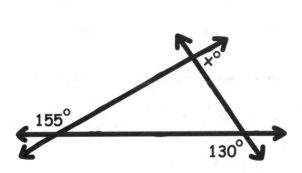

(c) 20. If $\overline{AC} \cong \overline{AD}$ and $\overline{BC} \cong \overline{BD}$, find y.

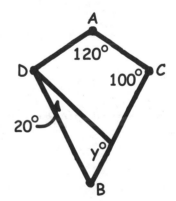

449

Answer each question below.

21.   The ratio of a pair of consecutive sides of a parallelogram is $3:5$. If the longer of the two consecutive sides is 35 inches, find the perimeter of the parallelogram.

(d) 22.   The measures of a pair of consecutive angles of a parallelogram have a ratio of $1:2$. Find the measure of each angle of the parallelogram.

Do each proof below. Number 24 will become a corollary to our Theorem 51.

23.   Given: $\overline{KI} \cong \overline{IL}$, $\overline{NM} \cong \overline{ML}$, $\angle KIL \cong \angle NML$
      Prove: $\triangle KIL \sim \triangle NML$

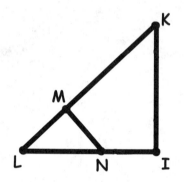

(e) 24.   Given: $\triangle ABC \sim \triangle PLM$, $\triangle PLM \sim \triangle XYZ$
      Prove: $\triangle ABC \sim \triangle XYZ$

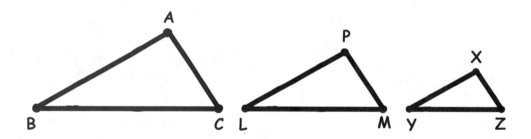

| Corollary 51.1 | Two triangles similar to a third triangle are similar to each other. |

Lesson 70—Using Similar Triangles

For quite a few chapters now, we've been using "Congruent Parts of Congruent Triangles are Congruent (C.P.C.T.C.) to prove things. You know how it works. First, we prove that two triangles are congruent, and then we can prove that certain parts of those triangles—such as a pair of sides or a pair of angles—are also congruent.

Proving Corresponding Sides of Similar Triangles Proportional

As it turns out, we can do the same kind of thing with similar triangles. Once we've proven that two triangles are similar, we can use that information to prove that sides of those triangles are proportional or that the triangle's angles are congruent. Let's look at a specific example.

We have a parallelogram, and we're supposed to prove that two sets of line segments inside the parallelogram ($\overline{TS}$, $\overline{SR}$ and $\overline{TM}$, $\overline{RK}$) are proportional. At first, it's not obvious how to do the proof. But notice that the line segments are actually corresponding sides of the triangles $\triangle KSR$ and $\triangle MST$. So if we can prove that those triangles are similar, by the definition of similar figures, we can then prove that the segments are proportional (since corresponding sides of similar triangles are always proportional). That's the method to use. Here's an informal version of the proof.

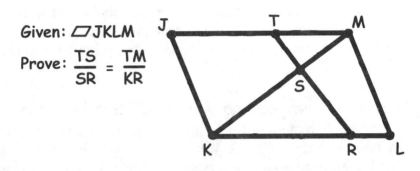

Given: $\square JKLM$

Prove: $\dfrac{TS}{SR} = \dfrac{TM}{KR}$

First, $\angle KSR \cong \angle MST$ (Pairs of vertical angles are congruent.) Next, since $JKLM$ is a parallelogram (Given), $\overline{KR} \parallel \overline{TM}$. It follows that $\angle RKS \cong \angle TMS$ (If two parallel lines are cut by a transversal, then their alternate interior angles are congruent.) That gives us two corresponding angles, so $\triangle KSR \sim \triangle MST$ by A.A. Similarity.

Therefore, $\dfrac{TS}{SR} = \dfrac{TM}{KR}$ (Converse of Definition of Similar Triangles)

Notice that the reason for the final step was **"Converse of Definition of Similar Triangles."** The definition of similar triangles says that "if two triangles have their corresponding sides in proportion, then they are similar." Here we're reversing that by saying that "if two triangles are similar, then their corresponding sides are proportional." Since all good definitions are reversible, we know that the converse is true. We could have also written the reason in longer form as "Corresponding Sides of Similar Triangles are Proportional (or

C.S.S.T.P.). But it would still have been just the converse of the definition of similar triangles by another name.[8] And since by this point in the course, you may have too many letters in your head already, we'll just state the reason as "Converse of Definition of Similar Triangles." Here's the formal version.

Converse of Definition of Similar Triangles

Definition 56	If two triangles are similar, then their vertices can be paired in a correspondence so that all pairs of corresponding angles are congruent and all pairs of corresponding sides are proportional.

The main point, though, is that we can use similar triangles to prove that line segments are proportional in much the same way that we use congruent triangles to prove things. Instead of C.P.C.T.C., the reason is the "Converse of the Definition of Similar Triangles."

Proving Corresponding Angles of Similar Triangles Congruent

In addition to using similar triangles to prove that two line segments are proportional, we can also use them to prove that two angles are congruent. This works because in similar triangles, all three pairs of corresponding angles have to be congruent. To do the proof, we just need to make sure that the angles in question are corresponding angles in two similar triangles.

To show an example of how to use similar triangles to prove congruent angles, let's go back to the diagram given previously. This time instead of proving $\dfrac{TS}{SR} = \dfrac{TM}{KR}$, we'll prove that $\angle SRK$ and $\angle STM$ are congruent. The process will be exactly the same as before. We'll prove that $\triangle KSR$ and $\triangle MST$ are similar by A.A. Similarity. But then, in the last step, instead of proving that the line segments are proportional, we'll prove that $\angle SRK$ and $\angle STM$ are congruent. Here's the informal proof of this one.

Given: ▱JKLM

Prove: $\angle SRK \cong \angle STM$

First, $\angle KSR \cong \angle MST$ (Pairs of vertical angles are congruent.)

Next, since $JKLM$ is a parallelogram (Given), $\overline{KR} \parallel \overline{TM}$. It follows

---

[8]And, if you remember, C.P.C.T.C. is really just the converse of the definition of congruent triangles.

that $\angle RKS \cong \angle TMS$ (If two parallel lines are cut by a transversal, then their alternate interior angles are congruent.) That gives us two corresponding angles, so $\triangle KSR \sim \triangle MST$ by A.A. Similarity. Therefore, $\angle SRK \cong \angle STM$ (Converse of Definition of Similar Triangles)

Notice that the reason is the same as it was when we proved that the line segments were proportional: Converse of Definition of Similar Triangles. The only difference is that here we're concentrating on the angle part of the converse instead of on the proportional sides part.

Cross-Multiplying Again

There's one last point we should make in this lesson. Sometimes, instead of proving that line segments are proportional, we have to prove that the product of certain line segments are equal. To explain how that works, let's look at a quick example.[9]

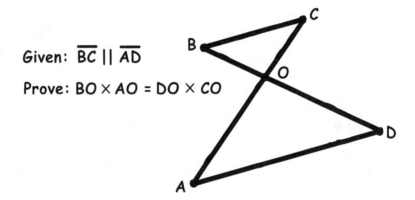

Given: $\overline{BC} \parallel \overline{AD}$

Prove: $BO \times AO = DO \times CO$

See, here we're supposed to prove that BO times AO is equal to DO times CO. But since there's nothing in the definition of similar triangles about line segments being multiplied together, it's hard to see what to do. The big thing to notice, though, is that the diagram has two triangles, $\triangle CBO$ and $\triangle ADO$, and the multiplied line segments are corresponding sides of those triangles: $\overline{BO}$ and $\overline{DO}$ are corresponding, and so are $\overline{CO}$ and $\overline{AO}$. If $\triangle CBO$ and $\triangle ADO$ turn out to be similar triangles, then the ratios of those corresponding sides will have to be equal. Specifically, $\dfrac{BO}{DO}$ will equal $\dfrac{CO}{AO}$. But then is there any way to get from $\dfrac{BO}{DO} = \dfrac{CO}{AO}$ to $BO \times AO = DO \times CO$? Absolutely. All we have to do is cross-multiply. To do this proof, then, we should first show that $\triangle CBO$ and $\triangle ADO$ are similar. That will tell us that $\dfrac{BO}{DO} = \dfrac{CO}{AO}$. The final step will be to cross-multiply to get $BO \times AO = DO \times CO$. Here's the complete (informal) proof.

---

[9] When multiplying the measures of line segments, the old multiplication symbol ($\times$) from arithmetic is often used, instead of the dot or parentheses.

Since $\overline{BC} \parallel \overline{AD}$ (Given), $\angle A \cong \angle C$ (If two parallel lines are cut by a transversal, then their alternate interior angles are congruent.) Also, $\angle COB \cong \angle AOD$ (Pairs of vertical angles are congruent.) It follows that $\triangle CBO \sim \triangle ADO$ (A.A. Similarity). So $\dfrac{BO}{DO} = \dfrac{CO}{AO}$ (Converse of the Definition of Similar Figures). Finally, we cross-multiply to get $BO \times AO = DO \times CO$.

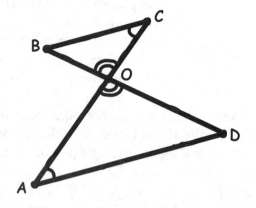

The key step of the whole process was figuring out that the line segments in the multiplication ($\overline{BO}$, $\overline{DO}$ and $\overline{CO}$, $\overline{AO}$) were corresponding sides of $\triangle CBO$ and $\triangle ADO$. All you have to do is mark off those sides on the diagram and see which triangles they're part of. Then prove that those triangles are similar.

Practice 70

a. Change the equation $AB \times JK = CD \times LM$ to a proportion.

b. State which shortcut can be used to prove that $\triangle FKH$ and $\triangle FGK$ below are similar. If no method applies, say "none."

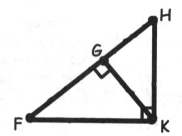

c. From the given statement below, tell the definition, property, postulate, or theorem that justifies the prove statement.

Given $\triangle PTS \sim \triangle PCT$ (on the right);
Prove: $\dfrac{TS}{CT} = \dfrac{PS}{PT}$

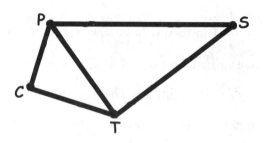

d. Write a proportion to represent the question below; then solve the proportion to get your answer.

d. Write a proportion to represent the question below; then solve the proportion to get your answer.

The ratio of the corresponding sides of two similar hexagons is $3:7$. If the length of the shortest side of the smaller hexagon is 36 inches, find the length of the shortest side of the larger hexagon.

e. Do the proof below.

Given: $\overline{KL} \parallel \overline{MN}$ and $\overline{JL} \parallel \overline{ON}$
Prove: $KL \times ON = MN \times JL$

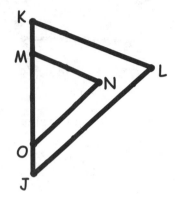

Problem Set 70

Tell whether each sentence below is True or False.

1. Similar triangles can be used to prove that two sets of line segments are proportional.

2. Similar triangles can be used to prove that two angles are congruent.

Complete each sentence below by filling in the blanks.

3. If two triangles are _____, then their vertices can be paired in a correspondence so that all pairs of corresponding angles are congruent and all pairs of corresponding sides are proportional.

4. If a line intersects two sides of a triangle and divides those sides proportionally, then the line is _____ to the third side.

5. The sum of the measures of the interior angles of a polygon with n sides is _____.

Find the sum of the exterior angles of each polygon below.

6.

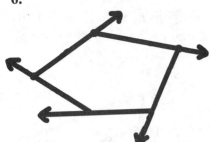

7.

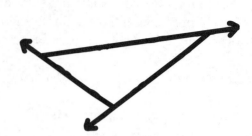

Change each equation below to a proportion

8. $3 \cdot 12 = 2 \cdot 18$

(a) 9. $AT \times EK = EG \times AN$

Find the perimeter of each polygon below.

10. If *ABCDEFGH* is a regular octagon, find the perimeter of polygon *ABCDEGH* in terms of *k*.

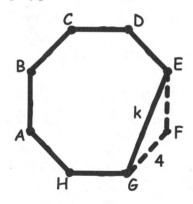

11. $\triangle ABC$

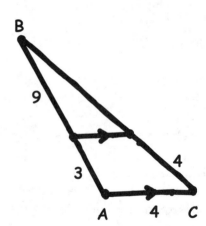

Answer each question below.

12. In $\triangle PLM$, $PL < PM$ and $LM > PM$. If one of the angles in $\triangle PLM$ is obtuse, which angle is it?

13. In $\triangle XYZ$, $m\angle Z = 64$ and the measure of the exterior angle at *X* is 138. Which is the longest side of the triangle?

State which shortcut can be used to prove that each pair of triangles below are similar. If no method applies, say "none."

14.

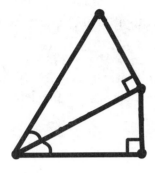

15.

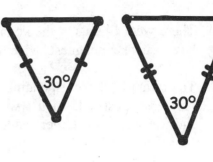

(b) 16. $\triangle ABC$ and $\triangle DAC$

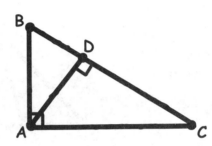

From each given statement below, tell the definition, property, postulate, or theorem that justifies each prove statement.

(c) 17. Given $\triangle ERQ \sim \triangle RJQ$ (on the right);

Prove: $\dfrac{ER}{RJ} = \dfrac{EQ}{RQ}$

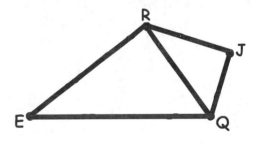

18. Given $\triangle ERQ \sim \triangle RJQ$ (on the right);
Prove: $\angle RQE \cong \angle JQR$

Answer each question below.

19. Find x.

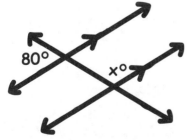

20. Find y.

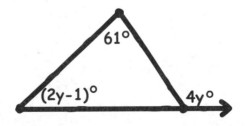

Write a proportion to represent each question below; then solve the proportion to get your answer.

21. There were 14 cats at the kennel. If the ratio of cats to total kennel guests was $2:11$, how many kennel guests were there?

(d) 22. The ratio of the corresponding sides of two similar quadrilaterals is $2:5$. If the length of the shortest side of the smaller quadrilateral is 28 inches, find the length of the shortest side of the larger quadrilateral.

Do each proof below.

23. Given: $\triangle JKL \sim \triangle STV$, $\overline{KP}$
bisects $\angle JKL$, and
$\overline{TO}$ bisects $\angle STV$
Prove: $\triangle KPL \sim \triangle TOV$

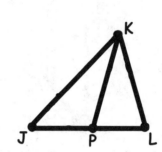 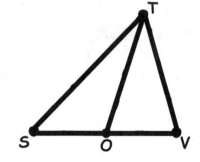

(e) 24. Given: $\overline{AB} \parallel \overline{DE}$ and $\overline{CB} \parallel \overline{FE}$
Prove: $DE \times CB = AB \times FE$

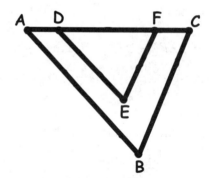

Lesson 71—Altitudes, Medians, and Perimeters

In the previous lesson, we learned how to use our knowledge of similar triangles to prove that line segments are proportional and that angles are congruent. As it turns out, we can also prove some other things by using similar triangles.

Altitudes are Similar

You remember that an altitude of a triangle is a line drawn from a vertex to the other side of the triangle so that it makes a perpendicular angle with that side. Here are two similar triangles with an altitude drawn in each.

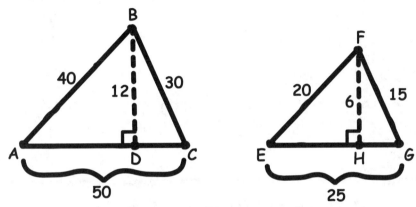

ΔABC and ΔEFG are similar.

Since ΔABC and ΔEFG are similar, we know that the ratios of their corresponding sides are all equal.[10] Specifically,

$$\frac{AB}{EF} = 2, \ \frac{BC}{FG} = 2, \text{ and } \frac{AC}{EG} = 2.$$

But what about the altitudes? Altitude $BD = 12$ and altitude $FH = 6$. So their ratio equals 2 as well.

$$\frac{BD}{FH} = 2$$

And that was no coincidence. According to a rule of geometry, for any pair of similar triangles, whatever the ratio of their corresponding sides, the corresponding altitudes must have that same ratio.[11] Here's a proof of the rule.

---

[10] The ratio of all the corresponding sides of similar triangles is sometimes called the "ratio of similitude."

[11] "Corresponding" altitudes just means that the vertices on one end of each line segment correspond. For instance, the letter B is in the middle of ΔABC and F is in the middle of ΔEFG. Also, the sides AC and EG (that the altitudes extend to) are corresponding.

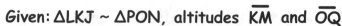

Given: △LKJ ~ △PON, altitudes $\overline{KM}$ and $\overline{OQ}$

Prove: $\dfrac{KM}{OQ} = \dfrac{KL}{OP} = \dfrac{KJ}{ON} = \dfrac{LJ}{PN}$

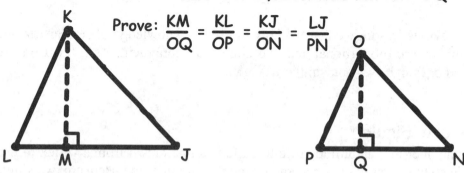

First, $\angle J \cong \angle N$ (Converse of Definition of Similar Triangles). $\angle KMJ \cong \angle OQN$ (All right angles are congruent). Therefore, $\triangle KMJ \sim \triangle OQN$ (A.A. Similarity). From that, we can conclude that $\dfrac{KM}{OQ} = \dfrac{KJ}{ON}$ (Converse of Definition of Similar Triangles). But we were given that $\triangle LKJ \sim \triangle PON$, which means that $\dfrac{KL}{OP} = \dfrac{LJ}{PN} = \dfrac{KJ}{ON}$. So $\dfrac{KM}{OQ} = \dfrac{KL}{OP} = \dfrac{LJ}{PN} = \dfrac{KJ}{ON}$ (Transitive).

Theorem 53	If two triangles are similar, then the lengths of a pair of corresponding altitudes have the same ratio as the lengths of any pair of corresponding sides.

With Theorem 53, we have another way of using similar triangles to prove that two line segments are proportional. The line segments don't have to be corresponding sides of the similar triangles. They could be corresponding altitudes. To do the proof, we would first show that the triangles are similar. Then, in the last step, we would use Theorem 53 to show that the altitudes are proportional.

Medians are Similar

If altitudes of similar triangles are proportional, what about medians? Remember, a median is a segment that starts at one vertex of a triangle and then goes to the midpoint of the opposite side. Not surprisingly, medians of similar triangles are proportional too. That means if we have two similar triangles whose corresponding sides all have a certain ratio, then the corresponding medians will have that same ratio. Here's the proof of this rule.

Given: $\triangle ABC \sim \triangle DEF$, medians $\overline{BR}$ and $\overline{ES}$

Prove: $\dfrac{BR}{ET} = \dfrac{AB}{DE} = \dfrac{BC}{EF} = \dfrac{AC}{DF}$

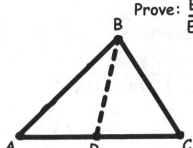
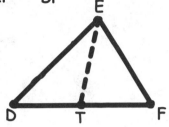

$\dfrac{AB}{DE} = \dfrac{AC}{DF} = \dfrac{BC}{EF}$ (Converse of definition of similar triangles).

Next, $\dfrac{AC}{DF} = \dfrac{\frac{1}{2}AC}{\frac{1}{2}DF}$ (Division). Point R is the midpoint of $\overline{AC}$ and

point T is the midpoint of $\overline{DF}$ (Definition of median). So $RC = \frac{1}{2}AC$ and $TF = \frac{1}{2}DF$ (Definition of midpoint). Substituting

gives us $\dfrac{RC}{TF} = \dfrac{BC}{EF}$. But we also know that $\angle C \cong \angle F$ (Converse

of definition of similar triangles for $\triangle ABC$ and $\triangle DEF$). There-

fore, $\triangle BRC \sim \triangle ETF$ (S.A.S. Similarity). Finally, $\dfrac{BR}{ET} = \dfrac{RC}{TF}$ (Con-

verse of definition of similar triangles). Then, by Transitive

$\dfrac{BR}{ET} = \dfrac{AB}{DE} = \dfrac{BC}{EF} = \dfrac{AC}{DF}$.

Theorem 54	If two triangles are similar, then the lengths of a pair of corresponding medians have the same ratio as the lengths of any pair of corresponding sides.

Theorem 54 gives us yet another way to prove that line segments are proportional. Now they can be medians of the similar triangles as well.

Perimeters are Similar

There's one more thing we need to cover in this lesson. It turns out that even the perimeters of similar triangles are proportional. In other words, if we take two similar triangles and calculate their perimeters, by going all the way around each one, the ratio of those perimeters will equal the ratios of the corresponding sides (and the ratios of the corresponding altitudes and medians). The proof of this one is tough, and it involves quite a bit of algebra.

Given: $\triangle RST \sim \triangle UVW$

Prove: $\dfrac{\text{perimeter } \triangle RST}{\text{perimeter } \triangle UVW} = \dfrac{RT}{UW}$

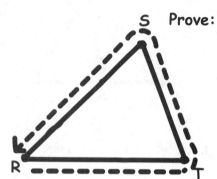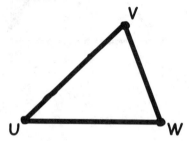

Since $\triangle RST \sim \triangle UVW$, $\dfrac{RT}{UW} = \dfrac{RS}{UV} = \dfrac{ST}{VW}$ (Converse of definition of similar figures). Next, let $\dfrac{RT}{UW} = k$. Then $\dfrac{ST}{VW} = k$ and $\dfrac{RS}{UV} = k$ (Substitution). Multiplying both sides of each equation gives us $RT = k \cdot UW$, $ST = k \cdot VW$, and $RS = k \cdot UV$. Adding the left side and right sides of each equation, gives us $RT + ST + RS = k \cdot UW + k \cdot VW + k \cdot UV$ (Addition). We can factor out a k from each term on the right to get $RT + ST + RS = k(UW + VW + UV)$ (Distributive). Since $RT + ST + RS$ equals the perimeter of $\triangle RST$ and $UW + VW + UV$ equals the perimeter of $\triangle UVW$, we have perimeter $\triangle RST = k \cdot$ perimeter $\triangle UVW$ (Substitution). It follows that $\dfrac{\text{perimeter } \triangle RST}{\text{perimeter } \triangle UVW} = k$. But since $\dfrac{RT}{UW} = k$, $\dfrac{\text{perimeter } \triangle RST}{\text{perimeter } \triangle UVW} = \dfrac{RT}{UW}$ (Transitive).

Theorem 55	If two triangles are similar, then their perimeters have the same ratio as the lengths of any pair of corresponding sides.

Even though our proof only covered triangles, the perimeters of a pair of any two polygons (whatever their shape) are also proportional. So Theorem 55 also works for quadrilaterals, pentagons, and on up.

Practice 71

a. Solve for x in terms of a and b in the proportion $\dfrac{4}{x-a} = \dfrac{3}{x+b}$ by cross-multiplying.

b. From the given statement below, tell the definition, property, postulate, or theorem that justifies the prove statement.

c. If $\triangle RTS \sim \triangle QTN$, find the perimeter of $\triangle QTN$.

Given: $\dfrac{JH}{JL} = \dfrac{MK}{ML}$ (below);

Prove: $\overline{JM} \parallel \overline{HK}$

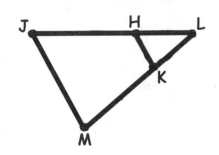

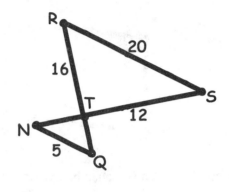

d. Assume $\triangle PLM \sim \triangle WRT$ with medians $\overline{PO}$ and $\overline{WC}$ to sides $\overline{LM}$ and $\overline{RT}$ respectively, $PL = 15$, and $WR = 12$. If PO is 2 greater than WC, find both medians.

e. Do the proof below.

Given: $\overline{GJ} \parallel \overline{DF}$, $\overline{GH} \parallel \overline{EF}$
Prove: $HG \times HF = IG \times EF$

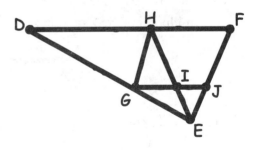

Problem Set 71

Tell whether each sentence below is True or False.

1. For any pair of similar triangles, the ratio of their corresponding altitudes is the same as the ratio of their corresponding sides.

2. For any pair of similar triangles, the corresponding altitudes are congruent to the corresponding medians.

3. The perimeters of any two similar triangles are always equal.

Complete each sentence below by filling in the blanks.

4. Two triangles similar to a third triangle are _____ to each other.

5. If a line is _____ to one side of a triangle and intersects the other two sides, then the line divides those sides proportionally.

Tell whether each figure below is a trapezoid, isosceles trapezoid, parallelogram, rectangle, rhombus, square, or just a plain quadrilateral.

6. 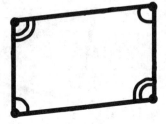 **7.**

Complete each sentence below with *always*, *sometimes*, or *never*.

8. A quadrilateral is _____ a rhombus.

9. A square is _____ a regular quadrilateral.

Answer each question below.

10. In $\overline{RW}$ (below), $RS = a$, $RW = d$, and $ST = c$. What is the distance from W to the midpoint of $\overline{RS}$, in terms of a and d?

11. If $\overrightarrow{OA} \text{-} \overrightarrow{OB} \text{-} \overrightarrow{OC}$ and if $m\angle AOB = 3y$, $m\angle BOC = 15$, and $m\angle AOC = 5y - 9$, then find $m\angle AOC$.

Solve in each proportion below by cross-multiplying.

12. Solve for x in terms of a in $\dfrac{x}{x+a} = \dfrac{3}{5}$.

(a) 13. Solve for y in terms of a and b in $\dfrac{3}{y+a} = \dfrac{2}{y-b}$.

From each given statement below, tell the definition, property, postulate, or theorem that justifies each prove statement.

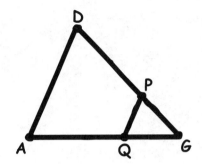

(b) 14. Given: $\dfrac{PG}{DG} = \dfrac{QG}{AG}$ (on the right);

Prove: $\overline{QP} \parallel \overline{AD}$.

15. Given: $\dfrac{PG}{DG} = \dfrac{QG}{AG} = \dfrac{QP}{AD}$ (on the right);

Prove: $\triangle ADG \sim \triangle QPG$.

State which shortcut can be used to prove that each pair of triangles below are similar. If no method applies, say "none."

16. $\triangle AEO$ and $\triangle UIO$

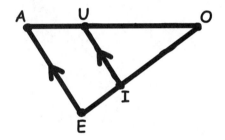

17.

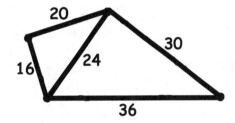

Answer each question below.

18. Find x.

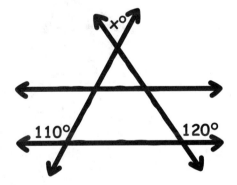

19. Find y.

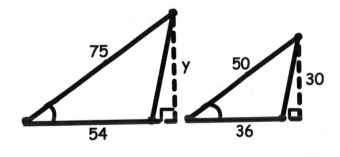

465

(c) 20. If $\triangle AOD \sim \triangle POJ$, find the perimeter of $\triangle POJ$.

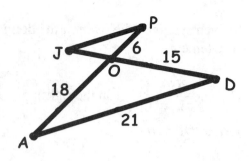

Answer each question below.

21. Assume $\triangle EBT \sim \triangle SDA$. If the perimeter of $\triangle EBT$ is 63, the perimeter of $\triangle SDA$ is 21, $BT = 6x$, and $DA = x + 3$, find BT and DA.

(d) 22. Assume $\triangle ABC \sim \triangle FGH$ with medians $\overline{AP}$ and $\overline{FQ}$ to sides $\overline{BC}$ and $\overline{GH}$ respectively, $AB = 9$, and $FG = 6$. If AP is 4 greater than FQ, find both medians.

Do each proof below.

23. Given: $\triangle DFC$, $\triangle BAC$, and $\dfrac{FC}{AC} = \dfrac{DC}{BC}$

Prove: $\dfrac{\text{perimeter } \triangle DFC}{\text{perimeter } \triangle BAC} = \dfrac{FD}{AB}$

(e) 24. Given: $\overline{VZ} \parallel \overline{TR}$, $\overline{ZU} \parallel \overline{ST}$

Prove: $ZU \times TU = ZW \times ST$

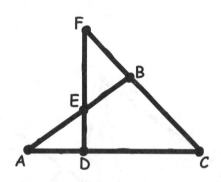

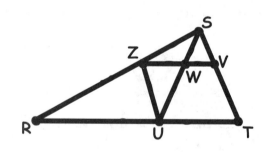

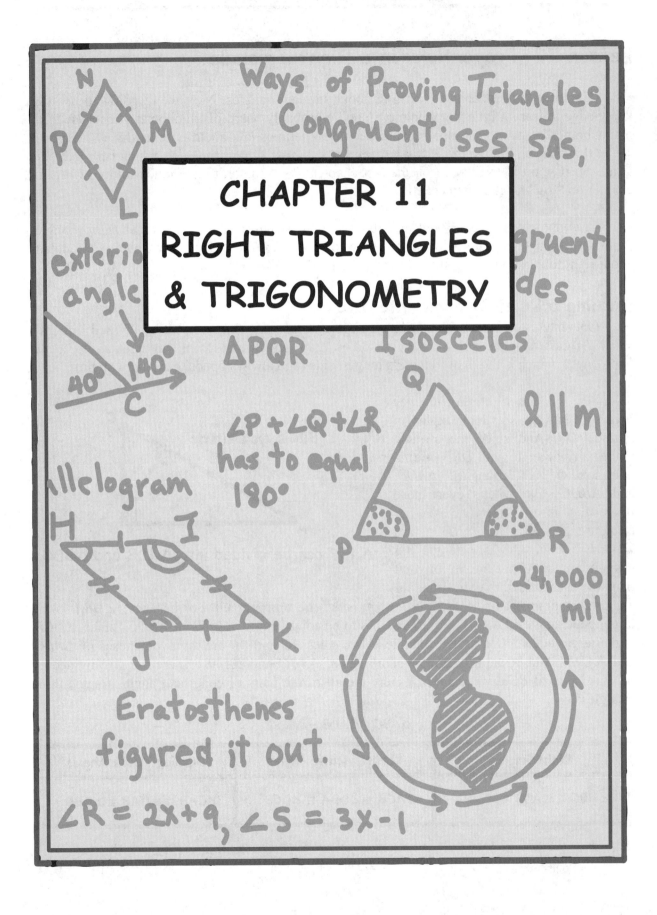

CHAPTER 11
RIGHT TRIANGLES
& TRIGONOMETRY

Lesson 72—Proportions in a Right Triangle

We spent the last chapter learning about similar triangles. Now we're going to use that knowledge to learn a little trigonometry. You've probably heard of trigonometry, because it's a major branch of math, and also because people sometimes talk about how hard it is. As you'll see in this chapter, though, basic trigonometry is all about similar triangles, which isn't that hard at all. So if you did fairly well on the last chapter, you shouldn't have much trouble with this chapter on "trig" (as it's often called).

Trigonometry is actually not just about similar triangles, it's about similar *right* triangles (with a 90° angle). That's why we're going to spend several lessons going over some details about right triangles before getting into trig itself.

Dividing a Right Triangle into Two

One interesting thing about right triangles is that they can always be divided into two smaller right triangles. All we have to do is draw an altitude from the right angle to the hypotenuse, which is the right triangle's longest side (and always opposite the right angle).

See, on the right, $\triangle ABC$ has been split into two smaller triangles by altitude DB. And since the altitude makes a right angle with DB, it forms two smaller right triangles: $\triangle ADB$ and $\triangle BDC$. But what's even more interesting is that the two smaller triangles, $\triangle ADB$ and $\triangle BDC$, are similar to each other and to the big triangle, $\triangle ABC$. That means for each pair of triangles, the corresponding

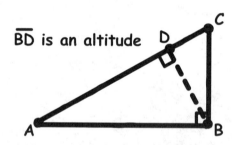

$\overline{BD}$ is an altitude

$\triangle ABC$ can be divided into $\triangle ADB$ and $\triangle BDC$.

angles are congruent and the corresponding sides are proportional. For instance, $\angle DBA$ is the larger acute angle of $\triangle ADB$. So $\angle DBA$ has to be congruent to $\angle DCB$ in $\triangle BDC$, since $\angle DCB$ is the larger acute angle in that triangle. Also, sides AC and AB are the hypotenuses of $\triangle ABC$ and $\triangle ADB$. And BC and BD are the short legs of $\triangle ABC$ and $\triangle ADB$. Therefore, AC divided by AB has to equal BC divided by BD. Here are all of the pairs of congruent angles for the three triangles.

$$\triangle ABC \sim \triangle ADB \sim \triangle BDC$$

Right Angles	Larger Acute Angles	Smaller Acute Angles
$\angle ABC \cong \angle ADB \cong \angle BDC$	$\angle ACB \cong \angle DBA \cong \angle DCB$	$\angle CAB \cong \angle DAB \cong \angle DBC$

To show you how the corresponding sides work, we'll list the ratios for $\triangle ABC$ and $\triangle ADB$. Proportions for other triangle pairs work the same way.

$$\triangle ABC \sim \triangle ADB$$

hyp. of $\triangle ABC$ / hyp. of $\triangle ADB$		long leg of $\triangle ABC$ / long leg of $\triangle ADB$		short leg of $\triangle ABC$ / short leg of $\triangle ADB$
$\dfrac{AC}{BA}$	=	$\dfrac{AB}{AD}$	=	$\dfrac{BC}{DB}$

A Quick Proof

This rule of dividing any right triangle into two more similar triangles can be proven fairly easily. Here's a quick and informal proof.

Both $\triangle EFG$ and $\triangle FHG$ are right triangles, so they have one pair of congruent angles. Then they also share $\angle G$. So by A.A. Similarity, $\triangle EFG \sim \triangle FHG$. Also, since $\triangle EFG$ and $\triangle EHF$ are both right triangles, they have one pair of congruent angles. Then $\triangle EFG$ and $\triangle EHF$ share $\angle E$ (continued). Therefore, $\triangle EFG \sim \triangle EHF$, by A.A. Similarity. Finally, $\triangle FHG \sim \triangle EHF$ (Two triangles similar to a third triangle are similar to each other.)

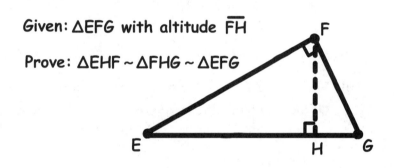

Given: $\triangle EFG$ with altitude $\overline{FH}$

Prove: $\triangle EHF \sim \triangle FHG \sim \triangle EFG$

Theorem 56	The altitude to the hypotenuse of a right triangle forms two triangles that are similar to each other and to the original triangle.

Practice 72

a. Use proportions to find *y* below.

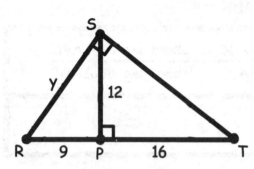

b. If $CD = DF$, find *a*.

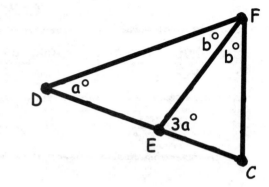

c. Find the perimeter of *LKNQ*, if $LM = 18$, $MQ = 10$, and $KN = 7$.

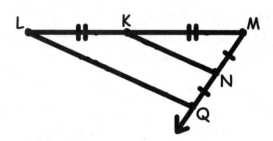

d. $\triangle JLN \sim \triangle RTV$ and the ratio of each pair of corresponding sides of the triangles is $2:3$. If the length of altitude $\overline{LM}$ is $x-4$ and the length of altitude $\overline{TS}$ is $x-1$, find *x*.

e. Do the proof below.

Given: $\overline{KM}$ bisects $\angle LMN$; $LK = KM$

Prove: $\dfrac{LN}{MN} = \dfrac{MN}{KN}$

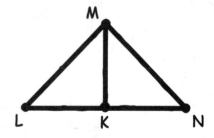

Problem Set 72

Tell whether each sentence below is True or False.

1. Basic trigonometry is all about similar triangles.

2. By drawing an altitude to its hypotenuse, any right triangle can be divided into two smaller right triangles.

Complete each sentence below by filling in the blanks.

3. The altitude to the hypotenuse of a right triangle forms two triangles that are _____ to each other and to the original triangle.

4. For any pair of _____ triangles, the ratio of their corresponding medians is the same as the ratio of their corresponding sides.

5. The line segment joining the midpoints of two sides of a triangle is _____ to the third side and _____ its length.

In the triangle below, find each of the ratios indicated. Do the ratios show that $\overline{RT} \parallel \overline{UV}$?

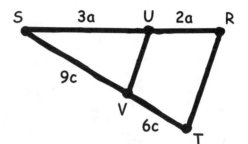

6. $\dfrac{RU}{US}$ and $\dfrac{TV}{VS}$

7. $\dfrac{US}{RS}$ and $\dfrac{VS}{TS}$

Use proportions to find the missing values below.

(a) 8. Find y.

9. Find x.

Answer each question below.

10. In $\triangle QWE$, $QE < WE$ and $QW > WE$. Which is the largest angle of $\triangle QWE$?

11. In $\triangle JHI$, $m\angle J = x$, $m\angle H = 2x$, and $m\angle I = x - 4$ (where $x > 4$). Find $m\angle H$. What is the longest side of $\triangle JHI$?

State which shortcut can be used to prove that each pair of triangles below are *congruent*. If no method applies, say "none."

12.

13.

From each given statement below, tell the definition, property, postulate, or theorem that justifies each prove statement.

14. Given: $\triangle ABC \sim \triangle TBY$

Prove: $\dfrac{TY}{AC} = \dfrac{TB}{AB}$

15. Given: $\triangle ABC \sim \triangle TBY$ with altitudes $\overline{BO}$ and $\overline{BP}$

Prove: $\dfrac{TB}{AB} = \dfrac{BP}{BO}$

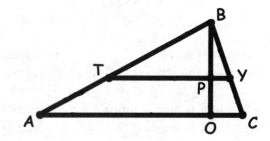

Answer each question below.

16. If $\ell_1 \parallel \ell_2$, find x.

17. Find y.

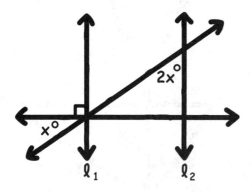

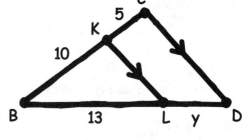

(b) 18. If $TU = UV$, find x.

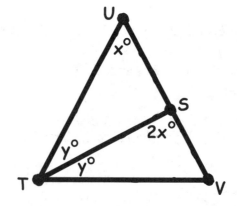

472

Find the perimeter of each polygon below.

19. $\triangle UTS$

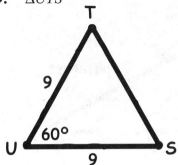

(c) 20. Find the perimeter of *DEHG*, if $BE = 6$, $BH = 12$, and $DG = 8$.

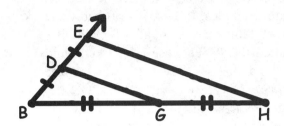

Answer each question below.

21. Four mimes were in the traveling circus. If the ratio of mimes to acrobats was $2:27$, how many acrobats were there?

(d) 22. $\triangle GHK \sim \triangle SDW$ and the ratio of each pair of corresponding sides of the triangles is $3:4$. If the length of altitude $\overline{HI}$ is $x-3$ and the length of altitude $\overline{DJ}$ is $x-1$, find the lengths *HI* and *DJ*.

Do each proof below.

23. Given: Right triangle $\triangle BCD$

with altitude $\overline{DE}$; *CD=BE*

Prove: $\dfrac{EC}{BE} = \dfrac{BE}{BC}$

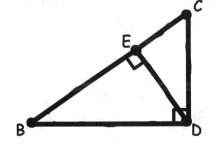

(e) 24. Given: $\overline{SR}$ bisects $\angle PRQ$; $PS = SR$

Prove: $\dfrac{PQ}{RQ} = \dfrac{RQ}{SQ}$

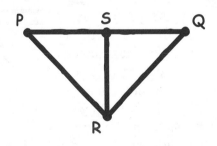

473

Lesson 73—The Pythagorean Theorem

We've been learning about right triangles. In this lesson, we're going to cover an extremely important rule on right triangles. In fact, it's probably the most famous rule in all of math. It's called the **Pythagorean Theorem**, and it says that for any right triangle the square of the two legs added together equals the square of the hypotenuse (on the right). You probably remember the Pythagorean Theorem from earlier math courses. But those books may have only showed you the theorem's equation. Since this is Geometry, we're actually going to prove the Pythagorean Theorem deductively. First, though, we should talk a little about why this theorem is so important.

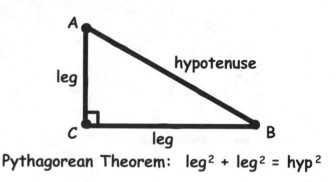

Pythagorean Theorem: $\text{leg}^2 + \text{leg}^2 = \text{hyp}^2$

Getting Practical

The Pythagorean Theorem is very practical, because it can be used to measure distances. Say, for example, that Tom is in his neighborhood park and wants to take a shortcut home, as shown in the diagram on the right. How far is the shortcut? As you can see, the dotted lines form a right triangle. The distance down Mulberry Lane, which is 4 miles, makes one leg of the triangle.

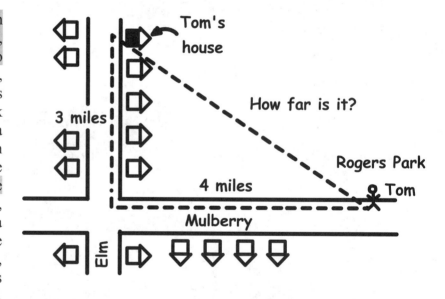

The distance up Elm Street to Tom's house, which is 3 miles, makes the other leg of the triangle. So to figure out the distance of Tom's shortcut, we really need to find the length of the hypotenuse of a right triangle. And we already know the lengths of the triangle's two legs. The Pythagorean Theorem will work here, because it's an equation that contains the legs and the hypotenuse.

$$\text{leg}^2 + \text{leg}^2 = \text{hyp}^2$$

We just need to put 3 and 4 in for the legs, and then let d represent the hypotenuse, which is the unknown distance of the shortcut.

$$3^2 + 4^2 = d^2$$

Since d is raised to the second power, this is a second-degree or quadratic equation (which you may remember from algebra). Some second-degree equations can be pretty tough, but this one isn't too bad. First, we simplify the left side.

$$9 + 16 = d^2$$

$$25 = d^2$$

Next, we need to get a plain d by itself on one side. The method is to undo the second power (or square) by taking the square root of both sides.[1]

$$\sqrt{25} = \sqrt{d^2}$$

$$\sqrt{25} = d$$

$$5 = d$$

We end up with 5 miles. So Tom will have to travel 5 miles to get home along the shortcut.

This was just a very simple example of how the Pythagorean Theorem can be used to measure things. We could have measured the distance across a river, to the top of a mountain, or the distance between two planets using the same method. Basically, if we know two sides of a right triangle, using the Pythagorean Theorem we can find the third side. It doesn't have to be the hypotenuse that's unknown. If we know the length of the hypotenuse and one leg, we can use the theorem to find the second leg. And the really neat thing about the Pythagorean Theorem is that it will work on any right triangle, no matter what its particular shape. But don't forget, the triangle has to be a right triangle.

Proving It

At the beginning of the lesson, we said we were going to prove the Pythagorean Theorem. Since this theorem is so famous, there are actually a lot of different proofs, and some of them are well known.[2] The informal proof below uses the fact that the altitude to the hypotenuse of a right triangle creates two smaller similar triangles. That's the theorem we learned in the last lesson.

---

[1] There are actually two square roots to 25: a positive and a negative. But we'll ignore the negative answer, since negative distances don't make much sense in this problem.

[2] One proof of the Pythagorean Theorem was created by a man who later became president of the United States (President Garfield).

Given: Right △ABC with right angle C

Prove: $a^2 + b^2 = c^2$

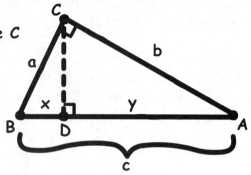

Draw altitude $\overline{CD}$ to hypotenuse $\overline{AB}$. (Through a given point not on a line, there exists exactly one perpendicular to the given line.) $\triangle ABC \sim \triangle ADC \sim \triangle CBD$. (The altitude to the hypotenuse of a right triangle forms two triangles that are similar to each other and to the original triangle.) Therefore, $\dfrac{c}{a} = \dfrac{a}{x}$ and $\dfrac{c}{b} = \dfrac{b}{y}$. (Converse of definition of similar triangles) Cross-multiplying in both equations gives $a^2 = cx$ and $b^2 = cy$ (Multiplication). Adding the left and right sides of $a^2 = cx$ to the left and right sides of $b^2 = cy$, we get $a^2 + b^2 = cx + cy$. Using the distributive property to factor the right side gives us $a^2 + b^2 = c(x + y)$. Since $x + y = c$, we know that $c(x + y) = c \cdot c$ or c^2 (Substitution). That means $a^2 + b^2 = c^2$ (Substitution).

The Pythagorean Theorem

Theorem 57	The square of the length of the hypotenuse of a right triangle is equal to the sum of the squares of the lengths of the legs.

It's also important to know the converse of the Pythagorean Theorem. The converse says that if the sum of the squares of two sides of any triangle equal the square of the third side, then the triangle has to be a right triangle. This theorem allows us to prove that an ordinary triangle is actually a right triangle, without knowing that one of its angles is 90°. We won't show the proof here. We'll let you do it yourself in the problem set (#24). But the formal theorem is stated below.

Converse of Pythagorean Theorem

Theorem 58	If the square of one side length of a triangle is equal to the sum of the squares of the other two side lengths, then the triangle is a right triangle.

Practice 73

a. Find x.

b. If $\triangle KLJ \sim \triangle PNQ$, $KJ = 9$, $PQ = 15$, and $JM = 12$, find QO.

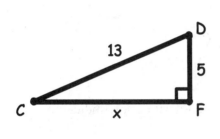

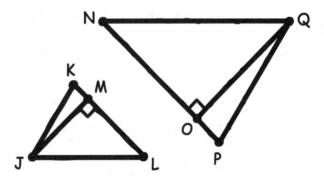

c. Assume $\triangle RST \sim \triangle KLM$. If the perimeter of $\triangle RST$ is 40, the perimeter of $\triangle KLM$ is 60, $RT = x + 7$, and $KM = 3x$, find RT and KM.

d. Find the length of the altitude drawn to a side of an equilateral triangle with perimeter of 30. Estimate your answer to 2 decimal places.

e. Do the proof below.

Given: $\triangle QMP$ and $p^2 + q^2 = m^2$
Prove: $\triangle QMP$ is a right triangle.

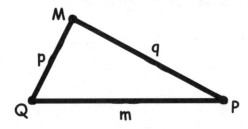

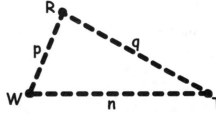

Problem Set 73

Tell whether each sentence below is True or False.

1. According to the Pythagorean Theorem, in any right triangle the square of the two legs added together equals the square of the hypotenuse.

2. The Pythagorean Theorem can be used to measure distances.

Complete each sentence below by filling in the blanks.

3. If the square of one side length of a triangle is equal to the sum of the squares of the other two side lengths, then the triangle is a _____.

4. For any pair of _____ triangles, the ratio of their corresponding perimeters is the same as the ratio of their corresponding sides.

5. A _____ is a parallelogram with four congruent sides.

Name each regular polygon below and find the measure of the interior angle indicated.

6.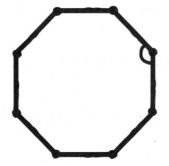

7.

Find the measures of the angles of each triangle described below.

8. A right triangle where one of the acute angles is x and the other is $4x$.

9. An isosceles triangle with a vertex angle of $26°$.

Find the missing lengths in the right triangles below.

10. Find *x*.

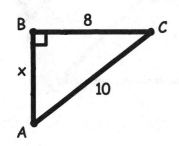

(a) 11. Find *x*.

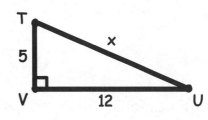

Calculate each ratio below.

12. Five of the 12 members of the Gleeful Singers are girls and the rest are boys. What is the ratio of boys to girls? Write your answer in the form $a:b$, where a and b are whole numbers.

13. Better than Bitter coffee costs $8.60 per pound. Buyer Beware coffee costs 43 cents per pound. What is the ratio of the price of Buyer Beware to the price of Better than Bitter? Write your answer in the form $a:b$, where a and b are whole numbers.

In the triangle below, find each of the ratios indicated. Do the ratios show that the sides are divided proportionally?

14. $\dfrac{DL}{KD}$ and $\dfrac{CM}{KC}$

15. $\dfrac{DL}{KL}$ and $\dfrac{CM}{KM}$

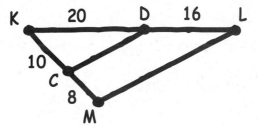

Answer each question below.

16. Find *y*.

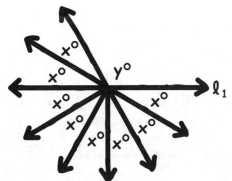

17. If $\triangle PRQ \sim \triangle TSV$, find *x*.

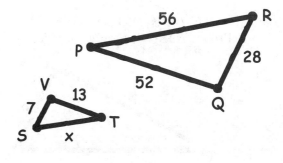

(b) 18. If $\triangle ABC \sim \triangle EFG$, $AB = 24$, $EF = 15$, and $BD = 16$, find FH.

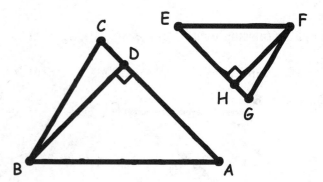

State which shortcut can be used to prove that each pair of triangles below are *similar*. If no method applies, say "none."

19.

20.

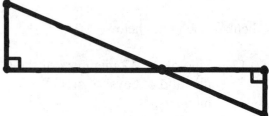

Answer each question below.

(c) 21. Assume $\triangle ABC \sim \triangle DEF$. If the perimeter of $\triangle ABC$ is 45, the perimeter of $\triangle DEF$ is 60, $BC = 2x$, and $EF = 3x - 2$, find BC and EF.

(d) 22. Find the length of the altitude drawn to a side of an equilateral triangle with perimeter of 36. Estimate your answer to 2 decimal places.

Do each proof below. Number 24 is the Converse of the Pythagorean Theorem.

23. Given: $\overline{DP}$ bisects $\angle ADS$
Prove: $DA > PA$

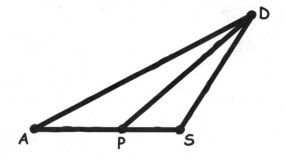

(e) 24. Given: $\triangle ABC$ and $a^2 + b^2 = c^2$
Prove: $\triangle ABC$ is a right triangle.

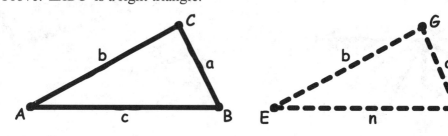

Lesson 74—Irrational Lengths and Pythagorean Triples

In the previous lesson, we used the Pythagorean Theorem to find the distance of Tom's shortcut, which turned out to be 5 miles. That problem was a fairly simple one, because all three sides of the right triangle had whole number lengths ($3, 4, 5$). But in most right triangles, at least one of the side lengths is a square root. Take the triangle below as an example.

To find the length of the hypotenuse, we can just use the Pythagorean Theorem. We put 1 in for each of the legs and let x represent the unknown.

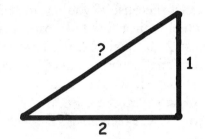

$$\text{leg}^2 + \text{leg}^2 = \text{hyp}^2$$

$$1^2 + 2^2 = x^2$$

Next, we simplify on the left.

$$5 = x^2$$

And, finally, we solve for x by taking the square root of both sides.[3]

$$\sqrt{5} = x$$

There's no whole number that equals the square root of 5. The number 2 is too small (since $2 \cdot 2 = 4$), and the number 3 is too large (since $3 \cdot 3 = 9$). You might think that the answer is some fraction or decimal between 2 and 3. But the surprising thing is that no fraction or decimal will work either. For instance, 2.2 is pretty close, but since $2.2 \cdot 2.2 = 4.84$ it's a little low. And 2.24 is even closer, since $2.24 \cdot 2.24 = 5.0176$, but it's slightly high.

The problem is that the square root of 5 is an irrational number. And, as you may remember from algebra, an **irrational number** can't be written precisely as a whole number, fraction, or decimal.[4] So the only way to write the length of our hypotenuse exactly is like this: $\sqrt{5}$. That's our final answer. It's pretty easy to tell when a square root is irrational, by the way. If the answer is not a whole number, then it has to be irrational. In that case, the only way to write the answer exactly is to leave it in square root form (like $\sqrt{5}$). By contrast, a square root that does have a whole number answer should be written as a whole number. For example, since $\sqrt{16}$ is equal to the whole number 4, it should be simplified to 4 and not left as a square root. But $\sqrt{13}$ is between the whole numbers 3 and 4, which means it's an irrational number and should be left as $\sqrt{13}$.

---

[3] We'll ignore the negative square root of 5.

[4] Technically, it can't be written as a whole number, fraction, or terminating or repeating decimal.

Estimating Irrationals

You may be wondering whether irrational answers like $\sqrt{5}$ are very practical. After all, when calculating an actual distance like Tom's shortcut, it's kind of strange to say that the answer is $\sqrt{5}$ miles. How far is that? On most real-world problems, irrational answers are estimated with a calculator. So if Tom's shortcut had come out to $\sqrt{5}$ miles, we could have punched square root of 5 into a calculator and found a decimal that was pretty close. To 4 decimal places, a calculator gives an answer of 2.2361, which is 2.2361 miles. That's still not exact, because if you square 2.2361, the answer won't be exactly 5. But it's extremely close, which is just fine for most practical problems. In fact, most people would round the answer to just 2 decimal places (2.24). So if an answer to a real-world problem comes out to be an irrational square root, which happens a lot when using the Pythagorean Theorem, feel free to estimate it with a calculator. (Just remember that the decimal isn't the exact answer.) When solving pure math problems in this textbook (or any math book), however, all your answers should be exact, unless the instructions say to give an estimate. That means you should write the square root of 2 as $\sqrt{2}$.

Simplifying Irrationals

Let's look at another right triangle with one of its sides missing shown in the diagram on the right. To find the missing leg, we should use the Pythagorean Theorem again.

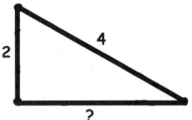

$$\text{leg}^2 + \text{leg}^2 = \text{hyp}^2$$

$$2^2 + x^2 = 4^2$$

$$4 + x^2 = 16 \qquad \text{simplifying}$$

$$x^2 = 12 \qquad \text{subtracting 4 from both sides}$$

$$x = \sqrt{12} \qquad \text{taking the square root of both sides}$$

There's no whole number that's equal to the square root of 12, because 3 is too small ($3 \cdot 3 = 9$) and 4 is too large ($4 \cdot 4 = 16$). Therefore, the square root of 12 is irrational and we have to leave it in square root form. But in this case, $\sqrt{12}$ can still be simplified. What we can do is use the rule for multiplying square roots. You may remember it from algebra. Any two square roots can be multiplied by multiplying the numbers under the square root signs and taking the square root of the result. For instance, to multiply $\sqrt{2} \cdot \sqrt{3}$, we multiply 2 and 3 to get 6 and then take the square root of 6 to get $\sqrt{6}$. To simplify a square root, all we do is reverse the multiplication rule. Starting with $\sqrt{12}$, we factor the 12.

$$\sqrt{12} = \sqrt{4 \cdot 3}$$

Next, we split $\sqrt{4 \cdot 3}$ into two square roots.

$$\sqrt{4} \cdot \sqrt{3}$$

This is just multiplying backwards (factoring, in other words). Then, since $\sqrt{4}$ is equal to 2, that gives us $2 \cdot \sqrt{3}$ or

$$2\sqrt{3}.$$

That's the fully simplified form of $\sqrt{12}$, because the number under the square root sign is as small as possible.

In general, then, whenever you get an irrational square root (using the Pythagorean Theorem), make sure that the square root is fully simplified by shrinking the number under the square root sign as small as possible. The method is to split it into two square roots, as we did with $\sqrt{12}$. One of the square roots needs to be something like $\sqrt{4}$ or $\sqrt{16}$ or $\sqrt{25}$, that simplifies to a whole number.

Pythagorean Triples

After learning about irrational square roots, you probably have a better appreciation for the simple right triangle from the last lesson (about Tom's shortcut), with its nice whole number lengths for all three sides. But are there other right triangles where all three side lengths come out to be whole numbers? Yes, there are. Here are several examples.

Each of these triangle's side lengths form a **Pythagorean Triple**, which is just three whole numbers that can be the side lengths of a right triangle. Any Pythagorean Triple will solve the Pythagorean Theorem. So if we put the three numbers in the right places, they'll make both sides of the

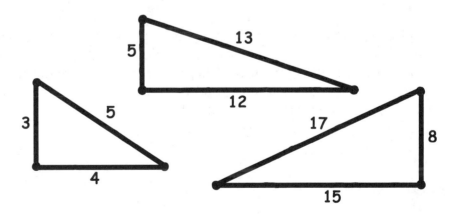

equation $\text{leg}^2 + \text{leg}^2 = \text{hyp}^2$ equal. There are many other Pythagorean Triples, but $\{3, 4, 5\}$, $\{5, 12, 13\}$, and $\{8, 15, 17\}$ are the most common. In fact, these three come up so often in geometry that it's worth memorizing them. Once they're lodged in your brain, you can name the missing side in a lot of right triangles instantly. If you saw a right triangle with legs equaling 3 and 4, for example, you would know immediately that the hypotenuse has to be 5, since $\{3, 4, 5\}$ is a well-known triple. Or if you saw a right triangle with one leg equal to 12 and the hypotenuse equal to 13, you'd know that the other leg must be 5, since $\{5, 12, 13\}$ is a common triple.

The other nice thing about Pythagorean Triples is that we can always find a new triple by multiplying all three of the numbers by any whole number. For instance, starting with $\{3, 4, 5\}$, we can find a new triple by multiplying 3, 4, and 5 by 2. That gives $\{6, 8, 10\}$. That's also a Pythagorean Triple. So there's a right triangle with legs equaling 6 and 8 and a hypotenuse of 10. Multiplying each number by 3 would give us another triple: $\{9, 12, 15\}$. The same process will work on $\{5, 12, 13\}$ and $\{8, 15, 17\}$. The table below shows how to get new Pythagorean Triples from the three most common ones. But remember, you don't have to multiply by 2 or 3. Any other whole number will do just as well.

Some Pythagorean Triples

	× 2	× 3
$\{3, 4, 5\}$	$\{6, 8, 10\}$	$\{9, 12, 15\}$
$\{5, 12, 13\}$	$\{10, 24, 26\}$	$\{15, 36, 39\}$
$\{8, 15, 17\}$	$\{16, 30, 34\}$	$\{24, 45, 51\}$

We've covered several important points, so let's do a quick summary. Most right triangles have at least one side with an irrational length, and that length pops up as a square root when solving for it with the Pythagorean Theorem. To write an irrational length precisely, it must be kept in square root form but fully simplified. Also, in some right triangles (the simple ones), all three sides have whole number lengths. Those sets of numbers are called Pythagorean Triples, and the most popular triples are worth memorizing.

Practice 74

a. Estimate the irrational number $6\sqrt{5}$ to two decimal places.

b. Use proportions or the Pythagorean Theorem to find *y*.

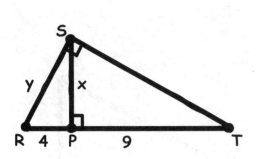

c. In the figure below, $AD = BD$. Find *x*.

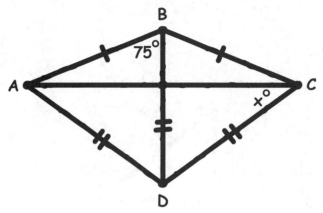

d. Rectangle *KLMN* is similar to rectangle *WXYZ*. If $KL = 36$, $LM = 28$, and $XY = 21$, find *WX* and *WZ*.

e. Do the proof below.

Given: *FGHJ* is an isosceles
trapezoid with $\overline{FJ} \cong \overline{GH}$.
Prove: $\overline{FH} \cong \overline{GJ}$

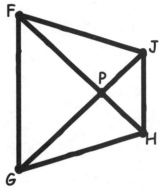

Problem Set 74

Tell whether each sentence below is True or False.

1. In all right triangles, every side has a whole number length.

2. Irrational numbers (such as $\sqrt{2}$) can be estimated using a calculator.

Complete each sentence below by filling in the blanks.

3. A _____ is three whole numbers that can be the side lengths of a right triangle.

4. The _____ of a parallelogram bisect each other.

5. If two triangles are _____, then their corresponding angles are congruent and the lengths of their corresponding sides are in proportion.

Estimate each irrational number below to two decimal places.

6. $\sqrt{11}$ **(a) 7.** $3\sqrt{7}$

Find the missing side of each Pythagorean Triple below.

8. 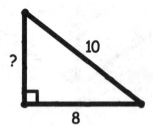   **9.**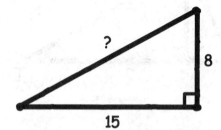

Use proportions or the Pythagorean Theorem to find the missing values below.

10. Find x.

(b) 11. Find y.

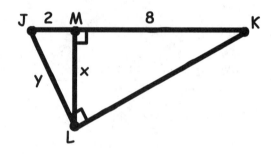

Find the perimeter of each polygon below.

12. A regular hexagon with sides of $y+2$.   **13.**
(Find the perimeter in terms of y.)

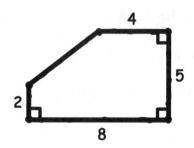

From each given statement below, tell the definition, property, postulate, or theorem that justifies each prove statement.

14. Given: Right $\triangle FKJ$
Prove: $a^2 + e^2 = d^2$

15. Given: $d^2 + c^2 = (a+b)^2$
Prove: $\triangle FHJ$ is a right triangle.

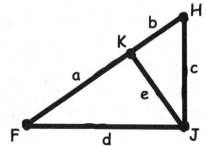

Solve in each proportion below by cross-multiplying.

16. Solve for x in terms of p and q in $\dfrac{x-p}{x+q}=\dfrac{3}{4}$.

17. Solve for y in terms of r and t in $\dfrac{y-t}{3}=\dfrac{y-r}{5}$.

Answer each question below.

18. Find x.

(c) 19.   If $GF=GJ$, find y.

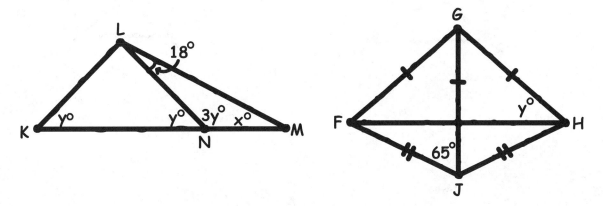

State which shortcut can be used to prove that each pair of triangles below are *congruent*. If no method applies, say "none."

20.

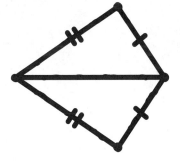

21.

Answer each question below.

22. $\triangle ABC \sim \triangle JKL$. If $AB=17$, $BC=24$, $AC=32$, and $KL=96$, find the lengths of the remaining sides of $\triangle JKL$.

(d) 23. Rectangle $DFGH$ is similar to rectangle $RSTV$. If $DF=15$, $FG=45$, and $RS=25$, find ST and TV.

Do each proof below.

24. Given: $\triangle TPS \sim \triangle VWR$

$\overline{UR}$ bisects $\angle WRT$

Prove: $\triangle TPS \sim \triangle VPR$

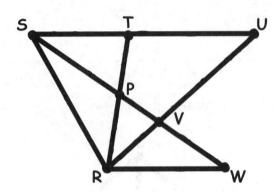

(e) 25. Given: $ABCD$ is an isosceles trapezoid with $\overline{AB} \cong \overline{CD}$.

Prove: $\overline{AC} \cong \overline{BD}$

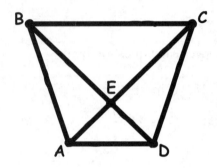

Lesson 75—The Isosceles Right Triangle

We've been learning about right triangles, but one point we haven't bothered to make—because it's pretty obvious—is that there are lots of different kinds of right triangles. Even though every right triangle has one right angle, the other two angles can have many different measurements, such as 45–45 or 50–40 or 60 – 30, and so on. Basically, the acute angles of a right triangle can be anything, as long as they add to equal 90° (since those two angles plus the right angle must equal 180°). So that makes for a whole bunch of right triangles of various shapes.

Finding the Angles

Out of all those right triangles, however, a few are really special. That's because they come up all the time in the real world, especially in science and engineering. One special right triangle is the **isosceles right triangle**, which is just a triangle that has both a right angle and two congruent sides. An example is shown on the right. The right angle is $\angle C$ and the congruent sides are $\overline{AC}$ and $\overline{BC}$. We can also figure out $\angle A$ and $\angle B$, though. According to the Base Angles Theorem, the angles opposite the congruent sides must also be congruent. So $\angle A \cong \angle B$. But since the measures of $\angle A$ and $\angle B$ must add to 90°, $m\angle A = 45$ and $m\angle B = 45$. In every isosceles right triangle, then, the other two angles (besides the right angle) have to both be 45°.

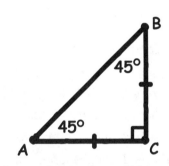

$\triangle ABC$ is an isosceles right triangle,

Relating the Sides

What about the sides? Are they related in any way? Yes, they are. Imagine a specific isosceles right triangle where the two congruent legs are both 1 inch long (on the right). Using the Pythagorean Theorem, we can find the length of the hypotenuse.

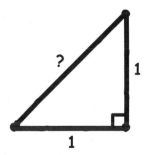

$$\text{leg}^2 + \text{leg}^2 = \text{hyp}^2$$

$$1^2 + 1^2 = x^2$$

$$2 = x^2$$

$$\sqrt{2} = x$$

We end up with a hypotenuse of $\sqrt{2}$, which is an irrational number (and fully simplified).

But what if the legs of the triangle had been 2 inches long? (on the right) We could still calculate the length of the hypotenuse using the Pythagorean Theorem.

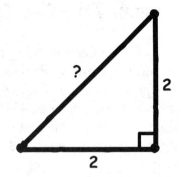

$$\text{leg}^2 + \text{leg}^2 = \text{hyp}^2$$

$$2^2 + 2^2 = x^2$$

$$8 = x^2$$

$$\sqrt{8} = x$$

This time the hypotenuse comes out to $\sqrt{8}$. That's an irrational number again. Only $\sqrt{8}$ can be simplified: $\sqrt{4 \cdot 2}$ equals $\sqrt{4} \cdot \sqrt{2}$ or $2\sqrt{2}$.

Now let's compare the side lengths of the two triangles. The first triangle was leg $=1$, leg $=1$, hypotenuse $= \sqrt{2}$. The second triangle was leg $=2$, leg $=2$, hypotenuse $= 2\sqrt{2}$. Do you see a pattern? The sides of the second triangle are all twice the length of the sides of the first triangle. It's not hard to figure out that an isosceles right triangle with 3 inch legs would have a hypotenuse that's $3\sqrt{2}$ inches long. An isosceles right triangle with 4 inch legs would have a hypotenuse that's $4\sqrt{2}$ inches long, and so on. Generally, whatever the length of the legs (and, remember, the legs have to be the same), the hypotenuse is just $\sqrt{2}$ times that length. That's true for any isosceles right triangle.

Here's a quick proof of this relationship (using the diagram on the right), followed by the official theorem.

Assume that the two legs of a right triangle have lengths of s, and that the hypotenuse has a length of c. Then, by the Pythagorean Theorem $s^2 + s^2 = c^2$ or $2s^2 = c^2$. Solving for c gives us $\sqrt{2s^2} = c$, which simplifies to $\sqrt{2}\sqrt{s^2} = c$ or $\sqrt{2}s = c$. Therefore, the hypotenuse equals $\sqrt{2}$ multiplied by the length of the triangle's legs.

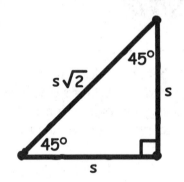

For any isosceles right triangle $\triangle ABC$

Theorem 59	In an isosceles right triangle, the length of the hypotenuse is $\sqrt{2}$ times the length of one leg.

Memorize It

You may be wondering why anyone would care how the sides of an isosceles right triangle are related. Actually, it helps a lot. Since isosceles right triangles come up so often (especially in real-world problems), it's worth your while to memorize the relationship between the sides. Certain kinds of problems can be solved much faster. Here's a simple example.

Herman is siding his house, and he needs a triangular piece of siding to fit in the top of the house's gable. If two of the sides form a right angle and measure 17 inches each, calculate the length of the third side.

We're given the lengths of the two legs of a right triangle. And since those legs are the same, we know it's an isosceles right triangle. The problem is asking us to find the length of the third side, which is the hypotenuse. Now remember the rule. In any isosceles right triangle, the hypotenuse must equal the length of each leg multiplied by $\sqrt{2}$. In other words, if each leg has a length of s, then the hypotenuse must have a length of $s\sqrt{2}$. The legs in our problem are each 17 inches, so the hypotenuse must be $17\sqrt{2}$ inches. That's the answer to the problem. We didn't even have to use the Pythagorean Theorem.

Since this is a real-world problem, though, we should probably find a decimal estimate for $17\sqrt{2}$ That way we could actually cut a piece of siding with that length. Punching $\sqrt{2}$ into a calculator, we get 1.414... (depending on how many digits the calculator shows). Rounding the decimal to two places gives us 1.41. Then, we multiply 1.41 by 17 to get 23.97 or about 24 inches. That's approximately the length that the third side of the triangular piece of siding should have.

So you see, memorizing the relationship between the sides of an isosceles right triangle speeds things up quite a bit. It keeps us from even having to use the Pythagorean Theorem. We can just write down the answer immediately.

Practice 75

a. The length of the hypotenuse of an isosceles right triangle is 11. Find the lengths of each leg.

b. Find y.

c. Find x.

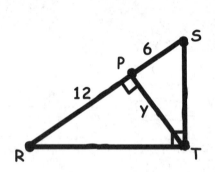

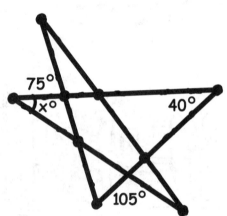

d. If the lengths of the diagonals of a rhombus are 14 and 20, find the perimeter of the rhombus. Estimate your answer to two decimal places.

e. Do the proof below.

Given: Quadrilateral $JKLM$ with diagonals $\overline{MK}$ and $\overline{JL}$; $\angle LJK \cong \angle JLM$; $\overline{MK}$ bisects $\overline{JL}$ at O.
Prove: $JKLM$ is a parallelogram.

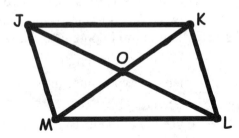

Problem Set 75

Tell whether each sentence below is True or False.

1. An isosceles right triangle is a right triangle that has all three sides congruent.

2. In an isosceles right triangle, the length of the hypotenuse is $\sqrt{2}$ times the length of one leg.

Complete each sentence below by filling in the blanks.

3. If a line is _____ to one side of a triangle and intersects the other two sides, then the line divides those sides proportionally.

4. According to the Pythagorean Theorem, in any right triangle the square of the two _____ added together equals the square of the _____.

5. If the original statement is in the form "If a, then b," then the converse is in the form _____.

Tell whether each figure below is a trapezoid, isosceles trapezoid, parallelogram, rectangle, rhombus, square, or just a plain quadrilateral.

6.

7.

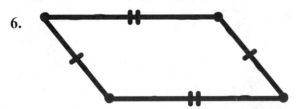

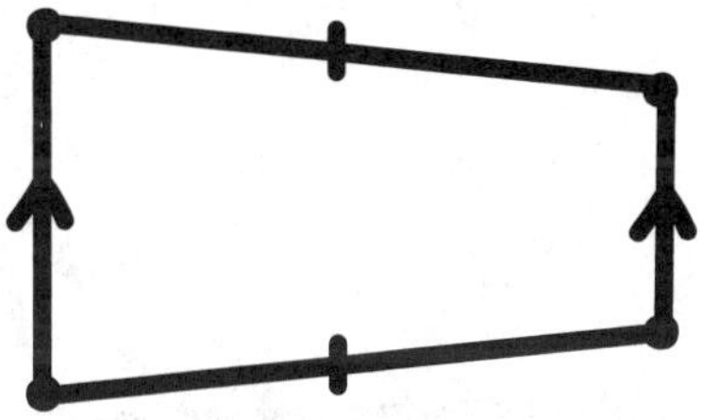

Tell whether each set of numbers below is a Pythagorean Triple.

8. {16,30,34}

9. {5,7,11}

Answer each question below.

10. The length of one leg of an isosceles right triangle is 14. Find the length of the hypotenuse.

11. In $\triangle QWE$, $m\angle Q = 45$ and $m\angle E = 90$. If $EW = 7$, find QE and QW.

(a) 12. The length of the hypotenuse of an isosceles right triangle is 17. Find the lengths of each leg.

Use proportions or the Pythagorean Theorem to find the missing values below.

(b) 13. Find y.

14. Find x.

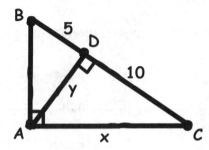

Answer each question below.

15. In the parallelogram below, find y and z.

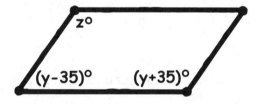

16. Find x.

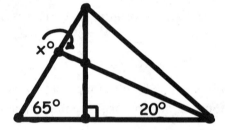

(c) 17. Find x.

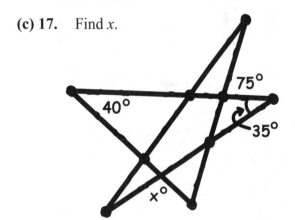

State which shortcut can be used to prove that each pair of triangles below are *similar*. If no method applies, say "none."

18.

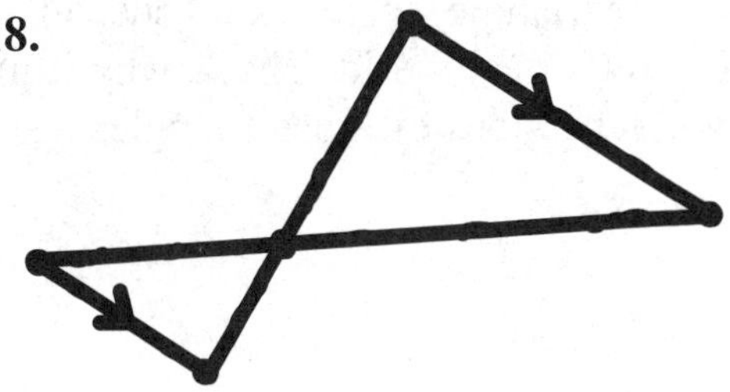

19.

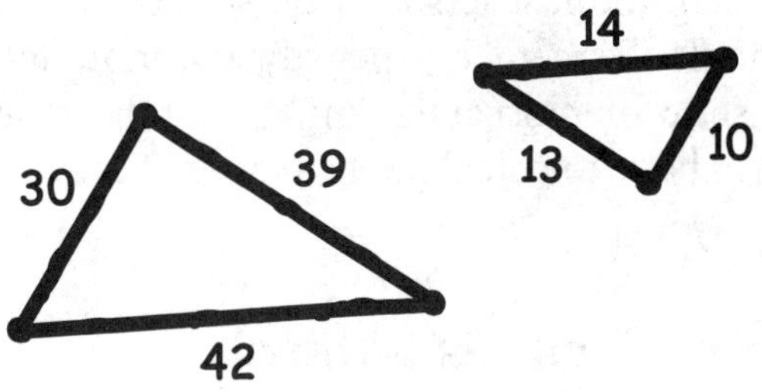

Answer each question below.

20. Quadrilateral *GHJK* and Quadrilateral *LPRT* are similar. If $m\angle G = 32$, $HJ = 9$, and the corresponding sides of *GHJK* to *LPRT* have a ratio of $3:2$ (the ratio of similitude), find $m\angle L$ and *PR*.

21. The longest side of a triangle is 3 greater than the longest side of a similar triangle. If the ratio of similitude is $5:4$, find the lengths of the longest side of each triangle.

(d) 22. If the lengths of the diagonals of a rhombus are 16 and 18, find the perimeter of the rhombus. Estimate your answer to two decimal places.

Do each proof below.

23. Given: parallelogram *DEFG*;
$\overline{KL} \cong \overline{MN}$
Prove: $\overline{GL} \cong \overline{EN}$

(e) 24. Given: Quadrilateral *QRST* with
diagonals $\overline{QS}$ and $\overline{RT}$;
$\angle SQT \cong \angle RSQ$;
$\overline{RT}$ bisects $\overline{QS}$ at *P*.
Prove: *QRST* is a parallelogram.

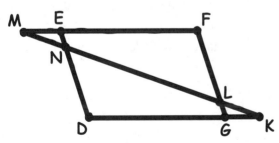

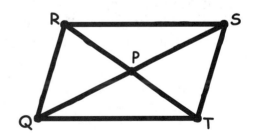

Lesson 76—The 30-60 Right Triangle

In the last lesson, we learned about the isosceles right triangle, which is a "special" right triangle. Remember, special right triangles come up a lot in the real world. That's why it makes sense to memorize the angles and the relationship between the sides of those triangles—so you don't have to calculate them every time.

Half of an Equilateral

Well, another special right triangle is the **30-60 right triangle**. As the name implies, this is just a right triangle whose acute angles (the angles other than the 90° angle) measure 30° and 60°. As it turns out, the easiest way to analyze a 30-60 right triangle is to put it inside an equilateral triangle (one with all 3 sides congruent). A diagram is given on the right. Equilateral $\triangle ABC$ has all three sides equal to 2 inches. We've drawn altitude $\overline{BD}$, and that has created two right triangles: $\triangle ABD$ and $\triangle CBD$. These are both 30-60 right triangles. Here's how we know. Since $\triangle ABC$ is equilateral, all of its angles must equal 60°. (Remember, equilateral triangles are also equiangular.) That means $\angle A$ is 60°. But since $\angle ADB$ is a right angle, $\angle ABD$ must be 30° (the three angles must add to 180°). The same argument holds for $\triangle CBD$: $\angle C$ is 60° and $\angle CDB$ is a right angle, so $\angle CBD$ is 30°.

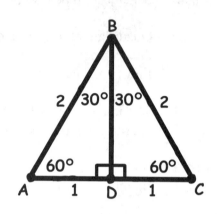

The other thing to notice is that altitude $\overline{BD}$ bisects $\overline{AC}$, making $AD=1$ and $DC=1$. We know that this is true, because $\triangle ABD$ and $\triangle CBD$ are congruent (by A.S.A.). And since AD and DC are corresponding parts of congruent triangles (C.P.C.T.C.), they also must be congruent. So an equilateral triangle cut in half becomes two 30-60 right triangles.

Now let's figure out all of the side lengths of our 30-60 right triangles. We'll concentrate on $\triangle ABD$, the right triangle on the left. We already know that its short leg, $\overline{AD}$, measures 1 inch and its hypotenuse, $\overline{AB}$, measures 2 inches. That just leaves the long leg, $\overline{BD}$. To find $\overline{BD}$, we can use the Pythagorean Theorem. We just need to make sure to let x be one of the legs and not the hypotenuse (which we already know is 2).

$$\text{leg}^2 + \text{leg}^2 = \text{hyp}^2$$

$$1^2 + x^2 = 2^2$$

$$1 + x^2 = 4$$

$$x^2 = 3$$

$$x = \sqrt{3}$$

The long leg measures $\sqrt{3}$ inches. So the sides of $\triangle ABD$ (and also of $\triangle CBD$) are 1, 2, and $\sqrt{3}$.

Finding the Pattern

Now let's look at two other cases of 30-60 right triangles, one where the hypotenuse is 4 inches long and the other where it's 6 inches long.

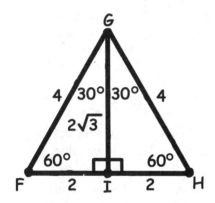
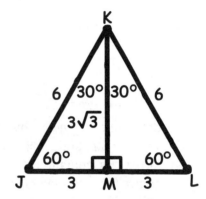

On the left, $\triangle FGI$ has a short leg of 2, a hypotenuse of 4 and a long leg of $2\sqrt{3}$. And the same goes for $\triangle GHI$. On the right, $\triangle JKM$ has a short leg of 3, a hypotenuse of 6, and a long leg of $3\sqrt{3}$. (And the same goes for $\triangle LKM$.)

Our three examples had sides of 1, 2, $\sqrt{3}$ and 2, 4, $2\sqrt{3}$ and 3, 6, $3\sqrt{3}$. Can you recognize a pattern in these? It's a little harder to detect than the pattern for isosceles right triangles that we found in the last lesson. As it turns out, for any 30-60 right triangle, the hypotenuse is always twice the length of the short leg. If the short leg is 1, as in our first example, then the hypotenuse has to be 2. If the short leg is 2, as in the second example, then the hypotenuse must be 4. And if the short leg is 3, as with the third example, the hypotenuse must be 6.

What about the long leg? The long leg always equals the short leg times $\sqrt{3}$. If the short leg is 1, the long leg is $\sqrt{3}$. If the short leg is 2, the long leg is

30-60 Right Triangles

short leg	long leg	hypotenuse
1	$\sqrt{3}$	2
2	$2\sqrt{3}$	4
3	$3\sqrt{3}$	6
$\vdots$	$\vdots$	$\vdots$
s	$s\sqrt{3}$	2s

497

$2\sqrt{3}$. And if the short leg is 3, the long leg is $3\sqrt{3}$. So that's the pattern for 30-60 right triangles.

Here's a proof of this relationship followed by the theorem.

Given: Right $\triangle ABC$ with $m \angle C = 90$,
$m \angle A = 60$, and $m \angle ABC = 30$
$BC = a$, $AC = b$, $AB = c$

Prove: $c = 2b$ and $a = b\sqrt{3}$

First, we draw $\overline{CD}$ and choose D so that $AC = CD$. Then, we draw $\overline{BD}$. Then, by S.A.S., $\triangle ABC \cong \triangle DBC$. That means $m\angle D = 60$ and $m\angle DBC = 30$ (C.P.C.T.C.). It follows that $\triangle ABD$ is equiangular and also equilateral. (All equiangular triangles are equilateral.) Because $AB = BD = AD$, $AB = c$ and $AD = 2b$, we know that $c = 2b$ (Substitution). According to the Pythagorean Theorem, $a^2 + b^2 = c^2$. By substitution, we get $a^2 + b^2 = (2b)^2$ or $a^2 + b^2 = 4b^2$. Subtracting b^2 from both sides gives $a^2 = 3b^2$. Taking the square root of both sides, we get $a = \sqrt{3b^2}$ or $a = b\sqrt{3}$.

Theorem 60	In a 30-60 right triangle, the length of the hypotenuse is twice the length of the short leg and the length of the long leg is $\sqrt{3}$ times the length of the short leg.

Practice 76

a. Simplify the irrational number $\sqrt{98}$, then estimate it to two decimal places.

b. The altitude of an equilateral triangle is $4\sqrt{3}$ inches long. What is the length of each side of the equilateral triangle?

c. Find p in terms of q.

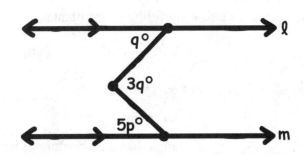

d. Write an equation to represent the question below; then solve the equation to get your answer.

A basketball hoop is 10 feet high. If Nina is 5 feet tall, and standing 13 feet away from the hoop, what is the distance from the top of Nina's head to the hoop? Estimate your answer to two decimal places.

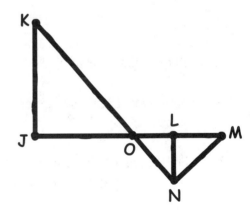

e. Do the proof below.

Given: $\overline{KJ} \perp \overline{JM}$; $\overline{MN} \perp \overline{KN}$; $\overline{LN} \perp \overline{JM}$
Prove: $\triangle KJO \sim \triangle MLN$

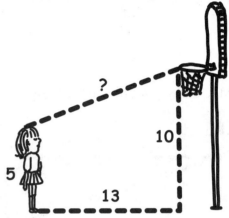

Problem Set 76

Tell whether each sentence below is True or False.

1. A 30-60 right triangle is a right triangle whose acute angles measure 30° and 60°.

2. In a 30-60 right triangle, the length of the hypotenuse is twice the length of the short leg, and the length of the long leg is $\sqrt{3}$ times the length of the short leg.

Complete each sentence below by filling in the blanks.

3. A(n) _____ is a triangle that has a right angle and two congruent sides.

4. If parallel lines are cut by a transversal, _____ angles on the same side of the transversal are _____.

5. A(n) _____ triangle has all three angles with measures less than 90°.

Simplify each irrational number below, then estimate it to two decimal places.

6. $\sqrt{32}$ **(a) 7.** $\sqrt{45}$

Find the missing lengths in the right triangles below.

8.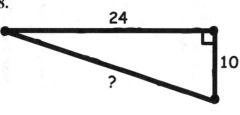

9.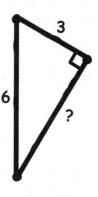

Answer each question below.

10. The diagonals of a square are $7\sqrt{2}$ inches long. What is the length of each side of the square?

(b) 11. The altitude of an equilateral triangle is $2\sqrt{3}$ inches long. What is the length of each side of the equilateral triangle?

Calculate each ratio below.

12. What is the ratio of 8 centimeters to 160 millimeters? Write your answer in the form $a:b$, where a and b are whole numbers.

13. Mr. and Mrs. Johnson took their three children to the movies. If adult tickets cost $7 and children's tickets cost $4, what is the ratio of the total cost of the parents' tickets to the total cost of the children's tickets? Write your answer in the form $a:b$, where a and b are whole numbers.

Find the perimeter of each polygon below.

14. $\triangle ABC$. Estimate your answer to 2 decimal places.

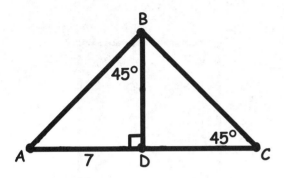

15. Quadrilateral *CPSW*. Estimate your answer to 2 decimal places.

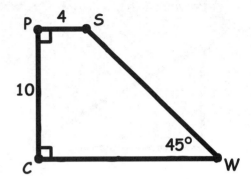

Answer each question below.

16. Find *x*.

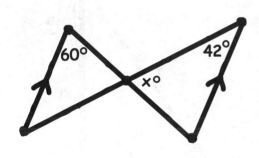

17. Find *y*.

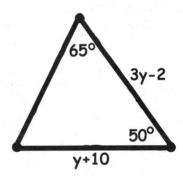

(c) 18. Find *t* in terms of *r*.

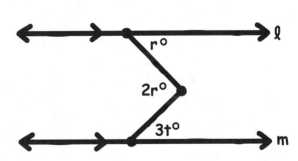

From each given statement below, tell the definition, property, postulate, or theorem that justifies each prove statement.

19. Given: $m\angle B = 30$;
Prove: $c = 2b$, $a = b\sqrt{3}$

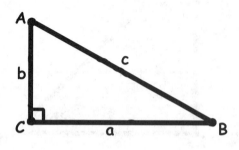

20. Given: Square $PQRS$
Prove: $QS = QR \times \sqrt{2}$

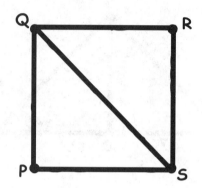

Write an equation to represent each question below; then solve the equation to get your answer.

21. A 20 foot tall flag pole is casting a shadow. If the distance from the top of the pole to the tip of the shadow is 25 feet, how long is the shadow?

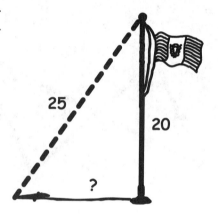

(d) 22. A basketball hoop is 10 feet high. If Toby is 4 feet tall, and standing 11 feet away from the hoop, what is the distance from the top of Toby's head to the hoop? Estimate your answer to two decimal places.

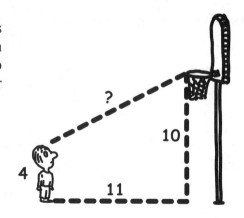

Do each proof below.

23. Given: $\overline{LP} \cong \overline{LK}$; $\overline{PK}$ bisects $\angle LKN$

Prove: $\dfrac{LP}{NK} = \dfrac{MP}{MK}$

24. Given: $\overline{AD} \perp \overline{DE}$; $\overline{AB} \perp \overline{BE}$;

$\overline{BF} \perp \overline{AD}$

Prove: $\triangle FAB \sim \triangle DEC$

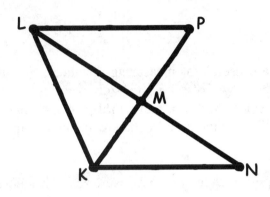

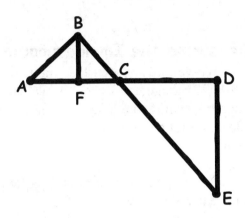

Lesson 77—Trigonometry: The Basics

This chapter is titled "Right Triangles and Trigonometry," but so far we've only talked about right triangles. You may be wondering what happened to the trigonometry. Well, here it comes. Starting with this lesson and continuing throughout the rest of the chapter, we'll be concentrating on trigonometry and nothing else.

Measuring the Immeasurable

We've already seen that right triangles are useful for measuring distances. For instance, with the Pythagorean Theorem, we can find the length of a missing side of a right triangle, as long as we know the lengths of the other two sides. And in a real-world problem, that missing side could represent some unknown distance, like the length of a shadow or the distance across town.

But even the Pythagorean Theorem isn't powerful enough to measure some distances. Look at the example below.

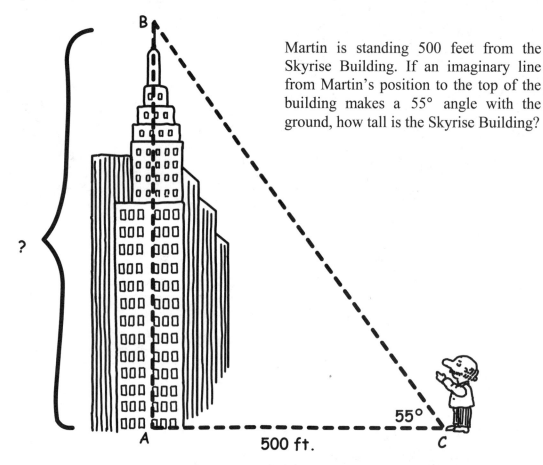

Martin is standing 500 feet from the Skyrise Building. If an imaginary line from Martin's position to the top of the building makes a 55° angle with the ground, how tall is the Skyrise Building?

As the diagram shows, we're really being asked to find the length of one leg of a giant right triangle (with right angle $\angle A$). Unfortunately, we know the length of just one of the other two sides: the horizontal leg. The hypotenuse is also unknown. Since we need two out of the three sides of a right triangle in order to use the Pythagorean Theorem, it won't help us here.

Situations like this are fairly common when trying to measure long distances. In this case, the Skyrise building is so tall that there's no easy way to measure either the vertical leg or the hypotenuse of our right triangle. It seems we're stuck. We shouldn't give up just yet, though, because there was one other important piece of information given in the problem: The angle where Martin is standing (angle *C*) has a measure of 55°. And, if you're wondering how Martin would know that angle, he could measure it pretty easily using a fancy protractor. But the real question is can we find the height of the Skyrise building, even though we only know one side length and one angle? Yes, we can—with trigonometry.

Same Shape, but Smaller

Here's how it works. Since we know two angles of the giant triangle (the right angle and the 55° angle), we can easily draw another triangle that is much smaller but similar to the giant triangle. (Remember, the third angle must be 35°.) Let's call the small triangle Δ*DEF* and draw it so that the bottom leg is 4 inches long (although any other small length would work just as well).

Since Δ*DEF* is small enough to fit on a piece of paper, we would have no trouble measuring the lengths of Δ*DEF* 's other two sides. Those measurements would show that Δ*DEF* 's hypotenuse ($\overline{EF}$) is 6.97 inches, and its other leg ($\overline{DE}$) is 5.71 inches.

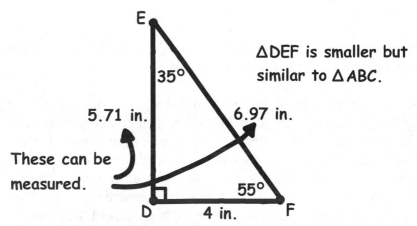

Importantly, since the small triangle and the giant one are similar, something else has to be true about them. Their sides must be proportional. That means we can take the ratio of the vertical and horizontal legs of the giant triangle (*AB* divided by *AC*) and make that equal to the ratio of the vertical and horizontal legs of the small triangle (*DE* divided by *DF*).

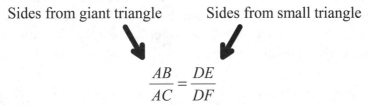

Sides from giant triangle   Sides from small triangle

$$\frac{AB}{AC} = \frac{DE}{DF}$$

These are different ratios than the ones we normally use for similar triangles. Normally, we have sides from different triangles in each ratio. But these ratios also must be equal for any two similar triangles. The reason is that with similar triangles, the ratio of any two sides of one triangle has to equal the ratio of the corresponding sides of the other triangle.[5] You can test this for yourself by drawing a couple of similar triangles and doing the measurements.

Now that we know these two ratios are equal to each other, finding the answer is easy. We measured *DE* as 5.71 inches. And we drew Δ*DEF* so that *DF* was equal to 4. Finally, according to the problem, *AC* is 500 feet. Putting those numbers in the appropriate places leaves only one unknown, *AB*, which is the height of the Skyrise Building.

$$\frac{AB}{500} = \frac{5.71}{4}$$

From here, we can just solve for *AB*.

$$\frac{AB}{500} = 1.428$$

$$500 \cdot \frac{AB}{500} = 500 \cdot 1.428$$

$$AB = 714$$

We end up with 714 feet. That's the height of the Skyrise building. That's also how trigonometry can be used to measure the immeasurable.

Let's summarize what we just did to make sure you've got it. We found the length of one side of a right triangle, knowing just one other side and an angle. (By contrast, the Pythagorean Theorem requires us to know two sides of a right triangle before we can calculate the third.) Our basic method was to draw a small triangle that was similar to the original one in the problem, and measure its sides. Then we set the ratios of two sides from the small triangle and from the original one equal to each other to make an equation. So you see, trigonometry really is all about similar right triangles, as we said at the beginning of the chapter.

Making a Table

One thing that may be bothering you about trigonometry is the hassle of drawing that extra triangle and measuring its sides. Is there any way around that? As a matter of fact, there is. The ancient Greek mathematicians who came up with trigonometry (that's right, Greeks again) realized how tiring it would be to draw a triangle and measure its sides on every problem. So they decided to calculate the ratios of the sides for a huge number of right triangles, of all different shapes, and record their answers in a table. That way, if anybody needed to know a ratio

---

[5] Actually, it's easy to show with algebra that $\frac{DE}{AB} = \frac{DF}{AC}$ is equivalent to $\frac{AB}{AC} = \frac{DE}{DF}$. Starting with the first equation, we just cross-multiply to get $DE \times AC = AB \times DF$. Next, we divide both sides by *AC* and finally we divide both sides by *DF*. That gives us the second equation, $\frac{AB}{AC} = \frac{DE}{DF}$.

of two sides of a particular triangle, instead of having to measure it for themselves, they could just look it up in the table. This was a tremendous time-saver, and another one of the Greeks' brilliant mathematical breakthroughs.

With a "trigonometric table," as it's called, the problem-solving process becomes a lot easier. To find the height of Skyrise, for example, we would only need to look up the ratio of the vertical leg to the horizontal leg of a right triangle that contains a 55° angle. Remember, the ratio has to be the same for all triangles of that shape, no matter how big or small they are (because they're all similar). If the table gave that ratio to 3 decimal places, it would show 1.428. Then, instead of including $\dfrac{DE}{DF}$ in the equation, we would just write 1.428, like this.

$$\frac{AB}{500} = 1.428$$

The other side of the equation would still have to be written as a fraction, since it contains an unknown. But from here, we could solve the equation and get AB (which would still equal 714). No need to draw any triangles.

Practice 77

    a.   Find the geometric mean of BC and CD.

    b.   Assume quadrilateral $PQRS \sim$ quadrilateral $TWVZ$. The lengths of the sides of $PQRS$ are 3, 9, 6, and 12. If $QR:WV$ equals $1:3$, what is the perimeter of $TWVZ$?

    c.   Find x.

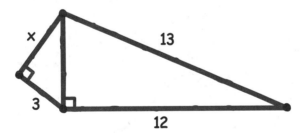

    d.   Everybody knows that there are only two types of ring tones: cool and annoying. If the ratio of cool ring tones to annoying ring tones on Tim's phone was 5 to 6 and there are 25 cool ring tones, how many ring tones does Tim have in total?

e. Do the proof below.

Given: ∠*JML* and ∠*KNL* are complements of
∠*JMN* ; $\overline{JL} \perp \overline{ML}$ and $\overline{KL} \perp \overline{NL}$;
$\overline{JM} \cong \overline{KN}$
Prove: Δ*LMN* is isosceles.

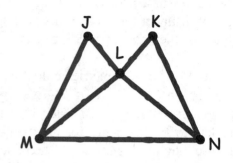

Problem Set 77

Tell whether each sentence below is True or False.

1. With similar triangles, the ratio of any two sides of one triangle has to equal the ratio of the corresponding sides of the other triangle.

2. To make trigonometry more efficient, the Greeks calculated the ratios of the sides for a huge number of right triangles and recorded their answers in a table.

Complete each sentence below by filling in the blanks.

3. If a quadrilateral is a parallelogram, then _____ angles are supplementary.

4. The measure of an exterior angle of a triangle is _____ the sum of the measures of the _____ remote interior angles.

5. If two lines form _____ alternate exterior angles with a transversal, then the lines are parallel.

If Δ*ABC* ~ Δ*DEF* , complete each proportion below.

6. $\dfrac{AB}{AC} = \dfrac{?}{?}$

7. $\dfrac{BC}{AB} = \dfrac{?}{?}$

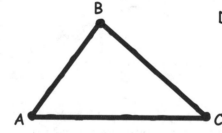

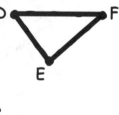

Find the geometric mean of each pair of quantities below.

8. Find the geometric mean of 3 and 15.

(a) 9. Find the geometric mean of *AB* and *CD*.

In the triangle, the missing length x can be found with several different proportions. Complete the possible proportions below, and find x for each.

10. $\dfrac{10}{x} = \dfrac{?}{12}$

11. $\dfrac{x}{x+10} = \dfrac{12}{?}$

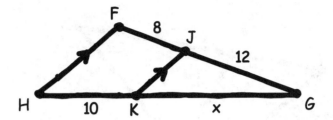

Answer each question below.

12. Assume $\triangle SDF \sim \triangle UVQ$. If $SD = 10$, $UV = 12$, $FS = x+8$, and $QU = 2x$, find FS and QU.

(b) 13. Assume quadrilateral $ABCD \sim$ quadrilateral $EFGH$. The lengths of the sides of $ABCD$ are 2, 5, 7, and 10. If $CD:GH$ equals $1:4$, what is the perimeter of $EFGH$?

Use proportions or the Pythagorean Theorem to find the missing values below.

14. Find x.

15. Find y.

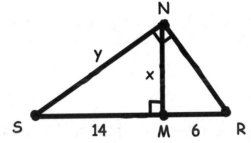

State which shortcut can be used to prove that each pair of triangles below are *congruent*. If no method applies, say "none."

16.

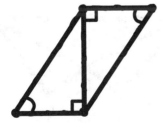

17.

Answer each question below.

18. Find *x*. **19.** Find *y*. **(c) 20.** Find *z*.

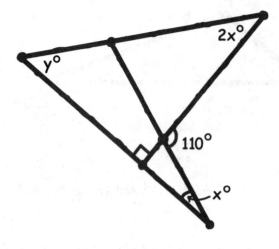

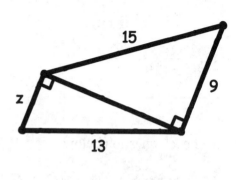

Write a proportion to represent each question below; then solve the proportion to get your answer.

21. Slugger got a hit 2 out of every 3 times he went to bat. If Slugger has gone to bat 36 times so far this season, how many hits has he had?

(d) 22. The candy dish contained only lemon drops and cinnamon drops in the ratio of 7 to 8. If there are 28 lemon drops, how many pieces of candy in total are in the dish?

Do each proof below.

23. Given: *T* is the midpoint of *PS*; $\angle P \cong \angle S$
Prove: $\triangle TVP \cong \triangle TVS$

(e) 24. Given: $\angle BCE$ and $\angle DFE$ are complements of $\angle BCF$; $\overline{BC} \perp \overline{BE}$ and $\overline{DE} \perp \overline{DF}$; $\overline{BC} \cong \overline{DF}$
Prove: $\triangle CEF$ is isosceles.

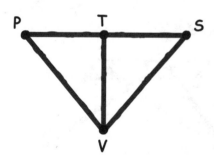

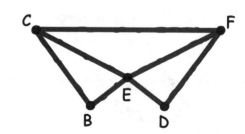

510

Lesson 78—The Tangent Ratio

In the last lesson, we learned how to apply trigonometry to find the side length of a right triangle when given only one other side and one angle. That can be really useful when measuring long, hard-to-reach, distances. In this lesson, we'll learn a few terms that are used a lot in trigonometry.

Tangent: Opposite Over Adjacent

You may remember the Skyrise example that we worked, with the ratio of the vertical leg to the horizontal leg of a right triangle. The diagram is included on the right again to refresh your memory. The only problem with the terms "vertical leg" and "horizontal leg" is that they depend on how the triangle is drawn. If the triangle were tilted on to one side, for instance, the vertical leg would become the horizontal leg and vice versa. That won't work, because when trigonometric ratios are listed in a table, the names have to be clear, regardless of how a particular triangle may have been drawn.

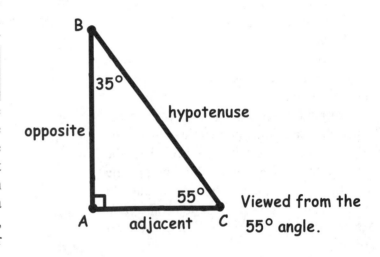

That's why the mathematicians came up with a unique naming system for the sides of a right triangle. Under this system, the hypotenuse is always just called the hypotenuse. That never causes any confusion, since the hypotenuse has to be opposite the right angle. To figure out the names for the legs, though, we start from the angle we were given (in this case, the 55° angle at vertex C). Then the leg that's next to that angle is called the **adjacent side**. (Adjacent means "lying next to.") So the adjacent side in this case is $\overline{AC}$. The leg that's opposite the given (55°) angle is called the **opposite side**. The opposite side here is $\overline{AB}$. Using these terms, the ratio $\dfrac{AB}{AC}$ is written $\dfrac{\text{opposite}}{\text{adjacent}}$, or $\dfrac{\text{opp.}}{\text{adj.}}$ for short. And the entire ratio is called the **tangent** ratio, or **tan** for short. Also, since we're starting from the 55° angle, we say that the "tangent of 55° equals $\dfrac{AB}{AC}$." And it's written as

$$\tan 55 = \frac{AB}{AC}.$$

The formal definition for the tangent ratio is shown below.

Definition 57	The *tangent* ratio is the ratio of the length of the opposite side to the length of the adjacent side of a right triangle, with respect to a given angle: $\tan = \dfrac{opp}{adj}$.

Be sure you understand the tangent ratio, because it can be a little confusing for beginners. Side *AC* is the "adjacent" side and side *AB* is the "opposite" side, only because we started from the vertex of the 55° angle. If we were to start from the 35° angle (at vertex *B* as indicated in the top right diagram), then *AB* would be the adjacent side (since it's connected to the 35° angle), and *AC* would be the opposite side (since it's opposite the 35° angle). In other words, the terms "adjacent" and "opposite" depend on which angle we start from.

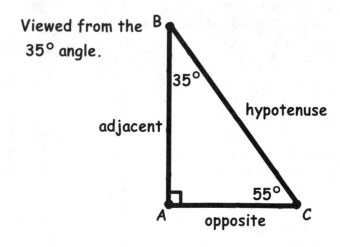

Viewed from the 35° angle.

Now let's go through a quick example shown on the bottom right, and this time we'll use all the proper terms. If in △*JKL*, *KL* equals 3 inches and ∠*J* measures 28°, what is the length of *JL*? Since we're viewing the sides from ∠*J*, *JL* is the adjacent side and *KL* is the opposite side. The tangent of 28° (or tan 28) is equal to $\dfrac{opp.}{adj.}$ or $\dfrac{KL}{JL}$. So that gives us the following equation.

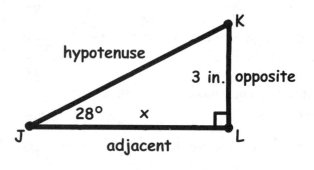

$$\tan 28 = \frac{3}{JL}.$$

Table of Trigonometric Ratios

Now we need to look up tan 28 in a table. Part of an actual trigonometric table is included on the right. We go down the Angle column to 28°, then straight across to the number in the Tangent column.[6] That takes us to 0.5317, which means that tan 28 is equal to 0.5317. The next step is to put 0.5317 in for the left side of our equation.

Angle	Sine	Tangent	Cosine
⋮	⋮	⋮	⋮
25°	0.4226	0.4663	0.9063
26	0.4384	0.4877	0.8988
27	0.4540	0.5095	0.8910
28	0.4695	(0.5317)	0.8829
29	0.4848	0.5543	0.8746
30	0.5000	0.5774	0.8660
⋮	⋮	⋮	⋮

$$0.5317 = \frac{3}{JL}.$$

From here, we solve for JL in the usual way.

$$0.5317 \times JL = 3 \qquad \text{multiplying both sides by } JL$$

$$JL = \frac{3}{0.5317} \qquad \text{dividing both sides by } 0.5317$$

$$JL = 5.6423$$

So JL is equal to about 5.6 inches.

From Table to Calculator

There's no doubt that the trigonometric table is easier than drawing another triangle and measuring its sides. We can thank the Greeks for that. But in today's electronic world, we have an even easier way to find trig ratios: with a calculator. And the calculator is even faster and easier than a table. Different calculators have different instructions for how to calculate a trig ratio. So you should look at the instruction book to find out exactly how your calculator works. But here's an example of how a typical calculator might be used to find the tangent of 28°. The tangent button on the calculator has "tan" on it. The first step is to press "tan." Next, we enter the measure of the angle, which for our problem would be 28. Finally, we press the equals button to get the answer. The calculator should then display the ratio of the opposite side divided by the adjacent side of any 28 – 62 right triangle (viewing the sides from the 28° angle), which is 0.5317, as we know. If the calculator is set to show more than four digits, the answer will go out even further.

---

[6] We'll explain about Sine and Cosine in the next lesson.

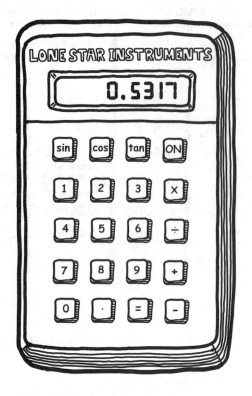

Calculating the tangent of 28:

1) press tan

2) press 2

3) press 8

4) press =

There's one thing, however, that you have to be careful about when using a calculator for trig ratios. You need to make sure that the angles are in the right units. In this book, we always measure angles in degrees. But there's another unit for angles called "radians" which are used a lot in higher math courses. Calculators are usually set in degree mode when they're first turned on. But if you're getting funny answers, the calculator might be in radians. To change it to degrees, press the "mode" button or the "dgr" (for degrees) button until "deg" is displayed on the bottom of the calculator screen instead of "rad," which means radians.

Practice 78

a. Find the perimeter of pentagon *LMNOP*.

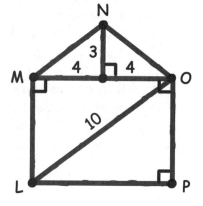

b. Calculate the trigonometric ratio tan 38 to 4 decimal places.

c. Use the tangent ratio to find the missing length *y* in the right triangle below.

d. Find *x*.

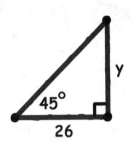

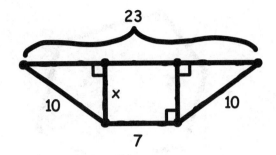

e. Given: *CDEF* is a parallelogram;
  $\overline{FG} \cong \overline{DH}$
  Prove: *CGEH* is a parallelogram

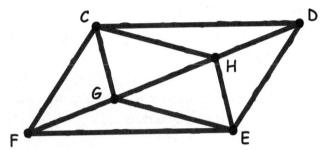

Problem Set 78

Tell whether each sentence below is True or False.

1. From a particular angle in a right triangle, the leg that connects to that angle is called the adjacent side and the leg opposite that angle is called the opposite side.

2. The only place to find a trigonometric ratio is in a table.

Complete each sentence below by filling in the blanks.

3. The tangent ratio for a particular angle in a right triangle is the _____ side to that angle divided by the _____ side.

4. A segment that is both an altitude and a median of a triangle is a _____.

5. The diagonals of an isosceles trapezoid are _____.

Find the sum of the interior angles of each polygon below.

6.

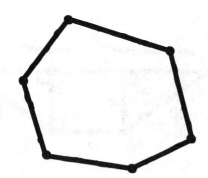

7.

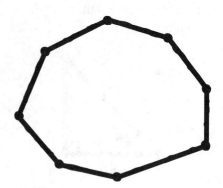

Answer each question below.

8. In right triangle PRQ, $\overline{PQ}$ is the hypotenuse and $m\angle P = 58°$. What is the shortest side of $\triangle PRQ$?

9. In $\triangle BCE$, $m\angle B = x + 10$, $m\angle C = 3x$, and $m\angle E = x$ (where $x > 0$). Find $m\angle C$. What is the longest side of $\triangle BCE$?

Find the missing lengths in the right triangles below.

10.

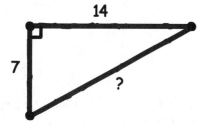

11.

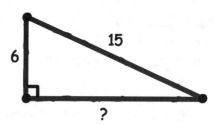

Find the perimeter of each polygon below.

12. parallelogram $ABCD$

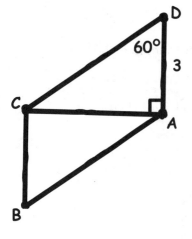

(a) 13. pentagon $QRSTU$

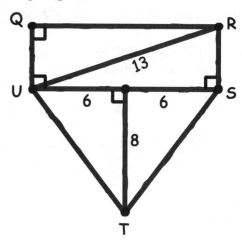

Calculate each trigonometric ratio below to 4 decimal places.

(b) 14. tan 22°

15. tan 68°

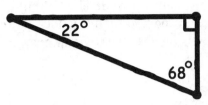

Use the tangent ratio to find the missing leg of each right triangle below. Estimate your answers to 2 decimal places.

(c) 16.

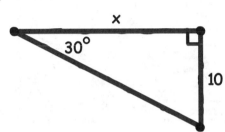

17.

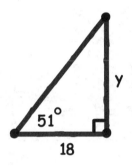

Answer each question below.

18. Find *x*.

19. Find *y*.

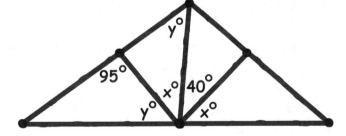

(d) 20. Find *x*.

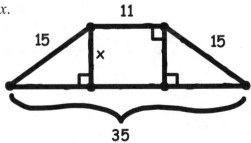

Write an equation to represent each question below; then solve the equation to get your answer.

21. A ladder is leaning up against a wall. The bottom of the ladder is 7 feet away from the bottom of the wall, and the top of the ladder is touching the wall 10 feet above the floor. How long is the ladder? Estimate your answer to 2 decimal places.

22. Central Park in New York City is $2\frac{1}{2}$ miles long and $\frac{1}{2}$ mile wide (which is rectangular). How far is it from corner to corner (see below). Estimate your answer to 2 decimal places.

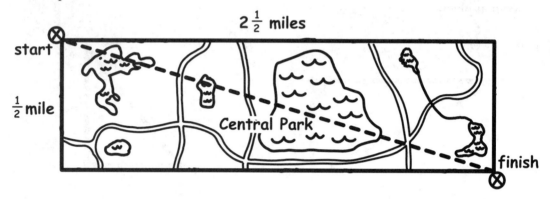

Do each proof below.

23. Given: $\dfrac{PS}{PT} = \dfrac{PR}{PQ}$

Prove: $\overline{SR} \parallel \overline{TQ}$

(e) 24. Given: *HIJK* is a parallelogram;

$$\overline{HL} \cong \overline{JM}$$

Prove: *LIMK* is a parallelogram

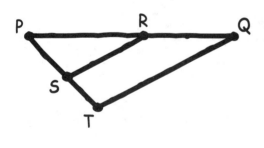

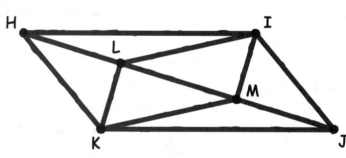

Lesson 79—The Sine and Cosine Ratios

In the previous lesson, we learned about the tangent ratio, which is the opposite side over the adjacent side of a right triangle. The tangent ratio is extremely valuable, especially when measuring long distances. Nevertheless, there are some problems where even the tangent won't work. Take a look at this example.

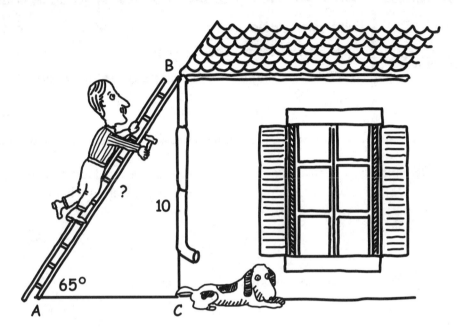

Jason is about to climb up on his roof to fix a leak. The ledge of the house is 10 feet high and the ladder makes a 65° angle with the ground. How long is the ladder?

The ladder, the house, and the ground make a right triangle, as you can see. And we're given the length of one leg and one angle. So this is exactly the kind of problem that we should be able to solve with trigonometry. Yet when we try to set up the equation using the tangent, watch what happens.

$$\frac{BC}{AC} = \tan 65$$

Opposite over adjacent gives us *BC* over *AC*. But the unknown side in our problem is the hypotenuse, which is *AB*. Tangent doesn't work. What now?

Sine: Opposite Over Hypotenuse

Easy. We just use a different trig ratio. There are actually six trig ratios in all. But in this book, we'll only learn about the three most popular ratios. Tangent is one of them. Another is the "sine" ratio.

519

Sine (or **sin** for short) is the opposite side divided by the hypotenuse.

$$\sin = \frac{\text{opposite}}{\text{hypotenuse}}$$

Here's the formal definition.

Definition 58	The *sine* ratio is the ratio of the length of the opposite side to the length of the hypotenuse of a right triangle, with respect to a given angle: $\sin = \dfrac{\text{opp}}{\text{hyp}}$.

Since it contains the hypotenuse, sine can be used to solve our ladder problem. So instead of finding the tangent of 65°, we'll need to find the sine of 65°. Here's what the equation should look like.

$$\sin 65 = \frac{BC}{AB}$$

Putting 10 in for *BC* (the height of the roof's ledge) gives us this.

$$\sin 65 = \frac{10}{AB}$$

Now to find sin 65, instead of looking it up in a table, we can just use a calculator. You may have noticed that the calculator picture in the last lesson had a "sin" button. Now you know what that stands for. We just press "sin" followed by 65 and then the equals sign to get 0.9063. This decimal goes into the left of the equation to get

$$0.9063 = \frac{10}{AB}$$

Now we have just one unknown and can solve for *AB* in the normal way.

$$0.9063 = \frac{10}{AB}$$

$$(0.9063)(AB) = 10 \qquad \text{multiplying both sides by } AB$$

$$AB = \frac{10}{0.9063} \qquad \text{dividing both sides by } 0.9063$$

$$AB = 11.03$$

The ladder is a little over 11 feet long.

Cosine: Adjacent Over Hypotenuse

The third major trig ratio is **cosine** (**cos** for short), which is the adjacent side divided by the hypotenuse.

$$\cos = \frac{\text{adjacent}}{\text{hypotenuse}}$$

Here's the formal definition of cosine.

Definition 59	The *cosine* ratio is the ratio of the length of the adjacent side to the length of the hypotenuse of a right triangle, with respect to a given angle: $\cos = \dfrac{\text{adj}}{\text{hyp}}$.

Let's do a quick problem involving cosine.

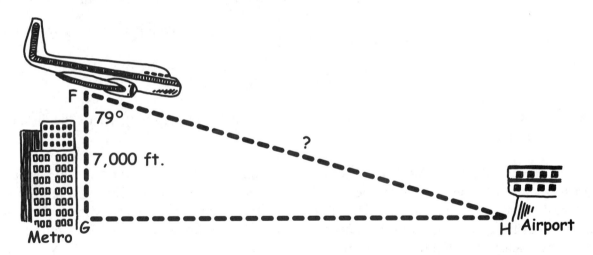

A plane is flying at an altitude of 7,000 feet, directly over Metro City. If the plane descends steadily, making an angle of 79° with a vertical line, how far will it have to fly to reach the airport?

Here we have a right triangle, ΔFGH. We know one angle, $\angle F$, and, viewing the sides from vertex F, we have the length of the adjacent side, FG, which is 7,000 feet. And we're supposed to find the hypotenuse, FH. The tangent ratio won't work, because it involves the adjacent side and the opposite side. We need the hypotenuse in our ratio. But the sine ratio won't work either. Even though it contains the hypotenuse, the other part of the ratio is the opposite side, which is unknown in our problem. So if we used sine, our equation would have two unknowns and be unsolvable.

The ratio to use is the cosine ratio, because it has the adjacent side (7,000 ft.) and the hypotenuse, which is what we're trying to find. The cosine of 79 is equal to *FG* divided by *FH*.

$$\cos 79 = \frac{FG}{FH}$$

Putting 7,000 in for *FG*, we have

$$\cos 79 = \frac{7,000}{FH}.$$

Now we solve in the usual way. The first step is to find cos 79. Since a calculator is faster than looking it up in a table, we could punch the "cos" button and then enter 79, followed by the equals sign. That gives 0.1908 to 4 decimal places. So we put 0.1908 in for the left side of the equation and then solve for *FH*.

$$0.1908 = \frac{7,000}{FH}$$

$$(0.1908)FH = 7,000 \qquad \text{multiplying both sides by } FH$$

$$FH = \frac{7,000}{0.1908} \qquad \text{dividing both sides by } 0.1981$$

$$FH = 36,687.6$$

We end up with 36,687.6 feet or about 6.7 miles (since 5,280 feet = 1 mile). That's the distance the plane has to fly to reach the airport.

To summarize, there are three main trig ratios: tangent, sine, and cosine. And it's not too hard to figure out which one is the best to use when solving a problem. The right ratio must contain the side you're trying to find. So if you're looking for the hypotenuse, you need a ratio that includes the hypotenuse. But the other requirement is that the second side in the ratio must be a known length (given in the problem). That way, when you write the equation, it will have just one unknown. If the second side of the ratio is also unknown, then your equation will have two unknowns and be unsolvable.

Practice 79

    a. An isosceles triangle has a base with length 16. If the altitude drawn to the base has a length of 12, find the length of each of the triangle's legs.

b. Find *x* in the figure below.

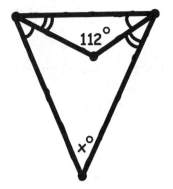

c. Find *y* in the figure below.

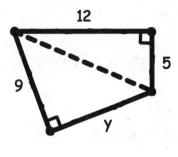

d. The baby slide makes a 31° angle with the ground. If the ground directly underneath the slide measures 9 feet, how long is the slide? Estimate your answer to two decimal places.

e. Given: $\overline{AB}$ and $\overline{CD}$ bisect each other at point *F*;
   $\angle CAE \cong \angle GBD$
Prove: $\overline{AE} \cong \overline{GB}$

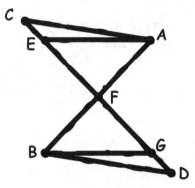

Problem Set 79

Tell whether each sentence below is True or False.

1. The sine ratio for a particular angle in a right triangle is the opposite side to that angle divided by the hypotenuse.

2. The cosine ratio for a particular angle in a right triangle is the adjacent side to that angle divided by the hypotenuse.

Complete each sentence below by filling in the blanks.

3. From a particular angle in a right triangle, the leg that connects to that angle is called the _____ side and the leg opposite that angle is called the _____ side.

4. The abbreviation for tangent is _____, the abbreviation for sine is _____, and the abbreviation for cosine is _____.

5. The _____ of a rhombus bisect the angles at the vertices which they join.

Simplify each irrational number below; then estimate it to two decimal places.

6. $\sqrt{72}$ **7.** $\sqrt{175}$

Calculate each trigonometric ratio below. Estimate your answers to four decimal places.

8. $\sin 23°$ **9.** $\cos 77°$ **10.** $\tan 81°$

Answer each question below.

11. Find the length of the sides of a rhombus whose diagonals are 40 and 96.

(a) 12. An isosceles triangle has a base with length 26. If the altitude drawn to the base has a length of 16, find the length of each of the triangle's legs.

From each given statement below, tell the definition, property, postulate, or theorem that justifies each prove statement.

13. Given: $\dfrac{AB}{CF} = \dfrac{DE}{CF}$; Prove: $AB \times CF = CF \times DE$.

14. Given: $m\angle R = m\angle S$ and $m\angle S > m\angle T$; Prove: $m\angle R > m\angle T$.

Answer each question below.

15. The length of one leg of an isosceles right triangle is 23. Find the length of the hypotenuse.

16. In $\triangle STM$, $m\angle S = 60$ and $m\angle M = 90$. If $ST = 12$, find SM and TM.

Answer each question below.

17. If *KLMN* is a parallelogram, find *x*.   **(b) 18.** Find *y*.   **(c) 19.** Find *y*.

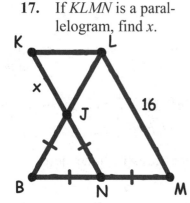

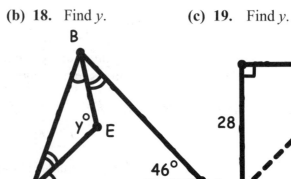

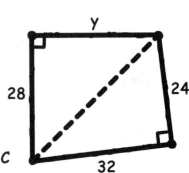

Write an equation to represent each question below; then solve the equation to get your answer.

20. A train track slopes upward at an angle of 12°. How many feet does the track rise over a horizontal distance of 150 feet? Estimate your answer to 2 decimal places.

21. A plane veered off its course at an angle of 14°. If the plane ends up 23 miles due west of its planned destination, how far did it fly? Estimate your answer to 2 decimal places.

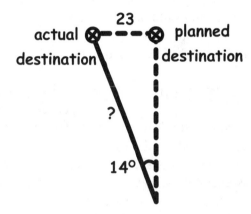

(d) 22. The power slide makes a 47° angle with the ground. If the ground directly underneath the slide measures 18 feet, how long is the slide? Estimate your answer to two decimal places.

Do each proof below.

23. Given: *ERDT* is a trapezoid
Prove: $DP \times TP = RP \times EP$

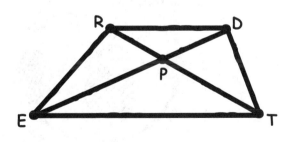

(e) 24. Given: $\overline{IJ}$ and $\overline{KL}$ bisect each other at point *N*;
$\angle LIO \cong \angle MJK$
Prove: $\overline{IO} \cong \overline{MJ}$

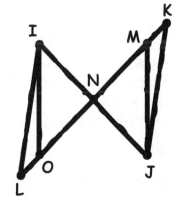

Lesson 80—Measuring the Solar System

So far, we've used trigonometry to measure things like the height of a building and the distance traveled by a plane. These are practical measurements that must be done from time to time, but they're not terribly exciting. However, the ancient Greeks actually created trigonometry to do some of the most exciting measurements imaginable—to measure the distances to the heavenly bodies.

Seemingly Impossible

The Greeks' motivation was mainly curiosity. Gazing up every night at the glowing moon, it was only natural to wonder how far away the moon was. And the warmth of each day made them curious about the distance from earth to that intensely bright fireball, the sun. They were also keenly interested in tracking the wandering stars known as planets.

But just think of how impossible such measurements must have seemed to people in the ancient world (and to most people today, if they took the time to think about it). The Greeks certainly couldn't look up the answer in an encyclopedia or on the Internet. Nor did they have rockets that could travel into space and clock the actual distance. They didn't even have telescopes to get a good look at the moon or any of the planets. The task of measuring such distances must have seemed overwhelming. Yet the brilliant Greek astronomers succeeded in measuring them with amazing accuracy, as you'll see. What's more, they performed their measurements with the very trig ratios that we've been talking about. So trig really does allow you to measure the immeasurable.

Measuring the Distance to the Moon

Let's go through one of their famous astronomical measurements to prove that trigonometry, along with a little basic geometry, really will do the job. Let's measure the distance to the moon. Here's a picture (although it's not drawn to scale).

E is at the center of the Earth and M is at the center of the moon. P and Q stand for two different positions on the earth's surface. The moon is directly overhead for a person standing at Q. The moon is barely visible in the horizon for a person standing at P. That's what makes $\angle P$ a right angle.[7]

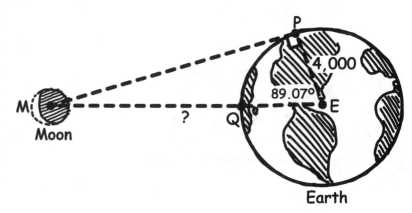

---

[7] This is actually a theorem of geometry that we'll be covering in the next chapter.

As you may remember from several chapters ago, the Greeks were also able to measure the distance around the earth, which was about 24,000 miles. Once that distance is known, calculating the distance to the earth's center is easy. It turns out to be 4,000 miles. That's why $PE = 4,000$. The distance between P and Q is not difficult to measure; it turns out to be 5,938 miles. The ratio of 5,938 to the distance all the way around the earth (24,000) has to equal the ratio of $\angle E$ to an angle that goes all the way around at point E (or $360°$). That gives us the proportion below.

$$\frac{m\angle E}{360} = \frac{5,938}{24,000}$$

Solving for $m\angle E$, we get the following.

$$(m\angle E)(24,000) = (360)(5,938) \qquad \text{cross-multiplying}$$

$$(m\angle E)(24,000) = 2,137,600$$

$$m\angle E = \frac{2,137,600}{24,000} \qquad \text{dividing both sides by 24,000}$$

$$m\angle E = 89.07$$

That's how we end up with 89.07° for $\angle E$. (Here's the diagram again, for you to see)

With this information, the problem becomes just simple trigonometry. ΔMPE is a right triangle. We know one side ($PE = 4,000$) and one additional angle ($m\angle E = 89.07$). Viewing the triangle from $\angle E$, PE is an adjacent side. We're trying to find QM, but since the

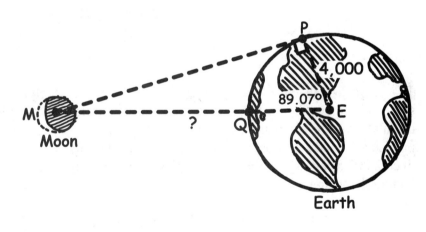

hypotenuse of the triangle is EM, we should find EM first and then we can subtract EQ to get QM. So we have the adjacent side and we're trying to find the hypotenuse. That means the appropriate trig ratio to use is cosine (adjacent over hypotenuse). Here's the equation.

$$\cos 89.07 = \frac{PE}{EM}$$

$$\cos 89.07 = \frac{4,000}{EM}$$

Next, we punch the cosine of 89.07 into the calculator. We press the "cos" button, then "89.07," and finally the equals sign, to get 0.0162 (to 4 places). That allows us to put 0.0162 in the left side of the equation.

$$0.0162 = \frac{4,000}{EM}$$

Now we have just one unknown and can solve normally.

$$(0.0162)EM = 4,000 \qquad \text{multiplying both sides by } EM$$

$$EM = \frac{4,000}{0.0162} \qquad \text{dividing both sides by } 0.0162$$

$$EM = 246,913$$

We end up with 246,913 miles for *EM*. We actually need *QM*, though, since we want to measure the distance to the moon from the earth's surface (not its center).[8] The distance to the earth's center is 4,000 miles, so all we have to do is subtract 4,000 from 246,913.

$$QM = 246,913 - 4,000$$

$$QM = 242,913$$

That gives us a distance to the moon of 242,913 miles, which is slightly off because we rounded some of the numbers. The actual number is a little lower. When the Greeks did the same calculation they came up with about 280,000 miles. Their measurement of $\angle E$ was not as precise as it needed to be, which threw their answer off. But considering that they were working over 2,000 years ago with no sophisticated measuring equipment and no calculator, that's an incredibly accurate answer.

We won't bother going through the measurement of the distance from the earth to the sun, because the method is basically the same one we used for the moon. Although since the sun is so much farther away than the moon, the measurement of $\angle E$ has to be really accurate to get a good answer. Even the smallest error will throw the number way off. The Greeks had trouble measuring $\angle E$ because of a lack of equipment. They came up with about 65,000,000 miles, although the actual distance is 93,000,000 miles.

But even 65,000,000 was a remarkable answer. That's because people in ancient times had no idea how big the universe was. They never dreamed that the moon was 240,000 miles away.

---

[8] We'll ignore the distance to the center of the moon, since it's smaller.

And then to learn that the sun was actually over 50 million miles from earth was absolutely astonishing. The Greek creators of trigonometry did more than develop a great mathematical tool for measurement. They forever changed the way human beings perceive the universe.

Practice 80

a. Find the measures of the angles of a right triangle with one leg having a length of 2 and the hypotenuse having a length of 4.

b. Find the perimeter of trapezoid *PQRS* below. Estimate your answer to 2 decimal places.

c. If $m\angle CBD = \dfrac{5}{7} m\angle CBA$, find *x*.

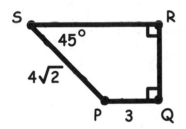

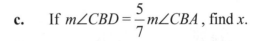
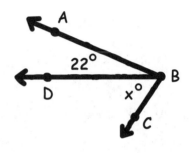

d. David is standing near a 30 foot oak tree. If the angle of elevation to the top of the tree is 46°, how far away is David standing? Estimate your answer to 2 decimal places.

e. Given: $\overline{PQ} \cong \overline{PT}$; $\overline{OQ} \cong \overline{OT}$
Prove: $\triangle RSO$ is isosceles.

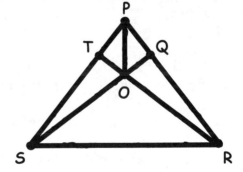

Problem Set 80

Tell whether each sentence below is True or False.

1. The ancient Greeks created trigonometry to measure the distances to the moon, sun, and planets.

2. The distance from the earth to the moon can be calculated by using the cosine ratio.

529

Complete each sentence below by filling in the blanks.

3. If a line is _____ to one side of a triangle and intersects the other two sides, then the line divides those sides proportionally.

4. If two sides of a triangle are not congruent, then the angles opposite those sides are _____ , and the _____ angle is opposite the _____ side.

5. The sum of the lengths of any two sides of a triangle must be _____ the length of the remaining side.

Complete each sentence below with *always*, *sometimes*, or *never*.

6. A parallelogram is _____ a quadrilateral.

7. A trapezoid _____ has both pairs of opposite sides parallel.

If $\triangle STR \sim \triangle UVW$, complete each proportion below.

8. $\dfrac{ST}{SR} = \dfrac{?}{?}$

9. $\dfrac{TR}{ST} = \dfrac{?}{?}$

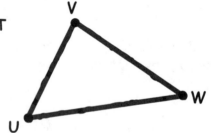

Find the measures of the angles of each triangle described below.

10. An isosceles triangle with one angle measuring $98°$.

(a) 11. A right triangle with one leg having a length of 1 and the hypotenuse having a length of 2.

Calculate each ratio below.

12. It is the red shirts versus the blue shirts. Both teams have a total of 21 players. If the red shirts have 9 players, what is the ratio of red shirts to blue shirts? Write your answer as a decimal.

13. A subscription to Living Longer magazine costs $39.95 per year. A subscription to Bouncing Babies magazine costs $49.95 per year. What is the ratio of the Living Longer subscription cost to the Bouncing Babies subscription cost? Write your answer as a decimal rounded to 2 places.

Find the perimeter of each polygon below. Estimate your answers to 2 decimal places.

14. right triangle *AFK*

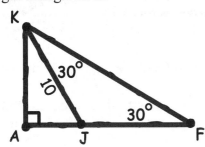

(b) 15. trapezoid *AMPR*

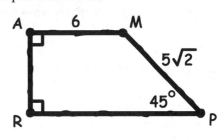

In the triangle, the missing length x can be found with several different proportions. Complete the possible proportions below, and find x for each.

16. $\dfrac{7.5}{x} = \dfrac{?}{9}$

17. $\dfrac{x}{x+7.5} = \dfrac{9}{?}$

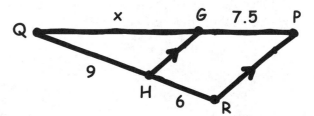

Answer each question below.

18. Find x.

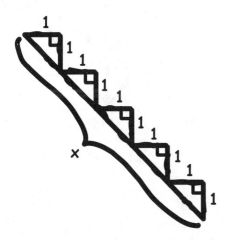

(c) 19. If $m\angle IJL = \dfrac{3}{4} m\angle IJK$, find x.

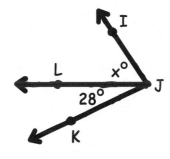

20.   Find *y*. Write your answer as a decimal rounded to 2 places.

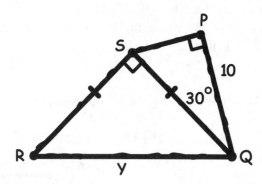

Write an equation to represent each question below; then solve the equation to get your answer.

(d) 21.   Annette is standing near a 25 foot oak tree. If the angle of elevation to the top of the tree is 58°, how far away is Annette standing? Estimate your answer to 2 decimal places.

22.   A firefighting crew needs to put a 38-foot ladder against the vertical wall of a high-rise building. The firefighters can't climb the ladder with all their equipment if the angle of the ladder from the ground is greater than 67°. How far from the building should they place the foot of the ladder in order to maintain an angle of 67°? Estimate your answer to 2 decimal places.

Do each proof below.

23.   Given: $\ell \parallel m$; $\overline{CB}$ bisects $\angle ABE$;
             D is the midpoint of $\overline{CB}$.
     Prove: $\overline{AD}$ bisects $\angle BAC$.

(e) 24.   Given: $\overline{KH} \cong \overline{LH}$; $\overline{JK} \cong \overline{JL}$
           Prove: $\triangle FGJ$ is isosceles.

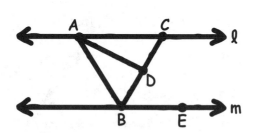

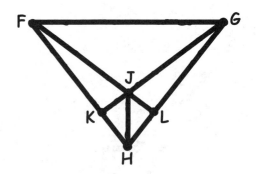

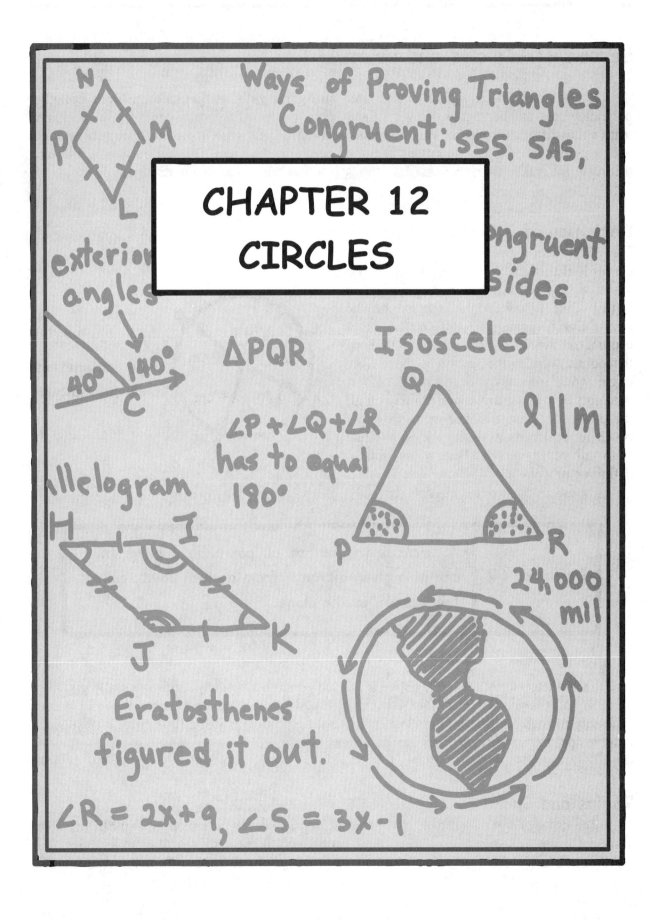

Ways of Proving Triangles Congruent: SSS, SAS,

CHAPTER 12
CIRCLES

exterior angles

ongruent sides

40° 140°
C

ΔPQR

∠P + ∠Q + ∠R has to equal 180°

Isosceles

ℓ ‖ m

llelogram

24,000 mil

Eratosthenes figured it out.

∠R = 2x + 9, ∠S = 3x - 1

Lesson 81—Circles and Lines

So far in this book, we've concentrated on figures with straight sides, such as triangles, parallelograms, and pentagons. Now it's finally time to take off the sharp edges (so to speak) and learn about circles. Circles are very common geometric figures, so it shouldn't surprise you that geometry has quite a few important theorems pertaining to them. But before getting into any theorems, we should first cover the definition of a circle and several technical terms.

Definition of a Circle

What sets a circle apart from all other curves is that every point along the circle has to be the same distance from the circle's center. Take a look at the diagram on the right. Every point on this circle is 4 centimeters away from the center. If some of the points were farther away or closer, the circle would obviously be distorted, and it wouldn't be a circle any more. So having all the points the same distance away from the center is really what distinguishes a circle from all other curves. Here's the formal definition of a circle.

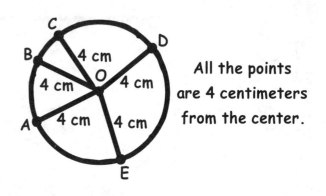

All the points are 4 centimeters from the center.

| Definition 60 | A *circle* is the set of all points in a plane that are at a given distance from a given point, called the *center*, in the plane. |

Notice that the center of the circle above is labeled point *O*. The entire circle is usually given the same name as the center. Therefore, this circle should be called circle *O*. Actually, it's not even necessary to spell out the word circle. The symbol for a circle is just a little circle with a center point inside: ⊙. So "circle *O*" can also be written as "⊙*O*."

Radius and Chord

The distance from the center to the edge of a circle is such an important number that it has a special name: it's called the **radius**. So 4 centimeters is the radius of the circle above. The word radius is also used to refer to an actual line segment extending from the center to the circle's edge, which means that line segments *OA*, *OB*, *OC*, and *OD* are all radii (that's plural for radius). Here's the formal definition of radius.

Definition 61	A *radius* is a line segment that joins the center of the circle to a point of the circle.

There's also a postulate that pertains to the radius. It says that all radii from the same circle have to be congruent. It's a pretty obvious point, really (which is why it's a postulate). If all radii were not congruent, the distance from center to edge wouldn't be everywhere the same. But here's Postulate 17 stated formally.

Postulate 17	All radii of the same circle are congruent (equal).

A radius runs from the center to the edge of a circle. But it's also possible for a line segment to run from one edge of the circle to another. Such a segment is called a **chord**. Check out the circle on the right. Segments *RS*, *TU*, and *VW* are all chords of circle *O*. Here's the formal definition of a chord.

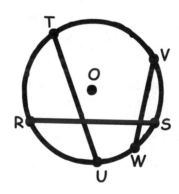

Chords RS, TU, and VW run from one edge to the other, but *not* through center O.

Definition 62	A *chord* of a circle is a line segment that joins two points of the circle.

A special kind of chord is one that goes right through the center of the circle. This is called a **diameter**. As shown in the circle O on the right, segments *EG*, *DH*, and *FI* are all diameters. As with a radius, the word diameter can mean two things. It can mean the distance from edge to edge (through the center) of the circle or an actual line segment covering that distance. Here is the formal definition of a diameter.

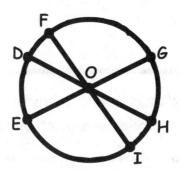

Diameters EG, DH, and FI run from one edge to the other, through center O.

Definition 63	A *diameter* of a circle is a chord that contains the center.

There's a simple relationship between the diameter and radius of any circle. Since the diameter (*d*) is twice the radius (*r*) in length, the following equation has to be true.

$$d = 2r$$

Tangent and Secant

So far we've talked about line *segments* (with end points) and circles. But lines (that go on forever) and circles can also go together. When working with circles, we deal with two kinds of lines: those that intersect the circle at one point and those that intersect it at two points. A line that intersects a circle just once is called a **tangent line**, as shown in the diagram on the right. Notice that *ST* is a line, because it goes on forever in both directions. But what makes *ST* a tangent to circle O is that it intersects the circle at point T, and nowhere else. Point T also has a special name. It's called the **point of tangency**. Here is the formal definition for a tangent line.

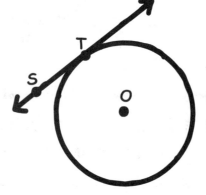

Tangent line ST intersects circle O at just one point.

Definition 64	A *tangent* line is a line which intersects a circle in exactly one point. The point of contact is called the *point of tangency*.

A line that intersects a circle at two points is called a **secant** line. An example is given on the right. See, since the line intersects the circle at both point L and point P, it qualifies as a secant. The formal definition of a secant line is shown below.

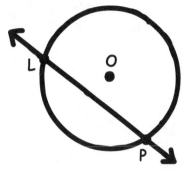

Secant line LP intersects circle O at two points.

Definition 65	A *secant* line is a line which intersects a circle in two different points.

Congruent and Similar Circles

Congruent figures, as you know, are figures that have the same shape and the same size. We've learned quite a few rules for determining when two triangles are congruent (S.A.S., S.S.S., and so on). You'll be glad to hear that there's just one rule for determining whether two circles are congruent: they just need to have the same radius. Since every circle is the same shape, when the radii are the same, the circles have to be both the same shape and the same size. That's all there is to it.

What about similar circles? That's even easier. Since every circle has the same shape, they're all similar! Nothing to memorize there.

Practice 81

a. A median of an equilateral triangle is $\dfrac{3\sqrt{3}}{4}$ inches long. What is the length of each side of the equilateral triangle?

b. Find *x*.

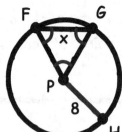

c. If $BD = BF$, find tan *x*.

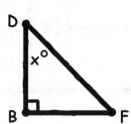

d. Write a proportion to represent the question below; then solve the proportion to get your answer.

The train that left Abilene at 7:45 pulled only oil tanker cars and cattle cars in the ratio of $45 : 7$. If there were 135 oil tanker cars, how many cars in total did the train pull?

e. Do the proof below.

Given: $\triangle MNO \cong \triangle QPO$; $LM = LQ$
Prove: $\triangle LNO \cong \triangle LPO$

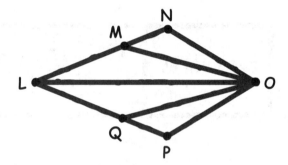

Problem Set 81

Tell whether each sentence below is True or False.

1. A circle is the set of all points in a plane that are a given distance from a given point, called the center, in the plane.

2. A radius is a line segment that joins the center of the circle to a point on the circle.

Complete each sentence below by filling in the blanks.

3. A _____ of a circle is a line segment that joins two points of the circle.

4. A _____ line is a line that intersects a circle in exactly one point. The point of contact is called the _____.

5. A _____ of a circle is a chord that contains the center.

Tell whether each figure below is a trapezoid, isosceles trapezoid, parallelogram, rectangle, rhombus, square, or just a plain quadrilateral.

6.

7.

Calculate each trigonometric ratio below. Estimate your answers to four decimal places.

8. sin 76°

9. cos 14°

Answer each question below.

10. The perimeter of a square is 84. Find the length of a diagonal.

(a) 11. A median of an equilateral triangle is $\dfrac{2\sqrt{3}}{3}$ inches long. What is the length of each side of the equilateral triangle?

Answer each question below.

12. The length of the hypotenuse of an isosceles right triangle is 14. Find the lengths of each leg.

13. In $\triangle JKL$, $m\angle K = 30$ and $m\angle J = 60$. If $JK = 26$, find JL and KL.

State which shortcut can be used to prove that each pair of triangles below are *congruent*. If no method applies, say "none."

14.

15.

Answer each question below.

16. In $\triangle VCF$, $VC > VF$ and $FC < VF$. Which is the largest angle of $\triangle VCF$?

17. In $\triangle SDG$, $m\angle S = 3x$, $m\angle D = 2x + 17$, and $m\angle G = x - 5$ (where $x > 0$). Find $m\angle D$. What is the longest side of $\triangle SDG$?

Answer each question below.

(b) 18. Find x.

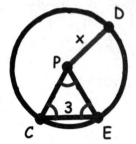

19. Find y.

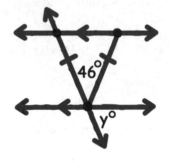

(c) 20. Find $\tan x$.

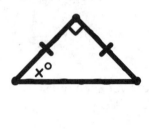

Write a proportion to represent each question below; then solve the proportion to get your answer.

21. The ratio of compacts to lipstick wearers was $15:19$. If there were 75 compacts, how many lipstick wearers were there?

(d) 22. The train that left Boise at 9:23 pulled only potato cars and lumber cars in the ratio of $23:9$. If there were 72 lumber cars, how many cars in total did the train pull?

Do each proof below.

23. Given: $\dfrac{QT}{QW} = \dfrac{QS}{QV}$; $\angle STQ \cong \angle RPQ$

Prove: $\overline{PR} \parallel \overline{VW}$

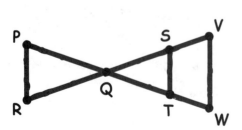

(e) 24. Given: $\triangle BCF \cong \triangle BHG$; $FE = GE$

Prove: $\triangle BCE \cong \triangle BHE$

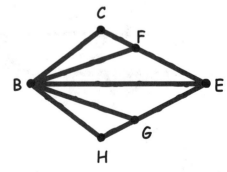

Lesson 82—Theorems on Chords

We introduced circles in the last lesson. Now it's time to go through some theorems. There are actually several important theorems about the chords of a circle. We'll show you the first one on the diagram below.

Bisecting a Chord

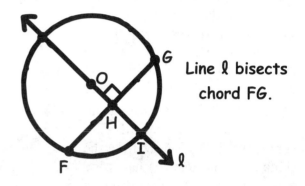

As you can see, this circle has a chord *FG* and a line ℓ (actually a secant) that's perpendicular to it. The other thing about line ℓ is that it runs through the center of the circle. Well, it turns out that in this situation, line ℓ also bisects chord *FG*. That means $FH = HG$. And what's really incredible is that this will work on any chord, whatever its length or position in the circle. If we run a line through the center of a circle so that it is perpendicular to a chord, that line will always cut the chord in half. Here's an informal proof of the theorem.

Line ℓ bisects chord FG.

Given: $\overleftrightarrow{OI} \perp \overline{FG}$
Prove: $\overleftrightarrow{OI}$ bisects $\overline{FG}$

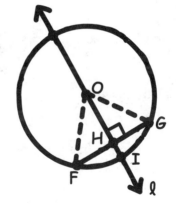

Draw $\overline{OF}$ and $\overline{OG}$. Given that $\overrightarrow{OI} \perp \overline{FG}$, $\angle OHG \cong \angle OHF$ (since they're both right angles). Therefore, $\triangle OHG$ and $\triangle OHF$ are right triangles. We know that $\overline{OF} \cong \overline{OG}$ (All radii of the same circle are congruent) and $\overline{OH} \cong \overline{OH}$ (Reflexive). So by Hypotenuse-Leg, $\triangle OHG \cong \triangle OHF$. It follows by C.P.C.T.C. that $\overline{FH} \cong \overline{GH}$. According to the definition of a segment bisector, then, $\overleftrightarrow{OI}$ bisects $\overline{FG}$.

Theorem 61	If a line through the center of a circle is perpendicular to a chord, it also bisects the chord.

Same Distance from the Center

Let's do another theorem. This one involves two chords instead of one. We'll use the diagram on the top right. The two chords are *AB* and *CD*, and $\overline{AB} \cong \overline{CD}$. But here's the main point. Since these chords are congruent, their distance from the center of the circle (*P*) has to be equal. Remember, the distance between a line segment and a point is measured by drawing a perpendicular segment between the two. So if we draw a segment from *P* to *AB*, making it perpendicular to *AB*, and then do the same thing to chord *CD*, those two perpendicular segments (*LP* and *PK* on the right) must be congruent as indicated in the bottom right diagram.

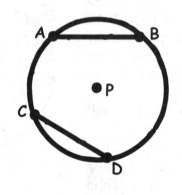

AB and CD
are chords
and $\overline{AB} = \overline{CD}$.

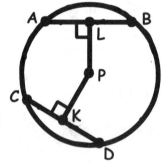

Since chords AB and CD
are congruent, they're
the same distance from
the center: $\overline{LP} \cong \overline{PK}$.

What's really interesting is that this rule works no matter where the chords are positioned inside the circle and no matter how long the chords are (as long as they're congruent). So it's very versatile. As always, though, before we can use the rule, it needs to be proven deductively. Here's an informal proof, followed by the official theorem.

Given: RS = TU, $\overline{RS} \perp \overline{JO}$,
$\overline{TU} \perp \overline{OQ}$

Prove: JO = OQ

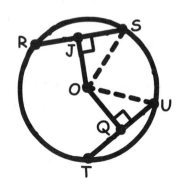

Draw radii OS and OU. Since all radii of a circle are equal, $OS = OU$. $\overline{JO}$ is perpendicular to $\overline{RS}$ and $\overline{OQ}$ is perpendicular to $\overline{TU}$ (Given). $\overline{JO}$ bisects $\overline{RS}$ and $\overline{OQ}$ bisects $\overline{TU}$ (If a line through the center of a circle is perpendicular to the chord, it also bisects the chord.) So $RJ = JS$ and $TQ = QU$ (Definition of segment bisector), and $JS = \frac{1}{2}RS$ and $QU = \frac{1}{2}TU$ (Definition of midpoint). Since $RS = TU$ (Given) and $\frac{1}{2}RS = \frac{1}{2}TU$ (Multiplication), $JS = QU$ (Substitution). Therefore, $\triangle OJS \cong \triangle OQU$ (Hypotenuse-Leg), which means that $JO = OQ$ (C.P.C.T.C.).

Theorem 62	**In the same circle, congruent (equal) chords are equidistant (the same distance) from the center of the circle.**

What about the converse of Theorem 62? If two chords are the same distance from the center of a circle, can we conclude that the chords are congruent? By now you know that the converse of a true statement isn't necessarily true itself. So we would have to prove the converse to be sure. It turns out that the converse is true as well, which means that if you're given that two chords in a circle are the same distance away from the center, the chords have to be congruent. We'll just state the converse theorem here. The proof will be left for you to do yourself in the problem set.

Theorem 63	**In the same circle, chords equidistant from the center of the circle are congruent (equal).**

Practice 82

a. Tell whether $\overleftrightarrow{TN}$ is a radius, diameter, chord, tangent line, or secant line of circle O.

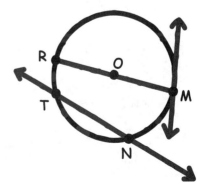

b. The length of a chord of a circle is 6 and its distance from the center is 4. Find the length of a diameter of the circle.

c. Find x. Write your answer as a decimal rounded to 2 places.

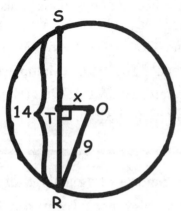

d. Farmer Brown needs to make a ramp to load a tool chest into the bed of his pickup. The incline of the ramp can't be more than 21° or the tool chest will tip over. The bed of the pickup truck is 1 foot above the ground. How long does the ramp need to be so that the angle of the ramp to the level ground below is 21°? Estimate your answer to two decimal places.

e. Do the proof below.

Given: $\overline{NP} \cong \overline{RP}$; $\overline{NP} \perp \overline{LM}$; $\overline{RP} \perp \overline{SQ}$
Prove: $\overline{ML} \cong \overline{QS}$

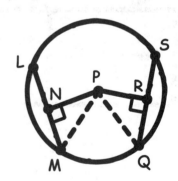

Problem Set 82

Tell whether each sentence below is True or False.

1. If a line through the center of a circle is perpendicular to a chord, it also bisects the chord.

2. In the same circle, congruent (equal) chords are equidistant from the center of the circle.

Complete each sentence below by filling in the blanks.

3. A _____ line is a line which intersects a circle in two different points.

4. Two circles are congruent if they have the same _____.

5. If a line is _____ to one side of a triangle and intersects the other two sides, then the line divides those sides proportionally.

Tell whether each of the following parts of circle O is a radius, diameter, chord, tangent line, or secant line.

(a) 6. $\overline{FG}$

7. $\overleftrightarrow{BD}$

8. $\overline{AO}$

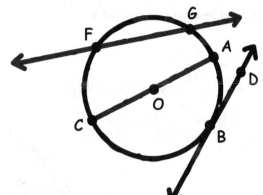

Answer each question below.

9. In right triangle SNV, $\overline{NV}$ is the hypotenuse and $m\angle N = 27°$. What is the shortest side of $\triangle SNV$? Estimate the length of that side to two decimals if $NV = 8$.

10. In $\triangle KGC$, $m\angle K = \dfrac{1}{2}x$, $m\angle G = 2x - 9$, and $m\angle C = 2x$ (where $x > 0$). Find $m\angle G$. What is the longest side of $\triangle KGC$?

Use proportions or the Pythagorean Theorem to find the missing values below. Write your answer as a decimal rounded to 2 places.

11. Find y.

12. Find x.

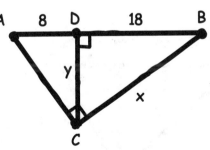

Answer each question below.

13. In $\triangle DCF$, $m\angle C = 60$ and $m\angle F = 30$. If $CF = 18$, find CD and DF.

(b) 14. The length of a chord of a circle is 16 and its distance from the center is 6. Find the length of a diameter of the circle.

Find the perimeter of each polygon below.

15.

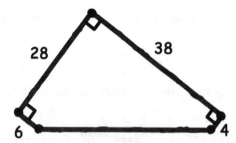

16.

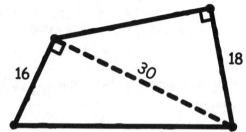

From each given statement below, tell the definition, property, postulate, or theorem that justifies each prove statement.

17. Given: $\overline{RS} \perp \overline{IO}$
Prove: $\overline{RJ} \cong \overline{SJ}$

18. Given: $\overline{RS} \cong \overline{ZV}$
Prove: $\overline{JO} \cong \overline{WO}$

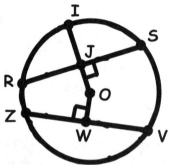

Answer each question below.

19. Find x.   **20.** Find y.   **(c) 21.** Find x. Write your answer as a decimal rounded to 2 places.

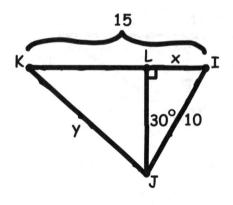

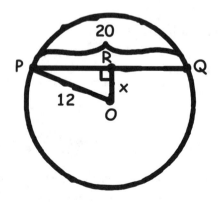

Write an equation to represent each question below; then solve the equation to get your answer.

22. Sandra spotted the sailboat from the shore and measured the angle from the water line to the top of the boat's mast to be 7°. If the top of the mast is 23 feet above the water, how far is the middle of the sailboat from the shore? Estimate your answer to the nearest foot.

(d) 23. Buford needs to make a ramp to load a refrigerator into the bed of his pickup truck. The incline of the ramp can't be more than 27° or the refrigerator will tip over. The bed of the pickup truck is 2 feet above the ground. How long does the ramp need to be? Estimate your answer to two decimal places.

Do each proof below. Number 25 is Theorem 64.

24. Given: $PRST$ is a parallelogram; $\overline{QT} \perp \overline{PR}$; $\overline{RU} \perp \overline{TS}$
Prove: $\overline{PQ} \cong \overline{SU}$

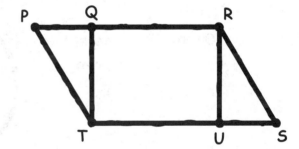

(e) 25. Given: $\overline{FO} \cong \overline{EO}$; $\overline{AB} \perp \overline{FO}$; $\overline{CD} \perp \overline{EO}$
Prove: $\overline{AB} \cong \overline{CD}$

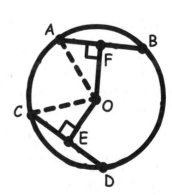

Lesson 83—Theorems on Tangents

In the last lesson, we learned about theorems on the chords of a circle. Now we're going to tackle theorems on tangent lines of a circle. Remember, a tangent line is a line that just intersects the circle at a single point.

Tangent Perpendicular to Radius

Our first theorem is a really important one. We'll explain it with the diagram below. Notice that circle O has a tangent line NP with a point of tangency at P. And inside the circle, there's a radius OP. It turns out that since radius OP intersects the tangent line at the point of tangency, OP has to be perpendicular to the tangent line. In other words, $\angle OPN$ is a right angle. This rule works no matter where a tangent line intersects a circle. Interestingly, the best way to prove this theorem is by the indirect method. Here is the proof (informally), along with the official theorem.

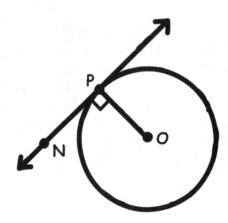

Tangent line NP
is perpendicular
to radius OP.

Given: $\overleftrightarrow{AB}$ is tangent to
$\odot O$ at point A.

Prove: $\overline{OA} \perp \overleftrightarrow{AB}$

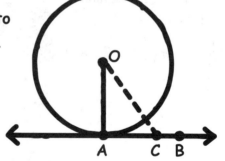

Assume that $\overline{OA}$ is not perpendicular to $\overrightarrow{AB}$. Then, there must be some other segment, $\overline{OC}$, which can be drawn from the center so that it's perpendicular to $\overrightarrow{AB}$. Since $\overline{OC} \perp \overrightarrow{AB}$, OC is the shortest distance from O to $\overrightarrow{AB}$. Therefore, $OC < OA$. But since $\overrightarrow{AB}$ intersects $\odot O$ only at A, C must be on the exterior of the circle. Yet $\overline{OA}$ is a radius, so OA must be less than OC. That contradicts $OC < OA$. Our assumption that $\overline{OA}$ is not perpendicular to $\overrightarrow{AB}$ must be false. Therefore, $\overline{OA} \perp \overrightarrow{AB}$.

Theorem 64	If a radius is drawn to the point of tangency of a tangent line, then the radius is perpendicular to the tangent line.

The reason Theorem 64 is so important is that it's used all the time in science. You may remember a few lessons ago, when we learned how the Greeks measured the distance to the moon with trigonometry. They used Theorem 64 to solve the problem. Look back at the diagrams in that lesson (80), and you'll see the radius of a circle (which represents the earth) drawn to a tangent line. Theorem 64 can help solve lots of other scientific problems, like analyzing the moon orbiting the earth or a planet orbiting the sun. This theorem is even needed to study the motion of a tether ball spinning around a pole. Theorem 64 is useful on just about any problem involving an object moving around in a circle.

Theorem 64 says that if a line is tangent to a circle, then the radius to the point of tangency is perpendicular to the tangent line. But what about the converse? If a radius is perpendicular to a line at the point where the line intersects the circle, does the line have to be a tangent? Yes it does. But of course the converse has to be proven separately. We'll let you do the proof yourself in the problem set. Here's the official theorem, though. It will be our Theorem 65.

Theorem 65	If a radius is perpendicular to a line at the point where the line intersects a circle, then the line is a tangent line.

Two Tangents

There's another theorem on tangents that we should discuss. This one involves two tangent lines rather than one. But they're actually not tangent lines, they're tangent segments. A **tangent segment** is just a tangent to a circle, but instead of being a line that goes on forever, it's a line segment with end points. And importantly, one of those end points is the point of tangency. As shown in the diagram on the right, $\overline{HJ}$ is a line segment but it's also tangent to circle O at point H (the point of tangency). That makes it a tangent segment. Here is the formal definition.

$\overline{HJ}$ is a tangent segment of $\odot O$.

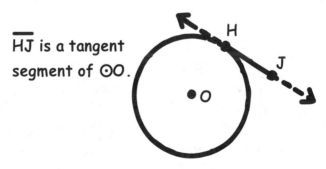

Definition 66	A *tangent segment* is a line segment that has a point on the tangent line and the point of tangency as an end point.

Getting back to our theorem, it turns out that if two tangent segments of a circle share an end point outside the circle, then the segments are congruent. It doesn't matter how long or short the segments are or where the points of tangency are on the circle. A picture is given on the right. Since $\overline{HJ}$ and $\overline{GJ}$ share an end point J, the segments must have the same length. An informal proof of this rule is shown below, along with the official theorem.

HJ and GJ are tangent segments, and HJ = GJ.

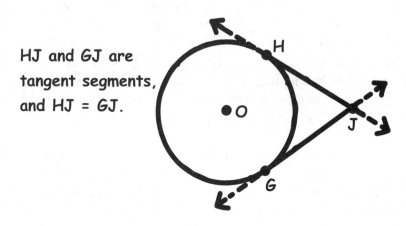

Given: $\overline{LM}$ and $\overline{EM}$ are tangent to $\odot P$ at points L and E.

Prove: $\overline{LM} \cong \overline{EM}$

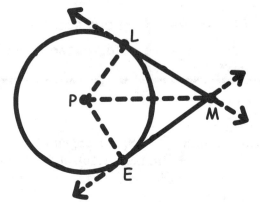

Given that $\overline{LM}$ and $\overline{EM}$ are tangent to $\odot P$, draw $\overline{MP}$ and radii $\overline{PL}$ and $\overline{PE}$. $\angle PLM$ and $\angle PEM$ are right angles (If a radius is drawn to the point of tangency to a tangent line, then the radius is perpendicular to the tangent line.) So $\triangle PLM$ and $\triangle PEM$ are right triangles. $\overline{PL} \cong \overline{PE}$ (All radii of the same circle are congruent.) and $\overline{MP} \cong \overline{MP}$ (Reflexive). Therefore, by Hypotenuse-Leg $\triangle PLM \cong \triangle PEM$. It follows that $\overline{LM} \cong \overline{EM}$ (C.P.C.T.C.).

Theorem 66	If two tangent segments are drawn to a circle from the same exterior point, then they are congruent.

Practice 83

a. Find the missing lengths in right triangle *MNO*. Estimate your answers to two decimal places.

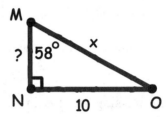

b. In $\triangle QRS$, $QS = 28$, $QR = 17$ and the altitude drawn to QS has a length of 15. Find the length *RS*.

c. Find x (on the right).

d. Quadrilateral *ABCD* and Quadrilateral *EFGH* are similar. If $m\angle D = 73$, $BC = 24$, and the ratio of similitude of *ABCD* to *EFGH* is $6:11$, find $m\angle H$ and *FG*.

e. Do the proof below informally and use the indirect method
   Given: $\overline{KL} \perp \overleftrightarrow{LW}$ at point *L*
   Prove: $\overleftrightarrow{LW}$ is tangent to $\odot K$

Problem Set 83

Tell whether each sentence below is True or False.

1. If a radius is drawn to the point of tangency of a tangent line, then the radius is perpendicular to the tangent line.

2. A tangent segment is a line segment that has a point on the tangent line and on the center of the circle.

Complete each sentence below by filling in the blanks.

3. If two _____ are drawn to a circle from the same exterior point, then they are congruent.

4. In the same circle, _____ equidistant from the center of the circle are congruent.

5. Since all circles have the same shape, they are all _____.

Find the missing lengths in the right triangles below. Estimate your answers to two decimal places.

6.   **7.**   **(a) 8.**

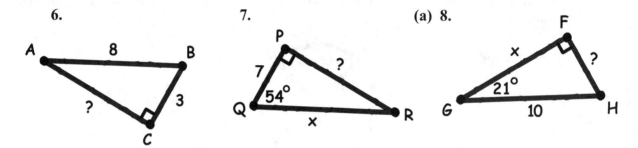

Tell which lines are tangent to each circle below.

9. ⊙O and ⊙P   **10.** ⊙Q and ⊙R

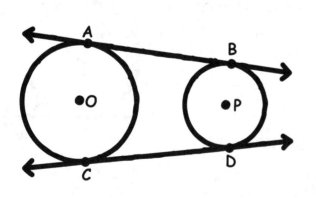
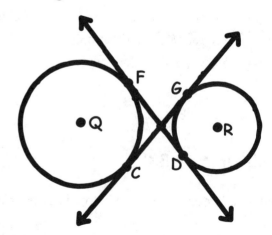

Find the measures of the angles of each triangle described below.

11. Right triangle *CDE* in which the tangent of ∠*C* is 1.

12. An isosceles triangle whose equal sides measure 8 and whose altitude drawn to the base measures 4.

Answer each question below

13. In Δ*FGH*, the exterior angle at *G* measures 105° and the exterior angle at *H* measures 126°. Which is the shortest side of Δ*FGH* ?.

14. In Δ*VBN*, $m\angle N = 90°$, $VB = 4\sqrt{5}$ and *VN* is twice *BN*. What is the length of the shortest side of Δ*VBN* ?

15. Find the perimeter of a rhombus whose diagonals are 48 and 90.

(b) 16. In Δ*HIJ*, $HJ = 14$, $HI = 13$ and the altitude drawn to *HJ* has a length of 12. Find the length *IJ*.

From each given statement below, tell the definition, property, postulate, or theorem that justifies each prove statement.

17. Given: Line ℓ is tangent to circle *P* at point *A*.
Prove: $ℓ \perp \overline{PA}$

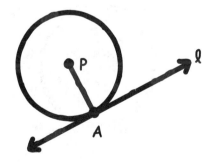

18. Given: $\overline{WV}$ and $\overline{TV}$ are tangent to circle *O*.
Prove: $\overline{WV} \cong \overline{TV}$

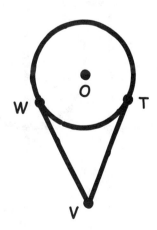

Answer each question below.

19. Find *x*.

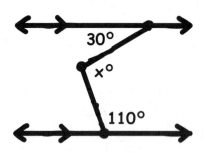

20. Find *y*.

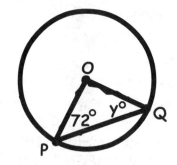

(c) 21. Find *x*.

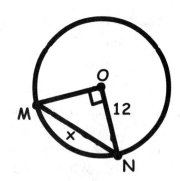

Answer each question below.

22. The shortest side of a triangle is 9 greater than twice the shortest side of a similar triangle. If the ratio of similitude is 7:3, find the lengths of the shortest side of each triangle.

(d) 23. Quadrilateral *KLMN* and Quadrilateral *PRST* are similar. If $m\angle M = 116$, $KN = 9$, and the ratio of similitude of *KLMN* to *PRST* is 3:14, find $m\angle S$ and *PT*.

Do each proof below. Number 25 is Theorem 65. Do an informal proof for problem 25 and use the indirect method.

24. Given: Rectangle *ABCD* and $\odot P$
Prove: $\overleftrightarrow{DC}$ is tangent to $\odot P$

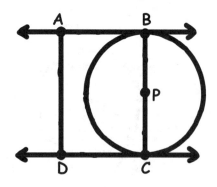

(e) 25. Given: $\overline{OP} \perp \overrightarrow{RP}$ at point *P*
Prove: $\overrightarrow{RP}$ is tangent to $\odot O$

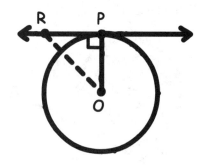

Lesson 84—Arcs and Angles

We've spent several lessons on lines in circles. Now we'll shift gears a bit and focus on angles and curves in circles. Of course, the most obvious curve in a circle is the circle itself. And there are plenty of rules about complete circles, as you know. However, sometimes instead of the complete circle, it's necessary to concentrate on only a part of the circle. A part of a circle is called an **arc**. An example

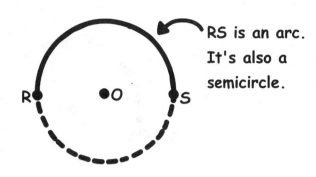

RS is an arc. It's also a semicircle.

is shown on the right. Arc *RS* represents half the circle, which is why it's also called a **semicircle**. Not all arcs are that size, though. An arc that's bigger than a semicircle is called a **major arc**, and an arc that's smaller than a semicircle is called a **minor arc**. Here is an example of each.

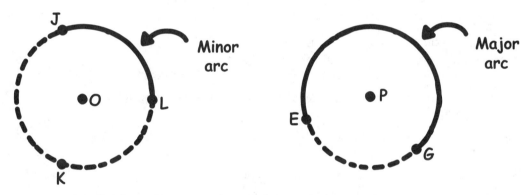

This is the formal definition of an arc.

Definition 67	An *arc* is a portion of a circle consisting of two end points and the set of points on the circle that lie between those points.

It's also important to know how to write an arc properly on paper. We use the end points and put a small arc above those letters. So arc *JL* is written as $\overset{\frown}{JL}$. Interestingly, every pair of points on a circle actually determines two arcs. For instance, in circle *O*, points *J* and *L* are the end points of the minor arc *JL*. But those points are also the end points of a major arc comprised of the rest of the circle (the part that's dashed). Similarly, in circle *P*, points *E* and *G* are the end points of the major arc shown. But they're also the end points of the minor arc, made up of the rest of that circle (the dashed part). Therefore, to avoid confusion, when an arc is written with two letters, we always assume that it represents the minor arc in the circle. That means to write a major arc, we need a third point between the end points. For example, to write the major arc in circle *P* we could add point *F* between *E* and *G* like this.

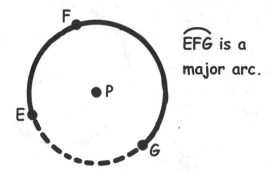

$\overparen{EFG}$ is a major arc.

Now we can write this major arc as $\overparen{EFG}$. The minor arc (the dashed part) would then be written as $\overparen{EG}$, and that eliminates the confusion. It also would have been okay to write $\overparen{EFG}$ as $\overparen{GFE}$ and $\overparen{EG}$ as $\overparen{GE}$. As long as the letters are in order, it doesn't matter which side we start with.

Measuring an Arc

Sometimes we need to be able to measure an arc. There are actually two ways to do the measurement. One way is just to measure the arc's length in inches, centimeters, feet, or whatever. This is called the linear measure of the arc. Using linear measurement, $\overparen{AB}$ on the right is about 1 inch.

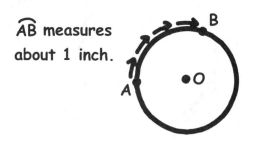

$\overparen{AB}$ measures about 1 inch.

When measuring an arc in this way, the bigger the circle the bigger the arc. For instance, watch what happens when we double the radius of circle *O*.

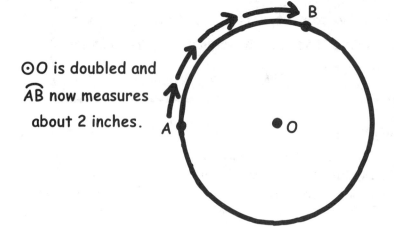

⊙*O* is doubled and $\overparen{AB}$ now measures about 2 inches.

The length of $\overparen{AB}$ has gone up as well. It's now about 2 inches. The point is that the bigger the circle, the longer will be any particular arc. To take an extreme example, a semicircle of the earth's equator is going to be a lot longer than a semicircle of a penny.

We said there are two ways to measure an arc. What's the other way? Well, with the second method, we measure the arc with an angle, in degrees. And interestingly, when using an angle, the size of the circle doesn't affect the measurement one bit. The way it works is that the arc equals the number of degrees of an angle that has its vertex at the center of the circle. Here's $\overset{\frown}{AB}$ again, measured with an angle this time.

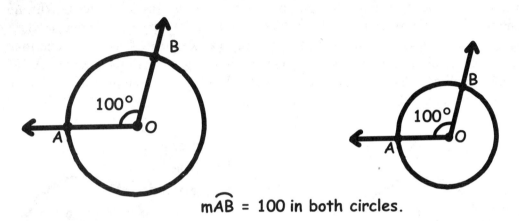

mÂB = 100 in both circles.

See, $\angle AOB$ has its vertex at the center of the circle and its sides cross the end points of the arc. Also, since $\angle AOB$ has a measure of 100 degrees, the measure of $\overset{\frown}{AB}$ has to be 100 degrees as well. That's how we measure an arc using an angle. And notice that $\overset{\frown}{AB}$ is 100 degrees in both the big circle and the small circle. Size makes no difference.

The angle with its vertex at the center of a circle is called a **central angle**. Here's the formal definition.

Definition 68	A *central angle* is an angle whose vertex is at the center of the circle.

And according to our second method of measurement, the degree measure of an arc is defined as the measure of its central angle.

Definition 69	The degree measure of a minor arc is the measure of its central angle.

One other small point is that when writing the measure of an arc in degrees, we put a little *m* in front of the arc symbol. So to show that $\overset{\frown}{AB}$ is 100 degrees, we write $m\overset{\frown}{AB}=100$. And there's

557

no need for a degree symbol after the 100 either. It's very similar to the way we write the measure of an angle.

Why in Degrees?

You may be wondering about the purpose of measuring arcs in degrees. Why not just measure an arc with inches or centimeters? When using a central angle (in degrees), what we're really doing is measuring how far around the circle the arc goes. A 90° arc goes one fourth the way around the entire circle. And that's true no matter how big or small the circle is. A 180° arc is a semicircle which goes half way around the circle. Again, that's true no matter what size the circle is. A 360° arc goes all the way around the circle.

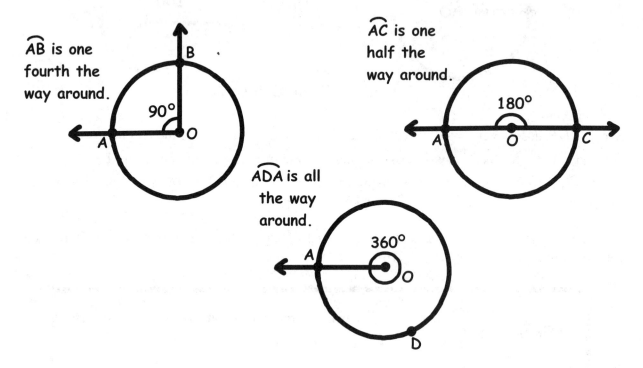

By contrast, when measuring the length of an arc (in inches, centimeters, etc.), we're just measuring the length of that particular arc. And that's going to depend on the size of the circle.

Practice 84

a. Find the degree measure of $\overarc{FG}$ below.

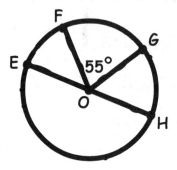

b. The vertex angle of an isosceles triangle measures 48°. If the length of the altitude drawn to the base is 10, find the length of the base and each leg of the triangle. Estimate your answers to 1 decimal place.

c. Find *y*.

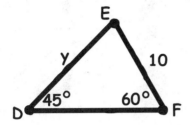

d. Write an equation to represent the question below; then solve the equation to get your answer.

Melvin needs to attach a support wire from the ground to the top of his HAM radio antenna to help hold it upright. He calculated that the best angle for the wire from the ground would be 52°. If the antenna is 39 feet high, how far from the base of the antenna should Melvin stake the wire? Estimate your answer to two decimal places.

e. Do the proof below.

Given: $\overline{MK}$ bisects $\angle JKL$, $\overline{JM} \cong \overline{IJ}$
Prove: $KI \times ML = KM \times IJ$

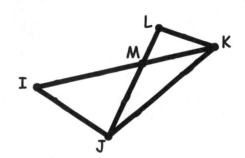

Problem Set 84

Tell whether each sentence below is True or False.

1. A central angle is a portion of a circle consisting of two end points and the set of points on the circle that lie between those points.

2. There are two ways to measure an arc: by linear measure or by degrees (with an angle).

Complete each sentence below by filling in the blanks.

3. A _____ is an angle whose vertex is at the center of the circle.

4. An arc that's longer than a semicircle is called a _____, and an arc that's shorter than a semicircle is called a _____.

5. If a radius is perpendicular to a line at the point at which the line intersects a circle, then the line is a _____.

Name each regular polygon below and find the measure of the interior angle indicated.

6.

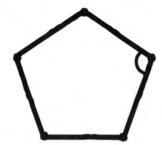

7.

Find the degree measure of each arc or central angle below.

8. ∠*ROS*

(a) 9. $\overset{\frown}{PQ}$

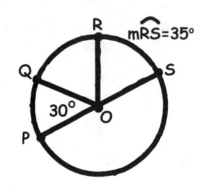

Answer each question below

10. Find the cosine of the largest acute angle of the triangle below. Estimate your answer to 4 decimal places.

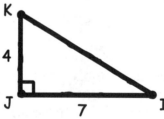

11. In $\triangle MNO$, $\overline{IJ}$ is drawn parallel to $\overline{MN}$ and intersects $\overline{MO}$ and $\overline{NO}$ at *I* and *J*, respectively. If $OI = 5$, $IM = 3$, and $NJ = 4$, find *JO*. Estimate your answer to 1 decimal place.

12. $\triangle HJK$ is a right triangle. $\angle H$ is a right angle and $\angle J$ measures $30°$. If $HK = 5$, find *HJ*.

(b) 13. The vertex angle of an isosceles triangle measures $68°$. If the length of the altitude drawn to the base is 14, find the length of the base and each leg of the triangle. Estimate your answers to 2 decimal places.

Find the perimeter of each polygon below. In 15, estimate your answer to 2 decimal places.

14.

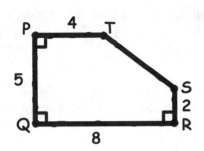

15.

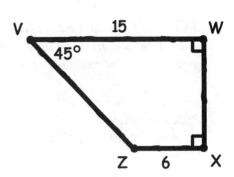

Answer each question below.

(c) 16. Find *x*.

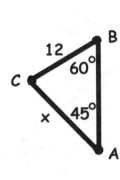

17. Find *y*.

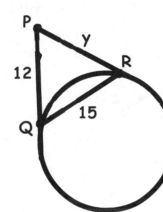

18. Find *x*.

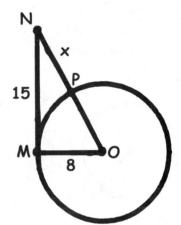

State which shortcut can be used to prove that each pair of triangles below are similar. If no method applies, say "none."

19.

20.

Write an equation to represent each question below; then solve the equation to get your answer. Estimate your answers to two decimal places.

21. Michelle's hamster has gotten too heavy to climb through its tube if it is sloped at more than a 24° angle. If the tube is 32 inches long, how high could Michelle raise the tube at one end so that her hamster can still climb through it?

(d) 22. Kelvin needs to attach a support wire from the ground to the top of his HAM radio antenna to help hold it upright. He calculated that the best angle for the wire from the ground would be 52°. If the antenna is 47 feet high, how long of a wire does Kelvin need?

Do each proof below.

23. Given: $\overrightarrow{JK}$ is tangent to $\odot P$ at J and to $\odot O$ at K.
Prove: $\angle 1 \cong \angle 2$

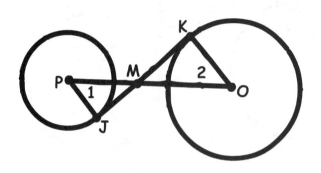

(e) 24. Given: $\overline{EC}$ bisects $\angle BCD$, $\overline{BE} \cong \overline{AB}$
Prove: $CA \times ED = CE \times AB$

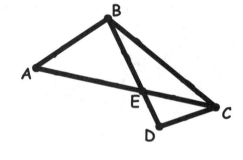

Lesson 85—More on Measuring Arcs

In the last lesson, we learned of the two methods for measuring an arc: by degree measure (with the central angle) and by linear measure, which is just measuring the actual length of the arc. Is it possible to find an arc's length without actually using a tape measure? Yes, but to understand how the process works, we first need to go over the concept of circumference.

Circumference

From earlier math courses, you probably remember that **circumference is the distance completely around a circle**. That means circumference is really just another name for the perimeter of a circle. Here's the formal definition of circumference.

Definition 70	The *circumference* of a circle is the distance around the circle, expressed in linear units of measurement (inches, centimeters, etc.)

To calculate the circumference (C) of a circle, we multiply 2 times the number π times the radius (r):

$$C = 2\pi r.$$

The Greek letter π (pi) is equal to about 3.14. That's not exact, because π is actually an irrational number (like $\sqrt{2}$), and so it can't be written precisely as a decimal or fraction. (That's the reason a Greek letter is used to represent it.) But most calculators have a π button that will give an estimate of π out to quite a few decimal places. Usually two places are enough. So to calculate the circumference of a circle with a radius of 4 inches, we can just put 4 in for r in $2\pi r$ and do the multiplication.

$$C = 2\pi r = 2(3.14)(4)$$

$$C = 25.12$$

The circumference comes out to about 25.12 inches. Again, that's not exact, because we estimated π. The only way to write the exact answer is to simplify $2\pi r$ without estimating π. Doing it that way, we would multiply 2 and 4 to get a circumference of 8π inches.

Using Circumference to find an Arc's Length

So what does the circumference of a circle have to do with calculating the length of an arc? Well, let's say we want to figure out the length of an arc whose central angle is 90°. That means the arc goes one fourth of the way around the circle, remember. If we know that the circumference of the circle is 12 inches, then the 90° arc must go one fourth of that distance around the circle, which means the arc has a length of 3 inches. Similarly, to measure a 180° arc of a circle with a circumference of 14 inches, we just take half of 14 (since 180° is half way around the circle) to get 7 inches.

What if the measure of an arc's central angle is a more unusual number like 32°? Easy. The ratio of the central angle to 360° (which is all the way around the circle) must equal the ratio of the arc's linear measure to the circumference (which also goes all the way around the circle). So we set up a proportion like this.

$$\frac{\text{Arc length (JL)}}{\text{Circumference}} = \frac{\text{Degree measure (32°)}}{360°}$$

If the circumference of the circle were 80 inches, that leaves us with just one unknown (JL)

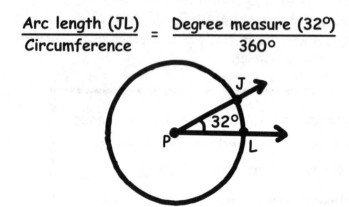

$$\frac{JL}{80} = \frac{32}{360}$$

Now we can cross-multiply and solve normally.

$$360 \times JL = (80)(32)$$

$$360 \times JL = 2,560$$

$$JL = \frac{2,560}{360}$$

$$JL = 7.11...$$

The answer comes out to be 7.11, with the 1s repeating. Rounding to two decimal places, the linear measure of $\overset{\frown}{JL}$ is about 7.11 inches. So if we know the circumference of the circle and the central angle (degree measure) of one of its arcs, we can always find the arc's length. Here's the official rule for doing the calculation.

Arc Length - Degree Measure Proportion

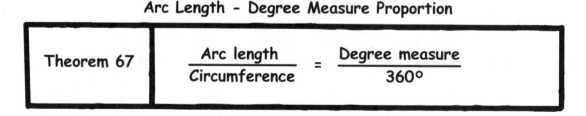

Theorem 67	$\dfrac{\text{Arc length}}{\text{Circumference}} = \dfrac{\text{Degree measure}}{360°}$

One other thing you should know is that sometimes circumference is calculated not using the circle's radius, but with its diameter. Since a diameter is always twice the radius, the equation is $C = \pi d$ (because d is the same as $2r$). Either way, you'll get the same answer.

Arc Addition Postulate

On certain problems, it's important to be able to add two arcs together. The process is pretty straightforward. Let's say we want to add $\overarc{AP}$ with degree measure of $40°$, to another arc, $\overarc{PB}$ (right next to it) with degree measure of $60°$. Common sense says that the total, $\overarc{AB}$, will be $100°$, which is right.

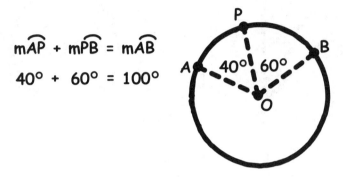

$$m\overarc{AP} + m\overarc{PB} = m\overarc{AB}$$
$$40° + 60° = 100°$$

Even though adding arcs is obvious, we need a postulate to cover it. It's called the Arc Addition Postulate, and it's very similar to Betweenness of Points. The Arc Addition Postulate works as long as the arcs are consecutive. In other words, they must have exactly one point in common. Here's the postulate stated formally.

Arc Addition Postulate

Postulate 18	If P is on $\overarc{AB}$, then $m\overarc{AP} + m\overarc{PB} = m\overarc{AB}$.

Practice 85

a. Find the degree measure of $\overarc{SP}$ below.   b. Find the linear measure of $\overarc{LMN}$ below.

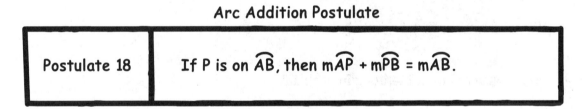

c. $\triangle GHJ \sim \triangle VXZ$ with a ratio of similitude of $5:2$. Also, VZ is 1 less than GH and HJ is 5 more than GJ. If $VX = 6$, what is XZ?

d. If $AB = CB$, find y. Estimate your answer to two decimal places.

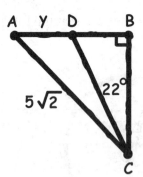

e. Do the proof below.

Given: $\overline{SP}$ is tangent to $\odot O$ at S;

$\overline{RQ}$ is tangent to $\odot O$ at R

Prove: $\triangle QRP \sim \triangle OSP$

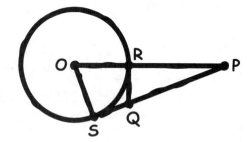

Problem Set 85

Tell whether each sentence below is True or False.

1. The circumference of a circle is the distance around the circle expressed in linear units of measurement (inches, centimeters, etc.)

2. If P is on $\overset{\frown}{AB}$, then $m\overset{\frown}{AP} + m\overset{\frown}{PB} = m\overset{\frown}{AB}$.

Complete each sentence below by filling in the blanks.

3. The Arc length-Degree measure proportion is _____.

4. A part of a circle is called a(n) _____.

5. The degree measure of a (minor) arc is the measure of its _____.

Find the degree measure of each arc or central angle indicated below.

6. $\overset{\frown}{GD}$

7. $\angle COF$

(a) 8. $\overset{\frown}{CD}$

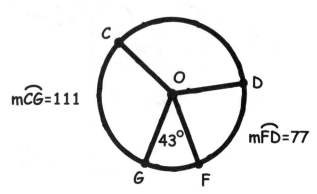

Find the linear measure of each arc indicated below.

9. $\overset{\frown}{ST}$

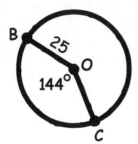

10. $\overset{\frown}{BC}$

(b) 11. $\overset{\frown}{KPL}$

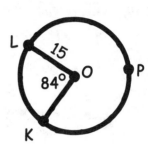

Answer each question below.

12. An isosceles right triangle has legs of length 6. What is the length of the altitude drawn to the hypotenuse?

13. If the vertex angle of an isosceles triangle measures $60°$ and the length of each leg is 18, find the length of the altitude drawn to the base.

(c) 14. $\triangle SDF \sim \triangle RTY$ with a ratio of similitude of $4:9$. Also, SF is 2 less than RT and TY is 9 more than RY. If $SD = 8$, what is DF?

15. In $\triangle JHN$, $m\angle J = x-1$, $m\angle H = 2x+3$, and $m\angle N = 3x-2$ (where $x > 1$). What are the measures of each angle of $\triangle JHN$?

16. Find x.

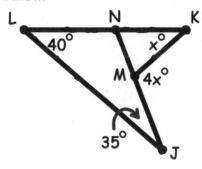

17. Find y.

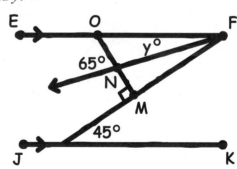

(d) 18. If $JK = LK$, find y. Estimate your answer to two decimal places.

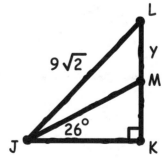

567

From each given statement below, tell the definition, property, postulate, or theorem that justifies each prove statement.

19. Given: $\overline{OG} \perp \overleftrightarrow{FG}$
Prove: $\overleftrightarrow{FG}$ is tangent to $\odot O$

20. Given: $\overline{PL} \cong \overline{PM}$; $\overline{PL} \perp \overline{HK}$; $\overline{PM} \perp \overline{DB}$
Prove: $\overline{DB} \cong \overline{HK}$

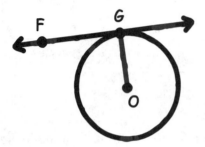

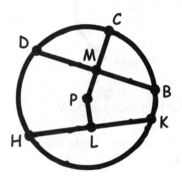

Write a proportion to represent each question below; then solve the proportion to get your answer.

21. The ratio of lampreys to oarfish in the marine aquarium was $27:22$. If there were 162 lampreys in the aquarium, how many oarfish were there?

22. Last basketball season, Nina outscored Toby. In fact, the ratio of Nina's total points to Toby's total points was $17:14$. Altogether, Nina and Toby scored 341 points for the season. How many points did Nina score last season?

Do each proof below.

23. Given: $\overline{HJ} \perp \overline{JK}$; $\overline{JL} \perp \overline{HK}$
Prove: $(HK)^2 - (JK)^2 = HL \times HK$

(e) 24. Given: $\overline{DH}$ is tangent to $\odot O$ at D;
$\overline{FG}$ is tangent to $\odot O$ at F
Prove: $\triangle GFH \sim \triangle ODH$

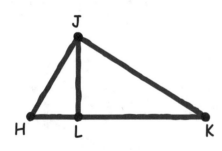

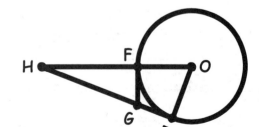

568

Lesson 86—Arcs and Chords

In the last lesson, we learned how arcs and angles are related. Now we're going to look at the connection between arcs and chords.

Congruent Arcs

But first we need to define congruent arcs. Those are arcs with the same shape and size (just as congruent figures are figures with the same shape and size). An example is given on the right. Arcs *AB* and *CD* are congruent, because their degree measures are the same—both are 55 degrees. But there's something else about them that must be true, before we can say for sure that the arcs are congruent. They also need to be in the same circle or in congruent circles (that have the same radius). Both $\overarc{AB}$ and $\overarc{CD}$ are in circle *O*, so they're definitely congruent. The reason for this second requirement is that even two arcs that have the same degree measure won't be congruent, if they're in different size circles. Check out the two arcs below, for example.

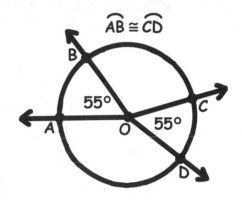

$\overarc{AB} \cong \overarc{CD}$

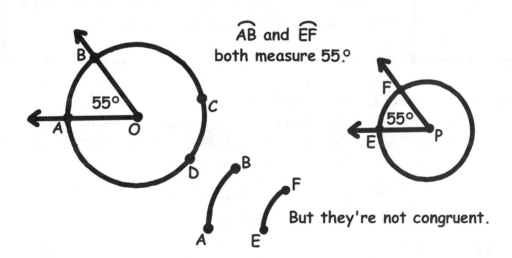

$\overarc{AB}$ and $\overarc{EF}$
both measure 55.°

But they're not congruent.

$\overarc{AB}$ and $\overarc{EF}$ both have a degree measure of 55°. But when they're shown right next to each other, it's easy to see that $\overarc{AB}$ is longer than $\overarc{EF}$, which means the arcs aren't congruent. The problem is that circle *O* is larger than circle *P*. So **congruent arcs** not only must have the same degree measure, but they also need to be in the same or congruent circles. Here's the formal definition.

Definition 71	*Congruent arcs* are arcs in the same or congruent circles which have the same degree measure.

Once congruent arcs are defined, the definition of the midpoint of an arc is really easy. The midpoint is just the point on an arc that divides it into two congruent arcs. Here's a quick example, followed by the formal definition.

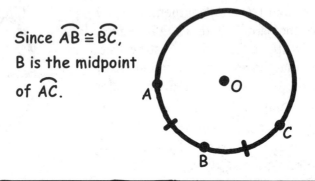

Since $\overarc{AB} \cong \overarc{BC}$, B is the midpoint of $\overarc{AC}$.

Definition 72	The *midpoint of an arc* is the point on the arc which divides the arc into two congruent arcs.

Congruent Chords Means Congruent Arcs

Now we're ready to talk about the connection between arcs and chords. Every chord of a circle determines or "cuts off" two arcs—a minor arc and a major arc. Here are a couple of examples.

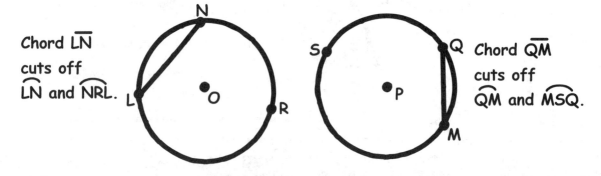

Chord $\overline{LN}$ cuts off $\overarc{LN}$ and $\overarc{NRL}$.

Chord $\overline{QM}$ cuts off $\overarc{QM}$ and $\overarc{MSQ}$.

Chord $\overline{LN}$ in the circle on the left has its end points at L and N, which are also the end points of arc LN. So $\overline{LN}$ "cuts off" minor arc $\overarc{LN}$. But L and N are also the end points of a major arc,

$\overparen{NRL}$, which means that chord $\overline{LN}$ cuts off $\overparen{NRL}$ too. We see the same thing in the circle on the right, where chord $\overline{QM}$ cuts off minor arc $\overparen{QM}$ and major arc $\overparen{MSQ}$.

A chord and the minor arc that it cuts off are related: the longer the chord, the longer the arc. The rule is that two congruent chords in the same circle (or congruent circles) always cut off congruent arcs. Let's look at an example given on the right. Since chords $\overline{LN}$ and $\overline{TR}$ are congruent, $\overparen{LN}$ and $\overparen{TR}$ (the arcs they cut off) must also be congruent. The nice thing about this rule is that we can use it to prove two arcs are congruent, without knowing their measures. Here's an informal proof of the rule, followed by the theorem.

Chord $\overline{LN}$ and chord $\overline{TR}$ are congruent, so $\overparen{LN}$ and $\overparen{TR}$ are congruent.

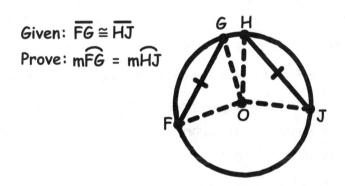

Given: $\overline{FG} \cong \overline{HJ}$
Prove: $m\overparen{FG} = m\overparen{HJ}$

$\overline{FG} \cong \overline{HJ}$ (Given). Draw radii $\overline{OG}$, $\overline{OH}$, $\overline{OF}$, and $\overline{OJ}$. $\overline{OG} \cong \overline{OH}$ and $\overline{OF} \cong \overline{OJ}$. (All radii in the same circle are congruent.) So $\triangle FGO \cong \triangle JHO$ (S.S.S.). That means $\angle FOG \cong \angle JOH$ (C.P.C.T.C.). Therefore, it follows that $m\overparen{FG} = m\overparen{HJ}$ (The degree measure of a minor arc is the measure of its central angle.)

Theorem 68	If two chords of the same circle or congruent circles are congruent, then their minor arcs are congruent.

The converse of Theorem 68 is also true. The converse says that if we know that two arcs in the same circle (or congruent circles) are congruent, then the chords that cut off those arcs also have to be congruent. Here's the proof of the converse (and the theorem).

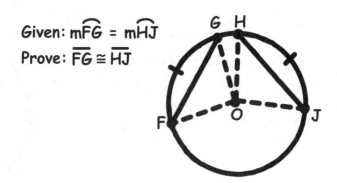

Given: $m\overarc{FG} = m\overarc{HJ}$
Prove: $\overline{FG} \cong \overline{HJ}$

Draw radii $\overline{OG}$, $\overline{OH}$, $\overline{OF}$, and $\overline{OJ}$. That means $\overline{OG} \cong \overline{OH}$ and $\overline{OF} \cong \overline{OJ}$. (All radii in the same circle are congruent.) $m\overarc{FG} = m\angle FOG$ and $m\overarc{HJ} = m\angle JOH$ (The degree measure of a minor arc is the measure of its central angle.) Since $m\overarc{FG} = m\overarc{HJ}$ (Given), $m\angle FOG = m\angle JOH$ (Substitution). Therefore, $\triangle FGO \cong \triangle JHO$ by S.A.S. It follows by C.P.C.T.C. that $\overline{FG} \cong \overline{HJ}$.

Theorem 69	If two minor arcs of the same or congruent circles are congruent, then their intersecting chords are congruent.

Practice 86

a. Find the degree measure of $\overarc{HIF}$ in $\odot O$. $\overline{FI}$ is a diameter of the circle.

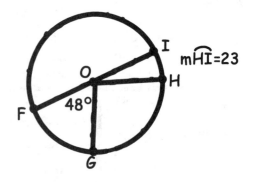

mĤÎ=23

48°

b. Find the linear measure of minor arc JK on $\odot O$, where $OK = 7$ and $m\angle KOJ = 62$. Estimate your answer to two decimal places.

c. If $b = 4a$, find y. Write your answer as a decimal rounded to 2 places.

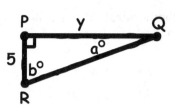

d. The weather report said that the wall cloud was at an altitude of 2,000 feet. From the barn, Farmer Brown measured the angle of the wall cloud above the horizon to be 12°. How many miles away was the wall cloud? Estimate your answer to two decimal places. (1 mile = 5,280 feet)

e. Do the proof below.

Given: $\overline{QS} \perp \overline{PR}$

Prove: $\overarc{PQ} \cong \overarc{RQ}$

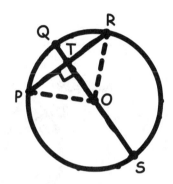

Problem Set 86

Tell whether each sentence below is True or False.

1. Congruent arcs are arcs in the same or congruent circles which have the same degree measure.

2. The midpoint of an arc is the center of the circle that contains the arc.

Complete each sentence below by filling in the blanks.

3. If two _____ of the same or congruent circles are _____, then their minor arcs are congruent.

4. If a line through the center of a circle is _____ to a chord, it also bisects the chord.

5. In the same circle, _____ equidistant from the center of the circle are congruent.

Tell whether each of the following parts of circle O is a radius, diameter, chord, tangent line, or secant line.

6. $\overline{PQ}$

7. $\overleftrightarrow{RS}$

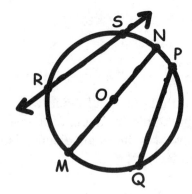

Find the degree measure of each arc or central angle below. $\overline{AD}$ is a diameter of $\odot O$.

8. $\angle BOC$

(a) 9. $\overarc{CDA}$

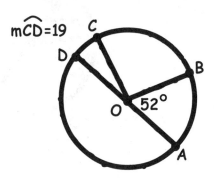

Find the linear measure of each arc described below. Estimate your answers to two decimal places.

(b) 10. Minor arc WV on $\odot O$, where $OV = 9$ and $m\angle WOV = 71$.

11. $\overarc{CD}$ on a circle of diameter 34, where central angle CPD measures $121°$.

Use proportions to find the missing values below. Write your answer as a decimal rounded to 2 places.

12. Find x.

13. Find y.

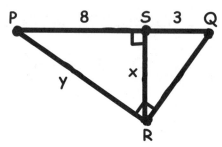

Answer each question below.

14. $\triangle BCD \sim \triangle PRQ$ and the ratio of each pair of corresponding sides of the triangles is $16:7$. If the length of altitude $\overline{CE}$ is $2x+4$ and the length of altitude $\overline{RS}$ is $x-1$, find CE and RS.

15. Quadrilateral $FGHJ \sim$ quadrilateral $WXYZ$. The lengths of the sides of $FGHJ$ are 12, 30, 18, and 24. If $FJ = 24$ and $WZ = 34$, what is the perimeter of quadrilateral $WXYZ$?

Find the perimeter of each polygon below. Estimate your answers to two decimal places.

16.

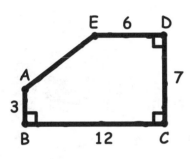

17.

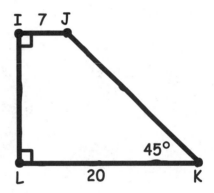

Answer each question below.

18. Find x.

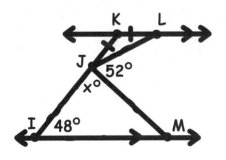

19. If GH is tangent to $\odot O$, find x.

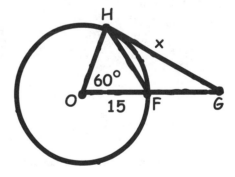

(c) 20. If $b = 4a$, find y. Write your answer as a decimal rounded to 2 places.

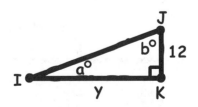

Write an equation to represent each question below; then solve the equation to get your answer. Estimate your answers to two decimal places.

21. Marcy rowed her boat across the lake and wanted to know how far she had rowed. She spotted her father standing on the shore across the lake where she had started. She measured the angle from the shore to the top of her father's head to be 2°. If her father was 6 feet tall, how far was it across the lake?

(d) 22. The weather report said that the wall cloud was at an altitude of 3,000 feet. From the barn, Farmer Jones measured the angle of the wall cloud above the horizon to be 11°. How many miles away was the wall cloud? (1 mile = 5,280 feet)

Do each proof below. Number 24 will be our Theorem 70.

23. Given: $OP > PR$
    Prove: $m\widehat{QR} > m\widehat{PR}$

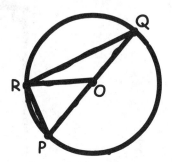

(e) 24. Given: $\overline{IJ} \perp \overline{KL}$
    Prove: $\widehat{KI} \cong \widehat{IL}$

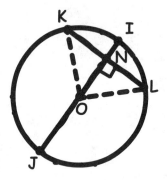

Theorem 70	In a circle, a diameter drawn perpendicular to a chord bisects the minor arc that the chord intercepts.

Lesson 87—Inscribed Angles

We've learned about central angles, which are angles with their vertex at the center of a circle. But it's also possible for angles to have their vertex at different places in the circle. Take the angle on the right, for example. See, the vertex of $\angle A$ is not at the center of circle O; it's on the circle itself. Angles of this type are called **inscribed angles**. The word inscribed means "inside of." Here's the formal definition.

∠A has its vertex on the circle itself.

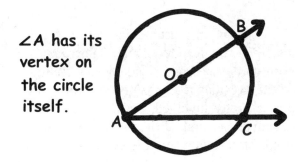

Definition 73	An *inscribed angle* is an angle whose vertex is on a circle and whose sides are chords (or secants) of the circle.

Inscribed Angle = ½Arc

We know that a central angle has the same measure as the minor arc it cuts off. Inscribed angles also cut off or "intercept" a minor arc: $\angle A$ intercepts $\overset{\frown}{BC}$. How do you think the measure of $\angle A$ compares to $\overset{\frown}{BC}$? To figure this out, let's draw in a central angle that cuts off $\overset{\frown}{BC}$ as well (on the right). Then we can compare the two. We'll say that the central angle measures $60°$. Since $m\angle BOC$ is a central angle, we know that $m\angle BOC = m\overset{\frown}{BC} = 60$. And it's not too hard to see that $m\angle A$ is less than $m\angle BOC$.

That means $m\angle A$ must be less than $m\overset{\frown}{BC}$. The question is how much less. Well, $\angle BOC$ is an exterior angle of $\triangle AOC$. And since exterior angles equal the sum of the two remote interior angles, $m\angle BOC = m\angle A + m\angle C$. And

m∠A is less than mB̂C.

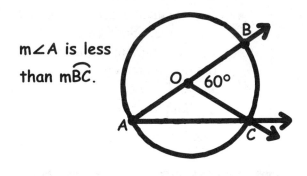

since $m\angle BOC = 60$, $m\angle A + m\angle C = 60$. But because $\overline{OA}$ and $\overline{OC}$ are radii (and congruent), $\triangle AOC$ has to be an isosceles triangle, Therefore, the base angles, $\angle A$ and $\angle C$, are congruent, with each of those measuring $30°$.

So $m\angle A = 30$ and $m\widehat{BC} = 60$. The inscribed angle is one-half the arc that it intercepts.

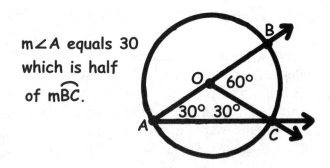

m∠A equals 30 which is half of m$\widehat{BC}$.

That wasn't just a coincidence. Any inscribed angle, no matter where its position on the circle, is equal to one-half of the arc that it intercepts. A proof of this is pretty involved, because we have to cover several different cases. The simplest case is where the center of the circle lies on one side of the inscribed angle. That was the situation in our example (since O was on $\overline{AB}$). The other cases are when the circle's center is inside the inscribed angle and when it's outside the inscribed angle. We'll show an informal proof of just the first case.

Given: ∠RST is inscribed in ⊙O.

Prove: $m\angle RST = \dfrac{1}{2} m\widehat{RT}$

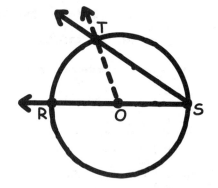

Draw $\overrightarrow{OT}$. Since $OS = OT$ (All radii of the same circle are equal.), then $m\angle OTS = m\angle RST$ (Base Angles Theorem). But we know that $m\angle OTS + m\angle RST = m\angle ROT$ (The measure of an exterior angle of a triangle is equal to the sum of the measures of the two remote interior angles.) Therefore, by substitution we have $m\angle RST + m\angle RST = m\angle ROT$ or $2m\angle RST = m\angle ROT$. Multiplying both sides by $\frac{1}{2}$, we get $m\angle RST = \frac{1}{2}m\angle ROT$. However, since $m\angle ROT = m\widehat{RT}$, we have $m\angle RST = \frac{1}{2}m\widehat{RT}$.

Theorem 71	An inscribed angle is equal in measure to one-half the measure of its intercepted arc.

Two Quick Corollaries

There are two corollaries to Theorem 71 that we should show you. The first is pretty obvious. It says that if inscribed angles intercept the same arc or congruent arcs, then the angles are congruent. On the right is a picture, and below is the official corollary.

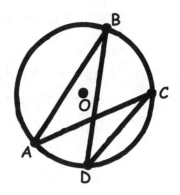

$\angle A \cong \angle D$ because they both cut off the same arc: $\overarc{BC}$.

Corollary 71.1	Inscribed angles that intercept the same or congruent arcs are congruent.

Another interesting corollary to Theorem 71 says that if an inscribed angle happens to cut off an arc that's a semicircle, then the inscribed angle must be a right angle. That's because a semicircle has a measure of 180°, remember, and the inscribed angle always has to equal half the measure of the arc it intercepts. Here's the official corollary.

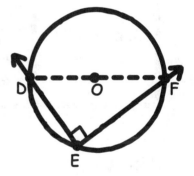

Since $\overarc{DF}$ is a semicircle, inscribed angle $\angle DEF$ is a right angle.

Corollary 71.2	An inscribed angle that intercepts a semicircle is a right angle.

One Side is a Tangent

We'll show you one last rule pertaining to inscribed angles. This one's a little more complicated. We know that an inscribed angle has to equal half of its intercepted arc. But imagine the angle becoming bigger and bigger until one of its sides is just tangent to the circle.

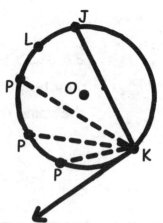

∠JKP is inscribed in ⊙O.

As P moves down, it eventually gets to K.

But ∠JKP is still half of $\overset{\frown}{JLK}$.

See, as P goes lower on the circle, $\angle JKP$ gets bigger. When P makes it all the way down to K, the bottom side of $\angle K$ becomes tangent to the circle. But, interestingly, that doesn't change the fact that the inscribed angle still equals half the intercepted arc. So $m\angle JKP$ is half of $m\overset{\frown}{JLK}$. We'll show you the formal theorem, but the proof is saved for the problem set.

Theorem 72	The measure of an angle formed by a tangent and a chord drawn to the point of tangency is equal to one-half the measure of the inter-cepted arc.

Practice 87

a. Find the degree measure of $\overset{\frown}{EG}$.

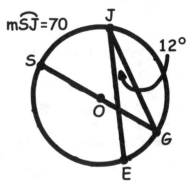

b. Find the linear measure of the arc described below. Estimate your answer to one decimal place.

$\overset{\frown}{DFE}$ on ⊙O, where $\overline{DF}$ is a diameter, $OF = 24$, and $m\angle DOE = 135$.

c. If the length of the diagonal of a square is $2\sqrt{6}$, find the perimeter of the square.

d. Find x.

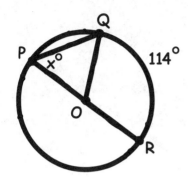

e. Given: $m\overset{\frown}{IJK} = m\overset{\frown}{LKJ}$
Prove: $m\angle IKJ = m\angle LJK$

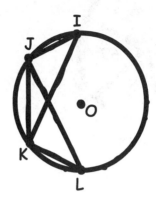

Problem Set 87

Tell whether each sentence below is True or False.

1. An inscribed angle is an angle whose vertex is on a circle and whose sides are chords (or secants) of the circle.

2. An inscribed angle is equal in measure to the measure of its intercepted arc.

Complete each sentence below by filling in the blanks.

3. Inscribed angles that intercept the same arc are _____.

4. If two _____ of the same or congruent circles are _____, then their intersecting chords are congruent.

5. A _____ line is a line which intersects a circle in two different points.

Find the degree measure of each arc or angle below.

6. $\overset{\frown}{ADC}$ **7.** $\angle KLR$ **(a) 8.** $\overset{\frown}{PL}$

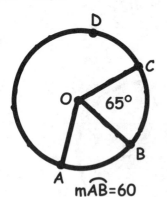

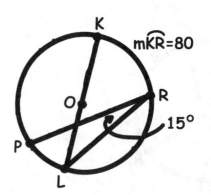

Find the linear measure of each arc described below. Estimate your answers to two decimal places.

9. $\overset{\frown}{SR}$ on $\odot P$, where $PR = 27$ and $m\angle RPS = 101°$.

(b) 10. $\overset{\frown}{KML}$ on $\odot O$, where $\overline{KM}$ is a diameter, $OM = 36$, and $m\angle KOL = 145°$.

Answer each question below.

(c) 11. If the length of the diagonal of a square is $5\sqrt{6}$, find the perimeter of the square.

12. In right $\triangle CDG$, $\angle C$ is a right angle and $m\angle D = 30$. If $CG = 11$, find DG.

13. In $\triangle KNP$, the exterior angle at P measures $114°$ and the exterior angle at K measures $131°$. Which is the longest side of $\triangle KNP$?

14. In $\triangle CDE$, $m\angle C = 90°$, $CD = 15$ and DE is 3 more than CE. What is the length of the longest side of $\triangle CDE$?

From each given statement below, tell the definition, property, postulate, or theorem that justifies each prove statement.

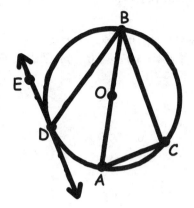

15. Given: $\overline{AB}$ is a diameter of $\odot O$.
Prove: $\angle ACB$ is a right angle.

16. Given: $\overrightarrow{ED}$ is tangent to $\odot O$ at point D.
Prove: $m\angle EDB = \dfrac{1}{2}m\widehat{DB}$

Answer each question below.

17. Find x.

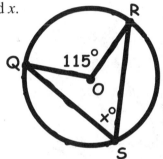

18. Find y.

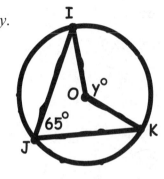

19. Find x.

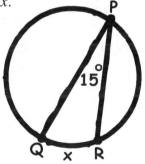

(d) 20. Find x.

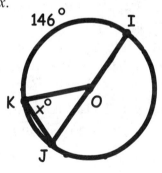

Write an equation to represent each question below; then solve the equation to get your answer. Estimate your answers to two decimal places.

21. The longest side of a triangle is 12 more than three times the longest side of a similar triangle. If the ratio of similitude is $11:3$, find the length of the longest side of each triangle.

22. Quadrilateral $ABCD$ and Quadrilateral $GHIJ$ are similar. If $m\angle B = 103°$, $DA = 28$, $CB = 14$, and $IH = 24$, find $m\angle H$ and JG.

583

Do the proof below.

(e) 23.   Given: $m\widehat{ABC} = m\widehat{DCB}$
Prove: $m\angle ACB = m\angle DBC$

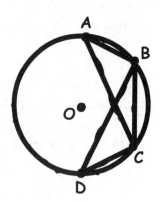

Fill in the blanks of the proof below. This is our Theorem 72.

24.   Given: $\overrightarrow{AC}$ is tangent to $\odot O$

Prove: $m\angle BAC = \dfrac{1}{2}m\widehat{AB}$

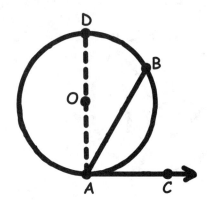

(1) Draw $\overleftrightarrow{DA}$ through center O (Two points determine a line.)
(2) $\overrightarrow{AC} \perp \overleftrightarrow{AD}$ (_____)
(3) $\angle DAC$ is a right angle. (Perpendicular lines intersect to form right angles.)
(4) $m\angle DAC = 90$ (Definition of right angle)
(5) $2m\angle DAC = 180$ (Multiplication)
(6) $m\widehat{DBA} = 180$ (Definition of semicircle)
(7) $m\widehat{DB} + m\widehat{BA} = m\widehat{DBA}$ (_____)
(8) $m\widehat{DB} + m\widehat{BA} = 2m\angle DAC$ (Substitution)
(9) $\frac{1}{2}m\widehat{DB} + \frac{1}{2}m\widehat{BA} = m\angle DAC$ (_____)
(10) $m\angle DAB = \frac{1}{2}m\widehat{DB}$ (_____)
(11) $m\angle DAB + \frac{1}{2}m\widehat{BA} = m\angle DAC$ (_____)
(12) $\frac{1}{2}m\widehat{BA} = m\angle DAC - m\angle DAB$ (_____)
(13) $m\angle DAC = m\angle DAB + m\angle BAC$ (_____)
(14) $m\angle DAC - m\angle DAB = m\angle BAC$ (_____)
(15) $m\angle BAC = \frac{1}{2}m\widehat{BA}$ (_____)

Lesson 88—Vertex Inside and Outside

We've been studying the relationship between angles and the arcs of circles. And so far we've learned about angles whose vertex is at the center of a circle and angles whose vertex is on the circle itself. What about angles where the vertex is in other places?

Vertex Inside

Well, take a look at the circles below.

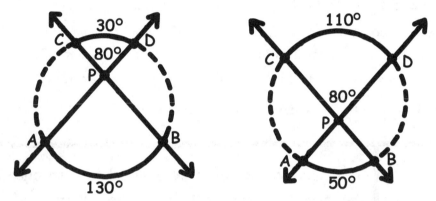

m∠CPD is equal to the sum of m$\widehat{CD}$ and m$\widehat{AB}$ multiplied by $\frac{1}{2}$.

Both of these diagrams have secants intersecting inside the circle at point P. But P is not at the center of the circle. Nor is it on the circle itself. Notice also that the angle at P is 80° in both circles. Basically, the only difference between the circles is that the secants are higher on the left than they are on the right. That puts the point of intersection in a different place in each circle.

But here's the question. What is the relationship between $\widehat{CD}$, $\widehat{AB}$, and ∠CPD? Basically, the measure of ∠CPD is the average of the measure of the two arcs. In the circle on the left, $m\widehat{CD} = 30$ and $m\widehat{AB} = 130$. Adding those (30 + 130) and multiplying by $\frac{1}{2}$ gives 80, which is the measure of ∠CPD. It's the same with the circle on the right. There, $m\widehat{CD} = 110$ and $m\widehat{AB} = 50$. Adding those (110 + 50) and multiplying by $\frac{1}{2}$ gives 80 again. Of course, since ∠CPD and ∠APB are vertical angles, the measure of ∠APB is also 80. So, really, the angles opening up to each arc must equal the average of those arcs.

Probably the most interesting thing is that this rule holds true no matter where the point of intersection is inside the circle. It can be anywhere. Here's an informal proof of this rule followed by the official theorem.

Given: Chords SR and QN

intersect at L.

Prove: $m\angle QLR = \frac{1}{2}(m\overset{\frown}{QR} + m\overset{\frown}{SN})$

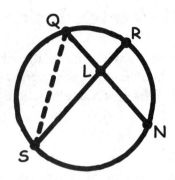

Draw $\overline{QS}$. $m\angle QLR = m\angle S + m\angle SQN$ (Exterior Angle of a Triangle Theorem). Also, $m\angle S = \frac{1}{2}m\overset{\frown}{QR}$ and $m\angle SQN = \frac{1}{2}m\overset{\frown}{SN}$ (An inscribed angle is equal in measure to one-half the measure of its intercepted arc.) Then, we get $m\angle QLR = \frac{1}{2}m\overset{\frown}{QR} + \frac{1}{2}m\overset{\frown}{SN}$ (Substitution). And finally, $m\angle QLR = \frac{1}{2}(m\overset{\frown}{QR} + m\overset{\frown}{SN})$ (Distributive).

Theorem 73	The measure of an angle formed by two chords (or secants) intersecting in the interior of a circle is equal to one-half the sum of the measures of the two intercepted arcs.

Vertex Outside

What's the relationship between the angle and the intercepted arcs when the vertex is completely outside the circle? Well, take a look.

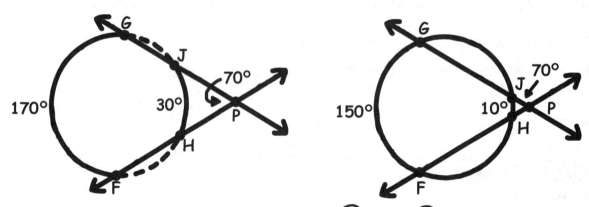

$m\angle JPH$ is equal to the difference of $m\overset{\frown}{GF}$ and $m\overset{\frown}{JH}$ divided by 2.

The vertex of $\angle JPH$ is outside the circle in both cases. And this time the pattern is to take the difference between the arcs and divide by 2. In the circle on the left, $m\overset{\frown}{GF} = 170$ and $m\overset{\frown}{JH} = 30$. Subtracting those $(170 - 30)$ and multiplying by $\frac{1}{2}$ gives us 70, which is the measure of $\angle JPH$. It works the same way for the circle on the right. With $m\overset{\frown}{GF} = 150$ and $m\overset{\frown}{JH} = 10$, we subtract $(150 - 10)$, and then multiply by $\frac{1}{2}$ to get 70 again. Here's an informal proof of this rule and then the official theorem.

Given: Secants AP and BP
intersect at P.

Prove: $m\angle BPA = \frac{1}{2}(m\overset{\frown}{AB} - m\overset{\frown}{CD})$

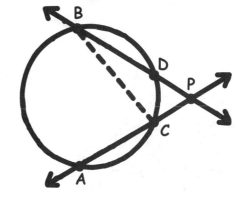

Draw $\overline{BC}$. $m\angle ACB = m\angle B + m\angle BPA$ (Exterior Angle of a Triangle Theorem). It follows that $m\angle ACB - m\angle B = m\angle BPA$ (Subtraction). But $m\angle ACB = \frac{1}{2}m\overset{\frown}{AB}$ and $m\angle B = \frac{1}{2}m\overset{\frown}{CD}$. (An inscribed angle is equal in measure to one-half the measure of its intercepted arc.) That means $m\angle BPA = \frac{1}{2}m\overset{\frown}{AB} - \frac{1}{2}m\overset{\frown}{CD}$ (Substitution). Finally, $m\angle BPA = \frac{1}{2}(m\overset{\frown}{AB} - m\overset{\frown}{CD})$ (Distributive).

Theorem 74	The measure of an angle formed by two secants (or tangents) intersecting in the exterior of a circle is equal to one-half the difference of the measures of the two intercepted arcs.

Notice that the theorem applies not just to secants but also to tangents. That means one or both of the lines can be tangents and the theorem will still work. Look at the following diagrams.

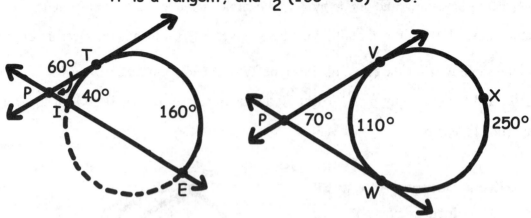

TP is a tangent, and $\frac{1}{2}(160 - 40) = 60$.

VP and WP are tangents, and $\frac{1}{2}(250 - 110) = 70$.

Practice 88

a. What is the length of a diagonal of a square whose side length is $\sqrt{8}$?

b. Find the degree measure of $\angle QPR$.

c. Find x.

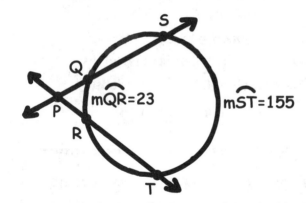

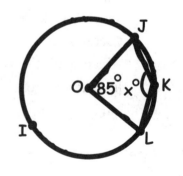

d. Find z.

e. Do the proof below.
   Given: $\overline{QS} \perp \overline{PR}$

   Prove: $m\widehat{RQ} = m\widehat{PQ}$

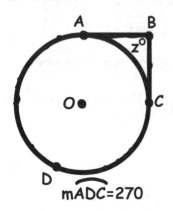

Problem Set 88

Tell whether each sentence below is True or False.

1. The measure of an angle formed by two chords (or secants) intersecting in the interior of a circle is equal to one-half the sum of the measures of the two intercepted arcs.

2. The measure of an angle formed by two secants (or tangents) intersecting in the exterior of a circle equals one-half the difference of the measures of the two intercepted arcs.

Complete each sentence below by filling in the blanks.

3. An inscribed angle that intercepts a _____ is a right angle.

4. If a radius is drawn to the point of tangency of a tangent line, then the radius is _____ to the tangent line.

5. The measure of an angle formed by a tangent and a chord drawn to the point of tangency is equal to _____ the measure of the intercepted arc.

Find the degree measure of each arc or angle below.

6. $\overset{\frown}{JK}$

7. $\angle JLK$

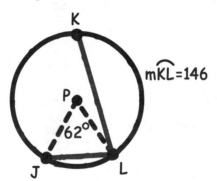

Calculate each ratio below.

8. Sam ate two corn dogs and five caramel apples at the fair. If corn dogs cost $2.25 each and caramel apples cost 95 cents a piece, what is the ratio of the total cost of corn dogs to the total cost of caramel apples? Write your answer in the form $a:b$, where a and b are whole numbers.

9. The new action comedy is 88 minutes long. The award-winning historical drama is 2.8 hours long. What is the ratio of the length of the drama to the length of the comedy? Write your answer in the form $a:b$, where a and b are whole numbers.

Answer each question below.

10. In $\triangle TUV$, $m\angle T = 21$ and $m\angle V$ is one-half $m\angle U$. What is the measure of the angle opposite the longest side of $\triangle TUV$?

(a) 11. What is the length of a diagonal of a square whose side length is $\sqrt{3}$?

Find the degree measure of each arc or angle below.

12. $\angle APB$

(b) 13. $\angle JPH$

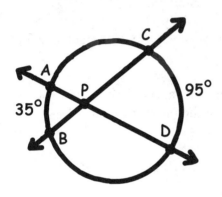

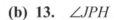

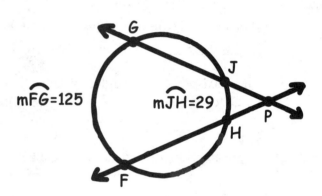

Find the perimeter of each polygon below.

14.

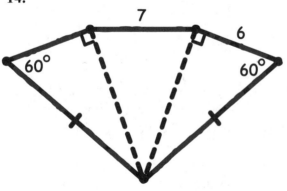

15.

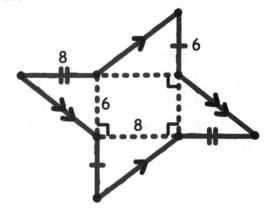

590

From each given statement below, tell the definition, property, postulate, or theorem that justifies each prove statement.

16. Given: $\overleftrightarrow{PS}$ and $\overleftrightarrow{QR}$ intersect at T

Prove: $m\angle RTS = \dfrac{1}{2}(m\widehat{RS} + m\widehat{PQ})$

17. Given: $\overleftrightarrow{NS}$ and $\overleftrightarrow{NR}$ intersect at N

Prove: $m\angle LNP = \dfrac{1}{2}(m\widehat{RS} - m\widehat{PL})$

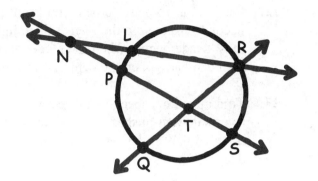

Answer each question below.

18. If $m\widehat{GH} = 54$, find d.

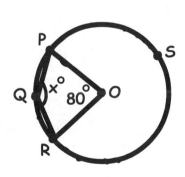

19. Find s.

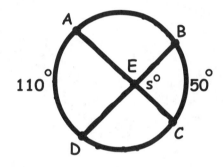

(c) 20. Find x.

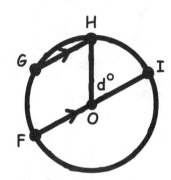

(d) 21. Find z.

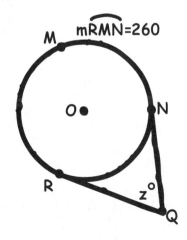

591

Write an equation to represent each question below; then solve the equation to get your answer. Estimate your answers to two decimal places.

22. Patty wants to plant some petunias in front of a 3-foot-high brick wall in her garden but needs to make sure they get full sunlight all summer. She noticed last summer that the most shade occurs when the sun is at a 29° angle above the horizon. How close to the wall can Patty plant the petunias and still be sure they are in full sunlight all summer?

23. Tom aimed his speedboat directly across the river at the dock on the other side. But the river's current pushed him off course by 52°. The odometer reading shows that the boat traveled 0.49 miles. How far does Tom need to walk along the riverbank to reach the dock?

Do each proof below.

24. Given: $m\widehat{AE} + m\widehat{DC} = 180°$
     Prove: $\overline{AC} \perp \overline{DE}$

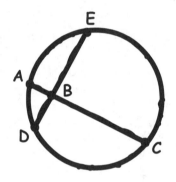

(e) 25. Given: $\overline{BE} \perp \overline{AC}$
        Prove: $m\widehat{CB} = m\widehat{AB}$

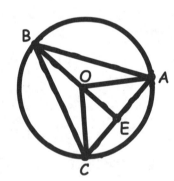

Lesson 89—Segment Products Inside and Out

We've learned that the angles formed by intersecting lines in circles are related to the arcs that they cut off. As it turns out, the line segments themselves are related to each other in interesting ways.

Products Inside

Look at the diagram below.

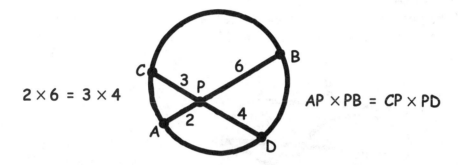

$2 \times 6 = 3 \times 4$

$AP \times PB = CP \times PD$

When chords *AB* and *CD* intersect, four line segments are created: *AP*, *PB*, *CP*, and *PD*. And if you look at the lengths of those segments, the pattern is clear. The product of the segments in the two chords are equal. And amazingly, this works no matter where the chords intersect inside the circle. The proof is actually fairly easy. Here is an informal version, along with the official theorem.

Given: Chords GH and JK
intersect at P.

Prove: GP × PH = JP × PK

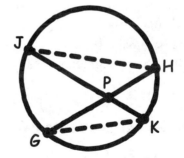

Draw $\overline{JH}$ and $\overline{GK}$. We know that $\angle J \cong \angle G$ and $\angle H \cong \angle K$ (Inscribed angles that intercept the same arcs are congruent.) It follows that $\triangle JHP \sim \triangle GKP$ (A.A. Similarity). That means $\dfrac{GP}{JP} = \dfrac{PK}{PH}$ (Converse of definition of similar triangles). Then, cross-multiplying gives us $GP \times PH = JP \times PK$.

Theorem 75	If two chords intersect in the interior of a circle, the product of the lengths of the segments of one chord is equal to the product of the lengths of the segments of the other.

Products Outside

What if the lines intersect outside the circle? Is there still a relationship between the line segments that are formed? Yes, there is. Look at this diagram.

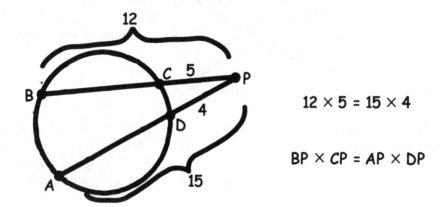

$$12 \times 5 = 15 \times 4$$

$$BP \times CP = AP \times DP$$

We have two secant segments that intersect outside the circle at point P. Notice the pattern on this one. If we take the entire length of each secant segment and multiply it by the part of the secant segment that's outside the circle, those products are equal. That's the rule. And it works no matter where the secant segments cross the circle. Here's an informal proof, along with the theorem.

Given: Secant segments PW and PS intersect at P.

Prove: PW × PT = PS × PR

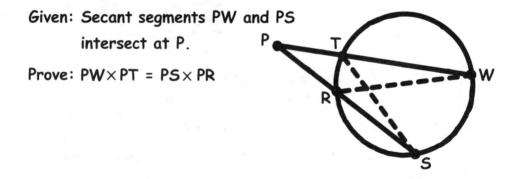

Draw $\overline{RW}$ and $\overline{ST}$. We know that $\angle S \cong \angle W$. (Inscribed angles that intercept the same arcs are congruent.) And since $\angle P \cong \angle P$

594

(Reflexive), $\Delta PST \sim \Delta PWR$ (A.A. Similarity). From that, we know that $\dfrac{PW}{PS} = \dfrac{PR}{PT}$ (Converse of definition of similar triangles). Finally, cross-multiplying, we get $PW \times PT = PS \times PR$.

Theorem 76	**If two secant segments are drawn to a circle from the same exterior point, then the product of the lengths of one secant segment and its external segment is equal to the product of the lengths of the other secant segment and its external segment.**

The neat thing about this secants theorem is that it works even when one of the secants is a tangent. Look at this example given on the right. $\overline{LP}$ is a secant segment, since it intersects the circle at two points (L and N). $\overline{PT}$ is a tangent segment, though, because it intersects the circle at only one point (T). Normally, we would take each entire segment and multiply it by the exterior portion and make those products equal. For $\overline{LP}$, that gives us $LP \times NP$.

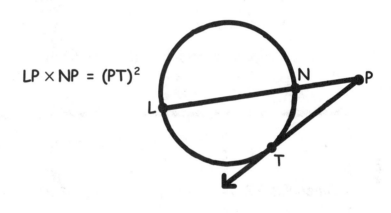

$$LP \times NP = (PT)^2$$

But since $\overline{PT}$ only crosses the circle once, there is no interior segment. So what we do is multiply the length of the exterior segment, $\overline{PT}$, by the entire segment, which is also $\overline{PT}$. Then, we get $PT \times PT$ or $(PT)^2$. That's how we end up with the equation $LP \times NP = (PT)^2$, shown in the diagram above. There's actually a separate proof of this. Here's the proof and the theorem.

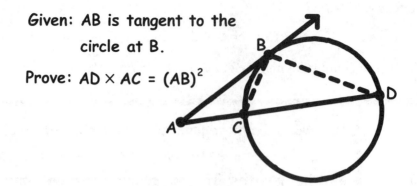

Given: AB is tangent to the
circle at B.

Prove: AD × AC = (AB)²

Draw $\overline{BC}$ and $\overline{BD}$. We know that $m\angle D = \frac{1}{2}m\widehat{BC}$ (An inscribed angle is equal in measure to one-half the measure of its intercepted arc). And $m\angle ABC = \frac{1}{2}m\widehat{BC}$ (The measure of an angle formed by a tangent and a chord drawn to the point of tangency is equal to one-half the measure of the intercepted arc). By substitution, $m\angle ABC = m\angle D$. But since $m\angle A = m\angle A$ (Reflexive), it follows that $\triangle ABD \sim \triangle ACB$ (A.A. Similarity). That means $\dfrac{AD}{AB} = \dfrac{AB}{AC}$ (Converse of definition of similar triangles). Cross-multiplying, we get $AD \times AC = AB \times AB$ or $AD \times AC = (AB)^2$.

Theorem 77	If a tangent segment and a secant segment are drawn to a circle from the same exterior point, then the square of the length of the tangent segment is equal to the product of the lengths of the secant segment and its external segment.

Practice 89

a. Find the degree measure of arc $\widehat{SQ}$ on the right.

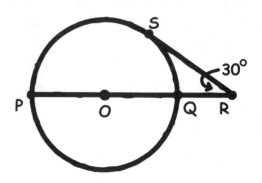

b. Find the linear measure of major arc $\overset{\frown}{ABC}$ on a circle of radius 50, where minor arc $\overset{\frown}{AC}$ has a linear measure of 10π. (Give your answer in terms of π.)

c. Find *b*.

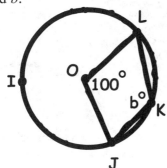

d. Find *DE*.

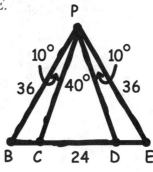

e. Do the proof below.

Given: $m\overset{\frown}{MI} = 2m\overset{\frown}{LJ}$
Prove: $\triangle MJK$ is isosceles.

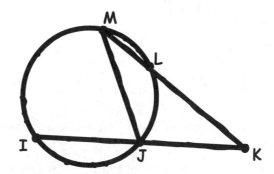

Problem Set 89

Tell whether each sentence below is True or False.

1. If two chords intersect in the interior of a circle, the chords bisect each other.

2. If two secant segments are drawn to a circle from the same exterior point, then the external segments are congruent.

Complete each sentence below by filling in the blanks.

3. If a _____ and a _____ are drawn to a circle from the same exterior point, then the square of the length of the _____ is equal to the product of the lengths of the _____ and its external segment.

4. The measure of an angle formed by two chords (or secants) intersecting in the interior of a circle is equal to one-half the _____ of the measures of the two intercepted arcs.

5. The measure of an angle formed by two secants (or tangents) intersecting in the exterior of a circle is equal to one-half the _____ of the measures of the two intercepted arcs.

Find the degree measure of each arc or angle indicated below.

6. $\overparen{KL}$ 7. $\angle JOL$ (a) 8. $\overparen{BD}$

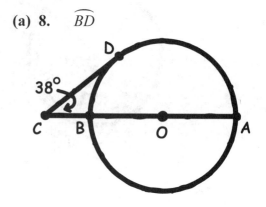

$mLI=145$

$m\overparen{IJ}=55$

Find the linear measure of each arc described below. Give your answers in terms of π.

9. On a circle having a radius of 18 meters, an arc whose central angle measures 80°.

(b) 10. Major arc $\overparen{RVT}$ on a circle of radius 72, where minor arc $\overparen{RT}$ has a linear measure of 16π.

Answer each question below.

11. In $\triangle XYZ$, $YZ = 30$ and $XZ = 28$. If the altitude drawn to XZ measures 24, what is the length XY?

12. If the length of the base of an isosceles right triangle is 2, what is the length of each congruent leg?

13. $\triangle EFG \sim \triangle BCD$. If $FG = 18$, $CD = 4$, EF is 3 more than BD, and BC is half of CD, find EG.

Find each missing line segment indicated below.

14. Find *AC.*

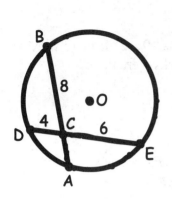

15. Find *AB*

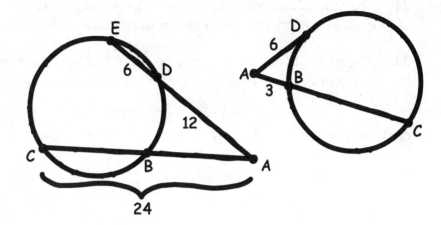

16. Find *AC*

Answer each question below.

17. Find *h.*

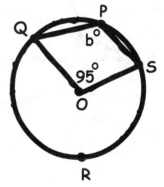

(c) 18. Find *b.*

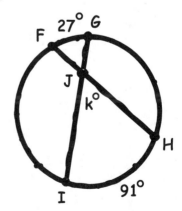

(d) 19. Find *x.*

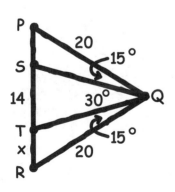

20. Find *k.*

Write a proportion to represent each question below; then solve the proportion to get your answer.

21. The ratio of chocolate bunnies to chocolate eggs was 9:14. If there were 98 chocolate eggs, how many chocolate bunnies were there?

22. The ratio of turnip trucks to hay trucks on Old Post Road was $19:12$. If there were 186 turnip trucks and hay trucks altogether, how many turnip trucks were there?

Do each proof below.

23. Given: $\overline{AC}$ and $\overline{AE}$ are secant segments, $AC = AE$
  Prove: $AB = AD$

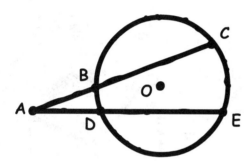

(e) 24. Given: $m\overparen{PT} = 2m\overparen{QS}$
  Prove: $\triangle RSP$ is isosceles.

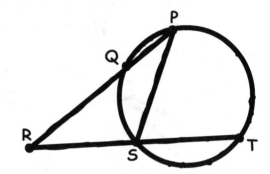

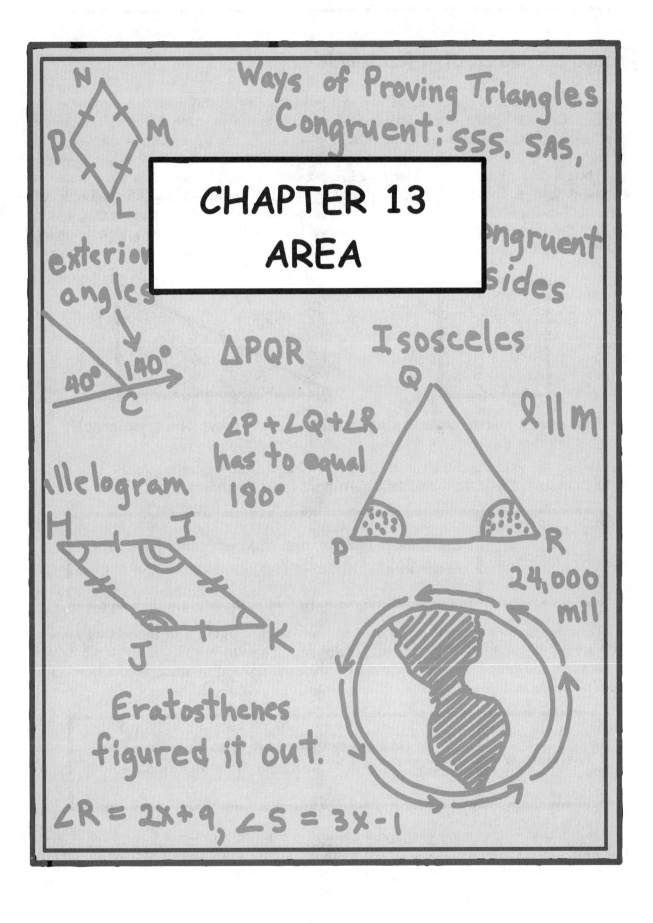

N

P

M

L

Ways of Proving Triangles Congruent: SSS, SAS,

ongruent
sides

exterior
angles

40° 140°
C

ΔPQR

∠P + ∠Q + ∠R
has to equal
180°

Isosceles

Q

ℓ ‖ m

P   R

24,000
mil

llelogram

H   I

J   K

Eratosthenes
figured it out.

∠R = 2x + 9, ∠S = 3x − 1

CHAPTER 13
AREA

Lesson 90—Area of a Rectangle

At the beginning of the book, we said that geometry has several main themes. One is the theme of congruent figures, which are figures that have the same shape and size. The second theme is similar figures. Those are figures that have the same shape but a different size.

There's also a third theme, which we'll concentrate on in Chapter 13. It's the theme of **equivalent figures.** Those are just figures with the same amount of flat space on the inside. Of course, the word for "flat space" is area. So we'll be spending this whole chapter learning how to calculate the areas of all the figures that we've been working with: rectangles, triangles, parallelograms, rhombuses, and so on. Here's a quick example of two equivalent figures.

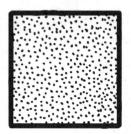 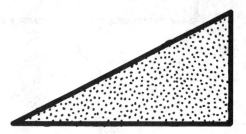

The square and triangle are equivalent figures (have the same area).

Even though the square and triangle are shaped differently, their areas are equal. That's why they're equivalent. This is the formal definition of equivalent figures.

Definition 74	*Equivalent figures* are figures that have the same area.

There is also a postulate that you need to know when working with area calculations. It says that two congruent figures must have the same area. It's pretty obvious, really. If the figures are the exact size and shape, they should have the same amount of space inside. Here's the official postulate, though.

Postulate 19	If two figures are congruent, then they have equal areas.

One thing to keep in mind when using Postulate 19 is that its converse is not true. In other words, just because two figures have the same area doesn't necessarily mean that they're congruent. The square and triangle we just showed are an example of that.

Measuring Area

Let's talk about how area is actually measured. Lengths are measured with lines. For instance, to measure the distance across a room, we could stretch a tape measure from one end to the other. If the tape measure were marked off in feet, we

A tape measure can be used for lengths because it's a straight line.

would measure the length of the room in feet. If it were marked off in inches, we would use inches. But lengths are measured with lines, because lengths are one-dimensional.

By contrast, flat spaces are two-dimensional. They have both length and width. That's why areas are not measured with a line. They're measured with little squares. For example, to measure the area of the rectangle at right (which is 3 feet long and 7 feet wide), we divide the space up into little squares, each with sides that are 1 foot long. Since there are 21 squares, the rectangle has an area of 21 square feet, which is often written as 21 sq. ft. or $21\,\text{ft}^2$ for short. A figure

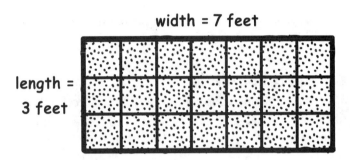

width = 7 feet

length = 3 feet

Surfaces are measured with little squares.

with an area of 48 square inches would have enough space inside of it to hold 48 squares, each with 1 inch sides. And a figure with an area of 14 square centimeters would have space enough inside for 14 squares, each with sides of 1 centimeter. You get the idea.

Why Count Little Squares?

Of course, nobody bothers to count all the little squares inside when figuring out the area of a rectangle. The fast way to do the calculation, as you've known for years, is to multiply the width by the length. On the example above, it would be $(3)(7) = 21$. In geometry, instead of using the words "width" and "length," we often call them "base" and "altitude" (or sometimes

"height"). Any of the rectangle's sides can be the base. You just have to choose one. Then either of the sides perpendicular to it can be the altitude, (because an altitude has to be perpendicular to the side it connects to, remember).

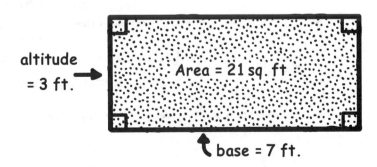

altitude = 3 ft.

Area = 21 sq. ft.

base = 7 ft.

So the area of a rectangle is the base multiplied by the altitude. And the units of the answer will depend on how the base and altitude were measured. If they were in feet, then the answer will be in square feet. If they were in inches, the answer will be in square inches, and so on. But the main point is that by multiplying the base and altitude, it's not necessary to count all the little squares inside. Multiplication is a shortcut. We won't prove this rule for calculating the area of a rectangle. We'll accept it as a postulate. We'll also assume that the postulate holds even for rectangles with sides that have fractional or decimal lengths.

Area of a Rectangle = ba

Postulate 20	The *area of a rectangle* (A) is the rectangle's base (b) multiplied by its altitude (a): A = ba

An Area Postulate

There's one more important postulate that we should show you before moving on. As it turns out, an easy way to figure out the area of a complicated figure is to break it up into simple parts. Take the figure below, for instance.

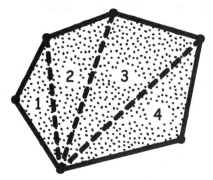

The 4 triangular parts add to equal the whole.

Calculating the area for this hexagon all at once would be pretty tough. We can simplify the task by drawing diagonals that break the hexagon up into triangles. Then we can calculate the area of each triangle (which is not so tough) and add those up to get the area for the entire hexagon.

Our next postulate is what allows us to add up those parts. It's called the **Area Addition Postulate**, and it basically says that the area of a figure equals the sum of the areas of all its parts. Here it is.

Area Addition Postulate

Postulate 21	The area of a closed region is equal to the sum of the areas of the nonoverlapping parts.

Practice 90

a. Calculate the area of a rectangle with an altitude of 6 feet and a diagonal of 10 feet.

b. If $\overline{BC}$ is tangent to $\odot O$ at B, $\overline{BD}$ is a diameter of $\odot O$, and BC is four times the radius of $\odot O$, which is the smallest angle of $\triangle BCD$?

c. Betty wants to be able to view two 8-inch-by-10-inch photos at full size side-by-side on her computer screen at the same time. She needs to view the photos with the 10-inch sides vertical and the 8-inch sides beside each other horizontally. What is the smallest diagonal screen size she should look for? Estimate your answer to one decimal place.

d. Find x.

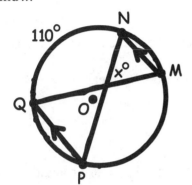

e. Do the proof below.
Given: $m\overset{\frown}{EF} = m\overset{\frown}{GH}$
Prove: $m\angle EFG = m\angle FGH$

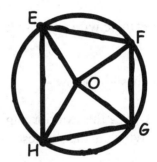

Problem Set 90

Tell whether each sentence below is True or False.

1. Equivalent figures are figures whose corresponding sides are proportional.

2. If two figures have equal areas, then they are congruent.

Complete each sentence below by filling in the blanks.

3. The area of a rectangle is its _____ multiplied by its _____.

4. If two chords intersect in the interior of a circle, the _____ of the lengths of the segments of one chord is equal to the _____ of the lengths of the segments of the other.

5. If two secant segments are drawn to a circle from the same exterior point, then the product of the lengths of one secant segment and its _____ are equal to the product of the lengths of the other secant segment and its _____.

Find the degree measure of each arc or angle below.

6. ∠QRN

7. $\overset{\frown}{RM}$

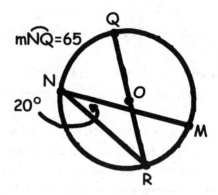

Calculate the area of each rectangle described below.

8. A rectangle with a base of 9 inches and an altitude of 8 inches.

(a) 9. A rectangle with an altitude of 12 feet and a diagonal of 20 feet.

Answer each question below.

10. In ΔHJK, the exterior angle at K measures 139° and the exterior angle at J measures 53°. Which is the shortest side of ΔHJK?

(b) 11. If $\overline{PQ}$ is tangent to $\odot O$ at Q, $\overline{RQ}$ is a diameter of $\odot O$, and $PQ = OR$, which is the smallest angle of ΔPQR?

Answer each question below.

12. The length of a chord of a circle is 24 and its distance from the center is 5. Find the length of a diameter of the circle.

(c) 13. Allison wants to be able to view two $8\frac{1}{2}$ in. × 11 in. pages at full size side-by-side on her computer screen. She needs to view the pages with the 11-inch sides vertical and the $8\frac{1}{2}$-inch sides beside each other horizontally. What is the smallest diagonal screen size she should look for? Estimate your answer to one decimal place.

Find the perimeter of each polygon indicated below.

14. $\triangle ABC$.

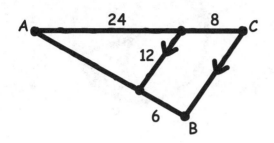

15. Hexagon *FGHIJK*, in terms of *a* and *d*.

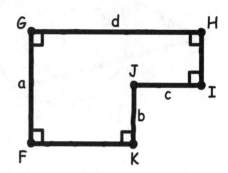

Find each missing line segment below.

16. Find *RT*.

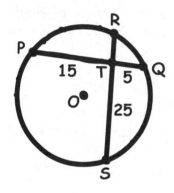

17. Find *RQ*.

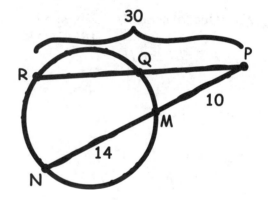

Answer each question below.

18. If *PO=OM*, find *a*.

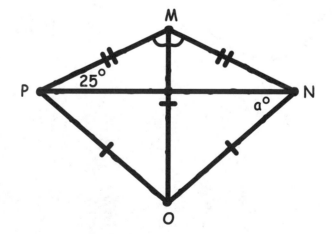

19. Find s.

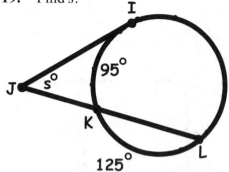

(d) 20. Find x.

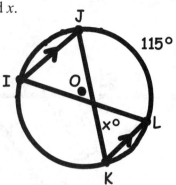

Write an equation to represent each question below; then solve the equation to get your answer.

21. The longest side of a triangle is 8 less than three times the longest side of a similar triangle. If the shortest sides of the triangles are 15 and 6, respectively, then what are the lengths of the longest side of each triangle?

22. Quadrilateral $ABCD$ is similar to Quadrilateral $FGHJ$ with a ratio of similitude of $7:11$. If $FJ = 11$, $AB = 2x$, $BC = 3x$, $CD = 4x$, and $AD = x$, what are the lengths of FG, GH, and HJ?

Do each proof below.

23. Given: $OP > PR$
Prove: $m\widehat{QR} > m\widehat{PR}$

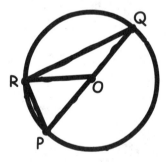

(e) 24. Given: $m\widehat{IJ} = m\widehat{KL}$
Prove: $m\angle IJK = m\angle JKL$

Lesson 91—Area of a Triangle and Parallelogram

In the last lesson we learned how to calculate the area of a rectangle. Now we're going to tackle the area of a triangle and a parallelogram.

Area of a Triangle

The formula for the area of a triangle is actually pretty easy to remember, because it's just half of the area of a rectangle. Since the area of a rectangle is just the base times the altitude, that means a triangle's area equals $\frac{1}{2} \times \text{base} \times \text{altitude}$. The proof of this is actually fairly involved. It has to be done in two steps. First, we have to prove that the area of any *right* triangle is $\frac{1}{2} \times \text{base} \times \text{altitude}$. Then we have to use that theorem to show that the area of *any* triangle

(whatever its shape) equals $\frac{1}{2} \times \text{base} \times \text{altitude}$. Let's start with the diagram on the right. Notice that $\triangle ABC$ is a right triangle, since $\angle C$ is a right angle. And we've drawn $\overline{BP}$ parallel to $\overline{AC}$ and $\overline{PA}$ parallel to $\overline{BC}$. That makes $APBC$ a parallelogram, which means that opposite angles are congruent and consecutive angles are supplementary. It follows that since $\angle C$ is a right angle, $\angle A$, $\angle P$, and $\angle B$ must also be right angles, and $APBC$ has to be a rectangle.

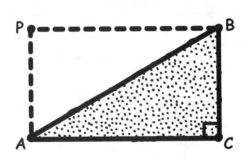

We know that the area of a rectangle is its base multiplied by its altitude. Letting AC be the base and AP the altitude, we get an area for $APBC$ of $AC \times AP$. But $\triangle ABC$ and $\triangle ABP$ are congruent by the Side-Side-Side shortcut (since opposite sides of the rectangle are congruent and the triangle share side AB). If the triangles are congruent, though, their areas must be equal. (Congruent figures have the same area.) Therefore, the area of $\triangle ABC$ must be one-half of the area of the entire rectangle or $\frac{1}{2} \times AC \times AP$. Since AC is the base and AP is the altitude, we've just proved that the area of any right triangle equals $\frac{1}{2}ba$.

Now for the second step of the process. We need to prove that $\frac{1}{2}ba$ will also work for the area of *any* triangle. To do that we need to cover the two major categories of "non-right" triangles: acute triangles, where all 3 angles are less than $90°$, and obtuse triangles, where 1 angle is greater than $90°$. Here are examples of both.

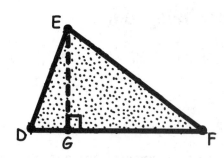

Acute △DEF with altitude on inside.

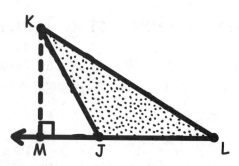

Obtuse △JKL with altitude on outside.

Notice that for the obtuse triangle, the altitude actually lies outside the triangle. That's the way it works for any obtuse triangle. It's not a problem, though. Altitude just means height, and $\overline{KM}$ is still the height of $\triangle JKL$, even though it's on the outside.

We need to do a separate proof for each of these cases. Here's the proof for the acute triangle case.

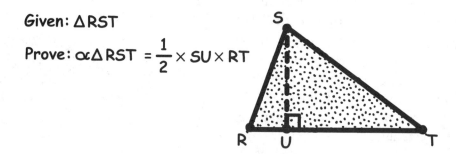

Given: △RST

Prove: $\alpha \triangle RST = \dfrac{1}{2} \times SU \times RT$

Draw altitude $\overline{SU}$ to side $\overline{RT}$. We know that $\overline{SU} \perp \overline{RT}$ (Definition of altitude). So $\angle SUR$ and $\angle SUT$ are right angles. (Perpendicular lines intersect to form right angles.) It follows that $\angle SUR \cong \angle SUT$ and $\triangle SUR$ and $\triangle SUT$ are right triangles and that $\alpha \triangle SUR = \frac{1}{2} \times RU \times SU$ and $\alpha \triangle SUT = \frac{1}{2} \times TU \times SU$ (The area of a right triangle is equal to one-half the product of the base and the altitude. But $\alpha \triangle RST = \alpha \triangle SUR + \alpha \triangle SUT$ (Area Addition Postulate). Therefore, $\alpha \triangle RST = \frac{1}{2} \times RU \times SU + \frac{1}{2} \times TU \times SU$ (Substitution) or $\alpha \triangle RST = \frac{1}{2} \times SU (RU + TU)$ (Distributive). But by Betweenness of points, $RU + TU = RT$. So $\alpha \triangle RST = \frac{1}{2} \times SU \times RT$. (Substitution)

Since the proof for the obtuse triangle case is very similar, we won't bother showing it. But after covering both the acute and the obtuse categories, we can state that the area of any triangle (regardless of its shape) is $\dfrac{1}{2} ba$. Here's the official theorem.

$$\text{Area of a Triangle} = \frac{1}{2}\, ba$$

Theorem 78	The area of a triangle is equal to one-half the product of the base and the altitude.

Area of a Parallelogram

Interestingly, the formula for the area for a parallelogram is exactly the same as the formula for the area of a rectangle: base times altitude. It makes some sense, when you study a diagram carefully. Check out the parallelogram and rectangle below.

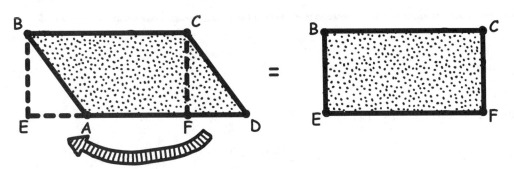

Moving △CFD to the left side changes ▱ABCD to rectangle EBCF.

Even though parallelogram *ABCD* leans to one side and rectangle *EBCF* is straight, the two have the same area because their bases and altitudes are the same: $AD = EF$ and $CF = BE$. One easy way to see that is to move $\triangle CFD$ from the right side to the left side of the parallelogram. That changes *ABCD* into a rectangle that's exactly the same size and shape as *EBCF*. Here's an informal proof of the rule that the area of any parallelogram equals base times altitude.

Given: ▱ABCD with base AD
and altitude CF.

Prove: $\alpha\, ▱ABCD = AD \times CF$

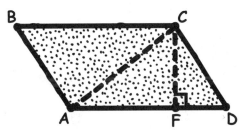

Draw diagonal $\overline{AC}$. Since opposite sides of a parallelogram are congruent, $AB = CD$ and $AD = BC$. Also, $AC = AC$ (Reflexive). That means $\triangle ACD \cong \triangle ACB$ (S.S.S.) and $\alpha\triangle ACD = \alpha\triangle ACB$ (Congruent figures have the same area.) $\alpha ABCD = \alpha\triangle ACD + \alpha\triangle ACB$

by the Area Addition Postulate. Then, substituting, we get $\alpha ABCD = \alpha\triangle ACD + \alpha\triangle ACD$ or $\alpha ABCD = 2\alpha\triangle ACD$. But we know that $\alpha\triangle ACD = \dfrac{1}{2} \times AD \times CF$ (The area of a triangle is equal to one-half the product of the base and the altitude.) Substituting again, gives us $\alpha ABCD = 2 \times \dfrac{1}{2} \times AD \times CF$, which simplifies to $\alpha ABCD = AD \times CF$

Area of a Parallelogram = ba

Theorem 79	The area of a parallelogram is equal to the product of the base and the altitude.

Practice 91

Calculate the area of each figure below.

a. $\triangle SVT$

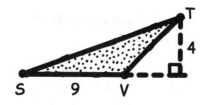

b. $\square MNOP$

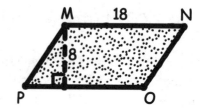

c. What is the area of an isosceles triangle that has a base measuring 12 and equal legs measuring 10?

d. If $AC = 3 \times BC$, find AC.

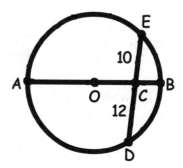

e. Do the proof below.

Given: $\overline{VT}$ is tangent to $\odot P$ at U;

$\overline{RT}$ is tangent to $\odot P$ at S;

$\overline{VR}$ is tangent to $\odot P$ at W;

$TS = SR$

Prove: $\angle T \cong \angle R$

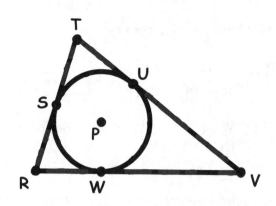

Problem Set 91

Tell whether each sentence below is True or False.

1. The area of a triangle is equal to one-half the product of the base and the altitude.

2. The area of a parallelogram is equal to the product of the base and the altitude.

Complete each sentence below by filling in the blanks.

3. _____ figures are figures that have the same area.

4. The area of a closed region is equal to the _____ of the areas of its non-overlapping parts.

5. A(n) _____ is an angle whose vertex is on a circle and whose sides are chords (or secants) of the circle.

Find the linear measure of each arc described below. Estimate your answers to two decimal places.

6. $\overset{\frown}{VW}$ on $\odot P$, where $PV = 32$ inches and $m\angle VPW = 84$.

7. $\overset{\frown}{CDE}$ on $\odot O$, where $\overline{CD}$ is a diameter, $CO = 21$, and $m\angle EOC = 155$.

Calculate the area of each figure below.

8. $\triangle IJK$

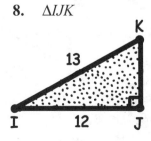

(a) 9. $\triangle EFG$

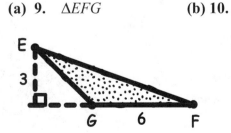

(b) 10. $\square ABCD$

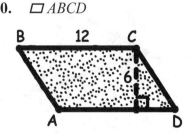

Answer each question below.

11. In right $\triangle DEF$, $DE = 28$, $DF = 14$, and $EF = 14\sqrt{3}$. What are the measures of each angle of $\triangle DEF$?

(c) 12. What is the area of an isosceles triangle that has a base measuring 10 and equal legs measuring 13?

From each given statement below, tell the definition, property, postulate, or theorem that justifies each prove statement.

13. Given: Chords $\overline{AC}$ and $\overline{BD}$ intersect at E.
Prove: $AE \times EC = BE \times ED$

14. Given: Secant segments $\overline{BF}$ and $\overline{AF}$ intersect at F
Prove: $FB \times FC = FA \times FD$

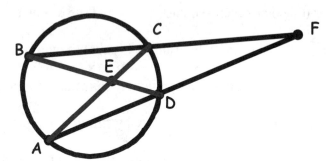

Find the degree measure of each angle indicated below.

15. $\angle MNL$

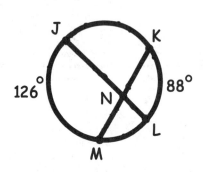

16. $\angle RPT$

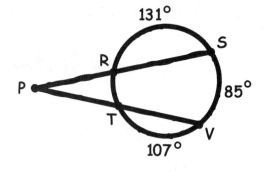

Answer each question below.

17. Find b.

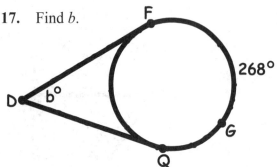

18. Find y.

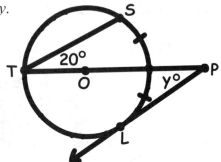

614

19. Find x.

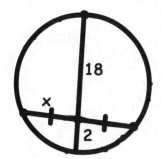

(d) 20. If $QJ = 4 \times PQ$, find QJ.

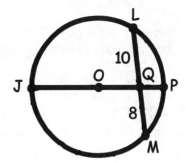

Write an equation to represent each question below; then solve the equation to get your answer. Estimate your answers to two decimal places.

21. To advertise for the big sale, a used car dealer has strung a banner with little flags on it from the top of the dealer's sign all the way to the ground. If the sign is 78 feet high, and the banner makes a 32° angle with the ground, how long is the banner?

22. Bill measured the shadow cast by the historical monument to be 71 feet long at the same time that Suzy measured the angle of the sun from the horizon to be 36°. How tall is the monument?

Do each proof below.

23. Given: $\overline{DC} \cong \overline{AB}$
  Prove: $\overline{DB} \cong \overline{AC}$

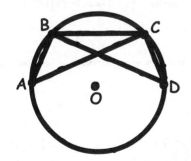

(e) 24. Given: $\overline{HF}$ is tangent to $\odot O$ at C; $\overline{GF}$ is tangent to $\odot O$ at D; $\overline{HG}$ is tangent to $\odot O$ at E; $FD = DG$
  Prove: $\angle F \cong \angle G$

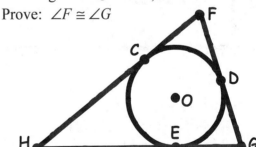

Lesson 92—Area of Other Quadrilaterals

In the last lesson, we learned how to calculate the area of a triangle and parallelogram. But what about other quadrilaterals, like squares, rhombuses, and trapezoids?

Area of a Square

Well, the area of a square is incredibly easy. A square is a rectangle, of course, so we could just multiply its base times its altitude. That would be $DG \times ED$ in the diagram at right. But since all four sides are equal, an easier way is just to multiply any side length (s) by itself. By that method, the formula for the area of a square is $A = s^2$. With this formula, we don't have to worry about whether a particular side is a base or an altitude. It doesn't matter (since they're all the same).

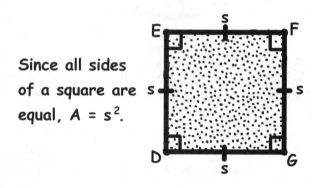

Since all sides of a square are equal, A = s².

The proof of the area of a square can be boiled down to a single step. Since a square is a rectangle, we know that its area equals $DG \times ED$. But we know that DG and ED are each equal to s, so substituting gives s^2. Here's the formal theorem.

Area of a Square = s²

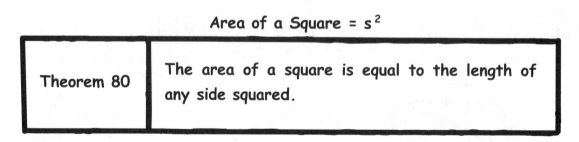

Theorem 80	The area of a square is equal to the length of any side squared.

Area of a Rhombus

Since a rhombus is also a parallelogram, multiplying the base and the altitude will work on it too. Like a square, though, a rhombus is a special kind of parallelogram: one where all four sides are equal (but the angles aren't right angles, as with a square). That means there's an alternative method for calculating the area of a rhombus, which is kind of neat. To show you how it works, check out the rhombus on the next page.

We've drawn the diagonals in, because this second method for area uses those. What we do is multiply the two diagonals together and then multiply that product by one-half. If we label one diagonal d_1 and the other one d_2, the formula is $A = \frac{1}{2}d_1d_2$. So with this second method, to calculate the area of a rhombus, we don't need to know the length of the sides at all. We just need to know the two diagonals. Here's an informal proof of this area rule, followed by the theorem.

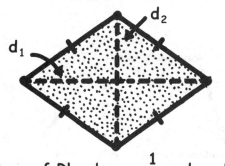

Area of Rhombus = $\frac{1}{2} \times d_1 \times d_2$

Given: Rhombus ABCD with diagonals $\overline{AC}$ and $\overline{BD}$.

Prove: $\propto$ ABCD = $\frac{1}{2} \times$ AC $\times$ BD

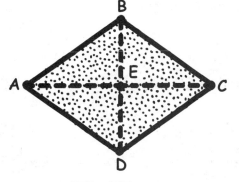

Since $ABCD$ is a rhombus, we know that $\overline{AC} \perp \overline{BD}$ (The diagonals of a rhombus are perpendicular to each other.) That means $\overline{BE}$ is an altitude of $\triangle ABC$ and $\overline{DE}$ is an altitude of $\triangle ADC$. $\overline{AC}$ is the base of both triangles. So $\alpha\triangle ABC = \frac{1}{2} \times AC \times BE$ and $\alpha\triangle ADC = \frac{1}{2} \times AC \times DE$. (The area of a triangle is equal to one-half of the product of the base and the altitude.) Therefore, we get $\alpha\triangle ABC + \alpha\triangle ADC = \frac{1}{2} \times AC \times BE + \frac{1}{2} \times AC \times DE$ (Addition), as well as $\alpha\triangle ABC + \alpha\triangle ADC = \frac{1}{2} \times AC(BE + DE)$ (Distributive). But since $\alpha ABCD = \alpha\triangle ABC + \alpha\triangle ADC$ (Area Addition Postulate), we know that $\alpha ABCD = \frac{1}{2} \times AC(BE + DE)$ (Substitution). Finally, we have $BE + DE = BD$ (Betweenness of Points), which means that $\alpha ABCD = \frac{1}{2} \times AC \times BD$ (Substitution).

Area of Rhombus = $\frac{1}{2} \times d_1 \times d_2$

Theorem 81	**The area of a rhombus is equal to one-half the product of the lengths of the two diagonals.**

Area of a Trapezoid

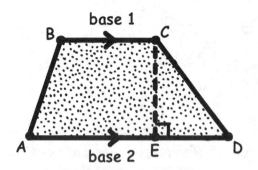

base 1

base 2

In a trapezoid, the bases are different lengths.

Finally, let's cover the area of a trapezoid. Remember, a trapezoid is a quadrilateral that has one pair of opposite sides parallel, as shown in the diagram on the left. You might guess that the formula is base times altitude, because a trapezoid is not all that different from a parallelogram or rectangle. Base times altitude won't work, though, because a trapezoid has two bases: here they're $\overline{BC}$ and $\overline{AD}$. What's worse, since those bases are different lengths, we wouldn't know which base to use in the calculation. Here's the actual formula for the area of a trapezoid.

$$\text{Area of a trapezoid} = \frac{1}{2} \times \text{altitude} \times (\text{base}_1 + \text{base}_2)$$

For trapezoid $ABCD$ above, that gives us $\frac{1}{2} \times CE(BC + AD)$.

This formula may seem kind of strange, but watch what happens when we switch the order of the $\frac{1}{2}$ and the altitude. We get $\text{altitude} \times \frac{1}{2}(\text{base}_1 + \text{base}_2)$. But an average of two numbers is just those numbers added together and divided by 2 (which is the same as multiplying by $\frac{1}{2}$). So the formula for the area of a trapezoid is really the same as $\text{altitude} \times \text{average of bases}$. Because the bases are different lengths, instead of using just one base, we use the average of the two. That makes sense. Here's the (tough) proof of the formula, along with the official theorem.

Given: Trapezoid ABCD with bases $\overline{AD}$ and $\overline{BC}$.

Prove: $\alpha ABCD = \frac{1}{2} \times CE(AD + BC)$

Draw $\overline{AC}$ and $\overline{CE}$. Since $\overline{CE}$ is an altitude of $\triangle ACD$ and $\overline{AD}$ is the base, $\alpha ACD = \frac{1}{2} \times AD \times CE$. (The area of a triangle is equal to one-half of the product of the base and the altitude.) Draw $\overrightarrow{CB}$. Draw $\overline{AF}$ so that $\overline{AF} \perp \overrightarrow{CB}$. $\overline{AF}$ is the altitude of $\triangle ABC$ and $\overline{BC}$ is the base. So $\alpha ABC = \frac{1}{2} \times BC \times AF$. (The area of a triangle is equal to one-half of the product of the base and the altitude.)

Since $\overline{AD} \parallel \overline{BC}$ (A trapezoid is a quadrilateral which has exactly one pair of parallel sides. The parallel sides are called bases.), $AF = CE$. But $\alpha ABCD = \alpha ACD + \alpha ABC$ (Area Addition Postulate). Therefore, $\alpha ABCD = \frac{1}{2} \times AD \times CE + \frac{1}{2} \times BC \times AF$ (Substitution) and $\alpha ABCD = \frac{1}{2} \times AD \times CE + \frac{1}{2} \times BC \times CE$ (Substitution). It follows that $\alpha ABCD = \frac{1}{2} \times CE(AD + BC)$

$$\text{Area of Trapezoid} = \frac{1}{2} a(b_1 + b_2)$$

Theorem 82	The area of a trapezoid is equal to one-half the product of the length of the altitude and the sum of the lengths of its bases.

Practice 92

Calculate the area of each figure below.

a.

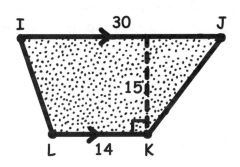

b. $MO = 6$ and $NP = 9$

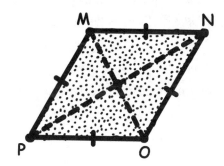

c. If $m\widehat{IJ} = 25\pi$, find a.

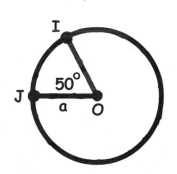

d. Find y.

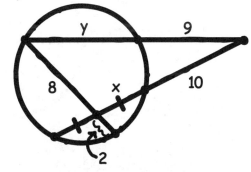

e. Do the proof below.

Given: $\overline{PR}$ is tangent to $\odot O$ at P;

$\overline{QR}$ is tangent to $\odot O$ at Q;

Prove: $\overrightarrow{RS}$ bisects $\angle PRQ$

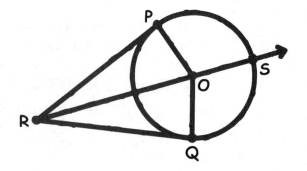

Problem Set 92

Tell whether each sentence below is True or False.

1. The area of a rhombus is equal to one-half the product of the two diagonals.

2. The area of a trapezoid is equal to one-half the product of the length of the altitude and the sum of the lengths of the bases.

Complete each sentence below by filling in the blanks.

3. The area of a _____ is equal to any side squared.

4. The area of a _____ is equal to one-half the product of the base and the altitude.

5. The measure of an angle formed by two chords (or secants) intersecting in the interior of a circle is equal to _____ the sum of the measures of the two intercepted arcs.

Find the degree measure of each arc or angle below.

6. $\overparen{LN}$ 7. $\angle POL$

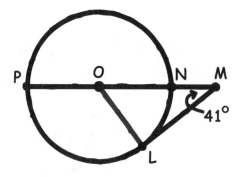

Calculate the area of each figure below.

8.

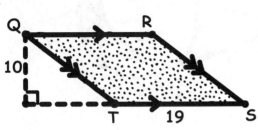
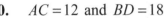

(a) 9.

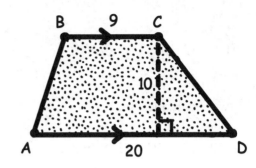

(b) 10. $AC = 12$ and $BD = 18$

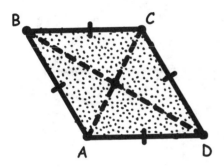

11.

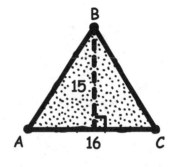

Answer each question below.

12. If the vertex angle of an isosceles triangle measures 60° and the length of each leg is 26, what is the length of the base?

13. $\triangle ABC \sim \triangle DEF$ with a ratio of similitude of $6:13$. If $AC = 72$, what is DF?

Find the perimeter of each polygon below. Estimate your answers to two decimal places.

14.

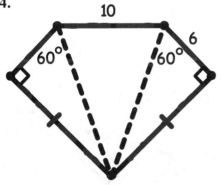

15.

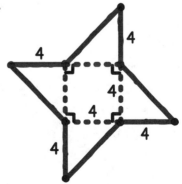

Find each missing line segment below.

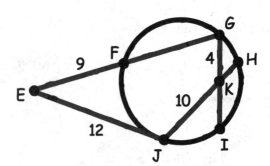

16. Find *FG*.

17. If $GI = 9$, find *HJ*.

Answer each question below.

(c) 18. If $m\overset{\frown}{BC} = 27\pi$, find *a*.

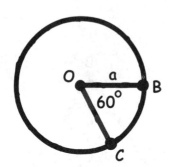

19. Find *x*.

(d) 20. Find *y*.

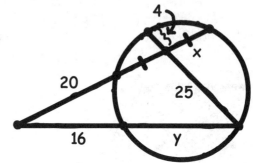

Write a proportion to represent each question below; then solve the proportion to get your answer.

21. The ratio of nail biters to spine tinglers was $9:14$. If there were 84 spine tinglers, how many nail biters were there?

22. The ratio of monkeys to organ grinders was $17:23$. If there were 840 monkeys and organ grinders altogether, how many monkeys were there?

Do each proof below.

23. Given: $\overline{JL}$ is tangent to $\odot P$ at *K*
and to $\odot O$ at *L*;
$\overline{JN}$ is tangent to $\odot P$ at *M*
and to $\odot O$ at *N*
Prove: $KL = MN$

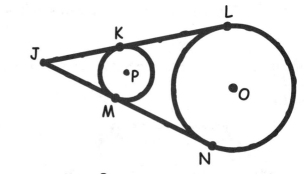

(e) 24. Given: $\overline{BD}$ is tangent to $\odot O$ at *B*;
$\overline{CD}$ is tangent to $\odot O$ at *C*;
Prove: $\overrightarrow{DE}$ bisects $\angle BDC$

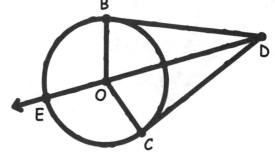

Lesson 93—Area of Polygons with More Sides

We've been learning how to calculate the area of triangles (which have 3 sides) and quadrilaterals (which have 4 sides). What about figures with more than 4 sides? Well, the greater the number of sides, the more complicated area calculations become, as you might guess.

Splitting into Triangles

And to be honest, even ordinary quadrilaterals can be pretty hard. In the last couple of lessons, we only learned to calculate the area of "special" quadrilaterals, like squares, rectangles, and parallelograms. Those are easier because some of their sides are congruent or parallel. That's why we were able to come up with fairly simple formulas for them. But there's really no easy formula for finding the area of a quadrilateral like the one on the right. See, this quadrilateral isn't a square, rectangle, parallelogram, or trapezoid. It's not special in any way. So there are no area formulas to use. That means the only way to find the area of $ABCD$ is to divide it into triangles by

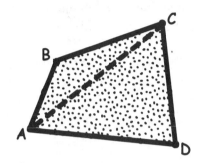

Draw a diagonal to split the quadrilateral into triangles.

drawing a diagonal, such as $\overline{AC}$. Then we could find the areas of $\triangle ABC$ and $\triangle ACD$ and add those together. We won't bother going through the process, because it's time-consuming—especially since we would have to measure altitudes of both triangles.

Regular Polygons Again

Fortunately, there are a few polygons with lots of sides that have a fairly easy area formula. These are the regular polygons. Remember, regular polygons have all sides and all angles congruent. Here's a picture of a regular pentagon and a regular hexagon.

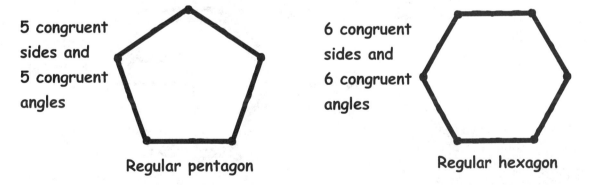

5 congruent sides and 5 congruent angles

Regular pentagon

6 congruent sides and 6 congruent angles

Regular hexagon

Before showing the area formula for these figures, we need to go over a few details. First, regular polygons are like circles in that they have a center and a radius. And the process for finding the center and radius is kind of interesting. What we do is "inscribe" the polygon inside a circle.

The word *inscribe* means to place the hexagon inside a circle that's just big enough to fit around the outside of the hexagon, so that the circle barely touches at the vertices.[1] We can also say that the circle is *circumscribed* about the hexagon. We use the word "inscribed" when talking about the figure on the inside and "circumscribed" when talking about the figure on the outside.

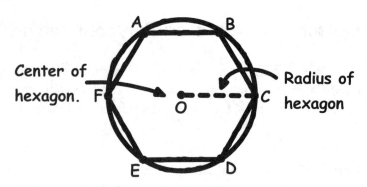

Hexagon inscribed in a circle.

The **center** of the hexagon is the center of the circle. The **radius** of the hexagon is the length of a segment going from the center of the hexagon to any one of its vertices. And notice that this radius is also equal to the radius of the circle. It works the same way for any regular polygon, no matter how many sides it has. Here are the formal definitions for the center and radius of any regular polygon.

Definition 75	The *center* of a regular polygon is the center of its circumscribed circle.
Definition 76	A *radius* of a regular polygon is a line segment that joins the polygon's center to a vertex.

Regular polygons also have **central angles**. These are formed by two radii that are next to each other, as shown in the diagram on the right. See, $\angle BOC$ is a central angle of hexagon *ABCDEF*. There are also 5 more central angles which we could show by drawing in the other radii. Notice there's another line in our hexagon called an **apothem**. That's a perpendicular line segment from the center of the hexagon to one of its sides.

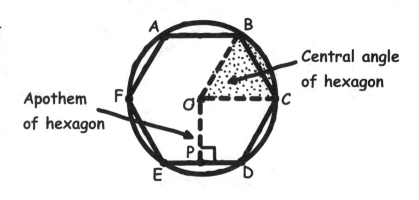

----

[1] It's basically the same concept as an inscribed angle (from the last chapter), whose vertex just touches the edge of a circle.

Here are the formal definitions of these terms.

Definition 77	The *central angle* of a regular polygon is an angle formed by radii drawn to two consecutive vertices.
Definition 78	An *apothem* of a regular polygon is a perpendicular line segment that joins the polygon's center to a side.

Area of a Regular Polygon

Now that all the necessary terms have been defined, we're ready to go over the formula for a regular polygon. Amazingly, the same formula will work on any regular polygon, no matter how many sides it has. It will even work on an equilateral triangle (which is a 3-sided regular polygon) and a square (which is a 4-sided regular polygon).

This area formula is to take one-half the product of the apothem and the perimeter of the regular polygon. Let's assume that each side of a hexagon is 5 units long.

The apothem, OP, is the altitude of $\triangle OED$, which turns out to be equilateral. That means $\triangle OEP$ is a 30-60-right triangle and OP must equal $2.5\sqrt{3}$ (EP times $\sqrt{3}$). So the area of hexagon $ABCDEF$ is $\frac{1}{2} \cdot 2.5\sqrt{3} \cdot 30$ or $37.5\sqrt{3}$.

$$\text{Area} = \frac{1}{2} \times \text{apothem } (OP) \times \text{perimeter } (5 \cdot 6)$$

You may be wondering why this formula works. Well, think of it this way. The radii divide the hexagon into 6 congruent triangles, each with an altitude equal to the hexagon's apothem and a base equal to one side of the hexagon. So the area of each of those triangles equals one-half times the apothem times the side length. But since there are 6 triangles around the hexagon, the total area is $6 \cdot \frac{1}{2}$(apothem)(side). Since the terms are multiplied, we can rearrange them like this: $\frac{1}{2}$(apothem)($6 \cdot$ side). However, $6 \cdot$ side is the perimeter of the polygon, so that gives us $\frac{1}{2}$(apothem)(perimeter).

And once again, this works no matter how many sides a regular polygon has. Look at the pentagon and octagon below.

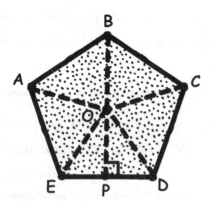

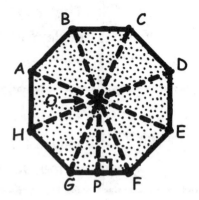

In the regular pentagon, there are 5 congruent triangles, each with an area of $\frac{1}{2}$(apothem)(side). Adding all 5 of those up will give us $5 \cdot \frac{1}{2}$(apothem)(side) or $\frac{1}{2}$(apothem)(perimeter) again. The octagon has 8 congruent triangles, each with an area of $\frac{1}{2}$(apothem)(side). Adding those up, we get $8 \cdot \frac{1}{2}$(apothem)(side), which still comes out to $\frac{1}{2}$(apothem)(perimeter). Here's the official theorem.

Area of Regular Polygon = $\frac{1}{2}$ × apothem × perimeter

Theorem 83	The area of a regular polygon is equal to one-half the product of the length of the apothem (a) and its perimeter (p).

Practice 93

a. Calculate the area of regular hexagon *LMNPQR*.

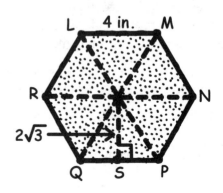

b. Find the measures of the angles of $\triangle RTV$, where $\overline{RT}$ is a diameter of $\odot O$, and chord $\overline{RV}$ intercepts an arc measuring $80°$.

c. Find x.

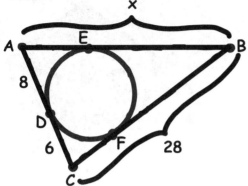

d. Find y.

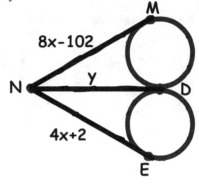

e. Do the proof below <u>informally</u>.
Given: A regular polygon
Prove: The central angles are congruent.

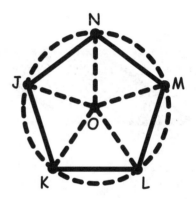

Problem Set 93

Tell whether each sentence below is True or False.

1. The area of a regular polygon is equal to one-half the product of its base and its diameter.

2. A radius of a regular polygon is a line segment that joins the polygon's center and intersects a side.

Complete each sentence below by filling in the blanks.

3. A(n) _____ of a regular polygon is an angle formed by radii drawn to two consecutive vertices.

4. A(n) _____ of a regular polygon is a perpendicular line segment that joins the polygon's center to a side.

5. The area of a _____ is equal to one-half the product of the two diagonals.

Calculate the area of each figure below.

6. △*XYZ*

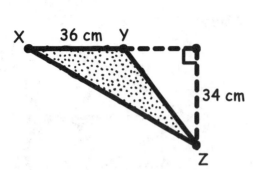

(a) 7. Regular pentagon *PQRST*

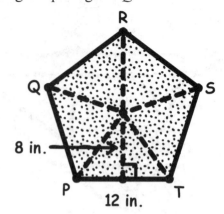

8.

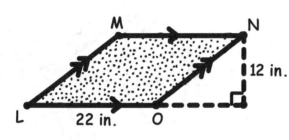

9.

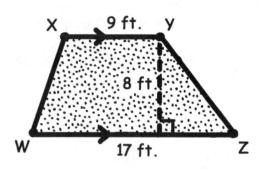

Answer each question below.

10. In △*MNO*, ∠*M* is obtuse and $m\angle N > m\angle O$. What is the shortest side of △*MNO*?

11. △*TUV* is inscribed in a circle in such a way that $\overline{TV}$ is a diameter and the length *UV* is equal to the radius of the circle. Which is the smallest angle of △*TUV*?

From each given statement below, tell the definition, property, postulate, or theorem that justifies each prove statement.

12. Given: △*ABC* ≅ △*DCB*
Prove: α△*ABC* = α△*DCB*

13. Given: △*ABE* is adjacent to △*BEC*
Prove: α△*ABC* = α△*ABE* + α△*BEC*

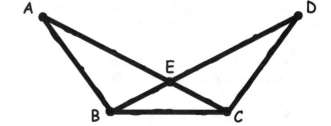

Find the measures of the angles of each triangle described below.

14. $\triangle BDE$, where $\overline{BD}$ is the altitude drawn to the hypotenuse of isosceles right $\triangle ABC$ and $\overline{DE}$ is the perpendicular bisector of $\overline{BC}$.

(b) 15. $\triangle GHJ$, where $\overline{GH}$ is a diameter of $\odot O$, and chord $\overline{GJ}$ intercepts an arc measuring $70°$.

Find the degree measure of each angle indicated below.

16. $\angle DCF$

17. $\angle RPQ$

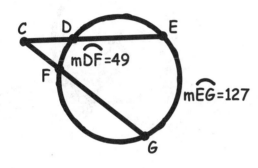

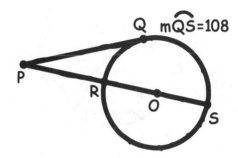

Answer each question below.

(c) 18. Find r.

19. Find x.

(d) 20. Find y.

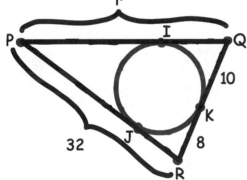

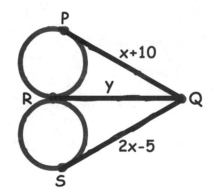

Write an equation to represent each question below; then solve the equation to get your answer. Estimate your answers to two decimal places.

21. Chuck measured the angle from the water level to the top of the deckhouse on the opposite side of the lake to be $4°$. If he knows that the top of the deckhouse is 28 feet above the water, how far is it across the lake?

22. Shelly wants the angle of the roof of her dog's house to be 28°. If the peak of the roof needs to rise 2 feet above the level of the walls, how long does the roof panel (one of the roof's slanted sides) need to be?

Do each proof below.

(e) 23. Do the following proof <u>informally</u>.
Given: A regular polygon
Prove: The central angles are congruent.

24. Given: *OABC* is a square
Prove: $m\overparen{MN} = m\overparen{SR}$

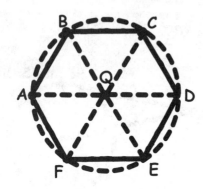

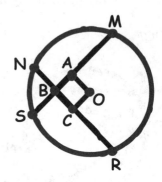

Lesson 94—Area of a Circle, Etc.

We've learned how to calculate the area of all sorts of polygons (with straight sides). But we haven't yet talked about the area of a circle. We'll cover that in this lesson, as well as some other things on area, to finish up the chapter.

Regular Polygon Becomes a Circle

The area of a circle is closely related to the area of a regular polygon. The reason is that as the number of sides of a regular polygon increases, it starts to look more and more like a circle. Check out the diagrams below.

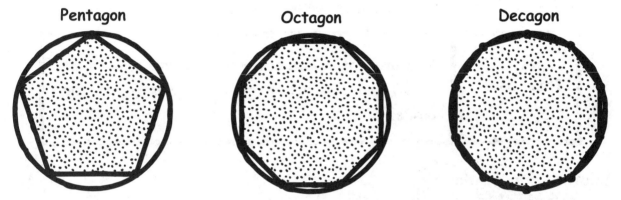

As the number of sides goes up, a regular polygon looks more like a circle.

The regular pentagon, which only has 5 sides, is shaped quite a bit differently from the circle that circumscribes it. The regular octagon, with its 8 sides, looks much more like the circle. The regular decagon, which has 10 sides, has practically the same shape as the circle. Imagine, then, what a polygon with 20 or 30 or 50 sides would look like. It would look almost exactly like the circle circumscribing it.

What does this have to do with area? Well, if a regular polygon with lots of sides is so much like a circle, then the formula for the area of a regular polygon and the formula for the area of a circle should be related. To refresh your memory, the formula for the area of a regular polygon is $\frac{1}{2} \times \text{apothem} \times \text{perimeter}$. As it turns out, the only difference between this formula and the one for the area of a circle is that the apothem is replaced by the circle's radius (r), and the perimeter is replaced by the circle's circumference ($2\pi r$). So $\frac{1}{2} \times \text{apothem} \times \text{perimeter}$ becomes

$$\frac{1}{2} \times r \times 2\pi r .$$

This can be simplified by multiplying $\frac{1}{2}$ and 2 to get πr^2. You've probably worked with the formula πr^2 many times. But in case you're rusty, we'll use it to calculate the area of a circle with a radius of 9 inches. All we have to do is put 9 in for r and then figure out the value of the expression on the right.

$$A = \pi(9)^2$$

Simplifying, we get $\qquad\qquad A = 81\pi.$

So the area of the circle is 81π square inches. (Notice that even a circle uses "square" units— inches in this case—to measure area.) Since π is an irrational number, 81π can't be simplified any further. We could estimate the answer, though, by punching π into a calculator. As you probably know, to two decimal places π equals 3.14. So that gives us $81 \cdot 3.14$ or about 254.34 square inches. Here's the formal theorem for calculating the area of a circle.

Area of a Circle = πr²

Theorem 84	The area of a circle is equal to the product of pi (π) and the square of the radius (r) of the circle.

Sector of a Circle

Sometimes, instead of finding the area of an entire circle, we need to find the area of just a part of the circle. Take the shaded area given on the right for example. The shaded area is called a **sector** of the circle. A sector is shaped like a piece of pie, as you can see. But we can find the area of a sector pretty easily. We start with the central angle of the sector, $\angle AOB$, which measures $60°$. Since $60°$ is one-sixth of the way around the entire

The shaded area is a sector of the circle

circle ($360°$), the sector must have an area equaling one-sixth of the area of the entire circle. The radius equals 7, so the circle has an area of $\pi(7)^2$ or 49π. Dividing that by 6 gives us $\dfrac{49\pi}{6}$ or about 25.64 square units. Here is the formal definition for a sector of a circle.

Definition 79	A sector of a circle is a region of a circle bounded by an arc of the circle and the two radii to the endpoints of the arc.

If the central angle isn't a nice round number like $60°$, then the calculation can be done more formally using the proportion in Theorem 85.

Proportion for Area of Sector of a Circle

Theorem 85	$\dfrac{\text{Area of sector}}{\text{Area of circle}} = \dfrac{\text{Degree measure}}{360°}$

It's really similar to the proportion for calculating the arc length of a circle. To use the sector area proportion, we put the area of the circle and the degree measure of the sector's central angle into the equation. That leaves the area of the sector as the only unknown: $\dfrac{\text{Area of sector}}{49\pi} = \dfrac{60}{360}$.

Solving will give us $\dfrac{49\pi}{6}$ or about 25.64, which we know is correct.

Segment of a Circle

There's also such a thing as a segment of a circle. A **segment** is the area between a chord and the minor arc that it cuts off, as shown in the diagram on the right. Calculating the area of a segment isn't as hard as it seems. All we have to do is find the area of the sector AOB and of triangle AOB, then subtract the two. We know that sector AOB has an area of $\dfrac{49\pi}{6}$. Let's say that $\triangle AOB$ has an area of 21 square units. We just subtract those two like this.

The shaded area is a segment of the circle

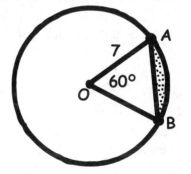

$$\text{Area of segment} = \frac{49\pi}{6} - 21$$

This answer can also be estimated. To two decimal places, it's equal to 4.64 square units. Here is the formal definition for a segment of a circle.

Definition 80	A segment of a circle is a region of a circle bounded by a chord and the minor arc that it intercepts.

Area and Similar Figures

There's one last concept we should talk about before finishing this chapter. It's the relationship between area and similar figures. We already know that congruent figures have the same area. But what about the area of similar figures? Let's take the very simple case of two similar squares.

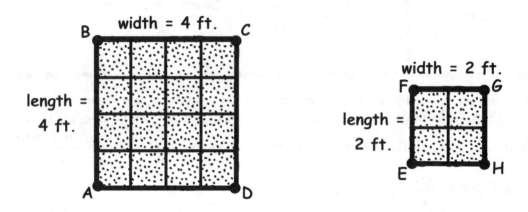

These are the same shape but a different size. And the ratio of the sides is 2 to 1. In other words, every side of square *ABCD* is twice as long as the corresponding side of square *EFGH*. But here's the important question. Is the ratio of the areas also 2 to 1? No it's not. Square *ABCD* has an area of 16 square feet and square *EFGH* has an area of 4 square feet. Dividing those gives us a ratio of 4 to 1. And notice that 4 is the square of 2 and 1 is the square of itself. So the ratio of the areas is the square of the ratio of the sides.

What's interesting is that it always works this way with the area of similar figures. To find the ratio of the areas, all we have to do is square the numbers in the ratio of the sides. For instance, if the sides have a ratio of 3 to 1, then the areas will have a ratio of 3^2 to 1^2 or 9 to 1. If the sides have a ratio of 1 to 4, then the areas will have a ratio of 1^2 to 4^2, which is 1 to 16. It even works when the ratios are more complicated: If the ratio of the sides is 2 to 3, then the ratio of the areas has to be 2^2 to 3^2 or 4 to 9.

The squares above show why this rule works. Both the length and the width of square *ABCD* are twice as long as the length and width of square *EFGH*. But when calculating the area of each, we multiply length and width together. That means for the larger square, we multiply 2 twice (for length and for width), which makes the area 4 times greater than the area of the smaller square. And importantly, this works no matter what shape the figures have. As long as they're similar, the ratio of the areas will always be the square of the ratio of the corresponding sides. Here's the official theorem.

$$\frac{\text{Area of polygon 1}}{\text{Area of polygon 2}} = \frac{(\text{Side of polygon 1})^2}{(\text{Side of polygon 2})^2}$$

Theorem 86	If two polygons are similar, then the ratio of their areas is equal to the square of the ratio of the lengths of any pair of corresponding sides.

Practice 94

a. Calculate the area of the shaded region.

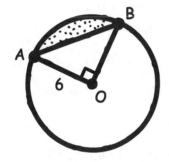

b. Find the perimeter of the figure below.

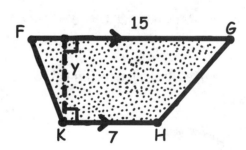

c. If the area of $FGHK = 55$, find y.

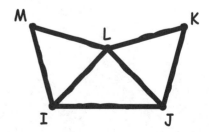

d. Trapezoid $WXYZ$ is similar to trapezoid $CDEF$. Trapezoid $WXYZ$ has $\overline{XY} \parallel \overline{WZ}$ and $\overline{XY} \perp \overline{YZ}$. If $XY = 16$, $WZ = 20$, $YZ = 12$, and $DE = 24$, what is the area of trapezoid $CDEF$?

e. Do the proof below.
Given: $\overline{JL} \cong \overline{IL}$; $\overline{KL} \cong \overline{ML}$; $m\angle JLM = m\angle KLI$
Prove: area of polygon $KLIJ$ = area of polygon $MLJI$

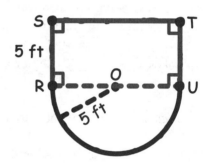

Problem Set 94

Tell whether each sentence below is True or False.

1. A sector of a circle is a region of a circle bounded by an arc of the circle and the two radii to the end points of the arc.

2. A segment of a circle is a region of a circle bounded by a chord and the minor arc that it intercepts.

Complete each sentence below by filling in the blanks.

3. The proportion for the area of a sector of a circle is _____.

4. If two polygons are similar, then the ratio of their areas is equal to the _____ of the ratio of the lengths of any two corresponding sides.

5. The _____ of a regular polygon is the center of its circumscribed circle.

Find the linear measure of each arc described below.

6. An arc whose central angle measures 144° on a circle of radius 35 inches.

7. Major arc $\overset{\frown}{BAC}$ on $\odot O$ where $m\angle BOC = 120$ and $OA = 36$ cm.

Calculate the area of each shaded region below.

8.

9.

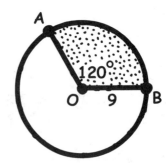

(a) 10.

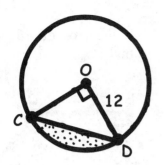

11.

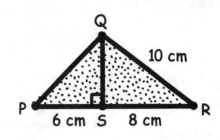

Answer each question below.

12. In right $\triangle FGH$, $m\angle G = m\angle F + m\angle H$ and $FG = GH$. If $FH = 8\sqrt{2}$ inches, what is the area of $\triangle FGH$?

13. In $\triangle TUV$, $TU = 51$ feet and $UV = 40$ feet. If the altitude drawn to side TV has length 24 feet, what is the length TV?

Find the perimeter of each figure below.

14.

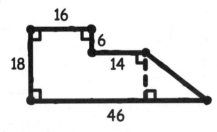

(b) 15.

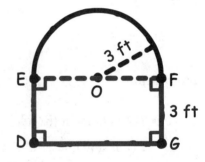

Find each missing line segment below.

16. Find TS.

17. If $PT = 16$, find QU.

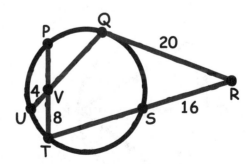

Answer each question below.

18. Find d.

19. Find n.

(c) 20. If the area of $ABCD = 30$, find x.

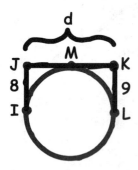

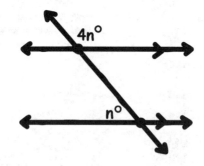

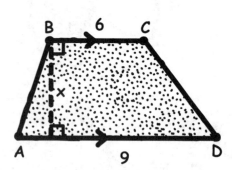

Write an equation to represent each question below; then solve the equation to get your answer.

21. In $\triangle BCD$, $\angle B$ is a right angle, $BC = 6$, $CD = 10$, and $BD = 8$. If $\triangle BCD \sim \triangle FGH$ and $FH = 32$, what is the area of $\triangle FGH$?

(d) 22. Trapezoid $JKLM$ is similar to trapezoid $QRST$. Trapezoid $JKLM$ has $\overline{JM} \parallel \overline{KL}$ and $\overline{JM} \perp \overline{ML}$. If $JM = 14$, $KL = 10$, $ML = 8$, and $QT = 21$, what is the area of trapezoid $QRST$?

Do each proof below.

23. Given: $\overline{TQ}$ is tangent to $\odot O$ at Q;
$\quad$ $\overline{PQ}$ is a diameter of $\odot O$;
$\quad$ Q is the midpoint of $\overset{\frown}{RQS}$
Prove: $\triangle QPT \sim \triangle QRP$

(e) 24. Given: $\overline{SQ} \cong \overline{RQ}$; $\overline{TQ} \cong \overline{PQ}$;
$\quad$ $m\angle SQP = m\angle TQR$
Prove: Area of polygon $TQRS =$
$\quad$ Area of polygon $PQSR$

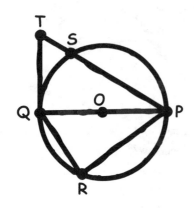

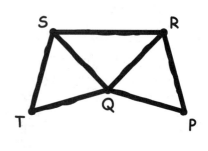

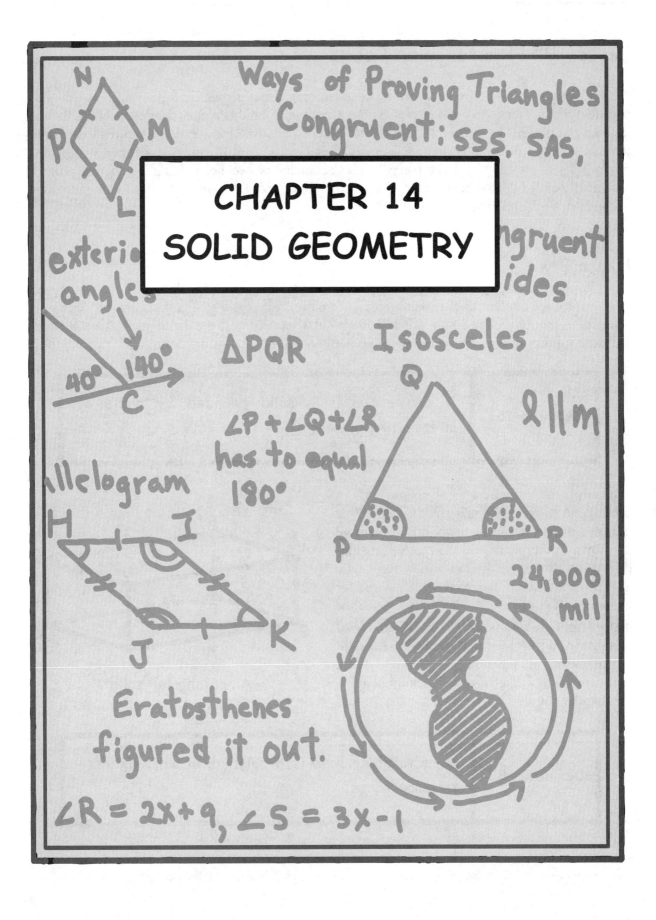

Ways of Proving Triangles Congruent: SSS, SAS,

CHAPTER 14
SOLID GEOMETRY

exterior angles

ngruent ides

40° 140°
C

ΔPQR

∠P+∠Q+∠R has to equal 180°

Isosceles
Q

ℓ ∥ m

P   R

llelogram
H   I

J   K

24,000 mil

Eratosthenes figured it out.

∠R = 2x + 9, ∠S = 3x − 1

Lesson 95—Rectangular Solids

Throughout this entire book, we've been learning about geometric figures such as triangles, parallelograms, rectangles, and circles. These are actually called "plane" figures, because they all lie on a flat plane (like a piece of paper). But it's also possible for geometric figures to be three-dimensional (or 3-D). 3-D figures are called geometric solids, and the geometry of three-dimensions is called "solid geometry." (The geometry we've been doing up to this point is technically called "plane geometry.") We're going to devote this whole chapter to learning some of the basics of solid geometry.[1]

Like a Box

In plane geometry, we work a lot with polygons, as you know. Polygons are just figures whose sides are straight lines (line segments, actually). There's also a solid geometry version of a polygon, though. Since solids are 3-D, their sides aren't lines; they're planes. A solid figure with sides made up of planes is called a **polyhedron**. Here's the formal definition.

Definition 81	A *polyhedron* is a solid bounded by parts of intersecting planes.

Probably the simplest polyhedron is a rectangular solid, which is basically shaped like a box (although it can be many different sizes) as shown in the picture on the right. The sides of a polyhedron are called *faces*. Rectangle *ABCD* is a face of the rectangular solid, for example. The edges of the sides are called *edges* (surprise, surprise). $\overline{AB}$ is an example of an edge. And the end points are called *vertices*, which means all the points *A* through *H* are vertices. Here's the formal definition of a rectangular solid.

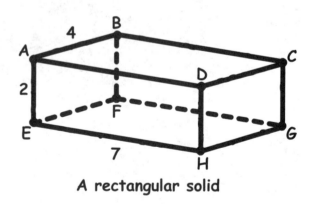

A rectangular solid

Definition 82	A *rectangular solid* is a polyhedron with six rectangular faces.

---

[1] Since solid geometry theorems can be messy, we won't prove every theorem in this chapter.

Surface Area

In the last chapter, we learned how to calculate the area of a flat figure. Well, it's also possible to calculate the area of a solid. What we do is add up the area of all the solid's sides (faces). The total is called the **surface area**. To show how the process works, let's calculate the surface area of the rectangular solid on the last page. Here's the diagram again, only this time we've included the lengths of the edges. Since all of the sides of the solid are rectangles and

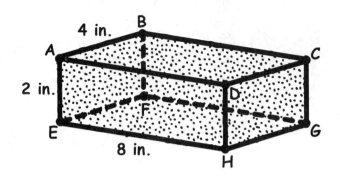

since opposite sides are congruent, the calculation is pretty easy. Faces *ADHE* and *BCGF* are opposite each other, so they have the same dimensions: a length of 8 inches and a width of 2 inches. Multiplying those gives us an area of 16 square inches for each of those sides. The other two sides are *ABFE* and *DCGH*. These have a width of 2 inches and a length of 4 inches, which comes out to an area of 8 square inches for each. Finally, the top and bottom are *ABCD* and *EFGH*. These have a width of 4 inches and a length of 8 inches for an area of 32 square inches for each. Now all we do is add these up.

$$16 \, (ADHE) + 16 \, (BCGF) + 8 \, (ABFE) + 8 \, (DCGH) + 32 \, (ABCD) + 32 \, (EFGH) = 112$$

The total is 112 square inches. That's the surface area of our rectangular solid.

Definition 83	The *surface area* of a rectangular solid is the sum of the areas of all six of its rectangular faces.

Volume

We also sometimes need to measure the amount of space inside a solid. This is called the **volume of the solid.** How do you think that process works? Well, we don't measure with little squares. That only works for flat spaces (areas). To measure volume (which is 3-D space) we use little cubes. In other words, the volume of a solid is basically the number of little cubes that will fit inside of it. For instance, a volume of 48 cubic inches means that the solid has room for exactly 48 little cubes with 1 inch sides. A volume of 8 cubic feet means that the solid has room for 8 not-so-little cubes with 1 foot sides. Here's a picture of our rectangular solid, filled up with 1 inch cubes.

One way to figure out the volume here would be to count all the cubes. That's time consuming, though. An easier way is to multiply the width by the length by the altitude (height).[2] For this rectangular solid, the width is 4, the length is 8 and the altitude is 2. That gives us this.

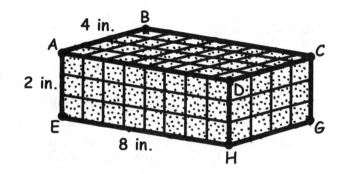

$$\text{Volume} = 4 \cdot 8 \cdot 2 = 64$$

There are 64 cubes inside, which means that the volume of the solid is 64 cubic inches. This can also be written as 64 in.[3].

The volume of any rectangular solid can be calculated in the same way. Instead of proving this rule, we'll accept it as a postulate.

Volume of Rectangular Solid = ℓwa

Postulate 22	The volume of a rectangular solid is equal to the product of the length (ℓ), the width (w), and the altitude (a).

Interestingly, there's another way to write this formula. And this version is very similar to the formula for the area of a flat rectangle. We calculate the area of a rectangle by multiplying the base by the altitude. Well, a solid can also have a base. But instead of a line, a solid's base is an entire side (face). For instance, we can let the bottom of our rectangular solid, *EFGH*, be the base. Then the volume of the solid can be calculated by multiplying the area of the base by the altitude: $V = $ (area of base)(altitude). Since the area of the base *EFGH* is its length times its width, (area of base)(altitude) is the same as ℓwa.

Practice 95

   a. Find the degree measure of arc $\overset{\frown}{AB}$ on the right.

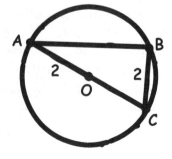

---

[2] Height means the same thing as altitude. But when calculating the volume of a rectangular solid, the word height is used a lot.

Calculate the area of each shaded region below.

b.

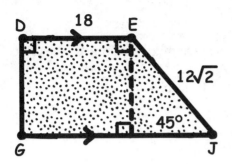

c.

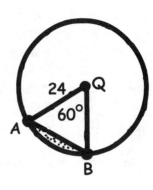

d. Find y.

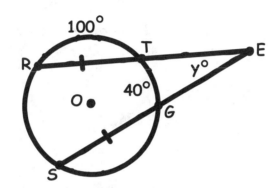

e. Do the proof below.
Given: $\overline{QR}$ is a diameter of $\odot O$; $\overline{PQ} \parallel \overline{AO}$;
$\overline{SQ} \parallel \overline{BO}$; $\overline{RA} \cong \overline{RB}$
Prove: $\overline{RP} \cong \overline{RS}$

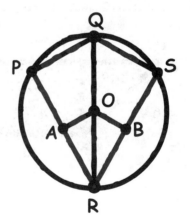

Problem Set 95

Tell whether each sentence below is True or False.

1. A polyhedron is a solid bounded by parts of intersecting planes.

2. A rectangular solid is a polyhedron with six rectangular faces.

Complete each sentence below by filling in the blanks.

3. The amount of space inside a solid is called its _____.

4. The _____ of a solid is the sum of the area of all the solid's sides (faces).

5. The volume of a rectangular solid is equal to the product of the _____, the _____, and the _____.

Find the degree measure of each arc or angle below.

(a) 6. $\overset{\frown}{JI}$

7. $\overset{\frown}{HIJ}$

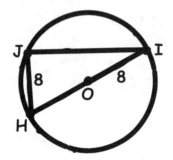

Calculate the area of each shaded region below.

(b) 8.

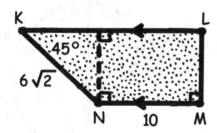

9.

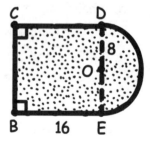

10.

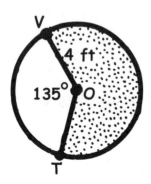

(c) 11.

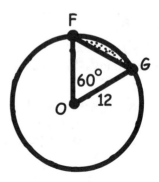

Answer each question below.

12. In $\triangle CDE$, $m\angle C$ is twice $m\angle D$ and $m\angle E$ is three times $m\angle D$. If $CD = 16$, what is DE?

13. Right $\triangle JKL$ has a hypotenuse of length 34 feet and one leg of length 16 feet. What is the area of $\triangle JKL$?

Calculate the surface area and volume of each rectangular solid below.

14.

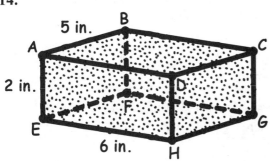

15.

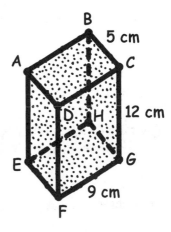

Find the measures of the angles of each triangle described below.

16. $\triangle CDF$ where $m\angle C = 4x$, $m\angle F = 3x$, and $m\angle D$ is twice $m\angle C$.

17. $\triangle RPT$ where R and T lie on $\odot P$ and $m\overset{\frown}{RT} = 108$.

Answer each question below.

18. Find x.

19. Find c in terms of a, b, and d.

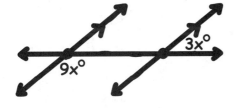

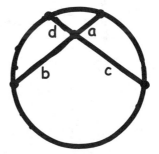

(d) 20. Find x.

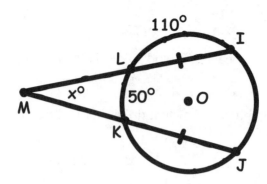

Write a proportion to represent each question below; then solve the proportion to get your answer.

21. The ratio of munchers to nibblers was $23:17$. If there were 612 nibblers, how many munchers were there?

22. The ratio of foot stompers to hand clappers was $15:19$. If there were 228 hand clappers, how many foot stompers were there?

Do each proof below.

23. Given: $\overline{AB}$ and $\overline{CB}$ are tangent segments to $\odot O$.

Prove: $m\angle B = 180 - m\overset{\frown}{AC}$

(e) 24. Given: $\overline{FG}$ is a diameter of $\odot O$; $\overline{EF} \parallel \overline{JO}$; $\overline{HF} \parallel \overline{KO}$; $\overline{GJ} \cong \overline{GK}$

Prove: $\overline{GE} \cong \overline{GH}$

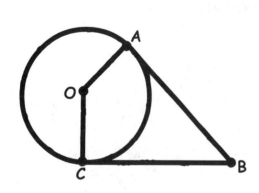

Lesson 96—Prisms

We learned about rectangular solids in the last lesson. Another well-known kind of solid is a prism. A **prism** is a solid where the top and bottom faces are congruent polygons that are parallel to each other (technically, they lie in parallel planes), as shown in the diagram on the right. Here the top and bottom are congruent hexagons, because they have 6 sides each. The top and bottom faces are called the **bases** of the prism, and the other faces are called **lateral faces**. The edges of the prism, where the lateral faces connect, are called lateral edges. And all of the lateral edges are parallel. Here's the formal definition of a prism.

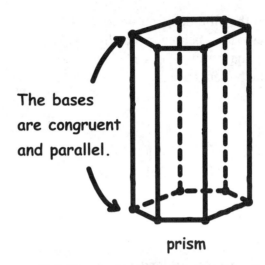

The bases are congruent and parallel.

prism

Definition 84	A *prism* is a polyhedron with two congruent faces, called bases, lying in parallel planes, and with all other faces as parallelograms.

Different Kinds of Prisms

There are lots of different kinds of prisms. These can be broken down into categories according to the shape of their bases. For example, since the bases of the prism above are hexagons, it is considered to be a "hexagonal" prism. There are also pentagonal prisms, with bases that are pentagons, octagonal prisms, with octagon-shaped bases, and so on. Actually, a rectangular solid qualifies as a quadrilateral prism, since its top and bottom bases are quadrilaterals (rectangles).

Another way to categorize prisms is according to their tilt. A prism that is straight up and down (like the one above) is called a *right prism*. The word "right" comes from the fact that the lateral edges of the prism make a right angle with each of the bases. The altitude of a right prism is just the length of one of the lateral edges.

A prism that is tilted to one side is called an *oblique prism*. The word "oblique" means non-right angle, and it refers to the fact that an oblique prism's lateral edges don't make a right angle with either one of the bases.

To find the altitude of an oblique prism, we just run a perpendicular line from the top base down to the plane containing the bottom base.

Another interesting thing about a prism is that the lateral edges are both congruent and parallel to each other. This is true whether the prism is right or oblique.

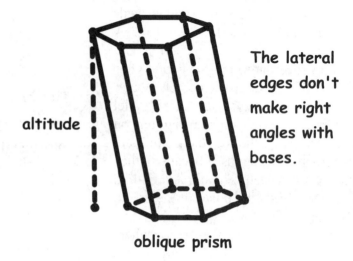

The lateral edges don't make right angles with bases.

altitude

oblique prism

Surface Area of a Prism

The surface area of a prism is just the sum of the areas of all the prism's faces, which includes the two bases and all the lateral faces. Sometimes, the surface area is called the **total area** of the prism and the sum of the area of the lateral faces is called the *lateral area*. Using those terms, the total area of a prism equals the lateral area plus the area of the two bases. Since the bases are congruent, their areas have to be equal. So that gives us the equation below.

Total Area of Prism = Lateral Area + 2 × Area of Base

There's a neat way to calculate the lateral area of a prism. We just multiply the perimeter of a base by the altitude of the prism to get this.

Lateral Area = Perimeter × Altitude

This is the same as adding base times altitude for every one of the lateral faces. And since the lateral faces are all parallelograms, that makes sense. Putting perimeter × altitude in for Lateral Area gives us a formula for the surface area (total area) of a prism. Here it is stated formally.

Total Area of Prism = ap + 2B

Theorem 87	The total area of a prism is equal to the product of the altitude (a) and the perimeter of a base (p) plus 2 times the area of a base (B).

Volume of Prism

Finding the volume of a prism is actually pretty easy. All we have to do is multiply the area of a base by the altitude.

> Volume = Area of Base × Altitude

And the neat thing about this formula is that it works whether a prism is right or oblique. It's kind of like the area formulas for rectangles and parallelograms. Those are both base times altitude, even though a rectangle is straight and a parallelogram is tilted. It's the same with right and oblique prisms, only it's the *area* of the base times the altitude. Here's the formal theorem.

Volume of Prism = Ba

Theorem 88	**The volume of a prism is equal to the product of the area of a base (B) and the altitude (a).**

Regular and Non-regular

You may have noticed that the bases of our two prisms were a little lopsided. That's because the hexagonal bases were not regular hexagons. In other words, their sides and angles were not all congruent. A prism where both bases are regular polygons is called a regular prism. So our examples were actually "non-regular" prisms. Just as regular polygons are simpler than non-regular ones, the same thing is true for regular prisms. For example, it's easier to calculate the surface (total) area or volume for a regular prism than it is for a non-regular prism.[3]

Practice 96

a. Calculate the area of the shaded region below.

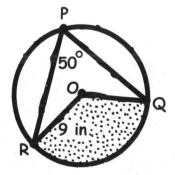

b. Calculate the total area of the prism below. Base is a regular pentagon of area 110.

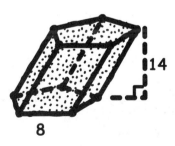

---

[3] That's mainly because it's simpler to calculate the area of a regular polygon than a non-regular polygon.

c. Calculate the volume of the prism.
Area of base = 100

d. Find a.

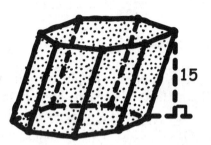

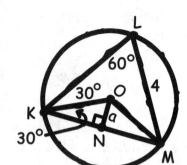

e. Do the proof below.
Given: $\overline{EC}$ is a diameter of $\odot O$; $\overline{DE} \perp \overline{DB}$;
$\overline{DE}$ is tangent to $\odot O$ at E
Prove: $\dfrac{DB}{BE} = \dfrac{BE}{EC}$

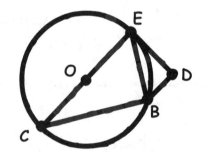

Problem Set 96

Tell whether each sentence below is True or False.

1. A prism is a solid where the top and bottom faces are congruent polygons that are parallel to each other.

2. The total (surface) area of a prism is its length times its width times its altitude.

Complete each sentence below by filling in the blanks.

3. The volume of a prism equals the product of the _____ and the _____.

4. A_____ is a polyhedron with six rectangular faces.

5. A _____ of a circle is a region of a circle bounded by a chord and the minor arc that it intercepts.

Calculate the area of each shaded region below.

6.

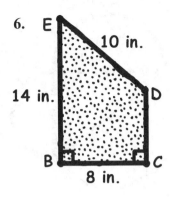

E

10 in.

14 in.

D

B

C

8 in.

7.

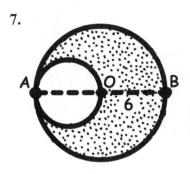

A   O   B

6

(a) 8.

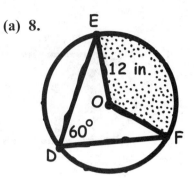

E

12 in.

O

60°

D   F

Identify each prism below.

9.

10.

11.

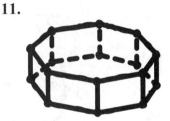

Calculate the total area of each prism below.

12.   Perimeter of base = 26;
       Area of base = 35

9

(b) 13.   Base is a regular pentagon;
           Area of base = 27.5

7

4

Calculate the volume of each prism below.

14.   Area of base = 35

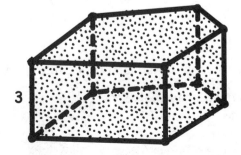

3

(c) 15.   Area of base = 127

14

Find the perimeter of each figure below. (All the arcs are semicircles.)

16.

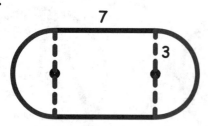

17.

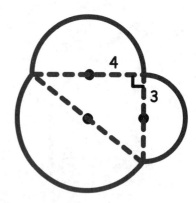

Answer each question below.

18. Find *m*.

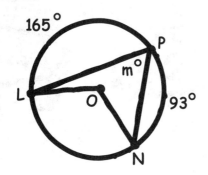

19. Find *x*.

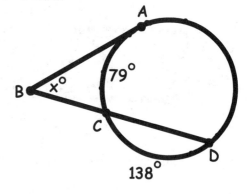

(d) 20. Find *a*.

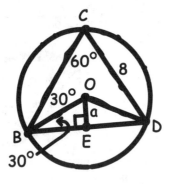

Find each ratio below.

21. The perimeter of a square with a side length of *s* is equal to the circumference of a circle of radius *r*. What is the ratio of *s* to *r*? (*Hint*: Set up an equation and solve for $\frac{s}{r}$.)

22. The area of a square with a side length of *s* is equal to the area of a circle of radius *r*. What is the ratio of *s* to *r*? (*Hint*: Set up an equation and solve for $\frac{s}{r}$.)

Do each proof below.

23. Given: $\overline{BC} \parallel \overline{AD}$; $\overarc{AB} \cong \overarc{CD}$

Prove: $\angle A \cong \angle D$

(e) 24. Given: $\overline{LN}$ is a diameter of $\odot O$; $\overline{KL}$ is tangent to $\odot O$ at L; $\overline{KL} \perp \overline{KM}$

Prove: $\dfrac{KM}{ML} = \dfrac{ML}{LN}$

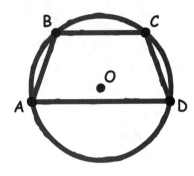

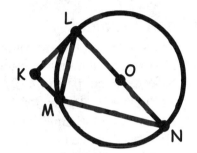

Lesson 97—Pyramids

The third geometric solid that we're going to study is the pyramid. Everybody knows the general shape of a pyramid because of the many pictures of Egyptian pyramids. In fact, we showed a drawing of an Egyptian pyramid way back in Lesson 1. You can flip back and take a quick look if you want.

Parts of a Pyramid

The parts of a pyramid are somewhat similar to those of a prism. For example, like a prism, a pyramid has a *base*. (In the diagram below, the base is on bottom.) The sides of a pyramid are called *lateral faces*, and the lines where those faces intersect are called *edges*. Those names are also the same for prisms. But one difference between a pyramid and a prism is that a **pyramid** has only one base. The other end of the pyramid is a point, which is called the *vertex* of the pyramid.

A pyramid also has an *altitude*. It's just a line segment that extends from the vertex to the base and makes a right angle with the base.

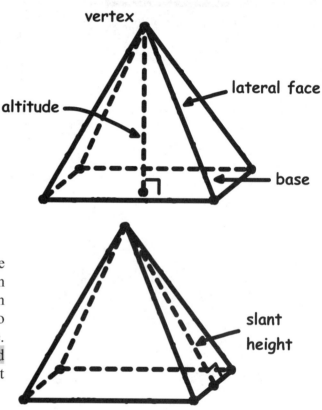

Not only does the entire pyramid have an altitude, but each lateral face has its own altitude. That's a line segment running from the vertex down to one side of the base, so that the segment is perpendicular to that side. The altitude of a lateral face is actually called the *slant height* of the pyramid (because that line segment is slanted).

Different Kinds of Pyramids

There are regular and non-regular pyramids. A *regular pyramid* has a regular polygon for a base and lateral edges that are all congruent. The Great Pyramid in Egypt is an example of a regular pyramid. It has a base that is a square (which is a regular quadrilateral).[4]

---

[4] Non-regular pyramids are actually pretty uncommon, so most of the pyramids you'll encounter will be regular.

When the lateral edges are not all the same length, a pyramid will tilt to one side. In this pyramid, the edges on the left are shorter than those on the right. Notice also that the base here is a pentagon, rather than a quadrilateral. That means this is a "pentagonal pyramid." It has 5 edges instead of 4. It's also possible for a pyramid to have a base that's a triangle, which would make it a "triangular pyramid," a hexagon base (hexagonal pyramid), an octagon base (octagonal pyramid), etc. In each case, the number of edges will be different. Here's the formal definition of a pyramid, which covers all the possible kinds.

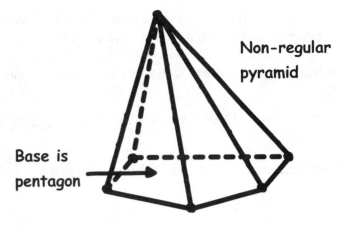

Non-regular pyramid

Base is pentagon

Definition 85	A *pyramid* is a polyhedron in which all faces but one have a point in common. That common point is called the vertex and the face that does not contain the vertex is called the base.

Total Area of a Regular Pyramid

The total area of a pyramid is the sum of the area of all the lateral faces (the lateral area) plus the area of the base. Since each lateral face is a triangle, the area of a face can be calculated using the formula $\frac{1}{2}ba$ (the formula for the area of a triangle). The altitude of a face is its slant height, remember.

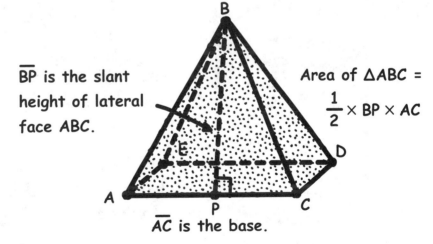

$\overline{BP}$ is the slant height of lateral face ABC.

Area of $\triangle ABC = \frac{1}{2} \times BP \times AC$

$\overline{AC}$ is the base.

And its base is the bottom of the face (one of the sides of the pyramid's base). So the area of a lateral face equals one-half the product of the slant height and the face's base.

When a pyramid is non-regular, the area of each lateral face has to be calculated separately, because each face might have a different altitude. But for a regular pyramid, we can get the area of all the lateral faces at once by multiplying one-half the product of the slant height—which has to be the same for every face—by the perimeter of the base of the pyramid.

$$\text{Lateral Area} = \frac{1}{2} \times \text{Slant Height} \times \text{Perimeter of Pyramid's Base}$$

That means we can calculate the total area of a regular pyramid with the following formula.

$$\text{Total Area of a Regular Pyramid} = \frac{1}{2}\ell p + B$$

Theorem 89	The total area of a regular pyramid is equal to one-half the product of the perimeter of the base (p) and the slant height (ℓ) plus the area of the base (B).

Volume of a Pyramid

The formula for the volume of a pyramid is surprisingly simple. You may remember that a prism's volume is the area of its base times its altitude (Ba). If we compare a prism and a pyramid that have the same base and altitude, it's pretty easy to see that the pyramid must have a smaller volume than the prism.

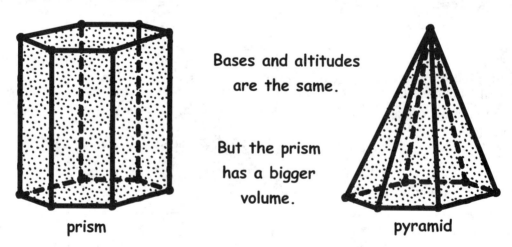

Bases and altitudes are the same.

But the prism has a bigger volume.

prism   pyramid

So it makes sense that the pyramid should have a volume which is less than Ba. Actually, the volume of the pyramid is one-third the volume of the prism. So the pyramid's volume is $\frac{1}{3}Ba$.

That means exactly three of the pyramids on the right would fit inside the prism on the left. This is the formal theorem for the volume of a pyramid.

$$\text{Volume of a Pyramid} = \frac{1}{3}\, Ba$$

Theorem 90	The volume of a pyramid is equal to one-third of the product of the area of the base (B) and the altitude (a).

Practice 97

a. Find the area of the shaded region.

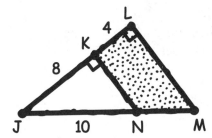

b. Calculate the total area of the solid. The top is a square.

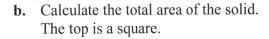
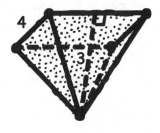

c. Calculate the volume of the solid The altitude of the pyramid is 10. The base is a regular pentagon of area 45.

d. Find *m* in terms of *n*, *p*, and *q*.

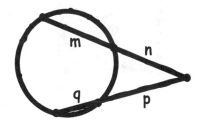

e. Do the proof below.

Given: A regular polygon
Prove: A radius of the polygon bisects an interior angle of the polygon.

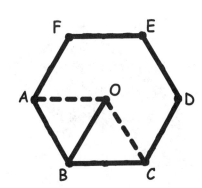

Problem Set 97

Tell whether each sentence below is True or False.

1. A pyramid has a base on one end and a point, called the vertex, on the other end.

2. The volume of any pyramid is equal to one-third the product of the area of its base and its altitude.

Complete each sentence below by filling in the blanks.

3. The altitude of a lateral face of a pyramid is called the _____ of the pyramid.

4. The total area of a prism is equal to the product of the _____ and the _____ of a base plus 2 times the _____.

5. If two polygons are similar, then the ratio of their areas is equal to the _____ of the ratio of the lengths of any two corresponding sides.

Calculate the area of each shaded region below.

6. *PQRS* is a square

7. *IML* and *JMK* are sectors

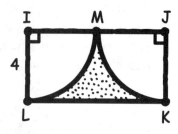

8.

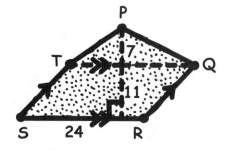

(a) 9.

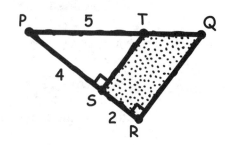

Identify each figure below.

10.

11.

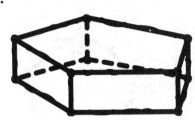

12.

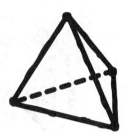

Calculate the total area of each solid below.

13.

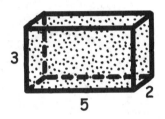

(b) 14. The base is a square.

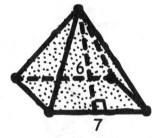

Calculate the volume of each solid described below.

15. Area of base = 94

16. Area of base = 27

(c) 17. Base is a regular pentagon of area 27.
The altitude of the pyramid is 7.

Answer each question below.

18. Find *a*.

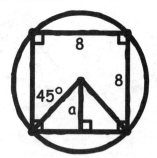

19. Find *b*.

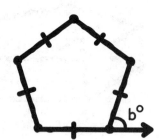

(d) 20. Find *s* in terms of *t*, *u*, and *v*.

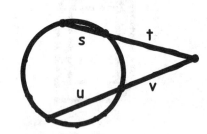

Find each missing line segment below.

21. Find *DO*.

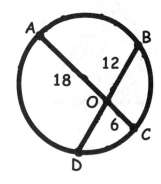

22. Find *AK*.

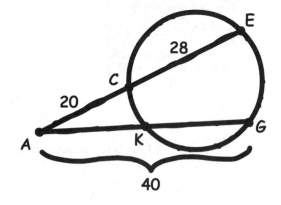

Do each proof below.

23. Given: $\overline{FG} \parallel \overline{DE}$

Prove: $\overset{\frown}{DF} \cong \overset{\frown}{EG}$

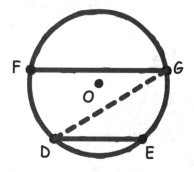

(e) 24. Given: A regular polygon

Prove: A radius of the polygon bisects an interior angle of the polygon

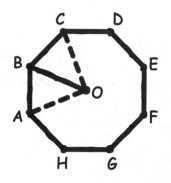

Lesson 98—Cylinders and Cones

So far, all of our solids have had polygons for sides. But there are also solids with circles for sides. One example is a cylinder. A **cylinder** is a lot like a prism in that the bases on the top and bottom are parallel and congruent to each other. But instead of being polygons, the bases of a cylinder are circles.

Cylinders

A cylinder is actually made up of three separate surfaces. The first two are the flat circular bases, and the third is the rounded middle section. Since it's round, the middle section doesn't have any edges, which means the cylinder has no lateral faces. The entire middle section is just called the *lateral surface*. A cylinder also has a *radius*. That's just the radius of each of the circular bases.

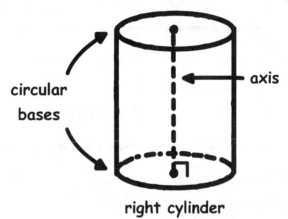

right cylinder

You may remember that there are right prisms and oblique prisms. Well, it's the same with cylinders. They can be right or oblique. Notice that we've drawn a line segment between the centers of the circular bases in both of the cylinders pictured. This segment is called the *axis* of the cylinder. The axis is what determines whether a cylinder is right or oblique. The cylinder on top is a *right cylinder*, because the axis makes a right angle where it intersects the bases. The cylinder on bottom is an *oblique cylinder*, because the axis doesn't make a right angle with the bases. And that causes the cylinder to tilt, as you can see. Here is the formal definition of a cylinder.

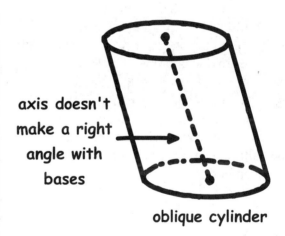

oblique cylinder

Definition 86	A *cylinder* is a solid with two congruent circular faces, called bases, lying in parallel planes. The surface lying between the bases is called the lateral surface.

Volume of a Cylinder

Since a cylinder is so much like a prism, it's not surprising that their volume formulas are very much alike. Remember, the volume of a prism is just the area of its base times its altitude. Well, the volume of a cylinder is also base times altitude. But since the bases of a cylinder are always circles, instead of writing "area of the base", we go ahead and stick in the formula for the area of a circle, which is πr^2. That gives us the following formal theorem.

Volume of a Cylinder = $\pi r^2 a$

Theorem 91	The volume of a cylinder is equal to the product of π (pi), the square of the radius (r), and the altitude of the cylinder (a).

For a right cylinder, the altitude is the same as the axis. So that makes things easy. But for an oblique cylinder, the altitude and axis are different lengths. To find the volume of an oblique cylinder, then, we need to measure the altitude, which is a segment that goes from the top base down to the plane that contains the bottom base. And depending on which point you start from on top, the altitude may fall outside the circle on bottom.

For an oblique cylinder, the altitude is not the same as the axis.

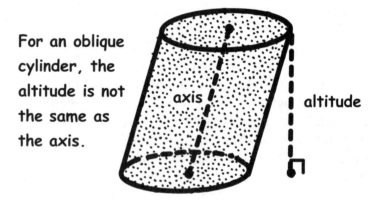

Cones

Just as a cylinder is a lot like a prism, a cone is a lot like a pyramid. You know that a pyramid has a polygon for a base at one end and a point, called the vertex, at the other end. Well, a **cone** has a circular base at one end and a point (again called the vertex) at the other end. But instead of having flat triangle-shaped faces (like a pyramid), a cone's middle section is a curved surface, called its *lateral surface*. The *slant height* of a cone is the length from the vertex down to the edge of the circular base. A cone also has an *axis*, which is the segment extending from the vertex on top to

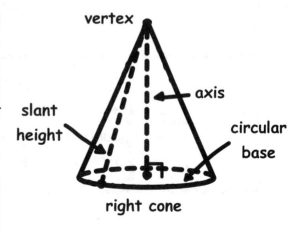

662

the base on bottom. And since, in the picture, the axis is perpendicular to the base, this qualifies as a *right cone*.

There's also such a thing as an oblique cone. An *oblique cone* is a cone whose axis is not perpendicular to the circular base. Oblique cones have a tilt, as you can see. Technically, an oblique cone doesn't have a slant height, since the distance from the vertex to the edge of the circular base is different as you go around the cone.

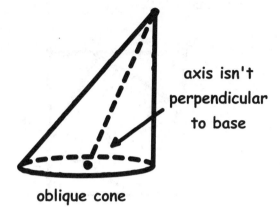

axis isn't perpendicular to base

oblique cone

The definition of a cone (whether it's right or oblique) is very similar to the definition of a pyramid.

Definition 87	A *cone* is a solid with a circular base on one end and a vertex on the other. The surface lying between the base and vertex is called the lateral surface.

Volume of a Cone

Since a cone is so similar to a pyramid, you might expect their volume formulas to be similar as well. Remember, the volume of a pyramid equals one-third times the area of the base times the altitude ($\frac{1}{3}Ba$). As it turns out, the volume of a cone is also $\frac{1}{3}Ba$. But since the base of a cone is always a circle, we use πr^2 for the area of the base. That gives us the formal theorem below.

$$\text{Volume of a Cone} = \frac{1}{3}\pi r^2 a$$

Theorem 92	The volume of a cone is equal to one-third the product of π (pi), the square of the radius (r), and the altitude of the cone (a).

Of course, if the cone is oblique, then the altitude will be a different length than the axis. And you'll need the length of the altitude to do the volume calculation.

Practice 98

a. Calculate the area of square *ABCD*.

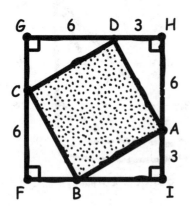

b. Calculate the total area of the prism.

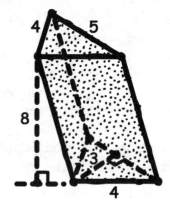

c. Calculate the volume of the solid.

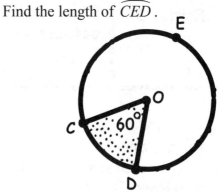

d. The area of the shaded region is $\dfrac{24}{\pi}$.

Find the length of $\overparen{CED}$.

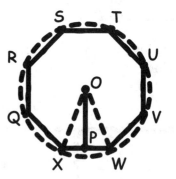

e. Do the proof below.
Given: A regular polygon
Prove: An apothem of the polygon bisects a central angle of the polygon.

Problem Set 98

Tell whether each sentence below is True or False.

1. A cylinder is like a prism, except it has circles for bases instead of polygons.

2. A cone is like a pyramid, except it has a circle for a base instead of a polygon.

Complete each sentence below by filling in the blanks.

3. The volume of a cylinder is equal to the area of the base times the altitude, but since the base is a circle, the formula is written as _____.

4. The volume of a cone is equal to one third of the area of the base times the altitude, but since the base is a circle, the formula is written as _____.

5. The total area of a prism is equal to the product of the _____ and the _____ of a base plus 2 times the area of a _____.

Calculate the area of each shaded region below.

(a) 6. Square *PQRS*

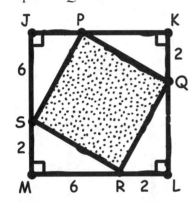

7. △*OIM*

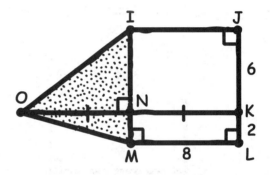

8.

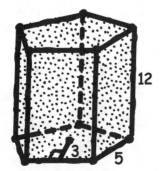

Calculate the total area of each solid below.

9. Base is a regular pentagon

(b) 10. Triangular prism

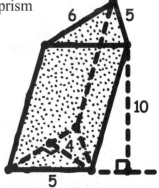

665

Calculate the volume of each solid described below.

11.

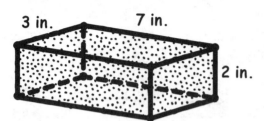

3 in.   7 in.

2 in.

12.

8

23

(c) 13.

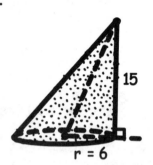

15

r = 6

Find the perimeter of each polygon below.

14.

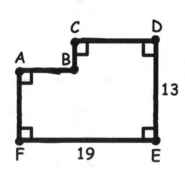

C   D

A   B

13

F   19   E

15.

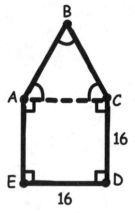

B

A   C

16

E   D

16

Find the degree measure of each arc or angle below.

16.   ∠BPD

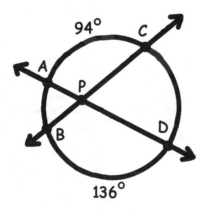

94°   C

A

P

B   D

136°

17.   ∠JPH

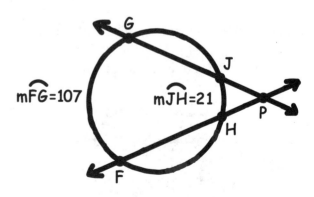

G

J

mFG=107   mJH=21

P

F   H

666

Answer each question below.

18. Find *a*.

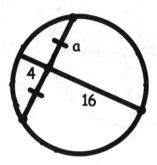

19. Find *c*.

(d) 20. The area of the shaded region is $\dfrac{6}{\pi}$. Find the length of $\overset{\frown}{IKJ}$.

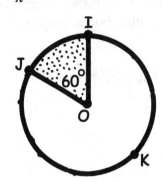

Write an equation to represent each question below; then solve the equation to get your answer. Estimate your answers to two decimal places.

21. Alex wants to build a skateboard ramp out of a 10-foot-long piece of plywood. For maximum performance, he wants the angle of the ramp to be 21°. How high does the piece of plywood need to be lifted at one end?

22. Viewed from the side, the frame of a soccer goal forms a right triangle. A horizontal bar on the ground measures 7 feet. If the diagonal bar is angled at 62° up from the ground, how long is the diagonal bar?

Do each proof below.

23. Given: $\overline{BC}$ is tangent to $\odot O$ at B;
        $\overline{AB}$ is a diameter of $\odot O$
Prove: $\triangle ABC \sim \triangle ADB \sim \triangle BDC$

(e) 24. Given: A regular polygon
Prove: An apothem of the polygon bisects a central angle of the polygon.

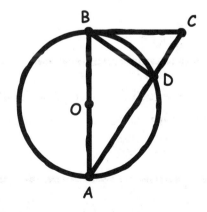

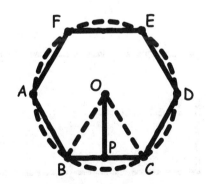

Lesson 99—Spheres

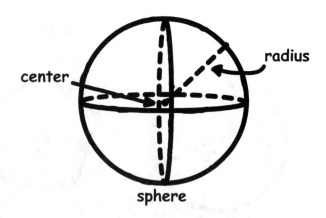

In the last lesson, we talked about cones and cylinders, which are solids with some round parts. But the simplest of all the round solids is the sphere. A **sphere** is shaped like a ball.

The definition of a sphere is very similar to the definition of a circle. Remember, a circle is defined as all the points in a plane that are the same distance from a point, which is the center of the circle. Well, a **sphere** is just all the points in 3-D space that are the same distance from the center. The distance from the center to the sphere's edge is the radius of the sphere. So, like a circle, a sphere also has a radius. Here's the definition stated formally.

Definition 88	A *sphere* is the set of all points in space that are at a given distance from a given point, called the center.

Volume and Surface Area of a Sphere

To do a complete proof of the formulas for the volume and surface area of a sphere requires a knowledge of calculus. So we'll skip the proofs and just show you the formulas for each. Both formulas have just one variable: the radius of the sphere. That means to calculate the volume or surface area of a sphere, all we need to know is the sphere's radius. It works just like a circle, where we only need to know the radius to calculate a circle's circumference or area. Here's the actual theorem for the formula for the volume of a sphere (which is $\frac{4}{3}\pi r^3$).

$$\text{Volume of a Sphere} = \frac{4}{3}\pi r^3$$

Theorem 93	The volume of a sphere is equal to four-thirds of the product of π (pi) and the cube of the radius of the sphere (r).

Once you have the formula for the volume of a sphere, you can find the formula for a sphere's surface area in a single step, using calculus. In fact, it's so easy, the step can actually be done in your head. The other interesting thing is that the formula looks very much like the formula for volume. Here's the actual surface area formula.

Surface Area of a Sphere = 4πr²

Theorem 94	The surface area of a sphere is equal to four times the product of π (pi) and the square of the radius of the sphere (r).

Volume and Surface Area of the Earth

To show you how easy these formulas are to use, let's calculate the surface area and volume of a really large sphere: the earth.[5] Even though the numbers are huge, the process is still pretty simple. All we need to do is plug the radius of the earth in for r in each formula. The earth's radius is about 4,000 miles. We'll figure out the surface area first. The formula is $4\pi r^2$. We could change the units from miles to something else, like feet or even inches. But since the radius is so long, we'll leave it in miles. So putting 4,000 in for r gives us

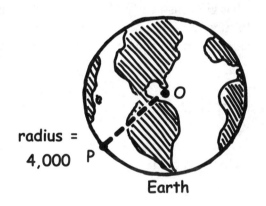

radius = 4,000

Earth

$$4\pi(4,000)^2.$$

Now we just simplify.

$$4\pi(16,000,000)$$

$$64,000,000\pi \text{ square miles}$$

We end up with 64 million π square miles. To estimate that, let's multiply 64 million by 3.14 (which is π to two decimal places).

Surface Area of Earth = 200,960,000 square miles

The earth's surface has enough room for nearly 201 million squares, each with sides that are 1 mile long! That's a lot of space.

---

[5] Technically, the earth is not a perfect sphere. But it's close enough for our purposes.

Now let's figure out the volume of the earth. We just put 4,000 miles into the formula for volume, which is $\frac{4}{3}\pi r^3$.

$$\frac{4}{3}\pi(4,000)^3$$

Simplifying gives us this.[6]

$$\frac{4}{3}\pi(64,000,000,000)$$

$$85,333,333,333.\bar{3}\pi \text{ cubic miles}$$

We end up with over 85 billion π cubic miles, which can be estimated by multiplying 85 billion by 3.14.

$$267,946,666,667 \text{ cubic miles}$$

That gives us nearly 268 billion cubic miles. In other words, there's enough room inside the earth to fit about 268 billion cubes, each with sides that are 1 mile long! Of course, if we had done the calculations in square feet and cubic feet, the numbers would have been a lot bigger.

Practice 99

a. Calculate the area of the shaded region.

b. Calculate the total area of the trapezoidal right prism below.

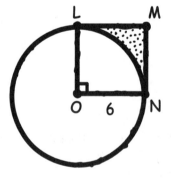

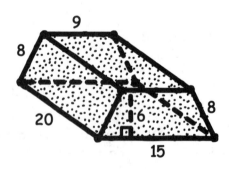

_____

[6] The little bar over the last 3 just means that the 3 repeats

c. Calculate the volume of the oblique prism below in cubic meters. The base is a regular hexagon.

d. Find x.

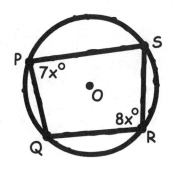

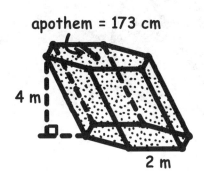

apothem = 173 cm

4 m

2 m

e. Do the proof below.
Given: Quadrilateral $FGHJ$ is inscribed in $\odot O$.
Prove: $m\angle F + m\angle H = 180$ and $m\angle G + m\angle J = 180$

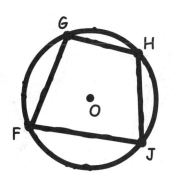

Problem Set 99

Tell whether each sentence below is True or False.

1. A sphere is the set of all points in space that are at a given distance from a given point, called the center.

2. The volume and surface area of a sphere can both be calculated if you know the radius of the sphere.

Complete each sentence below by filling in the blanks.

3. The volume of a rectangular solid is equal to the product of the _____, the _____, and the _____.

4. The volume of a pyramid is equal to one third of the area of the _____ times the _____.

5. The area of a trapezoid is equal to one-half the product of the length of the _____ and the _____ of the lengths of its bases.

Find the degree measure of each arc or angle below.

6. $\overarc{AB}$

7. $\angle BDC$

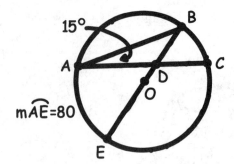

Calculate the area of each shaded region below.

8.

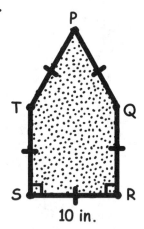

9.

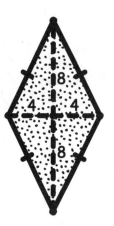

(a) 10.

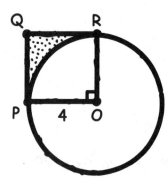

Calculate the total area of each solid below.

11. Sphere

(b) 12. Trapezoidal right prism

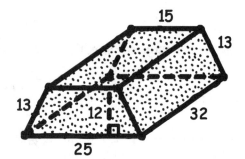

Calculate the volume of each solid described below.

13. Cube

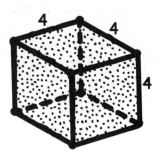

14. Sphere

(c) 15. Base is a regular hexagon. Find the volume in cubic meters.

apothem = 87 cm

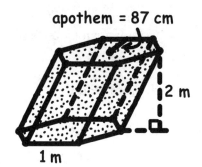

2 m

1 m

Find each missing line segment below.

16. Find *KM*.

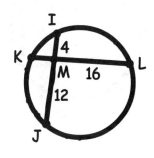

17. Find *IJ*.

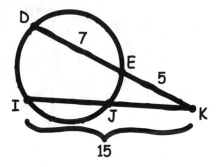

Answer each question below.

18. If $c = 3e$, find $b - d$.

19. If the area of the sector is 4π, find *n*.

(d) 20. Find *x*.

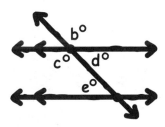

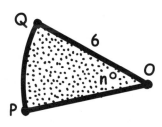

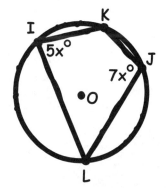

Write a proportion to represent each question below; then solve the proportion to get your answer.

21. The ratio of apples to oranges on the fruit stand was $31:11$. If there were 2940 apples and oranges altogether, how many apples were there?

22. There were 270 bananas on the fruit stand. If the ratio of bananas to grapes was $3:101$, how many grapes were there?

Do each proof below.

23. Given: $\overleftrightarrow{AB}$ is tangent to $\odot O$ at A and to $\odot P$ at B; $\overleftrightarrow{CD}$ is tangent to $\odot O$ and $\odot P$ at D

Prove: $\overline{CD}$ bisects $\overline{AB}$

(e) 24. Given: Quadrilateral $ABCD$ is inscribed in $\odot O$

Prove: $m\angle A + m\angle C = 180$ and $m\angle B + m\angle D = 180$

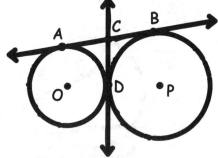

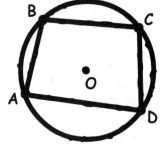

Lesson 100—Areas and Volumes of Similar Solids

We know that similar figures have the same shape but a different size. So far, though, we've only looked at similar *plane* figures, which are flat figures (triangles, quadrilaterals, circles, etc.). What about similar solids? Well, those are just solids with the same shape but a different size.

Comparing Surface Areas

One of the most interesting things about similar solids is how their surface areas compare. You may remember that the areas of flat similar figures have a different ratio from their corresponding sides. For example, take the two similar squares below.

The sides of the first square are twice the length of the sides of the second square: 4 is twice as big as 2. But the area of the first square is 4 times the area of the second square: 16 is 4 times as big as 4. It always works that way with similar figures. Generally, the ratio of the areas is always equal to the square of the ratio of the corresponding sides. We learned that in the last chapter.

Area = 16

Area = 4

The sides are twice as long, but the area is 4 times as big.

Well, it's the same for the surface area of similar solids. Look at the similar cubes below.

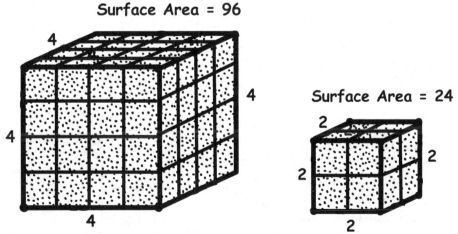

Surface Area = 96

Surface Area = 24

The edges are twice as long, but the surface area is 4 times as big.

675

The edges of the large cube are twice as long as the edges of the small cube. But now let's compare the surface areas. Each face of the large cube has an area of 16 square units (4×4). Since there are six faces in total, the surface area of the entire cube is 16×6 or 96 square units. Each face of the small cube has an area of 4 square units (2×2). Adding up all six of its faces gives us 4×6 or 24 square units. The surface areas are 96 and 24, so the large cube's surface area is 4 times as big as the small one's. In other words, the ratio of the edges is $2:1$, but the ratio of the surface areas is $4:1$ or $2^2 :1^2$. So the ratio of the surface areas is always the square of the ratio of the corresponding edges. And this works no matter what kinds of solids are involved. They could be similar pyramids, similar spheres, similar cones, similar prisms, or whatever. Here's the official theorem.

$$\frac{\text{Surface area of solid 1}}{\text{Surface area of solid 2}} = \frac{(\text{Edge of solid 1})^2}{(\text{Edge of solid 2})^2}$$

Theorem 95	If two solids are similar, then the ratio of their surface areas is equal to the square of the ratio of the lengths of any pair of corresponding edges.

Comparing Volumes

What about the volumes of two similar solids? How do they compare to the lengths of the edges? Well, let's go back to our cubes. We know that the edges of the large cube are twice as long as those of the small cube. Since a cube is a rectangular solid, its volume equals the product of its length, its width, and its altitude.

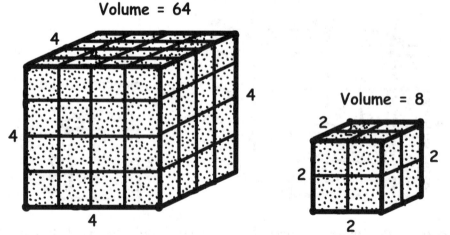

The edges are twice as long, but the volume is 8 times as big.

But of course, for a cube, all three of those measurements are the same. So the volume of the large cube is 4^3 or 64 cubic units. Since the small cube has side lengths of 2, its volume is 8 cubic units. The volume of the large cube, then, is 8 times as big as the volume of the small cube. Or, to say it another way, the ratio of the side lengths is $2:1$, but the ratio of the volumes is $2^3:1^3$. So the ratio of the volumes is the cube (or third power) of the ratio of the sides. This also works no matter what kind of similar solids you're dealing with. Here's the official theorem.

$$\frac{\text{Volume of solid 1}}{\text{Volume of solid 2}} = \frac{(\text{Edge of solid 1})^3}{(\text{Edge of solid 2})^3}$$

Theorem 96	If two solids are similar, then the ratio of their volumes is equal to the cube of the ratio of the lengths of any pair of corresponding edges.

Surface Areas and Volumes in Engineering

Surface areas and volumes of solids may seem theoretical, but they actually have many applications in the real world. One important area is in aviation. For instance, Orville and Wilbur Wright, the inventors of the first airplane, had to work with these geometric concepts.

THE WRIGHT BROTHERS

You've seen tiny model airplanes that fly around on a string. Some of them even run on fuel. It might seem like you could just increase the size of the airplane, keeping everything else the same, and create a real plane. But it doesn't work that way.

The reason is that when the length of the plane doubles, the volume (and weight) of the plane goes up 8 times. When the length of the plane quadruples, the volume (and weight) of the plane goes up 64 times. That's because of Theorem 96, which says that the ratio of the volumes equals the cube of the ratio of the edges. Because of this principle, you can't just increase the dimensions of a plane and assume that it will fly just like the smaller version. The larger the plane, the tougher and tougher it becomes to make it fly. The Wright brothers used their engineering and math skills to overcome this problem and build a working airplane.

There are many other examples in engineering where the ratios of side lengths, surface areas, and volumes are important. For instance, if two bridges are geometrically similar, and made out of the same material, the larger one will be weaker than the smaller one (and more likely to collapse). The reason is that as you increase the size of the bridge, the thickness of its supporting beams doesn't go up as quickly as the bridge's weight. And that's because surface area doesn't increase as quickly as volume. This principle makes the task of building a big bridge—such as the Brooklyn Bridge in New York or the Golden Gate in San Francisco—a very challenging one.

Golden Gate

Practice 100

a. Calculate the area of the shaded region.

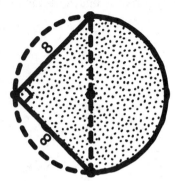

b. Calculate the total area of the solid.

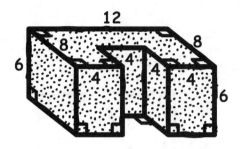

c. The altitude of a cylindrical soup can is 8 cm. The altitude of a similar cylindrical can is 32 cm. What is the ratio of the volume of the smaller can to the volume of the larger can?

d. If $V = 16\pi$, find s.

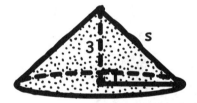

e. Do the proof below.
Given: $\square EFGH$ is inscribed in $\odot O$
of radius r.
Prove: $a\square EFGH = 2r^2$

Problem Set 100

Tell whether each sentence below is True or False.

1. For similar solids, the ratio of their surface areas is equal to the ratio of their corresponding edges.

2. For similar solids, the ratio of their volumes is equal to the ratio of their corresponding edges.

Complete each sentence below by filling in the blanks.

3. If two solids are _____, then the ratio of their surface areas is equal to the _____ of the ratio of any pair of corresponding edges.

4. If two solids are _____, then the ratio of their volumes is equal to the _____ of the ratio of any pair of corresponding edges.

5. A _____ is like a prism but instead of polygons for bases, it has circles.

Calculate the area of each shaded region below.

6.

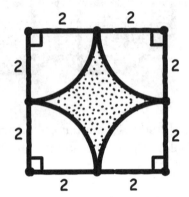

(a) 7.

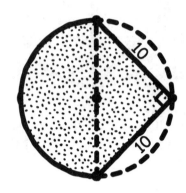

Calculate the total area of each solid below.

(b) 8.

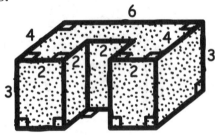

9.

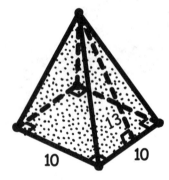

Calculate the volume of each solid below.

10.

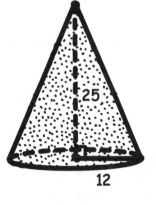

11.

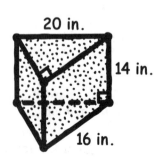

12.

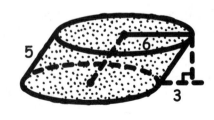

Answer each question below.

13. The edges of a large cube are five times as long as the edges of a smaller, similar cube. What is the ratio of the volume of the large cube to the volume of the small cube?

14. Two similar triangular prisms have edge lengths in the ratio of $2:3$. What is the ratio of the surface areas of the two prisms?

(c) 15. The altitude of a cylindrical soup can is 4 inches. The altitude of a similar cylindrical can is 12 inches. What is the ratio of the volume of the larger can to the volume of the smaller can?

Find the perimeter of each figure below.

16. The area of the semicircle is 2π

17. Find the perimeter of hexagon *AEFCGH*. Points *E*, *F*, *G* and *H* are midpoints of the sides of square *ABCD*, whose area is 4.

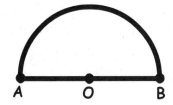

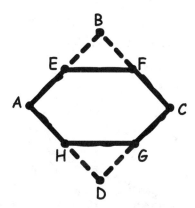

Find the degree measure of each angle indicated below.

18. $\angle QPS$

19. $\angle JKL$

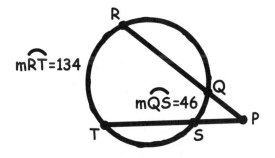

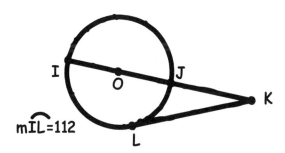

681

Answer each question below.

20. If $AB = 20$, $CO = 6$, find CD.

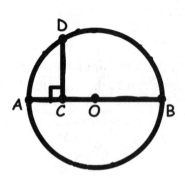

(d) 21. If $V = 320\pi$, find s.

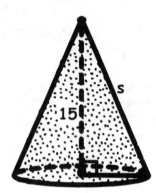

22. The hexagon is regular. Find r.

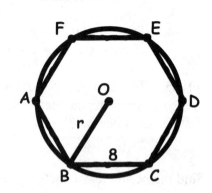

Do each proof below.

23. Given: N is the midpoint of $\overline{PQ}$
Prove: $\alpha\triangle PNM = \alpha\triangle QNM$

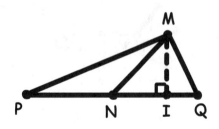

(e) 24. Given: $\square MNPQ$ is inscribed in $\odot O$ of radius r.
Prove: $\alpha\square MNPQ = 2r^2$

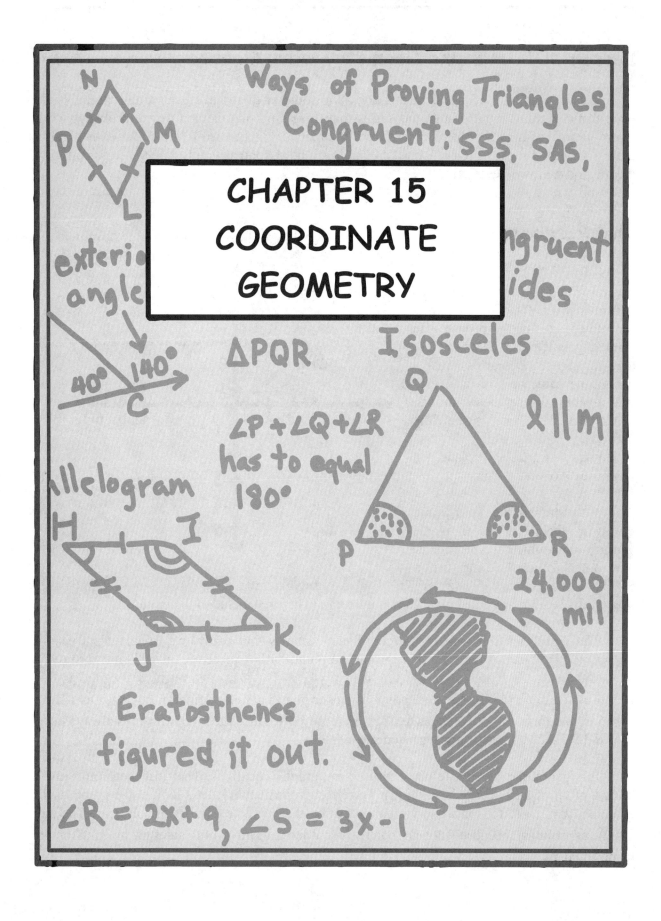

Ways of Proving Triangles Congruent: SSS, SAS,

CHAPTER 15
COORDINATE
GEOMETRY

ngruent ides

exterior angle

40° 140°
C

ΔPQR

Isosceles

Q

ℓ ∥ m

∠P+∠Q+∠R has to equal 180°

P   R

24,000 mil

allelogram

H   I

J   K

Eratosthenes figured it out.

∠R = 2x+9, ∠S = 3x-1

Lesson 101—Merging Geometry with Algebra

We've done a lot of proofs in this book and some of them have been tough. Probably the most difficult thing about proofs, though, is that there's no one method that will always work. Every proof requires a somewhat different approach. Algebra isn't like that. With algebra, there's a method for solving each kind of equation. And as long as you follow the steps correctly, the method will work every time.

The Coordinate Plane

A famous mathematician named Rene Descartes, who lived several hundred years ago, was frustrated by not having a method for doing geometry proofs. He wanted geometry to be more like algebra. Since Descartes was a genius, he came up with a way to use algebra on geometry proofs. What he did was invent the coordinate plane, which is also called the "Cartesian" plane, in Descartes' honor.

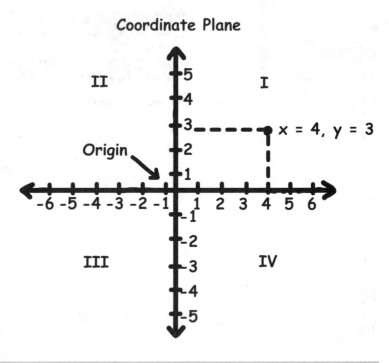

Coordinate Plane

You studied the **coordinate plane** in algebra. It has an **x-axis** and a **y-axis**, which are perpendicular to each other. The intersection of the two axes is called the **origin**. The axes separate the plane into four sections called **quadrants**, each represented by a Roman numeral. (They're labeled in the picture.)

The significant thing about the coordinate plane is that every one of its points can be represented by a pair of numbers. For instance, a point that's 4 places to the right and 3 units up from the origin is represented by the pair $x = 4$, $y = 3$. Those numbers are called the **x-coordinate** and **y-coordinate** of the point. The coordinates are also sometimes written as (4, 3). When in that form, they're referred to as an **ordered pair**: since the x-coordinate is always listed first and the y-coordinate is always listed second.

In algebra, the coordinate plane is used to "graph" equations. That just means to draw a picture of all of the equation's solutions. To refresh your memory, let's look at the graph of the equation $y = 2x + 1$. This is a two-variable equation that has lots of pairs of solutions. The pair (0, 1) is a solution, because when we put 1 in for x and 3 in for y, both sides of the equation are made equal.

Putting in 1 for x and 3 for y

$$y = 2x + 1$$

$$3 = 2(1) + 1$$

$$3 = 3$$

But the pair $(2, 5)$ is also a solution, because when we put those numbers in for x and y, they also make the sides of the equation equal. And the same is true for $(-3, -5)$, $(8, 17)$, and $(1, 3)$. All of those pairs will solve the equation as well. In fact, there are many, many more pairs that will work. So when graphing the equation $y = 2x + 1$, what we do is turn all those pairs of numbers into points on the coordinate plane. The graph is shown on the right. See, the points all run together and make a straight line. The line actually goes on forever, which is why it has arrows. This line is a picture or graph of the equation $y = 2x + 1$. That's how graphing is done in algebra.

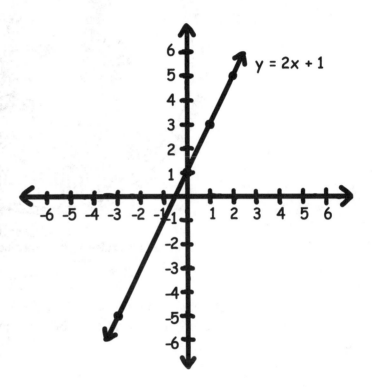

Proofs with Equations

So what does equation graphing have to do with geometry proofs? Well, Descartes realized that the coordinate plane could be used in two ways. We can either start with an equation, and then draw its picture (graph), which is what we did with $y = 2x + 1$. Or we can start with a picture (graph) and write an equation for it.

Descartes figured out that with the second approach, we could put geometric figures like a line or circle or a parallelogram on the coordinate plane and then write equations for them. Those equations could then be used to do proofs about the figures. The whole process is called **coordinate geometry**, because it uses the coordinate plane to do geometry proofs.

Rene Descartes
(Inventor of the coordinate plane)

Before we actually do any proofs with the coordinate plane ourselves, we need to go over some basics about the coordinate plane and about graphing. We'll cover those in the next few lessons.

Practice 101

a. Find the missing coordinates of the points on the diagram below.

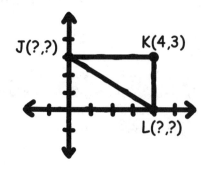

b. *DFGH* is a square with sides of length *b*. Calculate the area of the shaded region in terms of *b* and *c*.

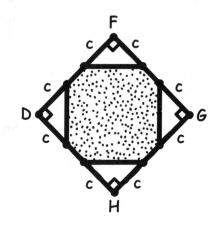

c. The surface areas of two spheres are 9π and 25π. What is the ratio of the volume of the smaller sphere to the volume of the larger sphere?

d. If the shaded area is 16π, find r.

e. Do the proof below.
Given: $\triangle PST \cong \triangle QRT$ and
$\quad\quad\quad \triangle PQT \cong \triangle SRT$
Prove: $\overline{PS} \parallel \overline{QR}$ and $\overline{PQ} \parallel \overline{SR}$

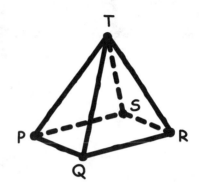

Problem Set 101

Tell whether each sentence below is True or False.

1. The coordinate plane has two axes, called the *x*-axis and the *y*-axis, which are perpendicular to each other.

2. The coordinate plane can be used to draw pictures of (graph) equations and to write equations for geometric figures.

Complete each sentence below by filling in the blanks.

3. On a coordinate plane, every point can be represented by a pair of numbers called the _____ and _____ of the point.

4. In _____, we use the coordinate plane to do geometry proofs.

5. A _____ is like a pyramid, except it has a circle for a base instead of a polygon.

Find the missing coordinates of the points on each diagram below.

(a) 6. Right triangle ABC

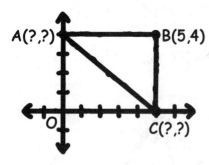

7. Rectangle $ABCD$

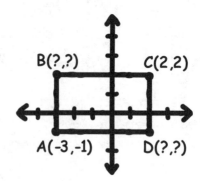

8. Parallelogram $OPQR$

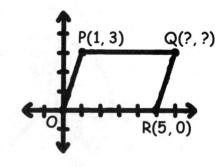

Find the degree measure of each arc or angle below.

9. $\overset{\frown}{PJ}$

10. $\angle JNK$

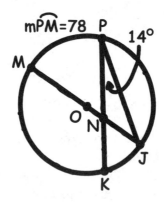

Calculate the area of each shaded region below.

11. The area of $\odot P$ is 48π.

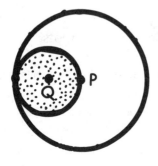

(b) 12. $PQRS$ is a square with sides of length y. Calculate the area of the shaded region in terms of y and z.

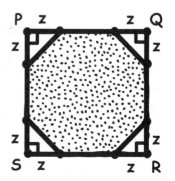

Answer each question below.

13. The side lengths of one cube are $4p$ and the side lengths of another cube are $6p$. What is the ratio of the surface area of the smaller cube to the surface area of the larger cube?

(c) 14. The surface areas of two spheres are 25π and 49π. What is the ratio of the volume of the smaller sphere to the volume of the larger sphere?

Calculate the volume of each solid described below.

15. An oblique prism having an altitude of 16 and a base that is an octagon with an area of 48.

16. A right pyramid with an altitude of 15 and a base which is a rhombus with diagonals measuring 8 and 11.

17. A right cylinder has a base with a radius of r. The altitude of the cylinder is the same length as the diameter of its base. Find the volume of the cylinder in terms of r.

Answer each question below.

18. *LMNP* is a square with an area of 8. Find r.

19. The total shaded area below is $\pi - 1$. Find r.

(d) 20. The total area of the 3 shaded sectors below is 25π. Find r.

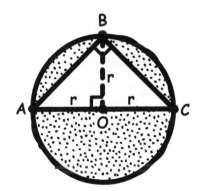

Write an equation to represent each question below; then solve the equation to get your answer. Estimate your answers to two decimal places.

21. The Manly Man spotted a grizzly bear on the opposite side of the clearing, which he knew was at a distance of 75 yards. When the grizzly stood upright, he calmly measured the angle from the ground to the top of its head to be 3°. How many feet tall was the grizzly bear?

22. Doug propped the back of a chair beneath his doorknob to keep the door closed. If the back of the chair is 41 inches high and forms a 41° angle with the door, how high from the floor is the doorknob?

Do each proof below.

23. Given: $\overline{MN}$ is a diameter of $\odot O$;
$\qquad \overparen{MP} \cong \overparen{NQ}$

Prove: $\triangle MNP \cong \triangle NMQ$

(e) 24. Given: $\triangle ADE \cong \triangle BCE$ and
$\qquad \triangle ABE \cong \triangle DCE$

Prove: $\overline{AD} \parallel \overline{BC}$ and $\overline{AB} \parallel \overline{DC}$

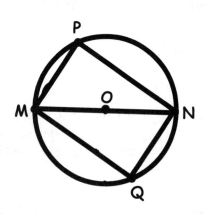

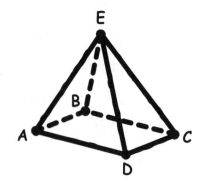

Lesson 102—Distance and Midpoint Formulas

In the last lesson, we learned that geometry proofs can actually be done with algebra. The trick is to put the geometric figure on a coordinate plane. Once a figure is on the coordinate plane, though, it's often necessary to find the distance between two of the figure's points. Let's go over the process for doing that.

The Distance between Two Points

It's fairly easy to find the distance between two points when they line up horizontally or vertically. All you have to do is subtract one pair of the coordinates. For instance, the distance between points A and B (on the right) is 4, because the x-coordinate of B is 6 and the x-coordinate of A is 2, and 6 minus 2 is 4. When the points line up vertically, then you just have to subtract their y-coordinates. The distance between points B and C is 5, since $2-(-3)$ equals 5. It's not even necessary to look at a graph to tell whether two points are lined up horizontally or vertically. If their y-coordinates are the same, then they are lined up horizontally. If their x-coordinates are the same, then they are lined up vertically. And so all you have to do to find the distance between them is to subtract the other pair of points.

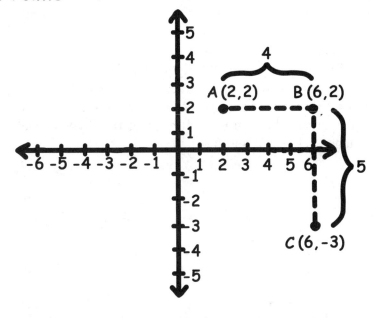

It's a little more challenging to find the distance between two points that are not lined up vertically or horizontally. For example, in the diagram to the right, points A and B are at a diagonal to each other. To find the distance between these points, we have to use the Pythagorean Theorem.

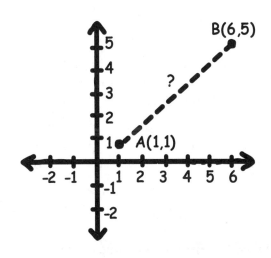

The first step is to make a right triangle out of the two points. That can be done by plotting a third point C that is directly across from point A and directly below point B. Connecting point C to A and to B gives us the legs of a right triangle, where the hypotenuse of the triangle is the distance between A and B. Since point C is directly across from A, it must have the same y-coordinate as A, which is 1. And since C is directly below B, it has the same x-coordinate as B, which is 6.

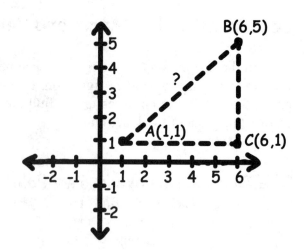

Now that we have the coordinates of C, we can find the lengths of the right triangle's legs very easily. All we do is subtract coordinates to get AC equals $6 - 1$ or 5 and BC equals $5 - 1$ or 4. That means we know the lengths of 2 out of the 3 sides of the right triangle and can use the Pythagorean Theorem to find the third (the hypotenuse). We'll use the letter d to represent the distance between A and B.

$$d^2 = AC^2 + BC^2$$

$$d^2 = 5^2 + 4^2$$

$$d^2 = 41$$

$$d = \sqrt{41}$$

The distance between points A and B is exactly $\sqrt{41}$ units. Of course, we can estimate that with a calculator. To one decimal place, that comes to 6.4 units.

The Distance Formula

This same method will work for any two points, no matter where they are on the coordinate plane. There's actually a formula that is used to calculate the distance between two points. It's just the Pythagorean theorem, which we used above, solved for d. Taking the square root of both sides of $d^2 = AC^2 + BC^2$ gives us $d = \sqrt{AC^2 + BC^2}$. Then, since AC is equal to the difference between the x-coordinates of the points and BC is equal to the difference between the y-coordinates of the points, we write the equation like this.

$$d = \sqrt{(x_2 - x_1)^2 + (y_2 - y_1)^2}$$

This is called the **distance formula**, because it can be used to quickly find the distance between any two points on a coordinate plane. The little 2 and 1 in x_2 and x_1 aren't exponents. The 2 just shows that x_2 is the x-coordinate of the *second* point and the 1 shows that x_1 is the x-coordinate of the *first* point. It works the same way for y_2 and y_1. Those represent the y-coordinates.

With the distance formula, all you have to do is plug in the coordinates of the points in the right places and calculate the value of the right side of the equation. There's no need to draw a right triangle or even to have a graph at all. All you need is the formula and the two points. Here's the theorem for the distance formula written formally.

| Theorem 97 | The distance (d) between point (x_1, y_1) and point (x_2, y_2) may be found with the following formula: $$d = \sqrt{(x_2 - x_1)^2 + (y_2 - y_1)^2}$$ |

The Midpoint Formula

When doing proofs on the coordinate plane, we sometimes need to find the midpoint between two points. To show you how that works, look at the two points on the right. To find the midpoint of *AB*, all we have to do is calculate the average of the x-coordinates and the average of the y-coordinates. Those averages are the coordinates of the midpoint.

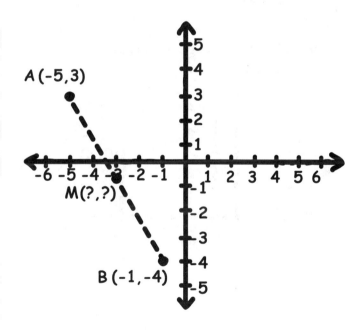

Let's go through it. The x-coordinates of A and B are -5 and -1. The y-coordinates of A and B are 3 and -4. The average of each pair is just those numbers added together and divided by 2. Here's what we end up with

$$\frac{-5+(-1)}{2}, \frac{3+(-4)}{2}.$$

Now simplifying, we get $\frac{-6}{2}, \frac{-1}{2}$ or $-3, -\frac{1}{2}$.

The coordinates of the midpoint of AB are $x = -3$ and $y = -\dfrac{1}{2}$ or, written as an ordered pair, $(-3, -\dfrac{1}{2})$.

That same procedure will work for finding the midpoint of any two points on the coordinate plane. Here's the formal theorem.

Theorem 98	The coordinates of the midpoint between points (x_1, y_1) and (x_2, y_2) are as follows: $(\dfrac{x_1 + x_2}{2}, \dfrac{y_1 + y_2}{2})$

Practice 102

a. Find the missing coordinates. $FGHI$ is a trapezoid.

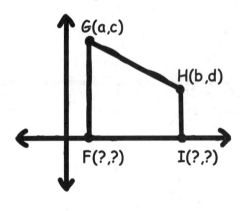

b. Find the midpoint of line segment $\overline{PQ}$.

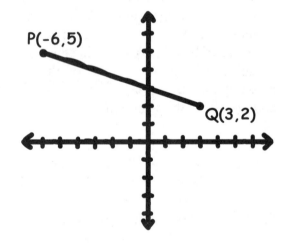

c. Find the lengths of the dashed sides of the diagram below.

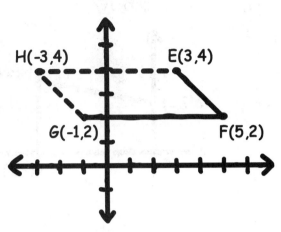

d. Calculate the area of the shaded region below.

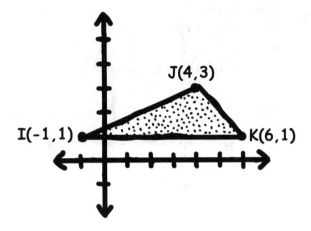

e. Do the proof below.
Given: $\overline{DF} \parallel \overline{VG}$
Prove: $\overline{FK} \cong \overline{DK}$

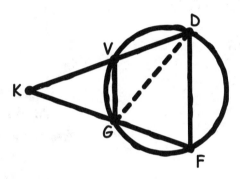

Problem Set 102

Tell whether each sentence below is True or False.

1. The distance (d) between points (x_1, y_1) and (x_2, y_2) may be found with the formula $d = \sqrt{(x_2 - x_1)^2 + (y_2 - y_1)^2}$.

2. The coordinates of the midpoint between points (x_1, y_1) and (x_2, y_2) are $(\dfrac{x_1 + x_2}{2}, \dfrac{y_1 + y_2}{2})$.

Complete each sentence below by filling in the blanks.

3. The volume of a prism equals the product of the _____ and the _____ .

4. The area of a circle is equal to the product of _____ and the square of the _____ of the circle.

5. The volume of a pyramid is equal to one third of the area of the _____ times the _____ .

695

Find the coordinates of the missing points on each diagram below.

6. Square *OUVW*

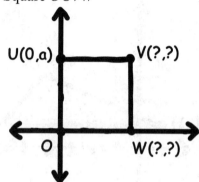

(a) 7. Trapezoid *OMNP*

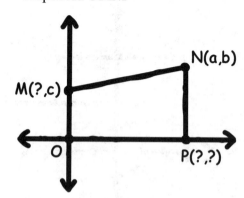

Find the midpoint of each line segment below.

8. $\overline{AB}$

(b) 9. $\overline{CD}$

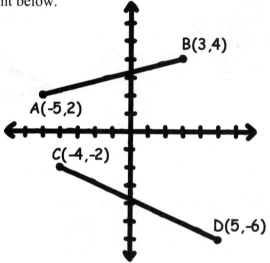

Find the lengths of the dashed sides of each diagram below.

10. Right triangle *ABC*   **11.** Rectangle *JKLM*   **(c) 12.** Parallelogram *RSTV*

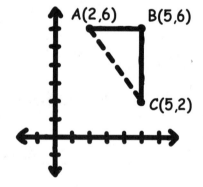

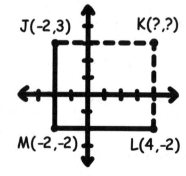

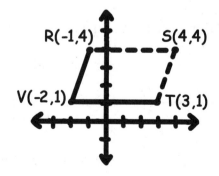

Calculate the area of each shaded region below.

(d) 13.

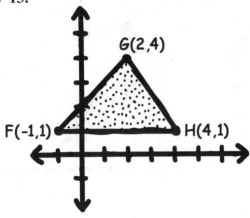

14. The area of $\triangle AOE$ is 72.

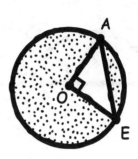

Find the perimeter of each polygon below.

15. Trapezoid *LQPO*

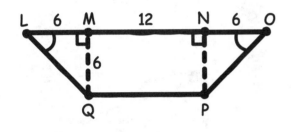

16. Regular hexagon *ABCDEF*

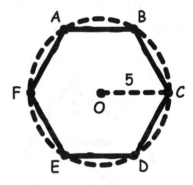

Calculate the total area of each solid described below.

17. A rectangular solid having a length of 12 inches, a width of 7 inches, and an altitude of 5 inches.

18. A regular pyramid whose base is an equilateral triangle with sides measuring 6, and whose lateral faces have a slant height of 4.

19. A heptagonal (7-sided base) right prism which has edge lengths in the ratio of $14:3$ to a similar heptagonal right prism that has a total area of 18 cm^2.

Answer each question below.

20. Find x.

21. Find $m\overset{\frown}{BC} + m\overset{\frown}{AD}$.

22. Find h.

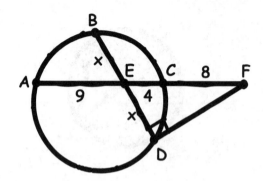

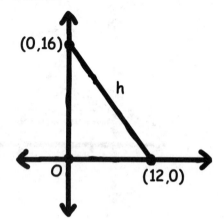

Do each proof below.

23. Given: $\overline{HM} \parallel \overline{IN}$, $\overline{HM} \parallel \overline{GJ}$, $\overline{GJ} \parallel \overline{IN}$,
$\overline{HI} \parallel \overline{MN}$, $\overline{HG} \parallel \overline{MJ}$, $\overline{GI} \parallel \overline{JN}$
Prove: $\triangle HGI \cong \triangle MJN$

(e) 24. Given: $\overline{TR} \parallel \overline{US}$
Prove: $\overline{RV} \cong \overline{TV}$

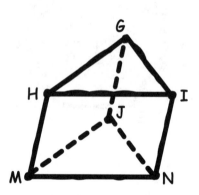

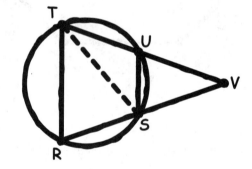

Lesson 103—Slope of a Line

Lines are used all the time in geometry, of course. When we put a line on a coordinate plane, it's easy to calculate the line's slope. **Slope is just a measure of the steepness of a line.**

Measuring Steepness

Figuring out the slope of a line isn't that hard. We just choose any two points on the line (any two will work). Then we calculate the change in the *y*-coordinates (going from one of the points to the other), and the change in the *x*-coordinates between the two points. Finally, we divide those changes.

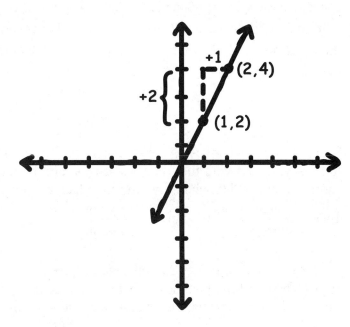

For the line to the right, we've chosen the points (1, 2) and (2, 4), which are both on the line. The change in the *y*-coordinates is 4 – 2 or 2. And the change in the *x*-coordinates is 2 – 1 or 1. Dividing the "change in *y*" (2) by the "change in *x*" (1), we get +2. So the slope of the line is positive 2.

$$\frac{\text{change in } y}{\text{change in } x} = \frac{4-2}{2-1} = \frac{+2}{+1} = +2$$

Here's the formal definition of the slope of a line.

Definition 89	The slope (m) of a nonvertical line which passes through the points (x_1, y_1) and (x_2, y_2) is the ratio of the change in y (Δy) to the change in x (Δx): $$m = \frac{\Delta y}{\Delta x} = \frac{y_1 - y_2}{x_1 - x_2}$$

Notice that to save space, "change in *y*" is written as Δy, and "change in *x*" as Δx.[1] So we could

---

[1] The symbol Δ is the Greek letter delta, which is often used in math and science to mean "change."

write the slope of the line above as $\frac{\Delta y}{\Delta x} = +2$. Also, notice that the letter m stands for slope. That's usually the letter used.

There are several things to be careful about when calculating the slope of a line. First, when subtracting to get the changes in y and x, you should always start with the same point for both. For instance, in the last example, when calculating the change in y we started with the y-coordinate of $(2, 4)$, which is 4. That's why when we calculated the change in x, we had to start with the x-coordinate of $(2, 4)$, which is 2. However, we could just as easily have started with the other point, $(1, 2)$. But then we would have had to start with that point for both the y's and the x's.

$$\frac{\text{change in } y}{\text{change in } x} = \frac{2-4}{1-2} = \frac{-2}{-1} = +2$$

See, that approach gives us the same answer. So it doesn't matter which point you start with, as long as you start with the same one on top and bottom. That's the key. The second thing to be careful about is that when dividing the changes, the y's are always on top. In other words, it's always $\frac{\text{change in } y}{\text{change in } x}$. It's *never* $\frac{\text{change in } x}{\text{change in } y}$.

Also, change in y is sometimes called the "rise" and change in x is sometimes called the "run." The word rise just means that the change in y refers to how much the line is rising upward. The word run means that the change in x refers to how much the line is running toward the right. Using these terms, the slope is sometimes called the "rise over the run" or just $\frac{\text{rise}}{\text{run}}$.

Another important point to make is that lines can have several different kinds of slopes. When the slope of a line is positive, the line slants upward from left to right. When the slope is negative, the line slants downward from left to right. And interestingly, when the line is perfectly horizontal, its slope is 0. Even more strange, a vertical line doesn't even have a slope at all. Its slope is said to be undefined.

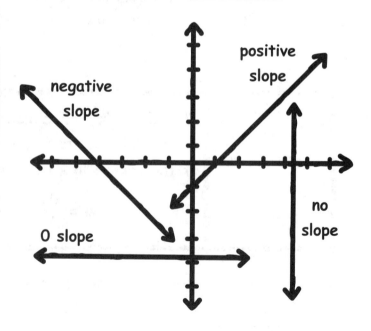

Slopes of Parallel and Perpendicular Lines

Since slope is a measure of the steepness of a line, parallel lines always have the same slope.[2] Take a look at the lines to the right. They're both parallel, and you can see from the calculations that they both have a slope of −2.

This works for any two parallel lines, no matter how they're slanted. Their slopes must always be equal. This fact turns out to be very helpful when doing geometry proofs on the coordinate plane, as you'll see. Here's the formal theorem for the slopes of parallel lines.

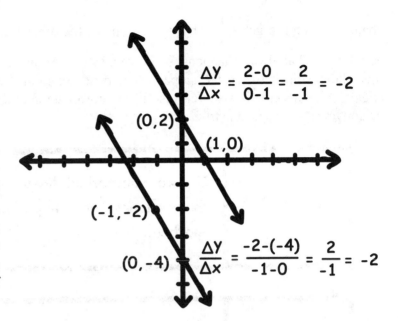

$$\frac{\Delta y}{\Delta x} = \frac{2-0}{0-1} = \frac{2}{-1} = -2$$

(0,2)

(1,0)

(−1,−2)

(0,−4)

$$\frac{\Delta y}{\Delta x} = \frac{-2-(-4)}{-1-0} = \frac{2}{-1} = -2$$

Theorem 99	If two nonvertical lines are parallel, then their slopes are equal.

The converse of Theorem 99 is also true. In other words, if we know that two lines have the same slope, then we can conclude automatically that they must be parallel. Here's the converse stated formally.

Theorem 100	If two nonvertical lines have the same slope, then they are parallel.

What about the slopes of perpendicular lines? Well, they aren't equal, but the slopes of perpendicular lines do have a relationship. As it turns out, their slopes are **negative reciprocals** of each other. That means if one line has a slope of +3, the other line will have a slope that's the

---

[2] The only exception is vertical lines. Since vertical lines don't even have a slope, their slopes technically can't be equal.

reciprocal of +3, with the sign changed. Since +3 is the same as $+\frac{3}{1}$, we just flip that over and change the sign to get $-\frac{1}{3}$. That's the slope of the other line. Notice that +3 multiplied by $-\frac{1}{3}$ equals −1. That always happens when we multiply negative reciprocals. So another way to state the relationship between the slopes of perpendicular lines is to say that their product always equals −1. This rule is also very useful in coordinate geometry. Here's the formal theorem and its converse, which is also true.

Theorem 101	If two nonvertical lines are perpendicular, then their slopes are negative reciprocals of one another.

Theorem 102	If the slopes of two nonvertical lines are negative reciprocals of one another, then the lines are perpendicular.

Practice 103

a. Find the midpoint of $\overline{IJ}$ below.

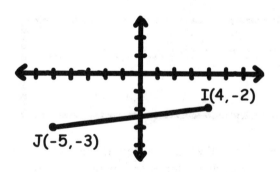

b. Find the length of the dashed side below.

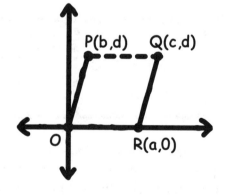

c. Tell whether the pair of lines described below are parallel, perpendicular, or neither.

Line m which has a slope of −6 and line n which has a slope of $\frac{1}{6}$.

d. Find *r*, the radius of the regular octagon below. Estimate your answer to two decimal places.

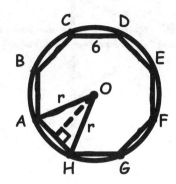

e. Do the proof below.

Given: $\overline{ZG}$ and $\overline{ZF}$ are secants to $\odot O$; $\overline{ZF} \cong \overline{ZG}$; $\overline{EY} \perp \overline{FG}$ at point *Y* and $\overline{HX} \perp \overline{FG}$ at point *X*

Prove: $\overline{EY} \cong \overline{HX}$

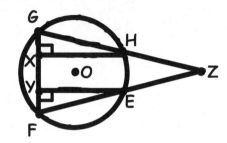

Problem Set 103

Tell whether each sentence below is True or False.

1. The slope (*m*) of a nonvertical line which passes through the point (x, y) is equal to the ratio of *y* to *x*: $m = \dfrac{y}{x}$.

2. If two nonvertical lines are perpendicular, then their slopes are equal.

Complete each sentence below by filling in the blanks.

3. If the slopes of two nonvertical lines are _____ of one another, then the lines are perpendicular.

4. The area of a _____ is equal to one-half the product of the base and the altitude.

5. The area of a _____ is equal to one-half the product of the two diagonals.

Answer each question below.

6. List the lines below in order by their slopes from least to greatest.

7. Which line(s) have a negative slope and which line(s) have a positive slope?

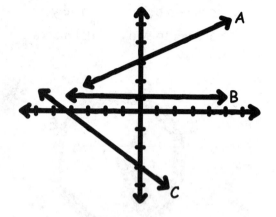

Find the midpoint of each line segment below.

8. $\overline{IJ}$

(a) 9. $\overline{PM}$

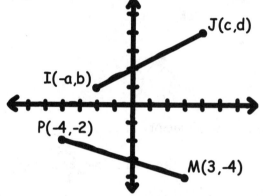

Find the lengths of the dashed sides of each diagram below.

10.   **(b) 11.**

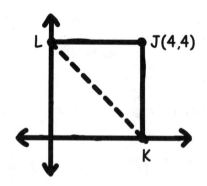   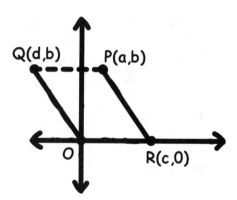

Calculate the slope of each line below.

12. Line *A*

13. Line *B*

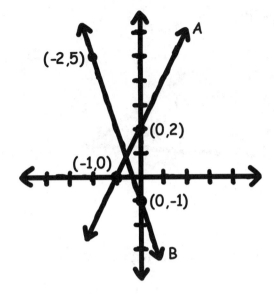

Tell whether each pair of lines described below are parallel, perpendicular, or neither.

14. Line *C* which has a slope of +2 and line *A* in the diagram above.

(c) 15. Line *E* which has a slope of 4 and line *F* which has a slope of $\frac{1}{4}$.

Calculate the area of each shaded region below.

16. *PQ, QR,* and *RS* are diameters with $SR = 4$, $RQ = 2SR$, $QP = 2RQ$

17. *PQR* is a semicircle

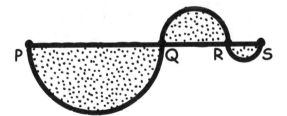

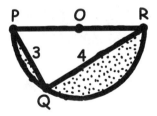

Calculate the volume of each solid described below.

18. A right octagonal (8-sided base) prism with an altitude of 17 in. and a base of area 48 sq. in.

19. An oblique pyramid with an altitude of 5 and a base that is a right triangle having sides of lengths 10, 24, and 26.

Answer each question below.

20. Find x.

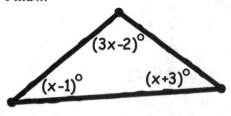

21. Find h.

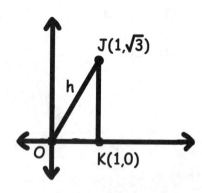

(d) 22. Find r, the radius of the regular octagon below. Estimate your answer to two decimal places.

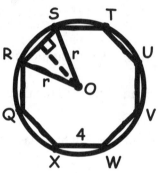

Do each proof below.

23. Given: $\overline{LN}$ and $\overline{RN}$ are secant segments; $\overrightarrow{NT}$ is tangent to both $\odot O$ and $\odot P$ at point T.
Prove: $LN \times MN = RN \times QN$

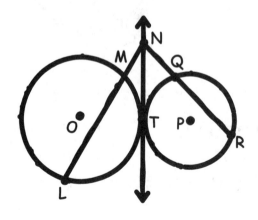

(e) 24. Given: $\overline{MQ}$ and $\overline{MS}$ are secants to $\odot O$; $\overline{MQ} \cong \overline{MS}$; $\overline{PI} \perp \overline{QS}$ at point I and $\overline{RJ} \perp \overline{QS}$ at point J
Prove: $\overline{PI} \cong \overline{RJ}$

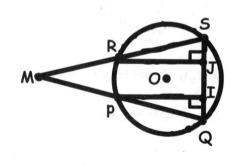

Lesson 104—Linear Equations

We're almost ready to do some proofs using the coordinate plane. But first we need to review some basics on equations for lines. You may remember from algebra that those are actually called **linear equations**.

A linear equation is always of the first degree. That means both x and y in the equation are raised to just the first power. A mathematician would say that a linear equation must have the form $ax + by = c$. In a real equation, there would be actual numbers in place of the letters a, b, and c, of course. But notice that both x and y have exponents of 1. If either of those variables were to have an exponent of 2 or above, then the equation would not be linear. Its graph would be a curve instead of a line.

Slope-Intercept Form

The most important thing we need to know about linear equations when doing coordinate geometry is how to write them. Fortunately, the process isn't too hard. If we're starting with a line on the coordinate plane and want to write its equation, all we need to know about the line is its slope and one point on the line.

Let's go through an example. The slope of the line to the right is 3 and we have the point $(0, -1)$, which is where the line crosses the y-axis. This point is called the *y*-**intercept** of the line, by the way. You may remember that from algebra.

When we know the slope and the *y*-intercept of a line, we can write the entire equation in this form.

$$y = mx + b$$

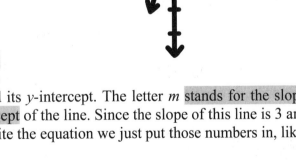

This is called the **slope-intercept form** of a linear equation, because it's easy to use when you know the line's slope and its y-intercept. The letter m stands for the slope and b stands for the y-coordinate of the y-intercept of the line. Since the slope of this line is 3 and the y-coordinate of the y-intercept is -1, to write the equation we just put those numbers in, like this.

$$y = mx + b$$

$$y = 3x + (-1)$$

That's the equation for our line. The coordinates of every point on the line will solve the equation when you put the numbers in for x and y.

The other neat thing about slope-intercept form is that when working with any linear equation, all we have to do to figure out its slope and y-intercept is write the equation in slope-intercept form and then read the numbers in the m and b positions. For instance, $2y = 4x + 10$ is a linear equation and let's say we want to know its slope and y-intercept. Instead of having to find two points on the line and calculate the change in y divided by the change in x to get the slope, we can just put $2y - 4x = 10$ in slope-intercept form by solving for y.

$$2y = 4x + 10$$

$$y = \frac{4x + 10}{2} \qquad \text{divide both sides by 2}$$

$$y = 2x + 5 \qquad \text{reduce the fraction}$$

Now the equation looks like $y = mx + b$. And since 2 is in the m position, we know automatically that the slope of the equation's line is +2. Also, since 5 is in the b position, we know that the y-intercept of the line has to be $(0,5)$.[3] Another way to find the y-intercept of a line is to put 0 in for x in the equation and then solve for y. For instance, putting 0 in for x in $y = 2x + 5$ gives us $y = 2(0) + 5$ or $y = 5$. So one point on the line is $(0,5)$. And that has to be the y-intercept, since its x-coordinate is 0.

Point-Slope Form

Sometimes we might be given the slope of a line and one of its points, but the point won't be the y-intercept. Is it still possible to write the entire equation? Yes, but we need to use a different form for the equation. Instead of slope-intercept form, we use the **point-slope form** of a linear equation. Here it is.

$$y - y_0 = m(x - x_0)$$

This isn't as hard as it looks. The letter m just stands for the slope of the line. And the symbols x_0 and y_0 stand for the x and y-coordinates of the point on the line that we're given.

To go through an example, let's say that some line has a slope of -2 and one point on the line is $(1,4)$. We know that $(1,4)$ isn't the y-intercept, because its x-coordinate is not 0. That means we can't use the slope-intercept form to write the equation. But we can use point-slope

---

[3] Remember, the x-coordinate of the y-intercept is always 0. The number in the b position is the y-coordinate of the y-intercept.

form. All we do is put −2 in for m, 1 in for x_0 (since that's the x-value of our point) and 4 in for y_0 (since that's the point's y-value).

$$y - y_0 = m(x - x_0)$$

$$\downarrow \quad \downarrow \quad \downarrow$$

$$y - 4 = -2(x - 1)$$

The equation for the line is $y - 4 = -2(x - 1)$. All of its solution pairs can be represented as points on the line that has a slope of −2 and contains the point $(1, 4)$. Of course, we could simplify this if we wanted by solving it for y and putting it into slope-intercept form. But we won't bother going through the process.

Practice 104

a. Calculate the shaded area below. Parallelogram $OAEI$

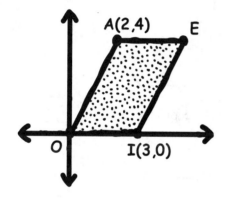

b. Find the length of the dashed side below.

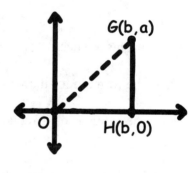

c. Write the equation for the line crossing the point $(-4, -2)$ and with slope 1.

d. Given that $\overline{CD}$ is a diameter, find the coordinates of the center point of the circle.

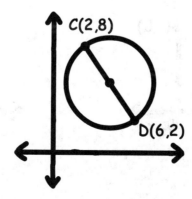

e. Do the proof below.

Given: $\overline{KJ}$ is tangent to $\odot O$ at point J; $\overline{IJ} \parallel \overline{LK}$;

secants $\overline{LJ}$ and $\overline{MI}$ intersect $\odot O$ at point N

Prove: $\dfrac{JL}{IM} = \dfrac{KL}{JM}$

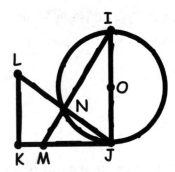

Problem Set 104

Tell whether each sentence below is True or False.

1. The slope-intercept form of a linear equation is $y = mx + b$, where m is the slope and b is the y-coordinate of the y-intercept of the line.

2. The point-slope for of a linear equation is $y - y_0 = m(x - x_0)$, where m is the slope and (x_0, y_0) is any point on the line.

Complete each sentence below by filling in the blanks.

3. The formula for the volume of a cylinder is _____.

4. The volume of a rectangular solid is equal to the product of the _____, the _____, and the _____.

5. The formula for the volume of a sphere is _____ .

Find the missing coordinates of the points on each diagram below.

6. Rectangle *ABCD*

7. Isosceles right triangle *OGH*

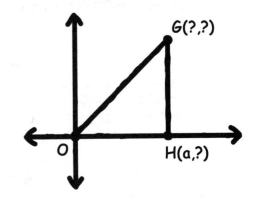

Calculate the area of each shaded region below.

8.

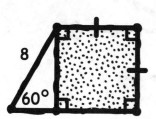

9.

(a) 10. Parallelogram *OBCD*

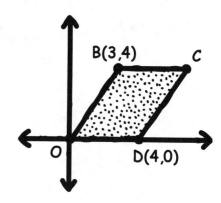

Find the lengths of the dashed sides of each diagram below.

11.

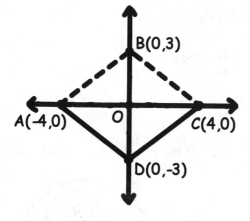

(b) 12.

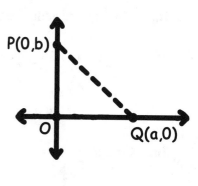

Find the degree measure of each arc or angle below.

13. ∠*QPS*

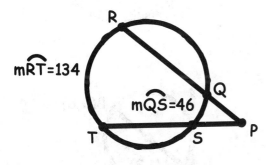

14. ∠*JKL*

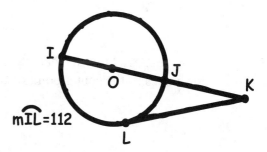

711

Calculate the slope of each line below.

15. Line ℓ

16. Line m

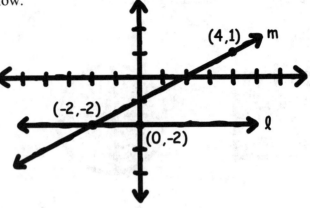

Write the equation for each line described below.

17. The line with slope -1 and y-intercept 3.

18. The line crossing the point $(0, -2)$ and with slope 4.

(c) 19. The line crossing the point $(-5, -3)$ and with slope 2.

Answer each question below.

20. Find a.

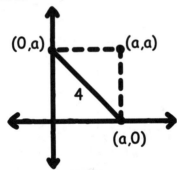

21. If the shaded area is 48π, find r.

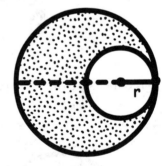

(d) 22. Given that $\overline{AB}$ is a diameter, find the coordinates of the center point of the circle.

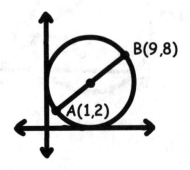

Do each proof below.

23. Given: $\overrightarrow{GH} \parallel \overrightarrow{JK}$

   Prove: $\alpha\triangle GJH = \alpha\triangle GKH$

(e) 24. Given: $\overline{RQ}$ is tangent to $\odot O$ at point Q;

   $\overline{PQ} \parallel \overline{SR}$; secants $\overline{SQ}$ and $\overline{UP}$

   intersect $\odot O$ at point V

   Prove: $\dfrac{QS}{PU} = \dfrac{RS}{QU}$

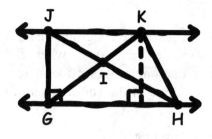

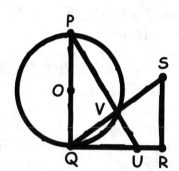

Lesson 105—Coordinate Proofs

Finally, we're ready to do some proofs using the coordinate plane. To start off, we'll prove that the diagonals of a square are congruent. If we were to do this proof with our usual methods, we'd have to think for a while to come up with the best approach. And then the proof would probably take several steps.

Use the Distance Formula

But watch how easy it is to prove that the diagonals of a square are congruent using the coordinate plane. The first step is to put the square on the plane itself. And, when doing coordinate proofs, it's usually a good idea to position a figure so that one of its vertices is on the origin and as many sides as possible are on an axis. That makes some of the coordinates of the points 0, which keeps things a little simpler. See, we have vertex A on the origin and two of the sides of the square run along an axis. Since this is a square, all four of its sides have to be equal. But notice that instead of making the sides a specific length like 5 or 6, we've used a to represent the side lengths. That's because this proof is going to cover all possible squares, no matter how long or short their sides. So we use a letter instead of a specific number.

Since we're using the coordinate plane to do this proof, all we have to do is use the distance formula to show that AC and BD are equal. Here's the distance formula again.

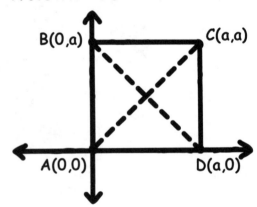

Given: Square ABCD

Prove: AC = BD

$$d = \sqrt{(x_2 - x_1)^2 + (y_2 - y_1)^2}$$

AC is just the distance from A to C and BD is the distance from B to D. Putting the coordinates of each pair of points into the formula gives us this.

$$AC = \sqrt{(a-0)^2 + (a-0)^2} \qquad\qquad BD = \sqrt{(0-a)^2 + (a-0)^2}$$

Now we simplify the right side of each equation.

$$AC = \sqrt{a^2 + a^2} \qquad\qquad BD = \sqrt{(-a)^2 + (a)^2}$$

$$AC = \sqrt{2a^2} \qquad\qquad BD = \sqrt{2a^2}$$

714

We could simplify these a little further, but there's no point. *AC* and *BD* are obviously equal and that finishes the proof. That's all there is to it.

The proof could have been done just as easily using the Pythagorean Theorem. Diagonal *AC* is the hypotenuse of right $\triangle ABD$, and diagonal *BD* is the hypotenuse of right $\triangle ABD$. The result would have been exactly the same. The nice thing about using the distance formula, though, is that it will work on all sorts of different figures, not just squares.

Calculate the Midpoints

Let's do another coordinate proof that's a little bit harder. This time let's prove that the diagonals of a parallelogram bisect each other. We proved this theorem back in Chapter 8, and it took several steps. We had to show that two triangles inside the parallelogram were congruent. Then, by C.P.C.T.C., we were able to show that the segments formed by the intersection of the diagonals were congruent, which proved that they bisected each other. It was a fairly involved proof.

We can do the same proof a lot easier using the coordinate plane. Here's the figure on the coordinate plane. And as you can see, we haven't used specific numbers for the side lengths, because this proof is going to cover *any* parallelogram, no matter what its size. Vertices *A* and *B* are at $(0,0)$ and $(a,0)$. Since the parallelogram is tilted, vertices *D* and *C* are not *a* units up on the *y*-axis. So we've used another letter, *c*, to represent the *y*-coordinates of those vertices. The *x*-coordinate of vertex *D* is represented by the letter *b*, and the *x*-coordinate of vertex *C* is $a+b$, because that's how far that point is from the *y*-axis.

Given: Parallelogram ABCD,

$\overline{AC}$ and $\overline{BD}$ intersect at P.

Prove: AP=PC and DP=PB

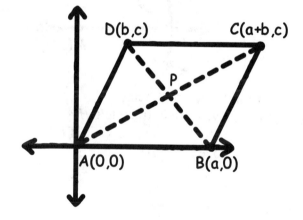

To do the proof, we just need to show that *P* is the midpoint of both *AC* and *DB*. If it is, then $AP = PC$ and $DP = PB$, which is what we're trying to prove. Remember, the coordinates of a midpoint always equal the averages of the *x*-coordinates and of the *y*-coordinates of the points on either end. The end points of *AC* are $(a+b,c)$ and $(0,0)$. The end points of *DB* are (b,c) and $(a,0)$. Using the midpoint formula, then, we have the following.

$$\text{Midpoint of } AC = (\frac{a+b}{2}, \frac{c}{2}) \qquad \text{Midpoint of } DB = (\frac{b+a}{2}, \frac{c}{2})$$

Since $a+b$ is the same as $b+a$, the midpoints are the same. Since *P* is the only point that *AC* and *DB* have in common, *P* must be the midpoint of both segments. That finishes our proof.

Practice 105

a. Find the missing coordinates below. $\triangle OAE$ is isosceles.

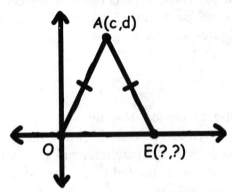

b. Find the midpoint of $\overline{OH}$ below.

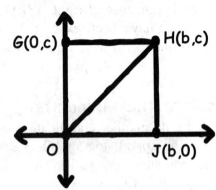

c. Find the length of the dashed side of the diagram below.

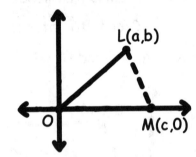

d. Write the equation for the line crossing the points $(-2,-7)$ and $(2,5)$.

e. Do the proof below.
Given: Right triangle GHI;
$\quad\quad\quad J$ is the midpoint of GH
Prove: $JI = JH$

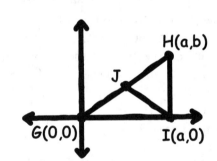

Problem Set 105

Tell whether each sentence below is True or False.

1. Coordinate proofs are often faster and easier than doing proofs in the traditional way.

2. When doing a coordinate proof, the position of the figure on the coordinate plane is not important.

Complete each sentence below by filling in the blanks.

3. The circumference of a circle is calculated with the formula _____.

4. The area of a trapezoid is equal to the product of the length of the _____ and _____ the sum of the lengths of its bases.

5. A _____ is the set of all points in space that are at a given distance from a given point, called the center.

Find the missing coordinates of the points on each diagram below.

6. Trapezoid *STVO*

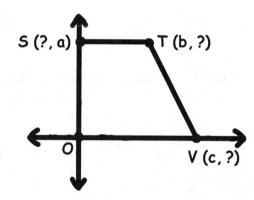

(a) 7. Δ*OIJ* is isosceles.

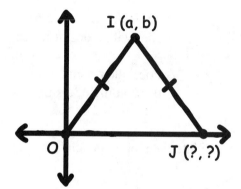

Answer each question below.

8. List the lines below in order by their slopes from least to greatest.

9. Which line(s) have a negative slope and which line(s) have a positive slope?

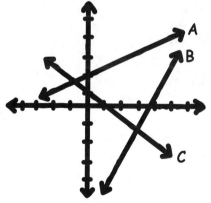

Find the midpoint of each line segment below.

10. $\overline{AB}$

(b) 11. $\overline{OB}$

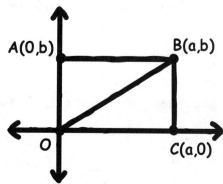

Find the lengths of the dashed sides of each diagram below.

12.

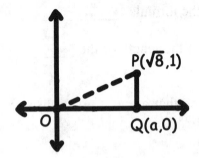

(c) 13.

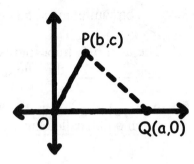

Answer each question below.

14. What is the total area of a regular pyramid whose slant height is 7 and whose base is a square with sides of length 8?

15. An oblique prism has an altitude of 16 inches and a volume of 128 cubic inches. What is the volume of a similar oblique prism that has a base of area 2 square inches?

Calculate the slope of each line below.

16. Line A

17. Line B

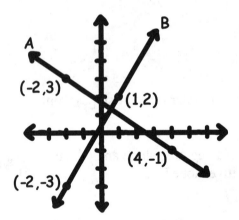

Write the equation for each line described below.

18. The line crossing the point $(-3, -5)$ and with slope $\frac{2}{3}$.

(d) 19. The line crossing the points $(-1, -4)$ and $(2, 3)$.

Answer each question below.

20. Find the area of $\triangle PQR$.

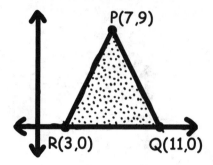

21. The volume of the sphere is 288π. Find the radius s.

22. Find r in terms of x, y, h, and k.

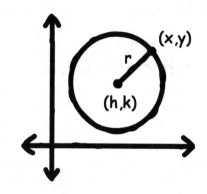

Do each coordinate proof below.

23. Given: Rectangle $FGHJ$
Prove: $FH = GJ$

(This is our Theorem 43: The diagonals of a rectangle are congruent.)

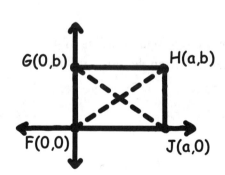

(e) 24. Given: Right triangle ABC;
D is the midpoint of BC
Prove: $AD = BD$

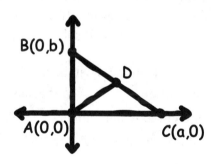

Lesson 106—Circles and Coordinate Proofs

In the previous lesson, we did a coordinate proof with a square and another one with a parallelogram. But it can be just as helpful to use the coordinate plane on proofs involving circles.

Equation of a Circle

Before going through an actual proof, though, we need to cover some basics on equations for circles. The definition of a circle is the set of points that are all the same distance from another point, which is the center of the circle. Using that definition, it's pretty easy to write an equation for any circle whose center is at the origin. The circle on the right has a radius of 3, which means all of its points are 3 places from the center at $(0,0)$.

If we choose any point (x, y) on the circle, it will be y units up and x units to the right of the origin. As you can see, the radius and other dashed lines form a right triangle. According to the Pythagorean Theorem, the sum of the square of the legs of that triangle must equal the square of the hypotenuse. That gives us $x^2 + y^2 = 3^2$. This is the equation for the circle. If we choose any point on the circle and put its coordinates in for x and y, those numbers will solve the equation.

The same process can be used to write the equation for a circle with a radius of 4. Only the equation will be $x^2 + y^2 = 4^2$, because the hypotenuse of the right triangle will be 4 instead of 3. And for a circle with a radius of 5, the equation turns out to be $x^2 + y^2 = 5^2$. More generally, any circle whose center is at the origin has an equation of the form $x^2 + y^2 = r^2$, where r is the radius of the circle.

The equation for a circle is a little different when its center is at some other point besides the origin. As an example, take the circle on the right. It has a radius of 3, but its center is at $(2,3)$. That means the lengths of the two legs of the right triangle are $x-2$ and $y-3$. Using the Pythagorean Theorem, we get the equation $(x-2)^2 + (y-3)^2 = 3^2$.

Likewise, if a circle with radius 3 had a center of $(4,1)$, the lengths of the right triangle's legs would be

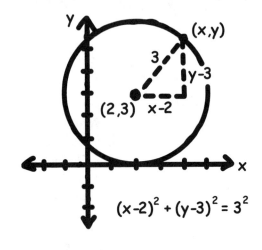

$x-4$ and $y-1$, and the circle's equation would be $(x-4)^2+(y-1)^2=3^2$. Generally, no matter where the center of the circle is, the equation comes out to be $(x-h)^2+(y-k)^2=r^2$, where the center is at the point (h,k) and the radius is r. This actually works even for a circle whose center is at $(0,0)$, because that makes the equation $(x-0)^2+(y-0)^2=r^2$, which simplifies to $x^2+y^2=r^2$. Here's the official theorem for the equation of a circle.

Theorem 103	The equation for a circle with radius r and its center at point (h,k) is (x-h)² + (y-k)² = r²

Another Proof

Now let's do another coordinate proof, this one involving a circle. Let's prove that line AB is tangent to circle O in the diagram. To prove this the old way, we might have to draw a radius to point P and then show that the radius makes a right angle with line AB, which would be time-consuming. But using the coordinate plane, we just need equations for the line and the circle.

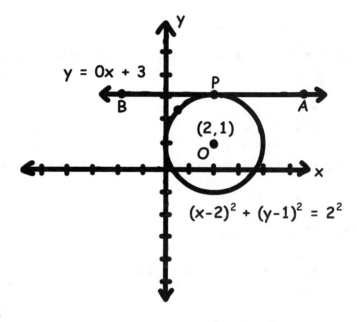

The circle has a radius of 2 and its center is at the point $(2,1)$, so the equation for the circle is $(x-2)^2+(y-1)^2=2^2$. The line is horizontal, which means it has a slope of 0. And the y-intercept of the line is $(0,3)$. Using the slope-intercept form, the equation can be set up like this.

$$y=mx+b$$

$$y=0x+3 \quad \text{or} \quad y=3$$

With these equations, the proof is easy. If $\overleftrightarrow{AB}$ is tangent to the circle, then the figures must have just one point in common. If that's true, then a system with our two equations should have only one solution pair.[4] To find out, let's solve this system.

$$\begin{cases} y = 3 \\ (x-2)^2 + (y-1)^2 = 2^2 \end{cases}$$

Since the first equation is solved for y, the easiest method is to substitute 3 for y in the second equation.

$$(x-2)^2 + (3-1)^2 = 2^2$$

Simplifying gives us this.

$$(x-2)^2 + 4 = 4$$

$$(x-2)^2 = 0$$

Now to solve for x, we take the square root of both sides.

$$x - 2 = 0$$

$$x = 2$$

There's just one solution pair: $x = 2$, $y = 3$. That proves that line AB is tangent to circle O.

Practice 106

a. Find the area of the shaded region.

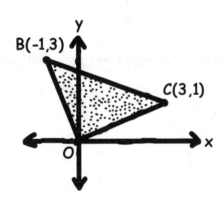

b. A right prism has an altitude of 10 cm and a base that is an isosceles right triangle with legs measuring 2 cm each. Find the volume of a similar right prism that has a base whose legs measure 4 cm.

---

[4] If the system had two solution pairs, then the line would cross the circle at two points and wouldn't be a tangent line. If the system had no solution pairs, then the line wouldn't cross the circle at all.

   c. Write the equation for the line that crosses the point $(2,2)$ and is perpendicular to the line $y = 2x - 1$.

   d. Equilateral $\triangle HIJ$ is inscribed in $\odot O$, with apothem $OK = 2$. Radius OH is perpendicular to PS. Find the perimeter of the square $PQRS$.

   e. Do the proof below.
      Given: $\odot O$ with center at $(3,3)$ and radius 2
      Prove: The line $y = x + 2$ is a secant to $\odot O$.

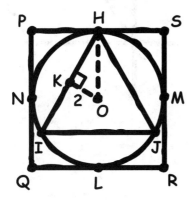

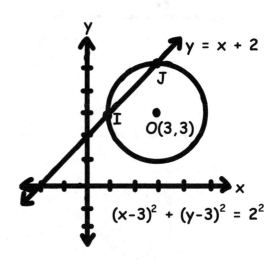

Problem Set 106

Tell whether each sentence below is True or False.

   1. The equation for a circle whose center is at the origin is $y - y_0 = m(x - x_0)$.

   2. The equation for a circle whose center is at (h, k) is $(x - h)^2 + (x - k)^2 = r^2$.

Complete each sentence below by filling in the blanks.

   3. The slope-intercept form of a linear equation is _____, where m is the slope and b is the y-coordinate of the y-intercept of the line.

   4. The volume of a sphere is calculated with the formula _____.

   5. A _____ of a circle is a region of a circle bounded by an arc of the circle and the two radii to the end points of the arc.

Find the lengths of the dashed sides of each diagram below.

6.

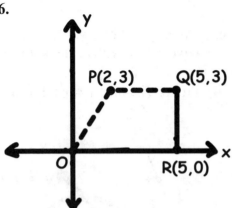

7. Rhombus *OABC*

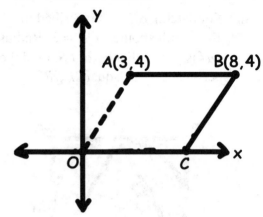

Calculate the area of each shaded region below.

8.

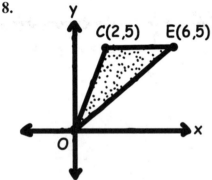

(a) 9.

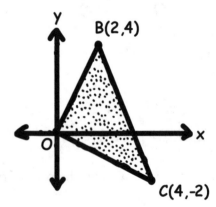

10.

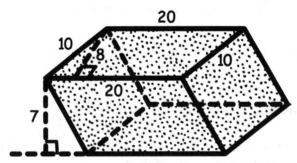

Answer each question below.

(b) 11. A right prism has an altitude of 20 cm and a base that is an isosceles right triangle with legs measuring 4 cm each. Find the volume of a similar right prism that has a base whose legs measure 8 cm.

12. A cone has an altitude of 10 and a base with radius 6. Find the volume of a similar cone that has a base with a radius of 9.

Find each missing line segment below.

13. Find *PR*.

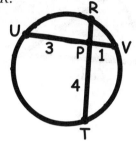

14. Find *HL*.

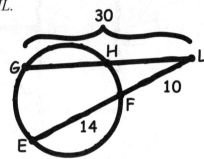

Calculate the slope of each line below.

15. Line *A*

16. Line *B*

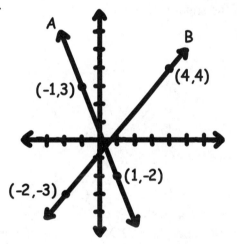

Write the equation for each line described below.

17. The line crossing the point $(-2, -3)$ and with slope $\frac{3}{2}$.

18. The line crossing the points $(-4, 5)$ and $(2, -1)$.

(c) 19. The line that crosses the point $(4, 1)$ and is perpendicular to the line $y = -2x - 3$.

Answer each question below.

20. *ABCD* and *EBFG* are squares. Find *z*.

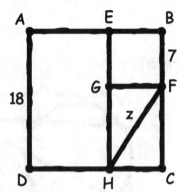

21. Find *x* if $\triangle QRS \sim \triangle DBC$.

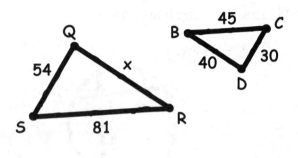

(d) 22. Equilateral $\triangle IJF$ is inscribed in $\odot O$, with apothem $OK = 1$. Radius *OF* is perpendicular to *GE*. Find the perimeter of the square *ACEG*.

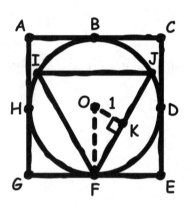

Do each coordinate proof below.

23. Given: Quadrilateral *ABCD* with coordinates shown
Prove: $AD = BC$ and $AB = DC$

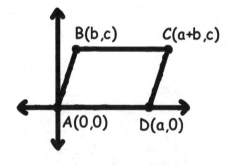

(e) 24. Given: $\odot O$ with center at (3, 2) and radius 2
Prove: The line $y = x + 1$ is a secant to $\odot O$.

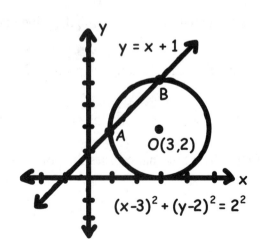

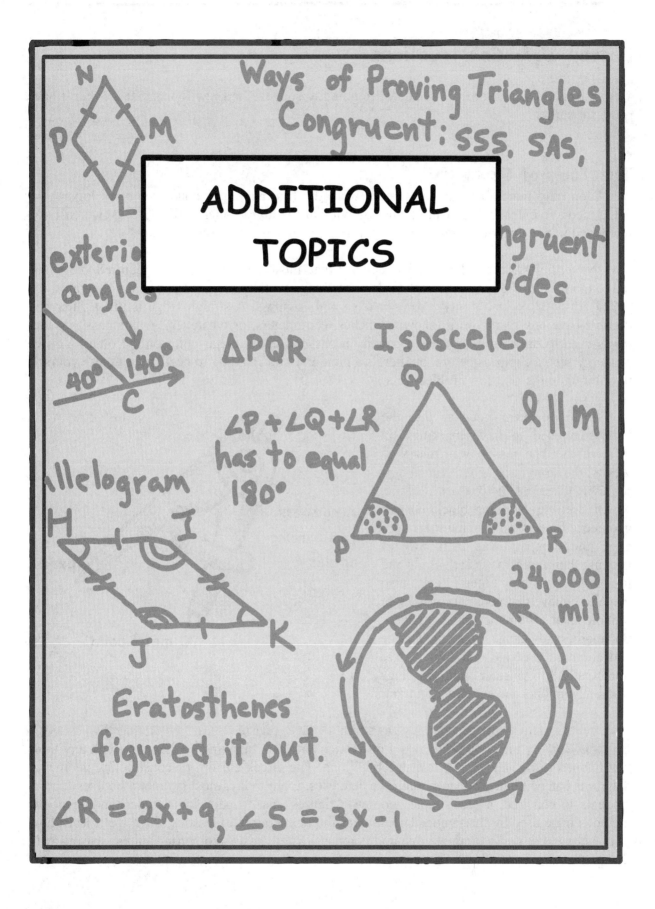

Ways of Proving Triangles Congruent: SSS, SAS,

ADDITIONAL TOPICS

ngruent ides

exterior angles

40° 140°
C

ΔPQR

Isosceles

ℓ ∥ m

∠P + ∠Q + ∠R has to equal 180°

allelogram

24,000 mil

Eratosthenes figured it out.

∠R = 2x + 9, ∠S = 3x - 1

Lesson 107—Constructions

In this last section of the book, we're going to squeeze in a few topics that we didn't have room for earlier.

The Tools of Geometry

You may remember that the Greeks were the first people to make geometry logical, by using deductive reasoning. Unlike the Babylonians and Egyptians, the Greeks weren't too interested in practical measurements; they were philosophers in search of truth.

Nevertheless, even the Greeks realized that most geometry proofs required diagrams. (although they would have preferred to do everything mentally.) In producing their diagrams, the Greeks insisted on using only a straight edge and compass. A straight edge is just a ruler that doesn't have any marks on it (showing inches, centimeters, or whatever). A compass is a tool that's used to draw circles. It has a pencil on one end and a metal point on the other. You've probably seen a compass before, but here's a picture. (You're going to need one of these yourself in order to do the next few problem sets.)

It might seem peculiar that the Greeks refused to have markings on their rulers. The reason was that they viewed the straight edge and compass as representatives of a line and circle, which are the building blocks of all geometric figures. So sticking to straight edge and compass was their way of keeping their mathematics as simple and logical as possible. Later Greeks also came to believe that geometry was more reliable than arithmetic (and numbers). So another advantage of straight edge and compass was that it didn't involve numbers at all. A ruler with markings contains numbers and so does a protractor.

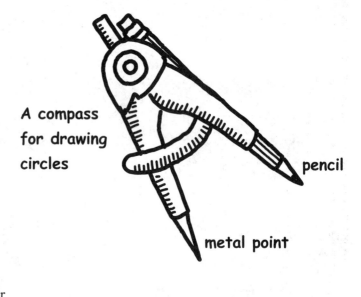

A compass for drawing circles

pencil

metal point

A diagram drawn with only a straight edge and compass is technically called a construction, by the way. So there's a difference between "drawing" a diagram (with any tools that happen to be handy) and "constructing" one. The Greek custom of constructing geometric diagrams has continued down through the centuries. Even today, most geometry courses require students to construct a few simple geometric figures, just to gain some understanding of the methods once used by the famous Greeks. For the next couple of lessons, then, we'll learn how to construct (with only straight edge and compass) a few basic geometric figures, starting with the simplest figure of all: the line segment.

Constructing a Line Segment

To construct a line segment what we do is use a compass to copy another line segment. Since the original line segment can be any length, this method can be used to create a line segment of whatever length we choose. The first step is to adjust the compass so that the metal end and pencil end are just far enough apart that each fits on the end points of $\overline{AB}$.

Adjust the compass so that it fits on the end points of line segment.

The distance between the two ends of the compass is called the radius of the compass (because if we drew a circle with the compass in that position, the distance would be the radius of the circle).

Now that the compass legs are set to the length of the original line segment, the next step is to draw a line and mark a point on it (C), and put the metal tip of the compass on that point. Using the compass, we then draw a small arc (part of a circle) that intersects the line segment at some other point, D.

The new line segment CD is congruent to $\overline{AB}$. We have "constructed" a line segment of a certain length, without having to use a ruler with marks on it. That's the way the Greeks did it.

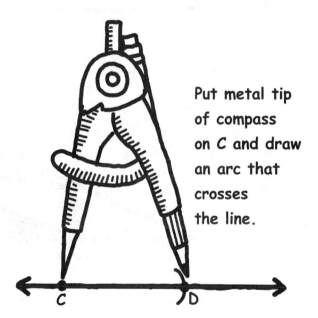

Put metal tip of compass on C and draw an arc that crosses the line.

Constructing an Angle

Next, let's learn how to construct another basic building block of geometry: an angle. When constructing an angle, it's not legal to use a protractor. The only tools allowed are straight edge and compass. And the procedure is to copy an angle of a certain measure.

We'll call the original angle $\angle A$. The first step is to put the metal point of the compass on the vertex of $\angle A$ and draw an arc that intersects both rays of the angle (below left). Then, we draw another ray, $\overrightarrow{BC}$, which will be one of the sides of the new constructed angle. The third step is to put the metal tip of the compass on point B and (without changing the distance between the legs of the compass) draw an arc through $\overrightarrow{BC}$, so that it intersects the ray at some point F (below right).

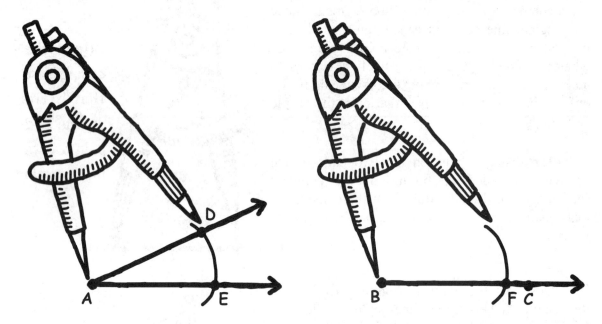

Next, the compass legs are adjusted so that the distance between metal point and pencil equals the length of $\overline{DE}$.

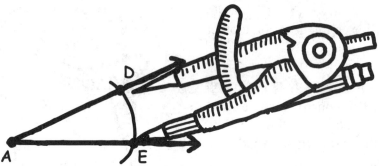

Then we put the metal point on F (without changing the distance between point and pencil) and draw another arc that intersects the first one.

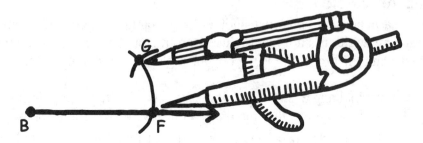

The final step is to draw another ray through B and G. That will be the second side of the new angle, $\angle B$, which is congruent to $\angle A$.

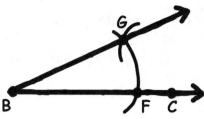

Practice 107

a. Construct an angle G congruent to $\angle F$.

b. Find the area of the shaded region.

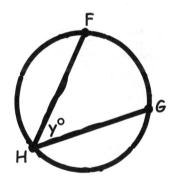

c. The surface areas of two spheres are 16π and 25π. What is the ratio of the volumes of the spheres?

d. If $\overset{\frown}{FG}$ has a length of 12π cm and the radius of the circle is 18 cm, find y.

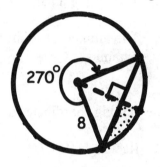

e. Do the proof below.

Given: $\triangle PQR$; S is the midpoint of $\overline{PQ}$;
T is the midpoint of $\overline{QR}$

Prove: $\overline{ST} \parallel \overline{PR}$ and $ST = \dfrac{1}{2}PR$

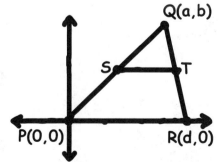

731

Problem Set 107

Tell whether each sentence below is True or False.

1. The Greeks used only a straight edge and compass in drawing their geometric figures.

2. A diagram drawn with only a straight edge and compass is technically called a construction.

Complete each sentence below by filling in the blanks.

3. The equation for a circle whose center is at the origin is _____.

4. The area of a parallelogram is the _____ multiplied by the _____.

5. The altitude of a lateral face of a regular pyramid is called the _____ of the pyramid.

Find the missing coordinates of the points on each diagram below.

6. Rectangle *ABCD*

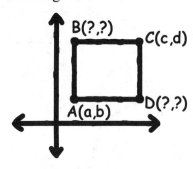

7. Right isosceles △*LJK*

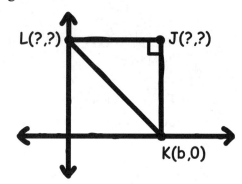

Find the midpoint of each line segment below.

8. $\overline{EF}$

9. $\overline{RQ}$

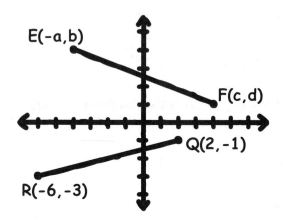

732

Use only a compass and straightedge to do each construction below.

10. Construct a line segment PQ congruent to $\overline{LM}$ on the right.

11. Construct an angle C congruent to $\angle B$.

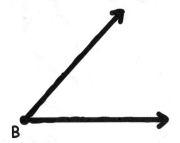

(a) 12. Construct an angle E congruent to $\angle D$.

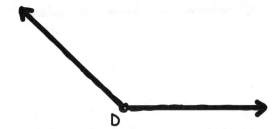

Answer each question below.

13. A rectangular solid has a length of 28 cm, a width of 16 cm, and a total area of 1424 cm^2. What is the total area of a similar rectangular solid with a length of 14 cm?

(c) 14. The surface areas of two spheres are 9π and 49π. What is the ratio of the volumes of the spheres?

Calculate the area of each shaded region below.

15. $a\triangle DEG = 18$

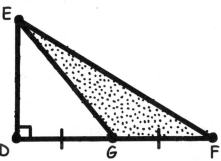

(b) 16.

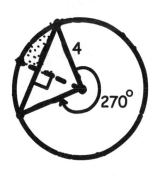

Write the equation for each line described below.

17. The line crossing the point $(-4, -3)$ and with slope $\dfrac{1}{3}$.

18. The line crossing the points $(-2, 6)$ and $(0, -4)$.

Answer each question below.

19. Find x.

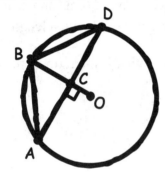

(d) 20. If $\overset{\frown}{RT}$ has a length of 9π cm and the radius of the circle is 15 cm, find y.

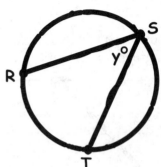

State which shortcut can be used to prove each statement below. If no method applies, say "none."

21. $\triangle ABC \cong \triangle DBC$

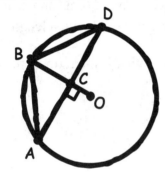

22. $\triangle PQR \sim \triangle ROS$

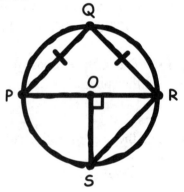

Do each coordinate proof below.

23. Given: Isosceles trapezoid $FGHJ$

Prove: The diagonals are congruent.

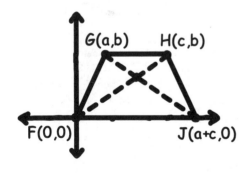

(e) 24. Given: $\triangle ABC$; D is the midpoint of $\overline{AB}$; E is the midpoint of $\overline{BC}$

Prove: $\overline{DE} \parallel \overline{AC}$ and $DE = \dfrac{1}{2}AC$

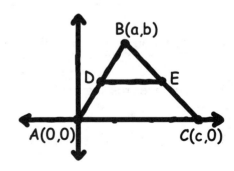

Lesson 108—More Constructions

In the last lesson, we learned how to construct a line segment and an angle. Remember, to "construct" a figure, using the Greek rules, we can use only a straight edge (an unmarked ruler) and a compass, nothing else. In this lesson, we're going to learn to construct a bisector of a line segment and a bisector of an angle.

Segment Bisector

To bisect segment *AB*, the first step is to put the metal point of the compass on one end-point of the segment and draw an arc that intersects the segment somewhere past the middle.

The second step is to do the same thing from the other endpoint without changing the compass setting. That creates two arcs that intersect above and below the segment, at points *C* and *D*.

The final step is to draw a line through *C* and *D*. Line *CD* bisects $\overline{AB}$.

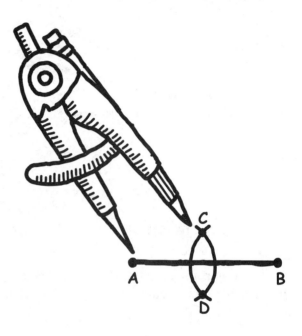

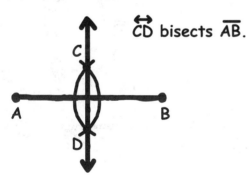

$\overleftrightarrow{CD}$ bisects $\overline{AB}$.

Angle Bisector

Constructing an angle bisector is a little bit harder. To bisect ∠*A*, we start by putting the metal point of the compass on the vertex, and then we draw an arc that intersects both sides of the angle (at points *B* and *C*).

Next, without moving the legs of the compass, we put the metal point on point *B* and make another arc inside the angle. Then we put

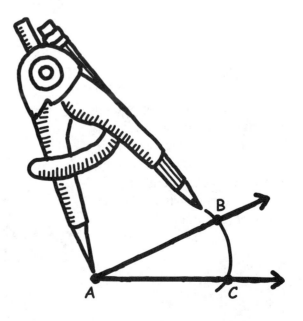

735

the metal point on point *C* and do the same thing (without changing the compass radius), making sure that the two new arcs intersect.

The last step is to draw ray *AD*, which is the bisector of ∠*A*.

$\overrightarrow{AD}$ bisects ∠A.

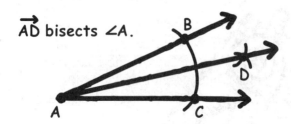

Line Perpendicular to Another Line

Another important construction is of a line that is perpendicular to another line. Let's go through that one.

Say that we have a line *m* and a point *P* not on the line, and that we want to construct a line running through *P* that is perpendicular to line *m*. The first step is to put the metal point of the compass on *P* and draw an arc that intersects line *m* at two points (*A* and *B*).

Next, we put the metal point on *A* and make an arc on the other side of line *m*. Then, without moving the legs of the compass, we do the same thing with the metal point on *B*, making sure that the two arcs intersect (at a point *C*).

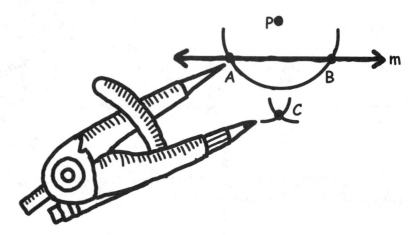

736

The final step is to run a line through points P and C. Line PC is then perpendicular to line m.

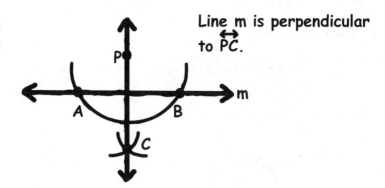

Line m is perpendicular to $\overset{\leftrightarrow}{PC}$.

Impossible Constructions

In the last couple of lessons, we've shown how to construct a few of the basic building blocks of all geometric figures, such as line segments, angles, and bisectors. Using these, many more complicated figures, like the various kinds of triangles and quadrilaterals, can also be constructed. In fact, once you've pinned down the building blocks, it seems reasonable that *any* geometric figure, no matter how complicated, could be constructed (with just a straight edge and compass) by just putting the segments and angles together in various ways. That's what the Greeks thought, even though they were never able to construct all the figures they wanted to, no matter how hard they tried. Actually, one favorite pastime of Greek intellectuals was to sit around and try to think of ingenious ways to construct complex geometric figures. (We told you they weren't very practical!)

Some constructions proved to be so difficult that they weren't discovered for many centuries, long after those original Greek philosophers were dead and gone. For instance, the famous mathematician Karl Friedrich Gauss was the first person to construct a 17-sided regular polygon (with straight edge and compass, of course) in the 1800s. The Greeks had worked on that one for a long time with no success.

But the biggest breakthrough came when modern mathematicians discovered that some of the most difficult constructions attempted by the Greeks were actually impossible. For example, one famous construction, which had frustrated not just the Greeks but many generations of mathematicians, was "squaring the circle." That means to construct a square with the same area as a given circle. The difficulty lies in the fact that the sides of the square must be based on the well-known irrational number π. So to square the circle amounts to constructing a line segment that is π units long. In 1882 (over 2,000 years after the Greeks first thought of the problem), a mathematician finally proved that squaring the circle was mathematically impossible.[1]

Interestingly, those modern mathematicians got to the bottom of the whole construction question by using algebra. They realized that the Greek straight edge and compass rules were the same mathematically as trying to solve certain algebra equations. So to say that a figure can't be constructed is roughly the same as saying that you can't find the solution to the problem using basic algebra. This connection between geometry and algebra shouldn't be all that surprising to you, now that you've studied coordinate geometry, and understand the usefulness of putting geometric figures on the coordinate plane.

---

[1] Even today the phrase "squaring the circle" is often used to mean performing an impossible task.

Practice 108

a. Find the shaded area below if $m\overarc{PR} = 90$ and the length of $\overarc{PR}$ is π cm.

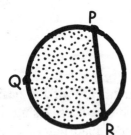

b. Construct a copy of $\angle K$ on your paper. Then construct the bisector of $\angle K$.

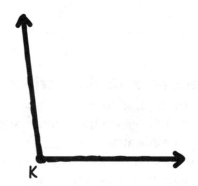

Find the missing coordinates of the points on each diagram below.

c. $\triangle OTV$ is equilateral

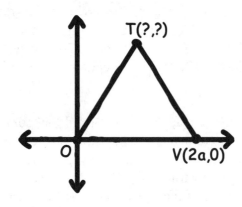

d. $\triangle CDE$ is isosceles

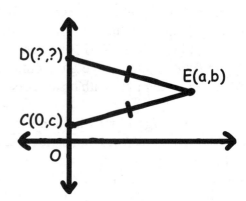

e. Do the coordinate proof below.

Given: Trapezoid $EFGH$; I is the midpoint of $\overline{EF}$ and J is the midpoint of $\overline{GH}$

Prove: $IJ = \dfrac{1}{2}(EH + FG)$

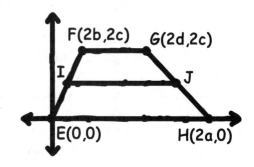

Problem Set 108

Tell whether each sentence below is True or False.

1. There were some constructions too difficult for the ancient Greeks to complete.

2. Modern mathematicians have discovered that it's possible to construct any geometric figure.

Complete each sentence below by filling in the blanks.

3. A pyramid has a _____ on one end and a point, called the _____, on the other end.

4. The circumference of a circle is equal to 2 times _____ times the _____ of the circle.

5. The equation for a circle of radius r whose center is at (h, k) is _____.

Find the lengths of the dashed sides of each diagram below.

6.

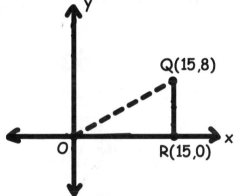

7.

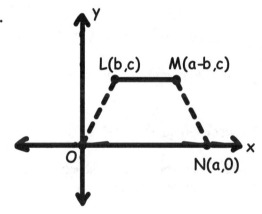

Calculate the area of each shaded region below.

8.

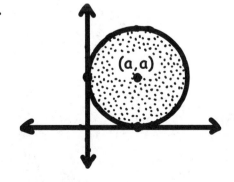

(a) 9. $m\overset{\frown}{ACB} = 270$ and the length of $\overset{\frown}{AB}$ is 4π inches.

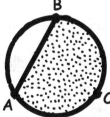

Use only a compass and straightedge to do each construction below.

10. Construct a copy of $\overline{FG}$ on your paper. Then construct the bisector of segment FG.

F   G

11. Construct a copy of $\angle H$ on your paper. Then construct the bisector of angle H.

(b) 12. Construct a copy of $\angle J$ on your paper. Then construct the bisector of angle J.

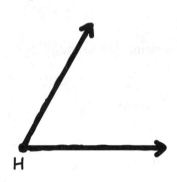

H

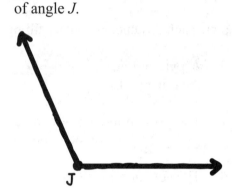

J

Calculate the total area of each solid described below.

13. A right prism whose altitude is 10 and whose base is an isosceles right triangle with sides of length 6, 6, and $6\sqrt{2}$.

14. A sphere with a radius of $2\sqrt{6}$ meters.

Answer each question below.

15. List the lines on the right in order by their slopes from least to greatest.

16. Which line(s) have a negative slope and which line(s) have a positive slope?

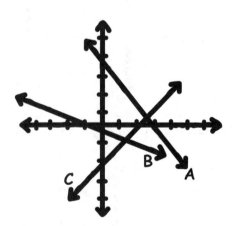

B

C

A

Write the equation for each line described below.

17. The line crossing the points $(1,11)$ and $(5,-3)$.

18. The line crossing the point $(8,7)$ and perpendicular to the line $y = -2x - 5$.

Find the missing coordinates of the points on each diagram below.

(c) 19. $\triangle ABC$ is equilateral.

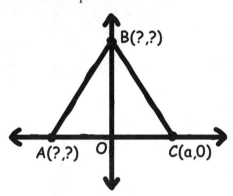

(d) 20. $\triangle LMN$ is isosceles.

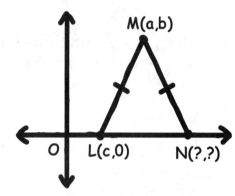

Answer each question below.

21. What is the area of an isosceles triangle that has a base measuring 40 cm and equal legs measuring 52 cm?

22. Right $\triangle RST$ has a hypotenuse of length 68 in. and one leg of length 60 in. What is the area of $\triangle RST$?

Do each coordinate proof below.

23. Given: Rhombus $OPQR$ with coordinates shown
Prove: The diagonals are perpendicular.

(e) 24. Given: Trapezoid $ABCD$; E is the midpoint of $\overline{AB}$ and F is the midpoint of $\overline{CD}$
Prove: $EF = \dfrac{1}{2}(AD + BC)$

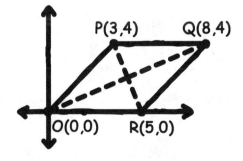

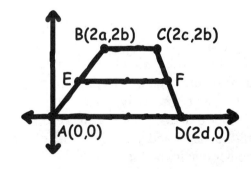

Lesson 109—Transformations

Throughout this book, we've talked about congruent figures, which are figures that have the same size and shape. Our technical definition of congruent figures has been that their corresponding sides and corresponding angles are congruent.

Redefining Congruent Figures

One problem with this definition is that it only works for polygons (whose sides are line segments). But what if we had two figures like this?

These appear to be the same shape and size, but since they aren't polygons, we don't have a technical definition that would allow us to make sure that the two are actually congruent. Remember, it's not enough for the figures to just look congruent. We need a mathematical way of determining it. Yet these two figures have no corresponding sides or angles to compare.

Congruent figures, but not polygons.

Interestingly, mathematicians were able to expand their definition of congruent figures to include non-polygons by going back to some of the ancient Greek ideas. The Greeks defined congruent figures as figures that could be made to "coincide." That just means that one figure will fit exactly on top of the other. This definition makes common sense, because we can always slide, spin, or flip one congruent figure to make it fit on top of another. For instance, what if our two non-polygons had been like this?

By sliding and spinning the figure on the right, we could have made it fit perfectly on top of the other figure. That would have shown that the two are congruent.

The only drawback of the Greek approach is that it isn't exact enough. How would we know whether the figures fit on top of each other precisely? And how would we actually pick a figure up off the page and put it on top of another one in the first place?

Slide and spin

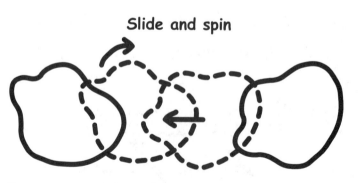

Put one congruent figure on top of the other.

To make things more precise, the mathematicians decided to use the coordinate plane. If two figures are placed on a coordinate plane, then every point on each can be represented by a pair of numbers. That makes it easy to tell whether the two figures can be made to fit perfectly on top of each other (and to decide if they're congruent). The mathematical term for matching up all the points of two figures is **transformation**. Here's the formal definition.

Definition 90	A *transformation* is a one-to-one correspondence between two sets of points.

Translations, Rotations, and Reflections

The mathematicians also came up with technical definitions for sliding, rotating, and flipping a figure. Sliding a figure, without turning it, is called a **translation**. An example of a translation on a coordinate plane is given on the right. ΔABC has been slid to the right 6 spaces and up 2 spaces. Notice how the *x*-coordinate of each point has increased by 6 and the *y*-coordinate of each point has increased by 2. By sliding a figure on a coordinate plane, you can know precisely how the positions of each point of the figure have changed, by looking at the change in their coordinates.

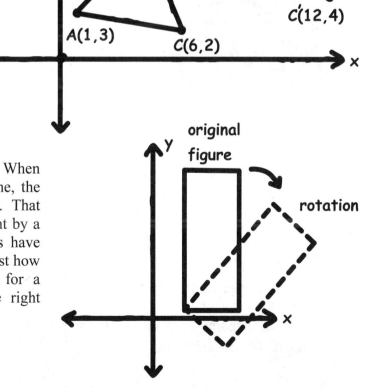

The technical term for spinning a figure around is **rotation**. When doing a rotation on a coordinate plane, the figure is turned by a certain angle. That changes the coordinates of every point by a specific amount. The mathematicians have worked out methods for calculating just how much each coordinate will change for a given rotation.[2] The picture on the right shows a rectangle being rotated.

---

[2] These methods use trigonometry.

Sometimes a figure needs to be flipped before it can be placed exactly on top of a congruent figure. This sort of flipping is called a reflection. In a line reflection, a figure is flipped onto the other side of a line. The resulting figure is a mirror reflection of the original (which is where the name comes from). To the right is a picture of a line reflection across the *y*-axis. Just as with translations and rotations, the mathematicians have devised ways to calculate how the coordinates of all the points of a figure will change for a particular reflection.

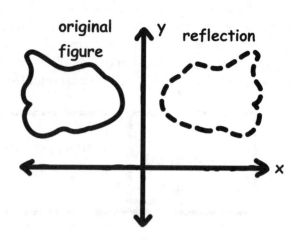

By working out how the coordinates of a figure will change for any translation, rotation, or reflection, mathematicians were able to define congruent figures for all sorts of different shapes. The concept wasn't just limited to polygons. Also, since all the points of a figure were represented by coordinates, this approach made it possible to study any transformation using all the techniques of algebra.

Practice 109

a. Find the shaded area.

b. In the diagram, the first figure is a translation of the second figure. Find the distance of the translation.

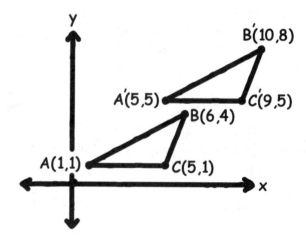

c. Write the equation for the line described below.

The line crossing the point $(1,-3)$ and perpendicular to the line that passes through the points $(4,-3)$ and $(2,1)$.

d. If $\overset{\frown}{IK}$ has a length of 2π cm, find JK.

e. Do the proof below.

Given: $\overline{PQ}$ is a diameter of $\odot O$.

Prove: $\triangle PRQ$ is obtuse.

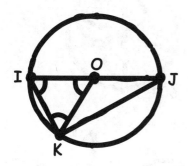

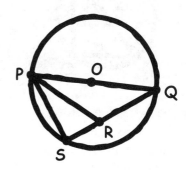

Problem Set 109

Tell whether each sentence below is True or False.

1. One drawback of our earlier definition of congruent figures is that it only applies to polygons (with line segments for sides).

2. Using the coordinate plane, mathematicians came up with a broader definition of congruent figures that works on non-polygons.

Complete each sentence below by filling in the blanks.

3. Sliding a figure without turning it is called a _____.

4. Flipping a figure so that it's upside down is called a _____.

5. The mathematical term for matching up all the points of two figures is _____.

Calculate the slope of each line below.

6. Line A

7. Line B

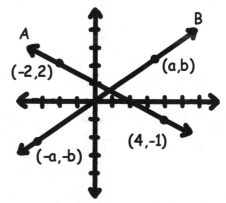

Calculate the area of each shaded region below.

8.

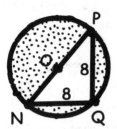

(a) 9.

Answer each question below.

10. Identify the relationship between figures *A* and *B*.

11. Identify the relationship between figures *A* and *C*.

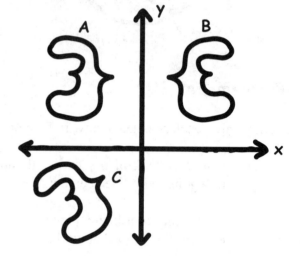

(b) 12. In the diagram below, the first figure is a translation of the second figure. Find the distance of the translation.

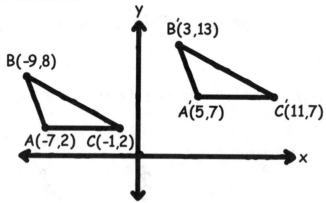

Use only a compass and straightedge to do each construction below.

13. Construct a copy of $\overline{KL}$ on your paper. Then construct the bisector of segment *KL*.

14. Construct a copy of $\angle P$ on your paper. Then construct the bisector of angle P.

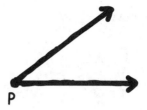

Find the measures of the angles of each triangle described below.

15. $\triangle ABC$ where $m\angle A = x + 12$, $m\angle B = 6x$, and $m\angle C$ is twice $m\angle A$.

16. $\triangle QOR$ where Q and R lie on $\odot O$ and $m\overset{\frown}{QR} = 134$.

Write the equation for each line described below.

17. The line crossing the point $(6, -4)$ and parallel to the line $3y = 2x + 6$.

(c) 18. The line crossing the point $(-2, -1)$ and perpendicular to the line that passes through the points $(-3, 5)$ and $(2, 0)$.

Answer each question below.

19. If $\overset{\frown}{MN}$ has a length of π cm, find MN.

(d) 20. Find LM.

21. Find the perimeter of quadrilateral $ABCD$.

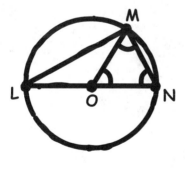

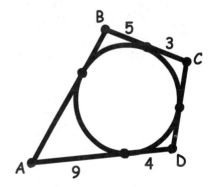

22. At the year-end pizza party, Greg has a choice between two pizzas. One pizza has a 20-inch diameter and is cut into 8 equal slices. The other pizza has an 18-inch diameter but is cut into 6 equal slices. Which pizza should Greg choose if he wants to get the slice with the larger area?

Do each proof below.

23. Given: $\overparen{JK} \cong \overparen{KL}$
Prove: $\triangle JKN \sim \triangle MKJ$

(e) 24. Given: $\overline{AC}$ is a diameter of $\odot O$.
Prove: $\triangle ABC$ is obtuse.

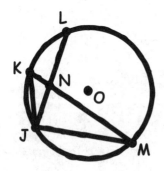

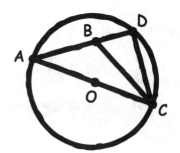

Lesson 110—Non-Euclidean Geometries

At the beginning of the book, we learned that geometry is based on a few postulates, which the Greeks believed were self-evident truths (so obvious that no one could disagree with them). The Greeks thought that if they started with self-evident truths and used only deductive reasoning that their theorems would also have to be true. This was important to them, because the Greeks were philosophers in search of truth. Euclid, the great Greek geometer, actually started with just 10 postulates, which are listed in Lesson 5.

Euclid's Not Perfect

In the 1800s, over 2,000 years after Euclid, mathematicians realized that geometry wasn't as certain as the Greeks had believed. And this realization changed math forever. Here's how it happened. After Euclid, some detail-minded mathematicians became troubled by Euclid's 5th postulate, which states that if there's a line ℓ and a point P not on the line, then only one line m can run through P without ever intersecting ℓ. That's just a fancy way of saying that two parallel lines never meet. It seems like a very reasonable statement, but these mathematicians didn't like it, because lines go on forever— for millions or even billions of miles. They argued that since no one can see that far away, the 5th postulate can't be self-evident (obviously true). How can anyone know for sure what happens at such great distances?

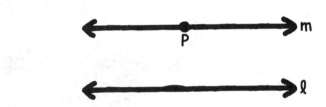

Just one line through P that never intersects ℓ.

Most mathematicians thought this was just an unimportant detail, but through the generations a few pioneers tried to eliminate Euclid's 5th postulate. Most of them attempted to prove that the 5th postulate was true using the other 9 postulates. That would do away with the problem, because then the statement about parallel lines would become a proved theorem instead of an assumed postulate. For hundreds and hundreds of years, no one succeeded.

Eventually, in the 1700s, one mathematician named Saccheri got a clever idea. He decided to try and prove the 5th postulate indirectly. In other words, he assumed that the 5th postulate about parallel lines never meeting was *not* true, and then hoped to get a contradiction in his proof.[3] Interestingly, Saccheri didn't get a contradiction, but he came up with several strange theorems that were different from any of the known theorems of geometry. These theorems were so strange that Saccheri thought his indirect proof worked and that he had successfully proved the 5th postulate. Saccheri published his results in a book titled *Euclid Vindicated of all Defects*.

---

[3] We did indirect proofs ourselves earlier in the book.

But a few generations later, Karl Friedrich Gauss, maybe the greatest mathematician of all time (and the man who proved the construction of a 17-sided polygon) looked at Saccheri's book and realized that since Saccheri didn't obtain a contradiction, those strange theorems had to be taken seriously. A couple of other mathematicians came to the same conclusion at about the same time.

Karl Friedrich Gauss
(Overall math genius)

Strange New Theorems

Gauss decided to create a whole new system of geometry, based on the other 9 postulates of Euclid, but on a different 5th postulate. For the 5th postulate, instead of assuming that only one line could run through point P and never intersect line ℓ, Gauss assumed that an infinite number of lines could run through P and still not intersect ℓ, no matter how far the lines extended!

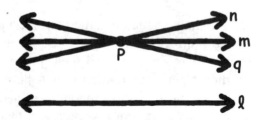

An infinite number of lines through P that never intersect ℓ.

As crazy as that seems, Gauss wasn't violating any of the rules of logic or of mathematics in choosing the new postulate. He just wanted to explore what kinds of theorems would be possible.

Since 9 of the 10 postulates were exactly the same as Euclid's, many of Gauss's theorems were the same as the ones you've learned. To name just two examples, the base angles of an isosceles triangle are still congruent and the exterior angle of a triangle is still greater than either of the remote interior angles. In fact, all of Euclid's theorems that don't use the 5th postulate were exactly the same in Gauss's new geometry as they were in Euclid's.

But those theorems that did rely on the 5th postulate came out different. For instance, one of Gauss's new theorems said that the sum of the angles of any triangle is always *less* than 180°.[4] What's more, the sum of the angles gets larger, the smaller the area of the triangle. So for a really small triangle, the sum is almost 180°, but not quite.

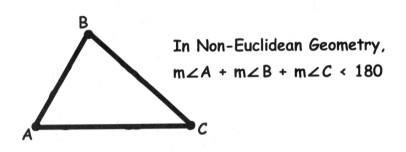

In Non-Euclidean Geometry,
$m\angle A + m\angle B + m\angle C < 180$

Another strange theorem of Gauss's was that if all three angles of two triangles are the same, then the triangles are congruent. In regular geometry, the triangles would just be similar. They wouldn't necessarily be congruent, because one triangle could be a lot bigger than the other one. Today Gauss's geometry is called Non-Euclidean Geometry. It's "Non-Euclidean" because it's different from Euclid's geometry.

Einstein Uses Non-Euclidean Geometry

Gauss knew that most mathematicians would think his theorems were silly. They would say that the angles of triangles obviously add to 180°. What purpose could a "new" geometry serve, if it contained theorems that didn't fit with real-world experience? Gauss didn't even publish his theorems for fear of being ridiculed by other mathematicians. He told only a few friends of his findings. The world didn't find out about Gauss's work on Non-Euclidean Geometry until after his death, when experts went through his papers.

Despite the opinions of others, Gauss knew that his new geometry was important. It showed that Euclid's geometry wasn't necessarily true. That it was possible to have other geometries with different postulates and different theorems. And who was to say which geometry was ultimately true. Even though triangles that human beings normally work with appear to have angles that add to 180°, a human being could never know the sum of the angles of a triangle whose sides were billions of miles long. Maybe Gauss's theorems weren't so silly after all.

In the 1900s, none other than Albert Einstein used Non-Euclidean Geometry in his General Theory of Relativity. According to Einstein, when large distances are considered and when space and time are viewed together (as in his theory), the universe is actually a much closer fit with

---

[4] Of course, in Euclidean Geometry, the sum is always equal to 180°.

Non-Euclidean Geometry than with Euclid's geometry. Gauss and a few other mathematicians who believed in Non-Euclidean Geometry were vindicated.

Today, mathematicians don't say that Euclid's postulates are "self-evident truths." They work with his postulates and with other postulates and deduce different theorems for different geometries. Some fit better in certain circumstances than others. And instead of just one Non-Euclidean Geometry, we now have many different Non-Euclidean Geometries. Each starts with a different set of postulates.

Practice 110

a. Find the shaded area below.

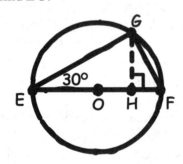

b. Copy $\triangle JKL$ on your paper. Then construct the segment bisector of each side of the triangle.

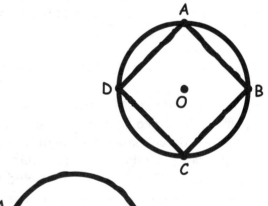

c. If $\overarc{EG}$ has a length of 6π in., find EG.

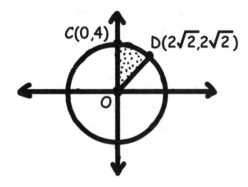

d. If the circumference of $\odot O$ is 4π, what is the area of square $ABCD$?

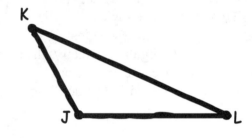

e. Do the proof below.

Given: $\overline{CO}$ is a diameter of $\odot P$;
$\overline{AC}$ is a chord of $\odot O$
Prove: $AB = BC$

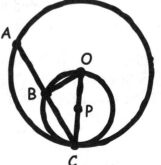

Problem Set 110

Tell whether each sentence below is True or False.

1. Mathematicians did not like Euclid's 5th postulate about parallel lines, because they didn't think it was self-evident (obvious) enough.

2. By changing the 5th postulate, modern mathematicians have created new geometries that are different from Euclid's.

Complete each sentence below by filling in the blanks.

3. Spinning a figure is called a _____.

4. _____ used Non-Euclidean Geometry to develop his General Theory of Relativity.

5. If the slopes of two nonvertical lines are _____ of one another, then the lines are perpendicular.

Find the lengths of the dashed sides of each diagram below.

6.

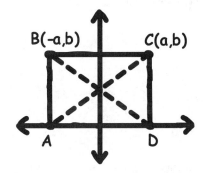

7.

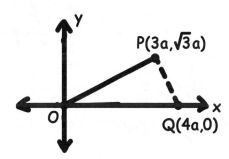

Calculate the area of each shaded region below.

8.

(a) 9.

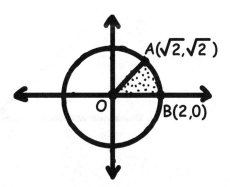

Answer each question below.

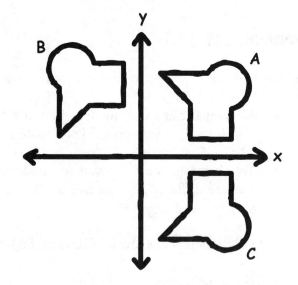

10. Identify the relationship between figures *A* and *B*.

11. Identify the relationship between figures *A* and *C*.

12. In the diagram below, the first figure is a translation of the second figure. Find the distance of the translation.

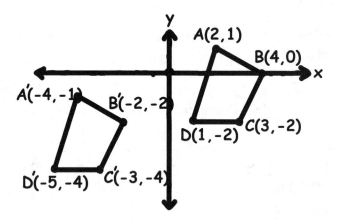

Use only a compass and straightedge to do each construction below.

13. Copy △*ABC* on your paper. Then construct the bisector of each angle of the triangle.

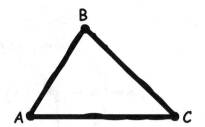

(b) 14. Copy △*DEF* on your paper. Then construct the segment bisector of each side of the triangle.

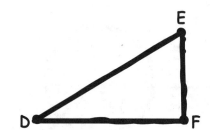

Calculate the total volume of each solid described below.

15. A right prism having an octagonal (8-sided) base of area 112 square inches and an altitude of 15 inches.

16. An oblique cone with a radius of $4\sqrt{3}$ feet and an altitude of 2 feet.

Write the equation for each line described below.

17. The line crossing the point $(-3, -2)$ and perpendicular to the line $y = -\dfrac{2}{3}x - 3$.

18. The line crossing the point $(0, 7)$ and perpendicular to the line that passes through the points $(-2, 4)$ and $(4, -5)$.

Answer each question below.

(c) 19. If $\overset{\frown}{AC}$ has a length of 4π in., find AC.

20. If $\overset{\frown}{AC}$ has a length of 4π in., find AD.

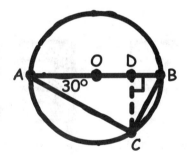

(d) 21. If the circumference of $\odot O$ is 10π, what is the area of square $LMNP$?

22. If diameters $IJ = JK = KL$ and $IO = 12$, what is the area of the shaded region?

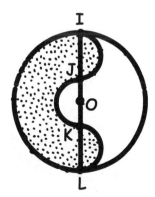

755

Do each proof below.

23.   Given: Chords $\overline{CF}$ and $\overline{DG}$ intersect at point E.
      Prove: $\dfrac{CG}{DF} = \dfrac{GE}{FE}$

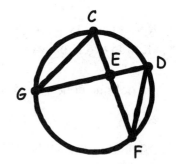

(e) 24.   Given: $\overline{QP}$ is a diameter of $\odot O$;
          $\overline{QS}$ is a chord of $\odot P$
      Prove: $QR = RS$

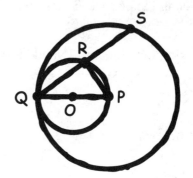

THE END

(Find the area and perimeter of the figure above... just kidding.)

Definitions, Theorems, and Postulates

Chapter 2: Lines and Angles

Definition 1: Collinear points are points that lie on the same line.

Definition 2: Noncollinear points are points that do not lie on the same line.

Definition 3: A line segment is a part of a line consisting of two points, called end points, and the set of all points between them.

Definition 4: Congruent line segments are line segments that have equal lengths.

Definition 5: Betweenness of Points: If F, G, and H are collinear, and if $FG + GH = FH$, then G is between F and H.

Definition 6: A ray is a part of a line consisting of a given point, called the end point, and the set of all points on one side of the end point.

Definition 7: An angle is the union of two rays having the same end point. The end point is called the vertex of the angle; the rays are called the sides of the angle.

Definition 8: Congruent angles are angles that have equal measures.

Definition 9: Betweenness of Rays: $\overrightarrow{PS}$ is between $\overrightarrow{PQ}$ and $\overrightarrow{PR}$, if point S lies in the interior of $\angle QPR$ and $m\angle SPR + m\angle QPS = m\angle QPR$.

Definition 10: A right angle is an angle with a measure of $90°$.

Definition 11: An acute angle is an angle with a measure of less than $90°$.

Definition 12: An obtuse angle is an angle with a measure of greater than $90°$ (and less than $180°$).

Definition 13: The midpoint of a line segment is the point that divides the line segment into two congruent line segments.

Definition 14: Segment Bisector: A bisector of $\overline{AB}$ is any line, ray, or line segment which passes through the midpoint of $\overline{AB}$.

Definition 15: Angle Bisector: $\overrightarrow{OR}$ is the bisector of $\angle PON$ if R lies in the interior of $\angle PON$ and $m\angle POR = m\angle RON$.

Postulate 1: Two points determine a unique straight line.

Postulate 2: Three noncollinear points determine a unique plane.

Postulate 3: The Ruler Postulate: (a) To every point on a line, there corresponds exactly one real number called its coordinate. (b) To every real number, there corresponds exactly one point of the line. (c) To every pair of points there corresponds exactly one real number called the distance between the points. (d) And the distance between two points is the absolute value of the difference between their coordinates.

Postulate 4: The Protractor Postulate (a) The rays in a half rotation (180 degrees) can be numbered so that to every ray there corresponds exactly one real number called its coordinate. (b) And to every real number from 0 to 180, there corresponds exactly one ray. (c) To every pair of rays there corresponds exactly one real number called the measure of the angle that they determine. (d) And the measure of the angle is the absolute value of the difference between the coordinates of its rays.

Addition Property:	If equals are added to equals, the results are equal: If $a = b$, then $a + c = b + c$.
Subtraction Property:	If equals are subtracted from equals, the results are equal: If $a = b$, then $a - c = b - c$.
Multiplication Property:	If equals are multiplied by equals, their products are equal: If $a = b$, then $ac = bc$.
Division Property:	If equals are divided by nonzero equals, their quotients are equal: If $a = b$, then $\dfrac{a}{c} = \dfrac{b}{c}$ as long as $c \neq 0$.
Substitution Property:	If $a = b$, then either a or b may be substituted for the other in any equation.
Transitive Property:	If two quantities are equal to the same quantity, then they are equal to each other: If $a = b$ and $b = c$, then $a = c$.
Reflexive Property:	Any quantity is equal to itself: $a = a$.
Symmetric Property:	The positions of the expressions on either side of an equals sign may be reversed. If $a = b$, then $b = a$.

Chapter 3: Angle Pairs and Perpendicular Lines

Definition 16: Complementary angles are angles with measures that add to $90°$.

Definition 17: Supplementary angles are angles with measures that add to $180°$.

Definition 18: Adjacent angles are angles that have the same vertex, share a common side, and have no interior points in common.

Definition 19: A linear pair is two adjacent angles whose exterior sides form a straight line.

Definition 20: Vertical angles are a pair of nonadjacent angles formed by two intersecting lines.

Definition 21: Perpendicular lines are lines which intersect to form right angles.

Definition 22: A perpendicular bisector is a line that is perpendicular to a line segment and intersects the line segment at its midpoint.

Definition 23: The distance between two points is the length of the line segment joining the points.

Definition 24: The distance between a line and a point not on the line is the length of the perpendicular segment drawn from the point to the line.

Theorem 1: If two angles are complementary to the same angle or equal (congruent) angles, then they are equal (congruent).

Theorem 2: If two angles are supplementary to the same angle or equal (congruent) angles, then they are equal (congruent).

Theorem 3: If two angles are a linear pair, then they are supplementary.

Theorem 4: Pairs of vertical angles are congruent (equal).

Theorem 5: Perpendicular lines intersect to form 4 right angles.

Theorem 6: All right angles are congruent (equal).

Theorem 7: Through a given point on a line, there exists exactly one perpendicular to the given line.

Theorem 8: If the exterior sides of a pair of adjacent angles are perpendicular, the angles are complementary.

Postulate 5: Through a given point *not* on a line, there exists exactly one perpendicular to the given line.

Chapter 4: Parallel Lines

Definition 25: Parallel lines are lines that lie in the same plane (coplanar) and that never intersect.

Definition 26: Lines, segments, rays, or points which lie in the same plane are said to be coplanar.

Definition 27: A transversal is a line that intersects two or more lines in different points.

Theorem 9: If two parallel lines are cut (crossed) by a transversal, then their corresponding angles are congruent (equal).

Theorem 10: If the two angles in a linear pair have equal measures (are congruent), then each is a right angle.

Theorem 11: If two parallel lines are cut (crossed) by a transversal, then their alternate exterior angles are congruent (equal).

Theorem 12: If two parallel lines are cut (crossed) by a transversal, then interior angles on the same side of the transversal are supplementary.

Theorem 13: If two lines form congruent corresponding angles with a transversal, then the lines are parallel.

Theorem 14: If two lines form congruent alternate exterior angles with a transversal, then the lines are parallel.

Theorem 15: If two lines form supplementary interior angles on the same side of a transversal, then the lines are parallel.

Postulate 6: If two parallel lines are cut by a transversal, then their alternate interior angles are congruent (equal).

Postulate 7: If two lines form congruent alternate interior angles with a transversal, then the lines are parallel.

Chapter 5: Triangles

Definition 28: A polygon is a geometric figure whose sides are line segments.

Definition 29: A triangle is a polygon that has three sides.

Definition 30: A scalene triangle has no congruent (equal) sides.

Definition 31: An isosceles triangle has two congruent (equal) sides.

Definition 32: An equilateral triangle has all three congruent (equal) sides.

Definition 33: An acute triangle has all three angles with measure of less than 90°.

Definition 34: A right triangle has one angle with a measure of 90°.

Definition 35: An obtuse triangle has one angle with a measure of greater than 90°.

Definition 36: An equiangular triangle has all three angles with equal measures.

Definition 37: An exterior angle of a polygon is an angle that forms a linear pair with one of the interior angles of the polygon.

Definition 38: Definition of Congruent Triangles: If the vertices of two triangles can be paired in a correspondence so that all pairs of corresponding angles are congruent and all pairs of corresponding sides are congruent, then the triangles are congruent.

Theorem 16: If two lines are parallel to a third line, then the lines are parallel to each other.

Theorem 17: The sum of the measures of the angles of a triangle is 180.

    Corollary 17.1: The acute angles of a right triangle are complementary.

    Corollary 17.2: The measure of each angle of an equiangular triangle is 60.

    Corollary 17.3: If two angles of a triangle are congruent to two angles of another triangle, then the remaining pair of angles are congruent.

Theorem 18: Exterior Angle of a Triangle Theorem: The measure of an exterior angle of a triangle is equal to the sum of the measures of the two remote interior angles.

Theorem 19: Angle-Angle-Side Theorem: If the vertices of two triangles can be paired so that two angles and the side opposite one of them in one triangle are congruent to the corresponding parts of the second triangle, then the two triangles are congruent.

Postulate 8: Through a given point not on a line, exactly one line may be drawn parallel to the line.

Postulate 9: Side-Angle-Side Postulate: If the vertices of two triangles can be paired so that two sides and the included angle of one triangle are congruent to the corresponding parts of the second triangle, then the two triangles are congruent.

Postulate 10: Angle-Side-Angle Postulate: If the vertices of two triangles can be paired so that two angles and the included side of one triangle are congruent to the corresponding parts of the second triangle, then the two triangles are congruent.

Postulate 11: Hypotenuse-Leg Postulate: If the vertices of two right triangles can be paired so that the hypotenuse and leg of one of them are congruent to the corresponding parts of the second right triangle, then the two right triangles are congruent.

Postulate 12: Side-Side-Side Postulate: If the vertices of two triangles can be paired so that three sides of one triangle are congruent to the corresponding sides of the second triangle, then the two triangles are congruent.

Chapter 6: Using Congruent Triangles

Definition 39: Converse of Definition of Congruent Triangles (C. P. C. T. C.): If two triangles are congruent, then their vertices can be paired in a correspondence so that all pairs of corresponding angles are congruent and all pairs of corresponding sides are congruent.

Definition 40: An altitude of a triangle is a segment drawn from any vertex of the triangle, perpendicular to the opposite side, extended outside the triangle if necessary.

Definition 41: A median of a triangle is a segment drawn from any vertex of the triangle to the midpoint of the opposite side.

Theorem 20: If two triangles are congruent to the same triangle, then they are congruent to each other.

Theorem 21: If a point lies on the perpendicular bisector of a segment, then the point is equidistant from the endpoints of the segment.

Theorem 22: If a point is equidistant from the endpoints of a segment, then the point lies on the perpendicular bisector of the segment.

Theorem 23: Base Angles Theorem: If two sides of a triangle are congruent (equal), then the angles opposite those sides are congruent (equal).

Corollary 23.1: If a triangle is equilateral, then it is also equiangular.

Theorem 24: The altitudes extending to the legs of an isosceles triangle are congruent (equal).

Theorem 25: Converse of Base Angles Theorem: If two angles of a triangle are congruent (equal), then the sides opposite those angles are congruent (equal).

Corollary 25.1: If a triangle is equiangular, then it is also equilateral.

Theorem 26: The medians extending to the legs of an isosceles triangle are congruent (equal).

Chapter 7: Inequalities

Theorem 27: Exterior Angle Inequality Theorem: The measure of an exterior angle of a triangle is greater than the measure of either of the remote interior angles.

Theorem 28: If Unequal Sides, then Unequal Angles: If two sides of a triangle are not congruent, then the angles opposite those sides are not congruent, and the greater angle is opposite the longer side.

Theorem 29: If Unequal Angles, then Unequal Sides: If two angles of a triangle are not congruent, then the sides opposite those angles are not congruent, and the longer side is opposite the greater angle.

Addition Property (Inequality):	If $a > b$, then $a + c > b + c$. Also, if $a > b$ and $c > d$, then $a + c > b + d$.
Subtraction Property (Inequality):	If $a > b$, then $a - c > b - c$.
Multiplication Property (Inequality):	If $a > b$ and $c > 0$, then $ac > bc$.
Division Property (Inequality):	If $a > b$ and $c > 0$, then $\dfrac{a}{c} > \dfrac{b}{c}$.
Substitution Property (Inequality):	If $a = b$, then a can be substituted for b in any inequality.
Transitive Property (Inequality):	If $a > b$ and $b > c$, then $a > c$.
Whole Greater than its Part:	If $c = a + b$ and $b > 0$, then $c > a$.

Postulate 13: Triangle Inequality Postulate: The sum of the lengths of any two sides of a triangle must be greater than the length of the remaining side.

Chapter 8: Quadrilaterals

Definition 42: A quadrilateral is a polygon that has four sides.

Definition 43: A trapezoid is a quadrilateral which has exactly one pair of parallel sides. The parallel sides are called bases and the nonparallel sides are called legs.

Definition 44: An isosceles trapezoid is a trapezoid that has both legs congruent (equal).

Definition 45: A parallelogram is a quadrilateral that has both pairs of opposite sides parallel.

Definition 46: A rectangle is a parallelogram with four right angles.

Definition 47: A rhombus is a parallelogram with four congruent sides.

Definition 48: A square is a parallelogram with four congruent sides and four congruent (right) angles.

Theorem 30: The sum of the measures of the angles of a quadrilateral is 360.

Theorem 31: The length of a line segment drawn from any vertex of an equilateral triangle to a point on the opposite side is less than the length of any side of the triangle.

Theorem 32: The lower (and upper) base angles of an isosceles trapezoid are congruent (equal).

Theorem 33: The diagonals of an isosceles trapezoid are congruent (equal).

Theorem 34: If a quadrilateral is a parallelogram, then pairs of consecutive angles are supplementary.

Theorem 35: If a quadrilateral is a parallelogram, then both pairs of opposite angles are congruent (equal).

Theorem 36: If a quadrilateral is a parallelogram, then both pairs of opposite sides are congruent (equal).

Theorem 37: If a quadrilateral is a parallelogram, then the diagonals bisect each other.

Theorem 38: If both pairs of opposite angles are congruent (equal), then a quadrilateral is a parallelogram.

Theorem 39: If both pairs of opposite sides are congruent (equal), then a quadrilateral is a parallelogram.

Theorem 40: If one pair of opposite sides is both parallel and congruent (equal), then a quadrilateral is a parallelogram.

Theorem 41: If the diagonals bisect each other, then a quadrilateral is a parallelogram.

Theorem 42: The line segment joining the midpoints of two sides of a triangle is parallel to the third side and is one-half its length.

Theorem 43: The diagonals of a rectangle are congruent.

Theorem 44: The diagonals of a rhombus are perpendicular to each other.

Theorem 45: The diagonals of a rhombus bisect the angles at the vertices which they join.

Chapter 9: Polygons

Definition 49: A regular polygon is a convex polygon that is both equilateral and equiangular.

Definition 50: The perimeter of a polygon is the sum of the lengths of its sides.

Theorem 46: The sum of the measures of the interior angles of a polygon with n sides is 180(n-2).

Theorem 47: The sum of the measures of the exterior angles of any polygon (one exterior angle per vertex) is 360.

Theorem 48: The measure of each interior angle of a regular polygon is $\dfrac{180(n-2)}{n}$, where n is the number of sides of the regular polygon.

Theorem 49: The perimeter of a regular polygon with n sides and side length s is equal to ns.

Chapter 10: Similar Triangles

Definition 51: The ratio of two numbers a and b (b ≠ 0) is the quotient of the numbers. It's written as $\dfrac{a}{b}$ or a : b.

Definition 52: A proportion is an equation which states that two ratios are equal to each other. It's written as $\dfrac{a}{b} = \dfrac{c}{d}$ or as a : b = c : d. (b ≠ 0, d ≠ 0)

Definition 53: In the proportion $\dfrac{a}{b} = \dfrac{c}{d}$, b and c are referred to as the means of the proportion, and a and d are referred to as the extremes of the proportion.

Definition 54: If $\dfrac{a}{b} = \dfrac{b}{c}$, then b is the geometric mean of a and c (where a, b, and c are positive).

Definition 55: Definition of Similar Figures: If the vertices of two polygons can be paired so that corresponding angles are congruent and the lengths of corresponding sides are in proportion, then the polygons are similar.

Definition 56: Converse of Definition of Similar Triangles: If two triangles are similar, then their vertices can be paired in a correspondence so that all pairs of corresponding angles are congruent and all pairs of corresponding sides are proportional.

Theorem 50: In a proportion, the product of the means is equal to the product of the extremes.

Theorem 51: Angle-Angle Similarity Theorem (A.A. Similarity): If two angles of one triangle are congruent to two angles of another triangle, then the triangles are similar.

Corollary 51.1: Two triangles similar to a third triangle are similar to each other.

Theorem 52: Side-Angle-Side Similarity Theorem (S.A.S. Similarity): If a pair of corresponding angles of two triangles are congruent and the sides including those angles are proportional, then the triangles are similar.

Theorem 53: If two triangles are similar, then the lengths of a pair of corresponding altitudes have the same ratio as the lengths of any pair of corresponding sides.

Theorem 54: If two triangles are similar, then the lengths of a pair of corresponding medians have the same ratios as the lengths of any pair of corresponding sides.

Theorem 55: If two triangles are similar, then their perimeters have the same ratio as the lengths of any pair of corresponding sides.

Postulate 14: If a line is parallel to one side of a triangle and intersects the other two sides, then the line divides those sides proportionally.

Postulate 15: If a line intersects two sides of a triangle and divides those sides proportionally, then the line is parallel to the third side.

Postulate 16: Side-Side-Side Similarity Postulate (S.S.S. Similarity): If all three pairs of corresponding sides of both triangles are proportional, then the triangles are similar.

Chapter 11: Right Triangles & Trigonometry

Definition 57: The tangent ratio is the ratio of the length of the opposite side to the length of the adjacent side of a right triangle, with respect to a given angle: $\tan = \dfrac{\text{opp}}{\text{adj}}$.

Definition 58: The sine ratio is the ratio of the length of the opposite side to the length of the hypotenuse of a right triangle, with respect to a given angle: $\sin = \dfrac{\text{opp}}{\text{hyp}}$.

Definition 59: The cosine ratio is the ratio of the length of the adjacent side to the length of the hypotenuse of a right triangle, with respect to a given angle: $\cos = \dfrac{\text{adj}}{\text{hyp}}$.

Theorem 56: The altitude to the hypotenuse of a right triangle forms two triangles that are similar to each other and to the original triangle.

Theorem 57: Pythagorean Theorem: The square of the length of the hypotenuse of a right triangle is equal to the sum of the squares of the lengths of the legs.

Theorem 58: Converse of Pythagorean Theorem: If the square of one side length of a triangle is equal to the sum of the squares of the other two side lengths, then the triangle is a right triangle.

Theorem 59: In an isosceles right triangle, the length of the hypotenuse is $\sqrt{2}$ times the length of one leg.

Theorem 60: In a 30-60 right triangle, the length of the hypotenuse is twice the length of the short leg and the length of the long leg is $\sqrt{3}$ times the length of the short leg.

Chapter 12: Circles

Definition 60: A circle is the set of all points in a plane that are at a given distance from a given point, called the center, in the plane.

Definition 61: A radius is a line segment that joins the center of the circle to a point of the circle.

Definition 62: A chord of a circle is a line segment that joins two points of the circle.

Definition 63: A diameter of a circle is a chord that contains the center.

Definition 64: A tangent line is a line which intersects a circle in exactly one point. The point of contact is called the point of tangency.

Definition 65: A secant line is a line which intersects a circle in two different points.

Definition 66: A tangent segment is a line segment that has a point on the tangent line and the point of tangency as an end point.

Definition 67: An arc is a portion of a circle consisting of two end points and the set of points on the circle that lie between those points.

Definition 68: A central angle is an angle whose vertex is at the center of the circle.

Definition 69: The degree measure of a minor arc is the measure of its central angle.

Definition 70: The circumference of a circle is the distance around the circle, expressed in linear units of measurement (inches, centimeters, etc.)

Definition 71: Congruent arcs are arcs in the same or congruent circles which have the same degree measure.

Definition 72: The midpoint of an arc is the point on the arc which divides the arc into two congruent arcs.

Definition 73: An inscribed angle is an angle whose vertex is on a circle and whose sides are chords (or secants) of the circle.

Theorem 61: If a line through the center of a circle is perpendicular to a chord, it also bisects the chord.

Theorem 62: In the same circle, congruent (equal) chords are equidistant (the same distance) from the center of the circle.

Theorem 63: In the same circle, chords equidistant from the center of the circle are congruent (equal).

Theorem 64: If a radius is drawn to the point of tangency of a tangent line, then the radius is perpendicular to the tangent line.

Theorem 65: If a radius is perpendicular to a line at the point where the line intersects a circle, then the line is a tangent line.

Theorem 66: If two tangent segments are drawn to a circle from the same exterior point, then they are congruent.

Theorem 67: Arc Length-Degree Measure Proportion: $\dfrac{\text{Arc length}}{\text{Circumferencec}} = \dfrac{\text{Degree measure}}{360°}$.

Theorem 68: If two chords of the same or congruent circles are congruent, then their minor arcs are congruent.

Theorem 69: If two minor arcs of the same or congruent circles are congruent, then their intersecting chords are congruent.

Theorem 70: In a circle, a diameter drawn perpendicular to a chord bisects the minor arc that the chord intercepts.

Theorem 71: An inscribed angle is equal in measure to one-half the measure of its intercepted arc.

    Corollary 71.1: Inscribed angles that intercept the same or congruent arcs are congruent.

    Corollary 71.2: An inscribed angle that intercepts a semicircle is a right angle.

Theorem 72: The measure of an angle formed by a tangent and a chord drawn to the point of tangency is equal to one-half the measure of the intercepted arc.

Theorem 73: The measure of an angle formed by two chords (or secants) intersecting in the interior of a circle is equal to one-half the sum of the measures of the intercepted arcs.

Theorem 74: The measure of an angle formed by two secants (or tangents) intersecting in the exterior of a circle is equal to one-half the difference of the measures of the two intercepted arcs.

Theorem 75: If two chords intersect in the interior of a circle, the product of the lengths of the segments of one chord is equal to the product of the lengths of the segments of the other.

Theorem 76: If two secant segments are drawn to a circle from the same exterior point, then the product of the lengths of one secant segment and its external segment is equal to the product of the lengths of the other secant segment and its external segment.

Theorem 77: If a tangent segment and a secant segment are drawn to a circle from the same exterior point, then the square of the length of the tangent segment is equal to the product of the lengths of the secant segment and its external segment.

Postulate 17: All radii of the same circle are congruent (equal).

Postulate 18: Arc Addition Postulate: If P is on $\overset{\frown}{AB}$, then $m\overset{\frown}{AP} + m\overset{\frown}{PB} = m\overset{\frown}{AB}$.

Chapter 13: Area

Definition 74: Equivalent figures are figures that have the same area.

Definition 75: The center of a regular polygon is the center of its circumscribed circle.

Definition 76: A radius of a regular polygon is a line segment that joins the polygon's center to a vertex.

Definition 77: The central angle of a regular polygon is an angle formed by radii drawn to two consecutive vertices.

Definition 78: An apothem of a regular polygon is a perpendicular line segment that joins the polygon's center to a side.

Definition 79: A sector of a circle is a region of a circle bounded by an arc of the circle and the two radii to the endpoints of the arc.

Definition 80: A segment of a circle is a region of a circle bounded by a chord and the minor arc that it intercepts.

Theorem 78: Area of a Triangle = $\frac{1}{2}ba$: The area of a triangle is equal to one-half the product of the base and the altitude.

Theorem 79: Area of a Parallelogram = ba: The area of a parallelogram is equal to the product of the base and the altitude.

Theorem 80: Area of a Square = s^2: The area of a square is equal to the length of any side squared.

Theorem 81: Area of Rhombus = $\frac{1}{2} \times d_1 \times d_2$: The area of a rhombus is equal to one-half the product of the lengths of the two diagonals.

Theorem 82: Area of Trapezoid = $\frac{1}{2}a(b_1 + b_2)$: The area of a trapezoid is equal to one-half the product of the length of the altitude and the sum of the lengths of its bases.

Theorem 83: Area of Regular Polygon = $\frac{1}{2} \times$ apothem $\times$ perimeter : The area of a regular polygon is equal to one-half the product of the length of the apothem (a) and its perimeter(p).

Theorem 84: Area of a Circle = πr^2: The area of a circle is equal to the product of pi (π) and the square of the radius r of the circle.

Theorem 85: Proportion for Area of Sector of a Circle: $\dfrac{\text{Area of sector}}{\text{Area of circle}} = \dfrac{\text{Degree measure}}{360°}$.

Theorem 86: $\dfrac{\text{Area of polygon 1}}{\text{Area of polygon 2}} = \dfrac{(\text{Side of polygon 1})^2}{(\text{Side of polygon 2})^2}$: If two polygons are similar, then the ratio of their areas is equal to the square of the ratio of the lengths of any pair of corresponding sides.

Postulate 19: If two figures are congruent, then they have equal areas.

Postulate 20: Area of a Rectangle = ba: The area of a rectangle (A) is the rectangle's base (b) multiplied by its altitude (a): A = ba.

Postulate 21: Area Addition Postulate: The area of a closed region is equal to the sum of the areas of the non-overlapping parts.

Chapter 14: Solid Geometry

Definition 81: A polyhedron is a solid bounded by parts of intersecting planes.

Definition 82: A rectangular solid is a polyhedron with six rectangular faces.

Definition 83: The surface area of a rectangular solid is the sum of the areas of all six of its rectangular faces.

Definition 84: A prism is a polyhedron with two congruent faces, called bases, lying in parallel planes, and with all other faces as parallelograms.

Definition 85: A pyramid is a polyhedron in which all faces but one have a point in common. That common point is called the vertex and the face that does not contain the vertex is called the base.

Definition 86: A cylinder is a solid with two congruent circular faces, called bases, lying in parallel planes. The surface lying between the bases is called the lateral surface.

Definition 87: A cone is a solid with a circular base on one end and a vertex on the other. The surface lying between the base and vertex is called the lateral surface.

Definition 88: A sphere is the set of all points in space that are at a given distance from a given point, called the center.

Theorem 87: Total Area of Prism = ap + 2B: The total area of a prism is equal to the product of the altitude (a) and the perimeter of a base (p) plus 2 times the area of a base (B).

Theorem 88: Volume of Prism = Ba: The volume of a prism is equal to the product of the area of a base (B) and the altitude (a).

Theorem 89: Total Area of a Regular Pyramid = $\dfrac{1}{2}lp + B$: The total area of a regular pyramid is equal to one-half the product of the perimeter of the base (p) and the slant height (l) plus the area of the base (B).

Theorem 90: Volume of a Pyramid = $\dfrac{1}{3}Ba$: The volume of a pyramid is equal to one-third of the product of the area of the base (B) and the altitude (a).

Theorem 91: Volume of a Cylinder = $\pi r^2 a$: The volume of a cylinder is equal to the product of π (pi), the square of the radius (r), and the altitude of the cylinder (a).

Theorem 92: Volume of a Cone = $\frac{1}{3}\pi r^2 a$: The volume of a cone is equal to one-third the product of π (pi), the square of the radius (r), and the altitude of the cone (a).

Theorem 93: Volume of a Sphere = $\frac{4}{3}\pi r^3$: The volume of a sphere is equal to four-thirds of the product of π (pi), the cube of the radius of the sphere (r).

Theorem 94: Surface Area of a Sphere = $4\pi r^2$: The surface area of a sphere is equal to four times the product of π (pi) and the square of the radius of the sphere (r).

Theorem 95: $\dfrac{\text{Surface area of solid 1}}{\text{Surface area of solid 2}} = \dfrac{(\text{Edge of solid 1})^2}{(\text{Edge of solid 2})^2}$: If two solids are similar, then the ratio of their surface areas is equal to the square of the ratio of the lengths of any pair of corresponding edges.

Theorem 96: $\dfrac{\text{Volume of solid 1}}{\text{Volume of solid 2}} = \dfrac{(\text{Edge of solid 1})^3}{(\text{Edge of solid 2})^3}$: If two solids are similar, then the ratio of their volumes is equal to the cube of the ratio of the lengths of any pair of corresponding edges.

Postulate 22: Volume of Rectangular Solid = lwa: The volume of a rectangular solid is equal to the product of the length (l), the width (w), and the altitude (a).

Chapter 15: Coordinate Geometry

Definition 89: The slope (m) of a nonvertical line which passes through the points (x_1, y_1) and (x_2, y_2) is the ratio of the change in y (Δy) to the change in x (Δx) :

$$m = \frac{\Delta y}{\Delta x} = \frac{y_1 - y_2}{x_1 - x_2}$$

Theorem 97: The distance (d) between point (x_1, y_1) and point (x_2, y_2) may be found with the following formula: $d = \sqrt{(x_2 - x_1)^2 + (y_2 - y_1)^2}$

Theorem 98: The coordinates of the midpoint between points (x_1, y_1) and (x_2, y_2) are as follows: $(\frac{x_1 + x_2}{2}, \frac{y_1 + y_2}{2})$

Theorem 99: If two nonvertical lines are parallel, then their slopes are equal.

Theorem 100: If two nonvertical lines have the same slope, then they are parallel.

Theorem 101: If two nonvertical lines are perpendicular, then their slopes are negative reciprocals of one another.

Theorem 102: If the slopes of two nonvertical lines are negative reciprocals of one another, then the lines are perpendicular.

Theorem 103: The equation for a circle with radius r and its center at point (h, k) is $(x - h)^2 + (y - k)^2 = r^2$

Additional Topics

Definition 90: A transformation is a one-to-one correspondence between two sets of points.